Safety Symbols

These symbols appear in laboratory activities. They warn of possible dangers in the laboratory and remind you to work carefully.

 Safety Goggles Wear safety goggles to protect your eyes in any activity involving chemicals, flames or heating, or glassware.

 Lab Apron Wear a laboratory apron to protect your skin and clothing from damage.

 Breakage Handle breakable materials, such as glassware, with care. Do not touch broken glassware.

 Heat-Resistant Gloves Use an oven mitt or other hand protection when handling hot materials such as hot plates or hot glassware.

 Plastic Gloves Wear disposable plastic gloves when working with harmful chemicals and organisms. Keep your hands away from your face, and dispose of the gloves according to your teacher's instructions.

 Heating Use a clamp or tongs to pick up hot glassware. Do not touch hot objects with your bare hands.

 Flames Before you work with flames, tie back loose hair and clothing. Follow instructions from your teacher about lighting and extinguishing flames.

 No Flames When using flammable materials, make sure there are no flames, sparks, or other exposed heat sources present.

 Corrosive Chemical Avoid getting acid or other corrosive chemicals on your skin or clothing or in your eyes. Do not inhale the vapors. Wash your hands after the activity.

 Poison Do not let any poisonous chemical come into contact with your skin, and do not inhale its vapors. Wash your hands when you are finished with the activity.

 Fumes Work in a ventilated area when harmful vapors may be involved. Avoid inhaling vapors directly. Only test an odor when directed to do so by your teacher, and use a wafting motion to direct the vapor toward your nose.

 Sharp Object Scissors, scalpels, knives, needles, pins, and tacks can cut your skin. Always direct a sharp edge or point away from yourself and others.

 Animal Safety Treat live or preserved animals or animal parts with care to avoid harming the animals or yourself. Wash your hands when you are finished with the activity.

 Plant Safety Handle plants only as directed by your teacher. If you are allergic to certain plants, tell your teacher; do not do an activity involving those plants. Avoid touching harmful plants such as poison ivy. Wash your hands when you are finished with the activity.

 Electric Shock To avoid electric shock, never use electrical equipment around water, or when the equipment is wet or your hands are wet. Be sure cords are untangled and cannot trip anyone. Unplug equipment not in use.

 Physical Safety When an experiment involves physical activity, avoid injuring yourself or others. Alert your teacher if there is any reason you should not participate.

 Disposal Dispose of chemicals and other laboratory materials safely. Follow the instructions from your teacher.

 Hand Washing Wash your hands thoroughly when finished with the activity. Use antibacterial soap and warm water. Rinse well.

 General Safety Awareness When this symbol appears, follow the instructions provided. When you are asked to [...] own procedure in a lab, have [...] approve your plan before you [...]

California
Focus on Life Science

PEARSON
Prentice
Hall

Boston, Massachusetts
Upper Saddle River, New Jersey

CALIFORNIA
SCIENCE
EXPLORER

Program Print Resources

Student Edition
Teacher's Edition
Teaching Resources
Color Transparencies
Reading and Note Taking Guide Level A
Reading and Note Taking Guide Level B
Inquiry Skills Activity Books I–III
Vocabulary Flashcards
Laboratory Manual
Laboratory Manual, Teacher's Edition
Probeware Lab Manual
Standards Review Transparencies
Progress Monitoring Assessments
Chapter Tests Level A and B
Teaching Guidebook for Universal Access

Program Technology Resources

Lab zone™ Easy Planner
PresentationExpress CD-ROM
StudentExpress with Interactive Textbook CD-ROM
TeacherExpress™ CD-ROM
ExamView® Computer Test Bank
Student Edition in MP3
Probeware Lab Manual CD-ROM

Program Video Resources

Lab Activity DVD
Discovery Channel DVD Library

Spanish Program Resources

Spanish Student Edition
Spanish Reading and Note Taking Guide
Spanish Teacher's Guide with Answer Keys
Spanish Student Edition in MP3

X 026878

Acknowledgments appear on pages 726–728, which constitute an extension of this copyright page.

PEARSON
Prentice
Hall

ISBN 0-13-201272-3

4 5 6 7 8 9 10 11 10 09 08 07

Program Authors

Michael J. Padilla, Ph.D.
Professor of Science Education
University of Georgia
Athens, Georgia

Michael Padilla is a leader in middle school science education. He has served as President of the National Science Teachers Association and as a writer of the National Science Education Standards. As lead author of Science Explorer, Mike has inspired the team in developing a program that meets the needs of middle grade students, promotes science inquiry, and is aligned with the National Science Education Standards.

Ioannis Miaoulis, Ph.D.
President
Museum of Science
Boston, Massachusetts

Originally trained as a mechanical engineer, Ioannis Miaoulis is in the forefront of the national movement to increase technological literacy. As dean of the Tufts University School of Engineering, Dr. Miaoulis spearheaded the introduction of engineering into the Massachusetts curriculum. Currently he is working with school systems across the country to engage students in engineering activities and to foster discussions on the impact of science and technology on society.

Martha Cyr, Ph.D.
Director of K–12 Outreach
Worcester Polytechnic Institute
Worcester, Massachusetts

Martha Cyr is a noted expert in engineering outreach. She has over nine years of experience with programs and activities that emphasize the use of engineering principles, through hands-on projects, to excite and motivate students and teachers of mathematics and science in grades K–12. Her goal is to stimulate a continued interest in science and mathematics through engineering.

Book Authors

Elizabeth Coolidge-Stolz, M.D.
Medical Writer
North Reading, Massachusetts

Jan Jenner, Ph.D.
Science Writer
Talladega, Alabama

Jay M. Pasachoff, Ph.D.
Professor of Astronomy
Williams College
Williamstown, Massachusetts

Donald Cronkite, Ph.D.
Professor of Biology
Hope College
Holland, Michigan

Michael Wysession, Ph.D.
Associate Professor of Earth
 and Planetary Sciences
Washington University
St. Louis, Missouri

Reading Consultants

Kate Kinsella

Kate Kinsella, Ed.D., is a faculty member in the Department of Secondary Education at San Francisco State University. A specialist in second-language acquisition and adolescent literacy, she teaches coursework addressing language and literacy development across the secondary curricula. Dr. Kinsella earned her master's degree in TESOL from San Francisco State University and her Ed.D. in Second Language Acquisition from the University of San Francisco.

Kevin Feldman

Kevin Feldman, Ed.D., is the Director of Reading and Early Intervention with the Sonoma County Office of Education (SCOE) and an independent educational consultant. At the SCOE, he develops, organizes, and monitors programs related to K-12 literacy. Dr. Feldman has a master's degree from the University of California, Riverside, in Special Education, Learning Disabilities, and Instructional Design. He earned his Ed.D. in Curriculum and Instruction from the University of San Francisco.

Mathematics Consultant

William Tate, Ph.D.
Professor of Education and
    Applied Statistics and Computation
Washington University
St. Louis, Missouri

Contributing Writers

Douglas E. Bowman
Health/Physical Education Teacher
Welches Middle School
Welches, Oregon

Jorie Hunken
Science Consultant
Woodstock, Connecticut

Evan P. Silberstein
Science Instructor
The Frisch School
Paramus, New Jersey

Patricia M. Doran
Science Instructional Assistant
State University of New York at Ulster
Stone Ridge, New York

James Robert Kaczynski, Jr.
Science Instructor
Jamestown School
Jamestown, Rhode Island

Joseph Stukey, Ph.D.
Department of Biology
Hope College
Holland, Michigan

Fred Holtzclaw
Science Instructor
Oak Ridge High School
Oak Ridge, Tennessee

Andrew C. Kemp, Ph.D.
Assistant Professor of Education
University of Louisville
Louisville, Kentucky

Thomas R. Wellnitz
Science Instructor
The Paideia School
Atlanta, Georgia

Theresa K. Holtzclaw
Former Science Instructor
Clinton, Tennessee

Beth Miaoulis
Technology Writer
Sherborn, Massachusetts

Reviewers

Content Reviewers

Paul Beale, Ph.D.
Department of Physics
University of Colorado
Boulder, Colorado

Jeff Bodart, Ph.D.
Chipola Junior College
Marianna, Florida

Michael Castellani, Ph.D.
Department of Chemistry
Marshall University
Huntington, West Virginia

Eugene Chiang, Ph.D.
Department of Astronomy
University of California – Berkeley
Berkeley, California

Charles C. Curtis, Ph.D.
Department of Physics
University of Arizona
Tucson, Arizona

Daniel Kirk-Davidoff, Ph.D.
Department of Meteorology
University of Maryland
College Park, Maryland

Diane T. Doser, Ph.D.
Department of Geological Sciences
University of Texas at El Paso
El Paso, Texas

R. E. Duhrkopf, Ph.D.
Department of Biology
Baylor University
Waco, Texas

Michael Hacker
Co-director, Center for
    Technological Literacy
Hofstra University
Hempstead, New York

Michael W. Hamburger, Ph.D.
Department of Geological Sciences
Indiana University
Bloomington, Indiana

Alice K. Hankla, Ph.D.
The Galloway School
Atlanta, Georgia

Donald C. Jackson, Ph.D.
Department of Molecular Pharmacology,
    Physiology, & Biotechnology
Brown University
Providence, Rhode Island

Jeremiah N. Jarrett, Ph.D.
Department of Biological Sciences
Central Connecticut State University
New Britain, Connecticut

David Lederman, Ph.D.
Department of Physics
West Virginia University
Morgantown, West Virginia

Becky Mansfield, Ph.D.
Department of Geography
Ohio State University
Columbus, Ohio

Elizabeth M. Martin, M.S.
Department of Chemistry and Biochemistry
College of Charleston
Charleston, South Carolina

Joe McCullough, Ph.D.
Department of Natural and
    Applied Sciences
Cabrillo College
Aptos, California

Robert J. Mellors, Ph.D.
Department of Geological Sciences
San Diego State University
San Diego, California

Joseph M. Moran, Ph.D.
American Meteorological Society
Washington, D.C.

David J. Morrissey, Ph.D.
Department of Chemistry
Michigan State University
East Lansing, Michigan

Philip A. Reed, Ph.D.
Department of Occupational & Technical
    Studies
Old Dominion University
Norfolk, Virginia

Scott M. Rochette, Ph.D.
Department of the Earth Sciences
State University of New York, College at
    Brockport
Brockport, New York

Laurence D. Rosenhein, Ph.D.
Department of Chemistry
Indiana State University
Terre Haute, Indiana

Ronald Sass, Ph.D.
Department of Biology and Chemistry
Rice University
Houston, Texas

George Schatz, Ph.D.
Department of Chemistry
Northwestern University
Evanston, Illinois

Sara Seager, Ph.D.
Carnegie Institution of Washington
Washington, D.C.

Robert M. Thornton, Ph.D.
Section of Plant Biology
University of California
Davis, California

John R. Villarreal, Ph.D.
College of Science and Engineering
The University of Texas – Pan American
Edinburg, Texas

Kenneth Welty, Ph.D.
School of Education
University of Wisconsin–Stout
Menomonie, Wisconsin

Edward J. Zalisko, Ph.D.
Department of Biology
Blackburn College
Carlinville, Illinois

Safety Reviewers

W. H. Breazeale, Ph.D.
Department of Chemistry
College of Charleston
Charleston, South Carolina

Ruth Hathaway, Ph.D.
Hathaway Consulting
Cape Girardeau, Missouri

Douglas Mandt
Science Education Consultant
Edgewood, Washington

Teacher Reviewers

David R. Blakely
Arlington High School
Arlington, Massachusetts

Jane E. Callery
Two Rivers Magnet Middle School
East Hartford, Connecticut

Melissa Lynn Cook
Oakland Mills High School
Columbia, Maryland

James Fattic
Southside Middle School
Anderson, Indiana

Dan Gabel
Hoover Middle School
Rockville, Maryland

Wayne Goates
Eisenhower Middle School
Goddard, Kansas

Katherine Bobay Graser
Mint Hill Middle School
Charlotte, North Carolina

Darcy Hampton
Deal Junior High School
Washington, D.C.

Karen Kelly
Pierce Middle School
Waterford, Michigan

David Kelso
Manchester High School Central
Manchester, New Hampshire

Benigno Lopez, Jr.
Sleepy Hill Middle School
Lakeland, Florida

Angie L. Matamoros, Ph.D.
ALM Consulting, INC.
Weston, Florida

Tim McCollum
Charleston Middle School
Charleston, Illinois

Bruce A. Mellin
Brooks School
North Andover, Massachusetts

Ella Jay Parfitt
Southeast Middle School
Baltimore, Maryland

Evelyn A. Pizzarello
Louis M. Klein Middle School
Harrison, New York

Kathleen M. Poe
Fletcher Middle School
Jacksonville, Florida

Shirley Rose
Lewis and Clark Middle School
Tulsa, Oklahoma

Linda Sandersen
Greenfield Middle School
Greenfield, Wisconsin

Mary E. Solan
Southwest Middle School
Charlotte, North Carolina

Mary Stewart
University of Tulsa
Tulsa, Oklahoma

Paul Swenson
Billings West High School
Billings, Montana

Thomas Vaughn
Arlington High School
Arlington, Massachusetts

Susan C. Zibell
Central Elementary
Simsbury, Connecticut

Activity Field Testers

Nicki Bibbo
Witchcraft Heights School
Salem, Massachusetts

Rose-Marie Botting
Broward County Schools
Fort Lauderdale, Florida

Colleen Campos
Laredo Middle School
Aurora, Colorado

Elizabeth Chait
W. L. Chenery Middle School
Belmont, Massachusetts

Holly Estes
Hale Middle School
Stow, Massachusetts

Laura Hapgood
Plymouth Community
    Intermediate School
Plymouth, Massachusetts

Mary F. Lavin
Plymouth Community
    Intermediate School
Plymouth, Massachusetts

James MacNeil, Ph.D.
Cambridge, Massachusetts

Lauren Magruder
St. Michael's Country
    Day School
Newport, Rhode Island

Jeanne Maurand
Austin Preparatory School
Reading, Massachusetts

Joanne Jackson-Pelletier
Winman Junior High School
Warwick, Rhode Island

Warren Phillips
Plymouth Public Schools
Plymouth, Massachusetts

Carol Pirtle
Hale Middle School
Stow, Massachusetts

Kathleen M. Poe
Fletcher Middle School
Jacksonville, Florida

Cynthia B. Pope
Norfolk Public Schools
Norfolk, Virginia

Anne Scammell
Geneva Middle School
Geneva, New York

Karen Riley Sievers
Callanan Middle School
Des Moines, Iowa

David M. Smith
Eyer Middle School
Allentown, Pennsylvania

Gene Vitale
Parkland School
McHenry, Illinois

Unit 1

Looking at Cells

Focus on the
BIG Idea

How do scientists make progress in understanding the natural world?

Focus on the
BIG Idea

How does light allow you to see?

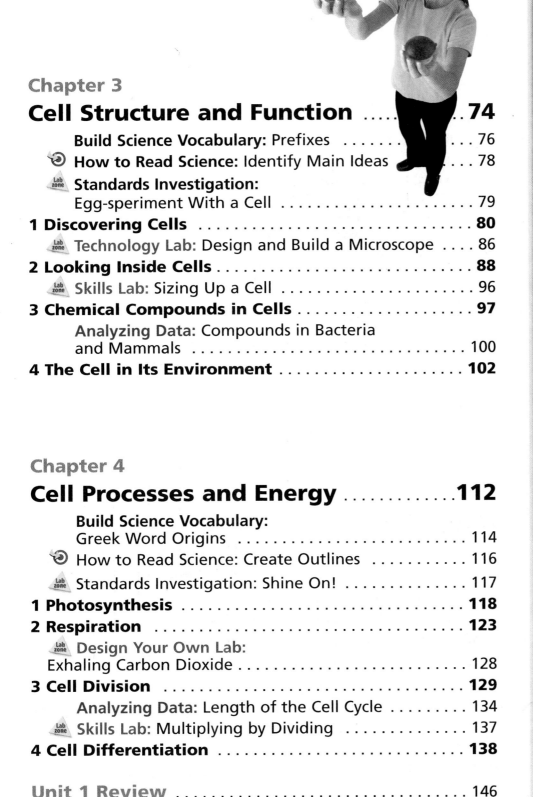

Focus on the
BIG Idea

What is the
structure of
a cell?

Focus on the
BIG Idea

How do cells
obtain the
energy they
need to carry
out all their
functions?

Unit 2

Genetics and Evolution

Focus on the BIG Idea

How are traits passed from parents to offspring?

Focus on the BIG Idea

How are traits inherited in people?

Focus on the
BIG Idea

What factors have caused the evolution and diversity of organisms?

Focus on the
BIG Idea

How does evidence from rocks help scientists understand Earth's history?

Unit 3

Structure and Function in Living Systems

Focus on the
BIG Idea

How do structure and function vary among organisms in different domains and kingdoms?

Focus on the
BIG Idea

How does the structure of a plant allow it to grow and reproduce?

Focus on the
BIG Idea

What major
functions do
animals' bodies
perform?

Focus on the
BIG Idea

How does the
structure of
vertebrates help
them to
function?

Unit 4

Focus on the
BIG Idea

How do organs
and other
structures
enable the
nervous system
to function?

Focus on the
BIG Idea

How do the
endocrine and
reproductive
systems work
together to
contribute to
reproduction?

xv

Activities

Try This **Activity**   Reinforcement of key concepts

Skills **Activity**   Practice of specific science inquiry skills

Lab zone At-Home **Activity** — Quick, engaging activities for home and family

• Tech & Design • — Design, build, test, and communicate

Math — Point-of-use math practice

active art Illustrations come alive online

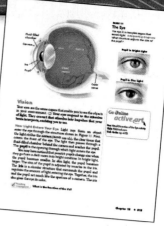

Video Field Trip
Discovery Channel School

VIDEO

Enhance understanding through dynamic video.

Preview Get motivated with this introduction to the chapter content.

Field Trip Explore a real-world story related to the chapter content.

Assessment Review content and take an assessment.

Go Online
Web Links

Get connected to exciting Web resources in every lesson.

SC*LINKS*™ NSTA Find Web links on topics relating to every section.

Active Art Interact with selected visuals from every chapter online.

Planet Diary® Explore news and natural phenomena through weekly reports.

Science News® Keep up to date with the latest science discoveries.

Interactive Textbook

Experience the complete textbook online and on CD-ROM.

Activities Practice skills and learn content.

Videos Explore content and learn important lab skills.

Audio Support Hear key terms spoken and defined.

Self-Assessment Use instant feedback to help you track your progress.

CALIFORNIA
Science Content Standards

This textbook is organized to support your learning of the California Science Content Standards. Understanding this organization can help you master the standards.

Focus on the BIG Idea

S 8.5

How do cells obtain the energy they need to carry out all their functions?

Every chapter begins with a Focus on the Big Idea question that is linked to a California Science Standard. Focus on the Big Idea poses a question for you to think about as you study the chapter. You will discover the answer to the question as you read.

CALIFORNIA
Standards Focus

S 7.1.d Students know that mitochondria liberate energy for the work that cells do and that chloroplasts capture sunlight energy for photosynthesis.

- How does the sun supply living things with the energy they need?

- What happens during the process of photosynthesis?

Each section begins with a Standards Focus. You will learn about these California Science Standards as you read the section.

The Standards Focus is broken down into two to four Key Concept questions. You will find the answers to these questions as you read the section.

Standards Key

Grade Level

Standard Set and Standard

S 7.1.d

Content Area
S for Science
E-LA for English-Language Arts
Math for Mathematics

The next several pages will introduce you to the California Science Content Standards for Grade 7. Seven sets of standards cover the material you will be learning this year. Each standard set contains several specific standards that tell what you need to know. For Grade 7, these standards focus mainly on life science. Some of the standards also help you learn about relationships between life science and other branches of science.

STANDARD SET 1

Cell Biology

1. All living organisms are composed of cells, from just one to many trillions, whose details usually are visible only through a microscope. As a basis for understanding this concept:

1. a. *Students know* cells function similarly in all living organisms.
1. b. *Students know* the characteristics that distinguish plant cells from animal cells, including chloroplasts and cell walls.
1. c. *Students know* the nucleus is the repository for genetic information in plant and animal cells.

What It Means to You

You will learn that all organisms are made up of cells. These cells have many functions and structures in common, but there are differences between cells from different organisms. You will learn about the important differences between plant and animal cells. You will also learn that cells have a nucleus that holds the cell's genetic information and controls the cell's functions.

Where You Will Learn It

Chapters 3 and 9

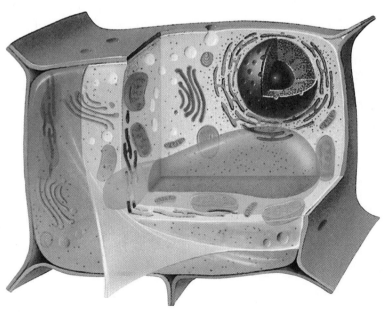

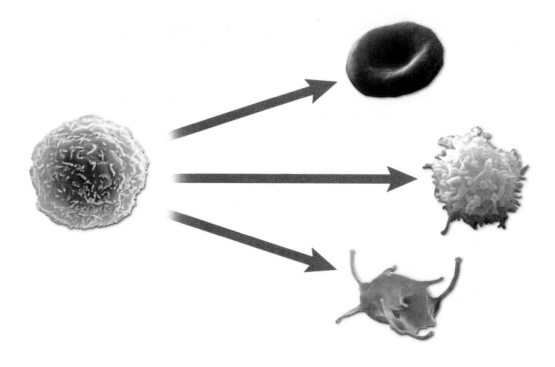

STANDARD SET 1, continued

1. d. *Students know* that mitochondria liberate energy for the work that cells do and that chloroplasts capture sunlight energy for photosynthesis.
1. e. *Students know* cells divide to increase their numbers through a process of mitosis, which results in two daughter cells with identical sets of chromosomes.
1. f. *Students know* that as multicellular organisms develop, their cells differentiate.

What It Means to You
You will learn how cells get the energy they need to perform their functions. Some cells, such as those in plants, have chloroplasts that capture energy from sunlight and use it to produce food that the cell can use. You will learn that both plant and animal cells have mitochondria that release energy from food. Cells use this energy to carry out many functions. You will also learn how cells divide to produce new cells. In multicellular organisms, cells may develop specialized structures that allow them to perform different functions.

Where You Will Learn It
Chapters 4, 10, and 16

2. **A typical cell of any organism contains genetic instructions that specify its traits. Those traits may be modified by environmental influences. As a basis for understanding this concept:**

2. a. *Students know* the differences between the life cycles and reproduction methods of sexual and asexual organisms.

2. b. *Students know* sexual reproduction produces offspring that inherit half their genes from each parent.

2. c. *Students know* an inherited trait can be determined by one or more genes.

2. d. *Students know* plant and animal cells contain many thousands of different genes and typically have two copies of every gene. The two copies (or alleles) of the gene may or may not be identical, and one may be dominant in determining the phenotype while the other is recessive.

2. e. *Students know* DNA (deoxyribonucleic acid) is the genetic material of living organisms and is located in the chromosomes of each cell.

What It Means To You

In this standard set, you will learn how organisms reproduce. You will learn that there are two main types of reproduction: asexual and sexual. You will also learn how parents pass their genetic information to their offspring in sexual reproduction. You will discover how DNA within a cell is divided into sections called genes. These genes determine an organism's traits.

Where You Will Learn It

Chapters 5, 6, 9, 10, 11, and 12

STANDARD SET 3

Evolution

3. **Biological evolution accounts for the diversity of species developed through gradual processes over many generations. As a basis for understanding this concept:**

3. a. *Students know* both genetic variation and environmental factors are causes of evolution and diversity of organisms.

3. b. *Students know* the reasoning used by Charles Darwin in reaching his conclusion that natural selection is the mechanism of evolution.

3. c. *Students know* how independent lines of evidence from geology, fossils, and comparative anatomy provide the bases for the theory of evolution.

3. d. *Students know* how to construct a simple branching diagram to classify living groups of organisms by shared derived characteristics and how to expand the diagram to include fossil organisms.

3. e. *Students know* that extinction of a species occurs when the environment changes and the adaptive characteristics of a species are insufficient for its survival.

What It Means to You

You will learn that the great diversity of organisms on Earth has developed over time through the process of evolution. You will learn how Charles Darwin developed the theory of natural selection, and how evidence from fossils, Earth's rock layers, and comparisons of organisms supports this theory. You will also learn how genetic variations and environmental changes interact in natural selection.

You will practice creating diagrams that show the relationship among living organisms and fossils. You will also learn that when a species of organisms cannot adapt to a change in the environment, the species may die out, or become extinct.

Where You Will Learn It

Chapters 7, 11, and 12

Earth and Life History

4. Evidence from rocks allows us to understand the evolution of life on Earth. As a basis for understanding this concept:

4. a. *Students know* Earth processes today are similar to those that occurred in the past and slow geologic processes have large cumulative effects over long periods of time.

4. b. *Students know* the history of life on Earth has been disrupted by major catastrophic events, such as major volcanic eruptions or the impacts of asteroids.

4. c. *Students know* that the rock cycle includes the formation of new sediment and rocks and that rocks are often found in layers, with the oldest generally on the bottom.

What It Means to You

You will learn how scientists use evidence found in layers of rock to study the evolution of life on Earth. You will learn how scientists study processes that occur on Earth today, such as the rock cycle, to understand what happened in earlier times. You will also learn how sudden events (such as volcanic eruptions and asteroid impacts) have changed the history of life on Earth.

Where You Will Learn It

Chapter 8

CALIFORNIA
Science Content Standards

CALIFORNIA

4. d.   *Students know* that evidence from geologic layers and radioactive dating indicates Earth is approximately 4.6 billion years old and that life on this planet has existed for more than 3 billion years.

4. e.   *Students know* fossils provide evidence of how life and environmental conditions have changed.

4. f.   *Students know* how movements of Earth's continental and oceanic plates through time, with associated changes in climate and geographic connections, have affected the past and present distribution of organisms.

4. g.   *Students know* how to explain significant developments and extinctions of plant and animal life on the geologic time scale.

What It Means to You

You will learn how scientists have determined the age of Earth and of early life forms by using radioactive dating and by comparing materials found in different rock layers. Fossils found in rock layers show how Earth's organisms and environments have changed over time. You will also learn how the movement of Earth's plates has changed Earth's environments, and how those changes have affected life on Earth. You will learn about the geologic time scale and how scientists determine when important events occurred.

Where You Will Learn It

Chapters 7 and 8

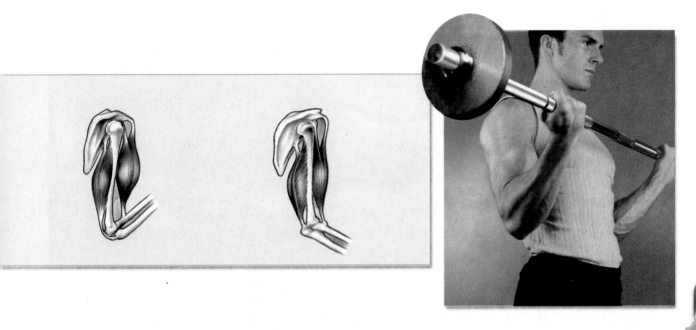

STANDARD SET 5

Structure and Function in Living Systems

5. **The anatomy and physiology of plants and animals illustrate the complementary nature of structure and function. As a basis for understanding this concept:**

5. a. *Students know* plants and animals have levels of organization for structure and function, including cells, tissues, organs, organ systems, and the whole organism.

5. b. *Students know* organ systems function because of the contributions of the individual organs, tissues, and cells. The failure of any part can affect the entire system.

5. c. *Students know* how bones and muscles work together to provide a structural framework for movement.

What It Means to You

You will learn about the structures found in organisms. These structures are organized into cells, tissues, organs, organ systems, and whole organisms. You will learn how different body parts work together to ensure that the whole organism survives. For example, you will explore how bones and muscles work together to allow animals to move. You will learn about a variety of structures in both plants and animals and how each structure helps the organism to carry out its life functions.

Where You Will Learn It

Chapters 1, 9, 10, 11, 12, 13, 14, 15, and 16

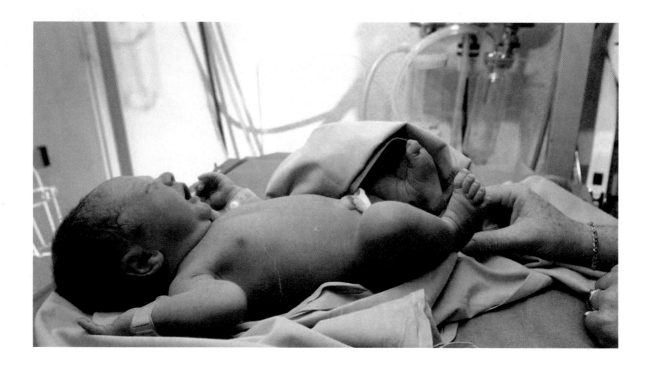

STANDARD SET 5, continued

5. d. *Students know* how the reproductive organs of the human female and male generate eggs and sperm and how sexual activity may lead to fertilization and pregnancy.

5. e. *Students know* the function of the umbilicus and placenta during pregnancy.

5. f. *Students know* the structures and processes by which flowering plants generate pollen, ovules, seeds, and fruit.

5. g. *Students know* how to relate the structures of the eye and ear to their functions.

What It Means to You
You will learn how humans reproduce, beginning with the production of egg and sperm cells. You will see how structures in the female reproductive system protect a developing fetus and transfer nutrients and other materials between the mother and the fetus. You will also learn how different plants reproduce. Finally, you will explore how the human eye and ear enable people to see and hear.

Where You Will Learn It
Chapters 10, 15, and 16

STANDARD SET 6

Physical Principles in Living Systems

6. **Physical principles underlie biological structures and functions. As a basis for understanding this concept:**

6. a. *Students know* visible light is a small band within a very broad electromagnetic spectrum.

6. b. *Students know* that for an object to be seen, light emitted by or scattered from it must be detected by the eye.

6. c. *Students know* light travels in straight lines if the medium it travels through does not change.

6. d. *Students know* how simple lenses are used in a magnifying glass, the eye, a camera, a telescope, and a microscope.

6. e. *Students know* that white light is a mixture of many wavelengths (colors) and that retinal cells react differently to different wavelengths.

6. f. *Students know* light can be reflected, refracted, transmitted, and absorbed by matter.

6. g. *Students know* the angle of reflection of a light beam is equal to the angle of incidence.

What It Means to You

This standard set includes some ways that concepts from physical science are important in life science. You will learn how light behaves and how your eye reacts to different kinds of light. You will explore tools, such as telescopes and microscopes, that allow people to observe objects that cannot be seen without these tools.

Where You Will Learn It

Chapters 1, 2, 3, and 15

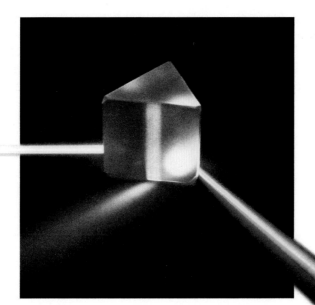

STANDARD SET 6, continued

6. h. *Students know* how to compare joints in the body (wrist, shoulder, thigh) with structures used in machines and simple devices (hinge, ball-and-socket, and sliding joints).

6. i. *Students know* how levers confer mechanical advantage and how the application of this principle applies to the musculoskeletal system.

6. j. *Students know* that contractions of the heart generate blood pressure and that heart valves prevent backflow of blood in the circulatory system.

What It Means to You

You will learn how the bones, muscles, and joints in your body are similar to machines such as levers. By exploring how simple machines work, you will learn how your own muscles and bones function. You will also learn how your heart moves blood through your body.

Where You Will Learn It

Chapters 13 and 14

7. **Scientific progress is made by asking meaningful questions and conducting careful investigations. As a basis for understanding this concept and addressing the content in the other three strands, students should develop their own questions and perform investigations. Students will:**

7. a. Select and use appropriate tools and technology (including calculators, computers, balances, spring scales, microscopes, and binoculars) to perform tests, collect data, and display data.

7. b. Use a variety of print and electronic resources (including the World Wide Web) to collect information and evidence as part of a research project.

7. c. Communicate the logical connection among hypotheses, science concepts, tests conducted, data collected, and conclusions drawn from the scientific evidence.

7. d. Construct scale models, maps, and appropriately labeled diagrams to communicate scientific knowledge (e.g., motion of Earth's plates and cell structure).

7. e. Communicate the steps and results from an investigation in written reports and oral presentations.

What It Means to You

You will learn how scientists gather, interpret, and communicate information. You will perform your own experiments and investigations and learn to draw conclusions from the data you collect. For instance, you will explore what conditions allow the stomach to digest protein. You will learn to find accurate information in print and electronic resources, and to create models and diagrams to communicate the information you learn.

Where You Will Learn It

This material is covered in Chapters 1, 3, and 9, and in the labs and activities in all chapters.

Your Keys to Success

Read for Meaning

This textbook has been developed to fully support your understanding of the science concepts in the California Science Standards. Each chapter contains built-in reading support.

Before You Read

Use the Standards Focus to preview the California Science Standards that are covered, the key concepts, and key terms in the section.

Standards Focus
The California Science Standards that you will learn are listed at the beginning of each section.

Key Concepts
Each science standard is broken down into smaller ideas called Key Concepts.

Key Terms Use the list of key terms to preview the vocabulary for each section.

Section

2

The Study of Life

CALIFORNIA
Standards Focus

S 7.5 The anatomy and physiology of plants and animals illustrate the complementary nature of structure and function.

S 7.6 Physical principles underlie biological structures and functions.

→ How are the branches of life science related?

→ What are some big ideas in life science?

Key Terms
• life science
• biology
• organism
• development
• structure
• function
• complementary

Lab zone Standards **Warm-Up**

How Is Structure Related to Function?

1. Study the photo of the bird and list its characteristics.
2. Next, study the photos of the three food items below.

Think It Over
Inferring Based on your observations, which of the food items do you think the bird feeds on? Explain your reasoning.

In a laboratory, detectives are solving a crime by comparing the genetic makeup of different suspects. On a beach, a scientist studies the nesting behavior of sea turtles. Deep in a tropical rain forest, another scientist discovers a new kind of beetle. In a hospital laboratory, doctors study a deadly form of bird flu. At a cancer research institute, a team of scientists develops new treatments for a rare form of cancer. What do all of these people have in common? All these people are working in the field of life science.

Life science is the study of living things. Another name for life science is biology. The word biology comes from two Greek words. *Bios* means "life" and *logos* means "reason" or "the study of." Thus **biology** is the study of life. Biologists are scientists who study living things.

Biologists study all kinds of living things. The general term for a living thing is an **organism**. An organism may be an animal, a plant, a fungus or a microbe.

As You Read

Key Concepts in boldface sentences allow you to focus on the important ideas of the chapter.

Look for the green and yellow keys to find the key concepts in each section.

Molecular biologists study the chemicals in cells.

Entomologists study insects.

Physiologists study the structure and function of organisms.

Ecologists study organisms in their environment.

FIGURE
Life Scientists at Work
You can find life scientists at work in such diverse places as forests, laboratories, zoos, and museums.

Go Online
SCiLINKS NSTA

For: Links on careers in life science
Visit: www.SciLinks.org
Web Code: cvn-1012

Branches of Life Science

Biologists can work outside or in a laboratory. They may work for universities, private companies, or government agencies. Biologists, like other scientists, usually work as part of a team studying a common topic.

Life science includes many different branches, or fields of study. Molecular biology, genetics, physiology, and ecology are just some fields of life science. Molecular biology is the study of the chemical building blocks of cells. Genetics is the study of how information about organisms is passed from parent to offspring. Physiology is the study of the structures and functions of organisms. Ecology is the study of how organisms interact with each other and with their surroundings. Other branches of life science include cell biology, plant biology, and microbiology. What do you think these fields involve?

⊙ **Though life science can be divided into branches, the different fields of study often overlap.** For example, understanding what controls plant development relies on concepts from molecular biology and plant biology. Progress in one field of life science often contributes to progress in another field.

The principles of physics also help explain life processes. Consider, for example, the relationship between the physics of light and the way that eyes function. To understand how eyes function, scientists must know what light is and how light travels. Scientists can compare the structure of an eye to that of a camera. Like a camera, an eye uses a lens to focus light and form an image. The principles that allow a camera to take a picture also allow an eye to see.

Compare the variety of eyes in Figure 9. Although each of the animals may see slightly differently, all of the eyes operate on similar physical principles.

If you can't answer these items, go back and review the section.

After You Read

The Section Assessment tests your understanding of the Key Concepts. Each bank of Reviewing Key Concept questions here focuses on one of the Key Concepts.

Section 2 Assessment

S 7.5, 7.6 E-LA: Reading: 7.2.0

⊙ **Target Reading Skill** Preview Text Structure When you took notes on Section 2, what question did you ask for the heading Change Over Time? What was your answer?

⊙ **Reviewing Key Concepts**
1. **a.** Defining What is life science?
   b. Describing List three branches of life science and describe what is studied in each.
   c. Making Judgments Your friend wants to be a plant biologist and says she only needs to take courses in plant biology. Why might it be a good idea for your friend to study other branches of life science as well?
2. **a.** Listing What are four big ideas in life science?
   b. Comparing and Contrasting What are some ways that a cat and a tree are similar? What are some ways they are different?

Lab zone At-Home **Activity**

It's Complementary Explain to a family member what "complementary structure and function" means. Then look through books or magazines for photos of organisms that illustrate this concept. Find five examples to show your family member. Describe how a structure on each of the organisms is adapted to its function.

Your Keys to Success

How to Read Science

 The target reading skills introduced on this page will help you read and understand information in this textbook. Each chapter introduces a reading skill. Developing these reading skills is key to becoming a successful reader in science and other subject areas.

Preview Text Structure By understanding how textbooks are organized, you can gain information from them more effectively. This textbook is organized with red headings and blue subheadings. Before you read, preview the headings. Ask yourself questions to guide you as you read. **(Chapter 1)**

Preview Visuals The visuals in your science textbook provide important information. Visuals are photographs, graphs, tables, diagrams, and illustrations. Before you read, take the time to preview the visuals in a section. Look closely at the titles, labels, and captions. Then ask yourself questions about the visuals. **(Chapter 2)**

Sequence Many parts of a science textbook are organized by sequence. Sequence is the order in which a series of events occurs. Some sections may discuss events in a process that has a beginning and an end. Other sections may describe a continuous process that does not have an end. **(Chapters 10 and 14)**

Compare and Contrast Science texts often make comparisons. When you compare and contrast, you examine the similarities and differences between things. You can compare and contrast by using a table or a Venn diagram. **(Chapters 9 and 12)**

Analyze Cause and Effect A cause makes something happen. An effect is what happens. When you recognize that one event causes another, you are relating cause and effect. **(Chapter 16)**

Identify Main Ideas As you read, you can understand a section or paragraph more clearly by finding the main idea. The main idea is the most important idea. The details in a section or paragraph support the main idea. Headings and subheadings can often help you identify the main ideas. **(Chapters 3, 6, and 15)**

Identify Supporting Evidence Science textbooks often describe the scientific evidence that supports a theory or hypothesis. Scientific evidence includes data and facts, information whose accuracy can be confirmed by experiments or observation. A hypothesis is a possible explanation for observations made by scientists or an answer to a scientific question. **(Chapter 7)**

Create Outlines You can create outlines to help you clarify the text. An outline shows the relationship between main ideas and supporting details. Use the text structure—headings, subheadings, key concepts, and key terms—to help you figure out information to include in your outline. **(Chapters 4 and 8)**

Take Notes Science chapters are packed with information. Taking good notes is one way to help you remember key ideas and see the big picture. When you take notes, include key ideas, a few details, and summaries. **(Chapters 5, 11, and 13)**

Target Reading Skills

Each chapter provides a target reading skill with clear instruction to help you read and understand the text. You will apply the skill as you read. Then you will record what you've learned in the section and chapter assessments.

Before You Read
Each chapter introduces a target reading skill and provides examples and practice exercises.

As You Read
As you read, you can use the target reading skill to help you increase your understanding.

After You Read
You can apply the target reading skill in the Section Assessments and in the Chapter Assessments.

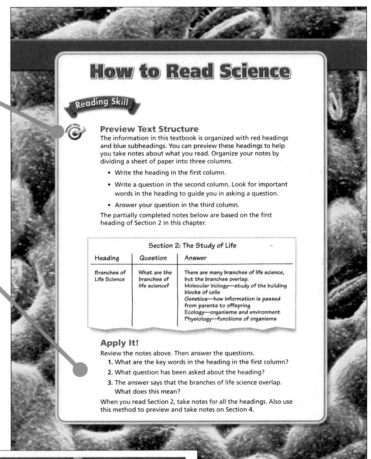

How to Read Science

Reading Skill

Preview Text Structure

The information in this textbook is organized with red headings and blue subheadings. You can preview these headings to help you take notes about what you read. Organize your notes by dividing a sheet of paper into three columns.

- Write the heading in the first column.
- Write a question in the second column. Look for important words in the heading to guide you in asking a question.
- Answer your question in the third column.

The partially completed notes below are based on the first heading of Section 2 in this chapter.

Section 2: The Study of Life

Heading	Question	Answer
Branches of Life Science	What are the branches of life science?	There are many branches of life science, but the branches overlap. Molecular biology—study of the building blocks of cells Genetics—how information is passed from parents to offspring Ecology—organisms and environment Physiology—functions of organisms

Apply It!

Review the notes above. Then answer the questions.
1. What are the key words in the heading in the first column?
2. What question has been asked about the heading?
3. The answer says that the branches of life science overlap. What does this mean?

When you read Section 2, take notes for all the headings. Also use this method to preview and take notes on Section 4.

Section 2 Assessment   S 7.5, 7.6 E-LA: Reading: 7.2.0

Target Reading Skill Preview Text Structure When you took notes on Section 2, what question did you ask for the heading Change Over Time? What was your answer?

Reviewing Key Concepts

1. a. Defining What is life science?
   b. Describing List three branches of life science and describe what is studied in each.
   c. Making Judgments Your friend wants to be a plant biologist and says she only needs to take courses in plant biology. Why might it be a good idea for your friend to study other branches of life science as well?
2. a. Listing What are four big ideas in life science?
   b. Comparing and Contrasting What are some ways that a cat and a tree are similar? What are some ways they are different?

Lab zone **At-Home Activity**

It's Complementary Explain to a family member what "complementary structure and function" means. Then look through books or magazines for photos of organisms that illustrate this concept. Find five examples to show your family member. Describe how a structure on each of the organisms is adapted to its function.

Build Science Vocabulary

Studying science involves learning a new vocabulary. Here are some vocabulary skills to help you learn the meaning of words you do not recognize.

Word Analysis You can use your knowledge of word parts—prefixes, suffixes, and roots—to determine the meaning of unfamiliar words.

Prefixes A prefix is a word part that is added at the beginning of a root or base word to change its meaning. Knowing the meaning of prefixes will help you figure out new words. You will practice this skill in **Chapters 3 and 9.**

Suffixes A suffix is a letter or group of letters added to the end of a word to form a new word with a slightly different meaning. Adding a suffix to a word often changes its part of speech. You will practice this skill in **Chapters 5 and 15.**

Word Origins Many science words come to English from other languages, such as Greek and Latin. By learning the meaning of a few common Greek and Latin roots, you can determine the meaning of new science words. You will practice this skill in **Chapters 2, 4, 12, and 13.**

Use Clues to Determine Meaning

When you come across a word you don't recognize in science texts, you can use context clues to figure out what the word means. First look for clues in the word itself. Then look at the surrounding words, sentences, and paragraphs for clues. You will practice this skill in **Chapters 8 and 11.**

Identify Multiple Meanings

To understand science concepts, you must use terms precisely. Some familiar words may have different meanings in science. Watch for these multiple-meaning words as you read. You will practice this skill in **Chapter 7.**

Identify Related Word Forms

You can increase your vocabulary by learning related forms of words or word families. If you know the meaning of a verb form, you may be able to figure out the related noun and adjective forms. You will practice this skill in **Chapter 16.**

Vocabulary Skills

One of the important steps in reading this science textbook is to be sure that you understand the key terms. Your book shows several strategies to help you learn important vocabulary.

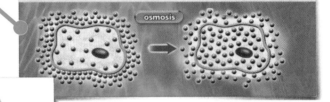

Build Science Vocabulary

The images shown here represent some of the Key Terms in this chapter. You can use this vocabulary skill to help you understand the meaning of some Key Terms in this chapter.

Vocabulary Skill

Prefixes

Words can sometimes be divided into parts. A root is the part of the word that carries the basic meaning. A prefix is a word part that is placed in front of the root to change the word's meaning. In the word *multicellular*, for example, *-cellular* is the root and *multi-* is the prefix. The prefix *multi-* means "many." *Multicellular* means "having many cells."

The prefixes below will help you understand some Key Terms.

Prefix	Meaning	Example Word
chlor-	green	**chloroplast** A cellular structure that captures energy from sunlight
cyto-	cell	**cytoskeleton** The framework inside a cell
multi-	many	**multicellular** Having many cells
uni-	one	**unicellular** Having one cell

Apply It!
1. A **chloroplast** is a structure in plant cells. What color do you think a chloroplast is?
2. What clue within the word **cytoplasm** lets you know that the word has something to do with cells?

osmosis

Before You Read

Each chapter introduces a Vocabulary Skill with examples and practice exercises. Key terms come alive through visuals. The beginning of each section lists the key terms.

Unicellular and Multicellular

Organisms may be composed of only one cell or many trillions of cells. **Unicellular,** or single-celled, organisms include bacteria (bak TIHR ee uh), the most numerous organisms on Earth. **Multicellular** organisms are composed of many cells.

In multicellular organisms, cells are often organized into tissues, organs, and organ systems. A **tissue** is a group of similar cells that work together to perform a specific function. For example, your brain is mostly made up of nervous tissue, which consists of nerve cells. An **organ,** such as your brain, is made up of different kinds of tissues that work together. In addition to nervous tissue, your brain contains other kinds of tissue that support and protect it. Your brain is part of your nervous system, an organ system that directs body activities and processes. An **organ system** is a group of organs that work together to perform a major function.

Unicellular

Multicellular

FIGURE 4
Cellular Organization
This dog is multicellular. The bacteria that live naturally on its teeth are unicellular. Each green sphere is a bacterial cell.

Reading Checkpoint What is an organ?

As You Read

Each key term is highlighted in yellow, appears in boldface type, and is followed by a definition.

Section 1 Assessment

S 7.1 E-LA: Reading 7.1.2, Writing 7.2.4

Vocabulary Skill Prefixes Complete the following sentences with Key Terms.
Because bacteria each have only one cell, they are _____ organisms.
Animals have many cells. Therefore, animals are _____ organisms.

Reviewing Key Concepts
1. a. Defining Define *structure* and *function*.
   b. Explaining Explain this statement: Cells are the basic units of structure and function in organisms.
   c. Applying Concepts In what important function are the cells in your eyes involved?
2. a. Reviewing What does a microscope enable people to do?
   b. Summarizing Summarize Hooke's observations of cork under a microscope.
   c. Relating Cause and Effect Why would Hooke's discovery have been impossible without a microscope?

3. a. Listing What does the cell theory state?
   b. Explaining What did Virchow contribute to the cell theory?
   c. Applying Concepts Use Virchow's ideas to explain why plastic plants are not alive.
4. a. Reviewing How do multicellular organisms differ from unicellular organisms?
   b. Explaining What is the relationship among cells, tissues, and organs?
   c. Inferring Would a tissue or an organ have more kinds of specialized cells? Explain.

Writing in Science

Writing an Award Speech Suppose you are a member of a scientific society that is giving an award to one of the early cell scientists. Choose the scientist, and write a speech that you might give at the award ceremony. Be sure to describe the scientist's accomplishments.

After You Read

You can practice the Vocabulary Skill in the Section Assessments. You can apply your understanding of the key terms in the Chapter Assessments.

Your Keys to Success

Build Science Vocabulary

High-Use Academic Words

High-use academic words are words that are used frequently in classroom reading, writing, and discussions. They are different from key terms because they appear in many subject areas.

Learn the Words

Each unit contains a chapter that introduces high-use academic words. The introduction describes the words, provides examples, and includes practice exercises.

Practice Using the Words

You can practice using the high-use academic words in Apply It! and the Section Assessments.

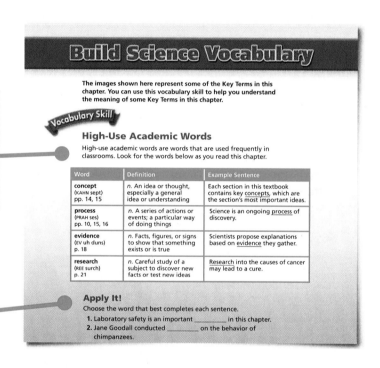

Focus on Life Science High-Use Academic Words

Learning the meanings of these words will help you improve your reading comprehension in all subject areas.

adjust	contract	flexible	normal	section
adult	contrast	focus	obvious	sequence
affect	contribute	function	occur	series
alter	convert	identical	percent	source
analyze	cycle	indicate	predict	specific
approach	detect	interact	process	stable
area	determine	interpret	range	structure
attach	device	involve	region	survival
communicate	distinct	label	regulate	technique
complex	diverse	layer	require	theory
concept	enable	locate	research	transport
conduct	environment	maintain	resource	unique
consist	evidence	mature	respond	vary
constant	expose	method	reverse	visible

Investigations

You can explore the concepts in this textbook through inquiry. Like a real scientist, you can develop your own scientific questions and perform labs and activities to find answers. Follow the steps below when doing a lab.

1 Read the whole lab.

5 Record your data.

2 Write a purpose. What is the purpose of this activity?

3 Write a hypothesis. What is a possible explanation? Hypotheses lead to predictions that can be tested.

4 Follow each step in the procedure. Pay attention to safety icons.

Lab zone | Skills Lab

Changing Colors

 S 7.6.e, 7.7.c

Problem
How do color filters affect the appearance of objects in white light?

Skills Focus
observing, inferring, predicting

Materials
- shoe box
- scissors
- flashlight
- removable tape
- red object (such as a ripe tomato)
- yellow object (such as a ripe lemon)
- blue object (such as blue construction paper)
- red, green, and blue cellophane, enough to cover the top of the shoe box

Procedure
1. Carefully cut a large rectangular hole in the lid of the shoe box.
2. Carefully cut a small, round hole in the center of one of the ends of the shoe box.
3. Tape the red cellophane under the lid of the shoe box, covering the hole in the lid.
4. Place the objects in the box and put the lid on.
5. In a darkened room, shine the flashlight into the shoe box through the side hole. Note the apparent color of each object in the box.
6. Repeat Steps 3–5 using the other colors of cellophane.

Analyze and Conclude
1. Observing What did you see when you looked through the red cellophane? Explain why each object appeared as it did.
2. Observing What did you see when you looked through the blue cellophane? Explain.
3. Inferring What color(s) of light does each piece of cellophane allow through?
4. Predicting Predict what you would see under each piece of cellophane if you put a white object in the box. Test your prediction.
5. Predicting What do you think would happen if you viewed a red object through yellow cellophane? Draw a diagram to support your prediction. Then test your prediction.
6. Communicating Summarize your conclusions by drawing diagrams to show how each color filter affects white light. Write captions to explain your diagrams.

Design an Experiment
Do color filters work like pigments or like colors of light? Design an experiment to find out what happens if you shine a light through both a red and a green filter. *Obtain your teacher's permission before carrying out your investigation.*

---

6 Analyze your results. Answering the questions will help you draw conclusions.

7 Communicate your results in a written report or oral presentation.
Your report should include
- a hypothesis
- a purpose
- the steps of the procedure
- a record of your results
- a conclusion

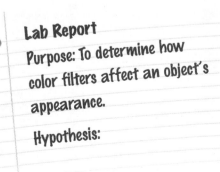

Lab Report

Purpose: To determine how color filters affect an object's appearance.

Hypothesis:

For more information on Science Inquiry, Scientific Investigations, and Safety refer to the Skills Handbook and Appendix A.

Chapter

1

What Is Life Science?

This food scientist is busy ▶ at work in a laboratory.

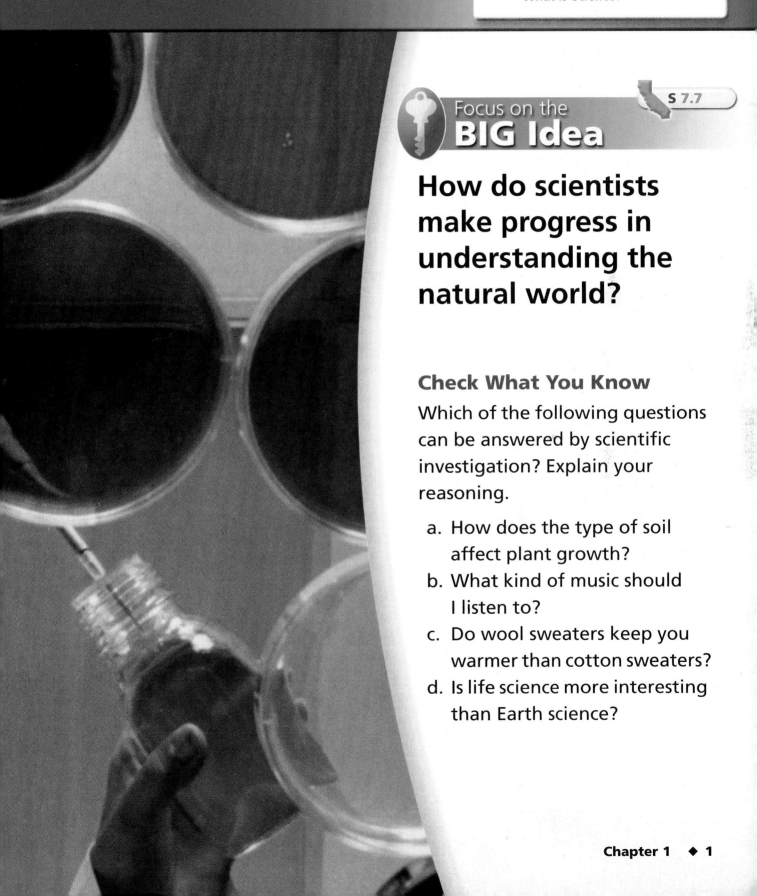

Focus on the
BIG Idea

S 7.7

How do scientists make progress in understanding the natural world?

Check What You Know

Which of the following questions can be answered by scientific investigation? Explain your reasoning.

a. How does the type of soil affect plant growth?
b. What kind of music should I listen to?
c. Do wool sweaters keep you warmer than cotton sweaters?
d. Is life science more interesting than Earth science?

Build Science Vocabulary

The images shown here represent some of the Key Terms in this chapter. You can use this vocabulary skill to help you understand the meaning of some Key Terms in this chapter.

Vocabulary Skill

High-Use Academic Words

High-use academic words are words that are used frequently in classrooms. Look for the words below as you read this chapter.

Word	Definition	Example Sentence
concept (KAHN sept) pp. 14, 15	*n.* An idea or thought, especially a general idea or understanding	Each section in this textbook contains key concepts, which are the section's most important ideas.
process (PRAH ses) pp. 10, 15, 16	*n.* A series of actions or events; a particular way of doing things	Science is an ongoing process of discovery.
evidence (EV uh duns) p. 18	*n.* Facts, figures, or signs to show that something exists or is true	Scientists propose explanations based on evidence they gather.
research (REE surch) p. 21	*n.* Careful study of a subject to discover new facts or test new ideas	Research into the causes of cancer may lead to a cure.

Apply It!

Choose the word that best completes each sentence.

1. Laboratory safety is an important _____ in this chapter.
2. Jane Goodall conducted _____ on the behavior of chimpanzees.
3. Scientists do research and gather _____ to test their ideas.

organisms

scale model

controlled experiment

observing

quantitative observation

Chapter 1 Vocabulary

Interactive Textbook

Build Science Vocabulary
Online
Visit: PHSchool.com
Web Code: cvj-1010

How to Read Science

Preview Text Structure

The information in this textbook is organized with red headings and blue subheadings. You can preview these headings to help you take notes about what you read. Organize your notes by dividing a sheet of paper into three columns.

- Write the heading in the first column.

- Write a question in the second column. Look for important words in the heading to guide you in asking a question.

- Answer your question in the third column.

The partially completed notes below are based on the first heading of Section 2 in this chapter.

Section 2: The Study of Life

Heading	Question	Answer
Branches of Life Science	What are the branches of life science?	There are many branches of life science, but the branches overlap. Molecular biology—study of the building blocks of cells Genetics—how information is passed from parents to offspring Ecology—organisms and environment Physiology—functions of organisms

Apply It!

Review the notes above. Then answer the questions.

1. What are the key words in the heading in the first column?

2. What question has been asked about the heading?

3. The answer says that the branches of life science overlap. What does this mean?

When you read Section 2, take notes for all the headings. Also use this method to preview and take notes on Section 4.

S 7.5, 7.7.c

Ideas and Scientific Evidence

Does fertilizer make plants grow taller? Is yawning contagious? Do fresh eggs sink in water, but older eggs float? Does moss always grow on the north side of trees? Do brightly colored flowers attract more insects? Each of these questions relates to a common idea about living things. But are those ideas true? What is the evidence? In this investigation, you will use scientific methods to find out.

Your Goal

To design and conduct a scientific experiment to test whether a common idea about living things is true or false

To complete this investigation, you must

- select one specific question to investigate
- determine the procedure you will follow to investigate your question
- collect data and use it to draw conclusions
- follow the safety guidelines in Appendix A

Plan It!

Make a list of some common ideas you could explore. Then preview the chapter to learn what types of questions can be explored by scientific methods. When you select a question, write the procedure you will follow. After your teacher approves your plan, begin your experiment.

Thinking Like a Scientist

CALIFORNIA
Standards Focus

S 7.7 Scientific progress is made by asking meaningful questions and conducting careful investigations.

What skills do scientists use to learn about the world?

Key Terms
- science
- observing
- quantitative observation
- qualitative observation
- inferring
- predicting
- classifying
- making models
- scale model

Lab zone Standards Warm-Up

How Keen Are Your Senses?
1. Your teacher has arranged for an unexpected event to occur. At the count of three, the event will begin.
2. List as many details as you can remember about the event.
3. Compare your list with those of your classmates.

Think It Over
Observing How many details could you list? Which of your senses did you use to gather information?

Once, as I walked through thick forest in a downpour, I suddenly saw a chimp hunched in front of me. Quickly I stopped. Then I heard a sound from above. I looked up and there was a big chimp there, too. When he saw me he gave a loud, clear wailing wraaaaah—a spine-chilling call that is used to threaten a dangerous animal. To my right I saw a large black hand shaking a branch and bright eyes glaring threateningly through the foliage. Then came another savage wraaaah from behind. Up above, the big male began to sway the vegetation. I was surrounded.

These words are from the writings of Jane Goodall, a scientist who studies wild chimpanzees in Gombe National Park in Tanzania, Africa. What would you have done if you were in Jane's shoes? Would you have screamed or tried to run away? Jane did neither of these things. Instead, she crouched down and stayed still so she wouldn't startle the chimps. Not feeling threatened by her, the chimps eventually moved on.

Jane Goodall was determined to learn all she could about chimps. Her studies are an example of science in action. **Science** is a way of learning about the natural world. Science also includes all of the knowledge gained by exploring the natural world. **Scientists use skills such as observing, inferring, predicting, classifying, and making models to learn more about the world and make scientific progress.** However, these skills are not unique to scientists. You, too, think like a scientist every day.

Go Online
PHSchool.com

For: More on scientific thinking
Visit: PHSchool.com
Web Code: cgd-6011

Observing

Jane Goodall has spent countless hours among the chimpanzees—quietly following them, taking notes, and carefully observing. **Observing** means using one or more of your senses to gather information. Your senses include sight, hearing, touch, taste, and smell. By using her senses, Jane learned what chimpanzees eat, what sounds they make, and even what games they play! During her time in Gombe, Jane made many surprising observations. For example, she observed how chimpanzees use sticks or long blades of grass as tools to "fish" out a tasty meal from termite mounds.

Like Jane, you use your senses to gather information. Look around you. What do you see? What do you hear and smell? You depend on your observations to help you make decisions throughout the day. For example, if it feels chilly when you wake up, you'll probably dress warmly.

Observations can be either quantitative or qualitative. **Quantitative observations** deal with a number, or amount. Seeing that you have eight new e-mails in your inbox is a quantitative observation. **Qualitative observations,** on the other hand, deal with descriptions that cannot be expressed in numbers. Noticing that a bike is blue or that a grape tastes sour are qualitative observations.

FIGURE 1 Observing
By patiently observing chimpanzees, Jane Goodall learned many things about chimpanzee behavior. The smaller photo shows one of Jane's earliest discoveries—that chimps use sticks as tools to fish for termites.

 **What senses can the skill of observation involve?**

Inferring

One day, Jane Goodall saw something peculiar. She watched as a chimpanzee peered into a hollow in a tree. The chimp picked off a handful of leaves from the tree and chewed on them. Then it took the leaves out of its mouth and pushed them into the tree hollow. When the chimp pulled the leaves back out, Jane saw the gleam of water. The chimp then put the wet leaves back in its mouth.

What was the chimpanzee doing? Jane reasoned that the chimpanzee might be using the chewed leaves like a sponge to soak up water. Seeing the chimp chew on leaves, put them in the hollow, and then squeeze the liquid out is an example of an observation. But Jane went beyond simply observing when she reasoned why the chimpanzee was doing these things. When you explain or interpret the things you observe, you are **inferring**, or making an inference.

Making an inference doesn't mean guessing wildly. Inferences are based on reasoning from what you already know. Jane knew that chimpanzees, like all other animals, need water, and that rainwater collects in tree hollows. She reasoned that the chimp was using chewed leaves to get the water out of the tree.

You, too, make inferences all the time. Because your brain processes observations and other information so quickly, you may not even realize when you have made an inference. For example, if you see your friend smile after getting back an exam, you might automatically infer that she got a good grade. Inferences are not always correct, however. Your friend's smile might not have anything to do with the test.

Reading Checkpoint What is inferring?

FIGURE 2
Inferring
When you explain or interpret your observations, you are making an inference. Inferring *List three inferences you can make about this chimp.*

Predicting

Sometimes, Jane could even predict what a chimp was going to do next. **Predicting** means making a forecast of what will happen in the future based on past experience or evidence.

Through her observations, Jane learned that when a chimpanzee is frightened or angry, its hairs stand on end. This response is sometimes followed by threatening gestures such as charging, throwing rocks, and shaking trees, or even an attack. Therefore, if Jane sees a chimp with its hairs on end, she can predict that the chimp might attack her in a short time. She then leaves the area.

Likewise, you would probably move away if you saw a dog growling or baring its teeth. Why? Because predicting is part of your everyday thinking. You might predict, for example, that your basketball team will win tonight's game if you have always beaten the other team in the past. Predictions, of course, are not always correct. New players this year may increase the other team's chances of winning.

Predictions are a type of inference. An inference is any explanation or interpretation. A prediction is an inference about the future. Suppose you see a broken egg on the floor by a table. Which of the following statements is a prediction?

- The egg rolled off the table.
- Somebody walking by will step on the egg.

FIGURE 3
Predicting
Predictions are forecasts of what will happen next. Like many animals, chimps bare their teeth when they are frightened or angry.
Predicting *What do you think the chimp will do next?*

Reviewing Math: Algebra and Functions 6.2.0

Math ▶ Analyzing Data

Chimp Food

This graph shows the diet of chimps at Gombe National Park during May of one year.

1. **Reading Graphs** According to the graph, what foods do chimps eat?

2. **Interpreting Data** Did chimps feed more on seeds or leaves during this month?

3. **Calculating** What percentage of the diet did blossoms, seeds, leaves, and fruit make up?

4. **Predicting** November is the main termite-fishing season, when chimps spend a large part of their time eating termites. Predict how the percentage of foods might change in November.

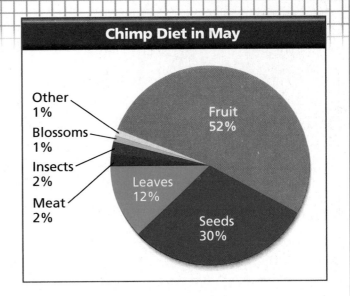

Chimp Diet in May

Other 1%
Blossoms 1%
Insects 2%
Meat 2%
Fruit 52%
Leaves 12%
Seeds 30%

FIGURE 4
Classifying

Field notes like these contain many details about a chimp's daily activities. By grouping together all the information related to resting, climbing, or feeding, Jane can better understand the chimp's behavior.

Resting

6:45 Jomeo in nest

6:50 Jomeo leaves nest, climbs, feeds on *viazi pori* fruit

7:16 Wanders along, feeding on *budyankende* fruits

8:08 Stops feeding, climbs, and feeds on *viazi pori* fruit again

8:35 Travels

Classifying

What do chimps do all day? To find out, Jane and her assistants followed the chimpanzees through the forest. They took detailed field notes about the chimps' behaviors. Figure 4 shows a short section of notes about Jomeo, an adult male chimp.

Suppose Jane wanted to know how much time Jomeo spent feeding or resting that morning. She could find out by classifying Jomeo's actions into several categories. **Classifying** is the process of grouping together items that are alike in some way. For example, Jane could group together all the information about Jomeo's feeding habits or his resting behavior. This would also make it easier to compare Jomeo's actions to those of other chimps. For instance, she could determine if other adult males feed or rest as much as Jomeo does.

You, too, classify objects and information all the time. Classifying things helps you to stay organized so you can easily find and use them later. When you put papers in a notebook, you might classify them by subject or date. And, you might have one drawer in your dresser for shirts and another for socks.

 Reading Checkpoint **How is classifying objects useful?**

Climbing

Feeding

Making Models

How far do chimpanzees travel? Where do they go? Sometimes, Jane's research team would follow a particular chimpanzee for many days at a time. Figure 5 illustrates Jomeo's journey through the forest over the course of one day. The diagram is one example of a model. **Making models** involves creating representations of complex objects or processes. Models help people study and understand things that are complex or that can't be observed directly. Using a model like the one in Figure 5, Jane and her assistants could share information that would otherwise be difficult to explain.

Types of Models Models are all around you. They include physical objects, such as globes or the sets used in filming your favorite TV show. Some models are generated by computer, like the ones some architects use to design new buildings. It's important to keep in mind that models are only representations of the real object or process. Because some information may be missing from a model, you may not be able to understand everything about the object or process the model represents.

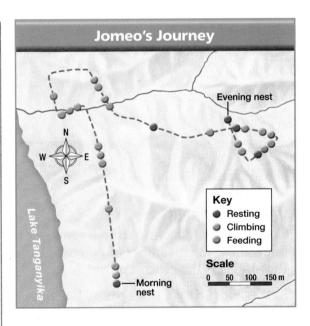

FIGURE 5
Making Models
This map is a model that traces Jomeo's journey through the forest. It represents information that would be hard to explain in words. Notice the scale on the map.
Interpreting Maps *Estimate the total distance that Jomeo traveled between his morning and evening nests.*

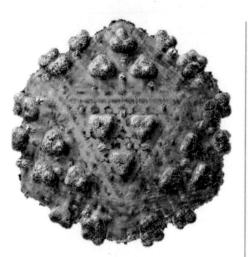

FIGURE 6
Model of a Virus
This scale drawing of the human immunodeficiency virus (HIV) shows the structures on its surface. The yellow knobs allow the virus to attach to a cell. Scientists use such models to develop ways to fight HIV.

Scale Models A **scale model** accurately shows the proportions between its parts. A scale is a proportion used in determining the relationship between a model and the object that it represents. You may be familiar with the scales on maps. A map may have a scale with the proportion of 1 centimeter to 1 kilometer. This means that 1 centimeter on the map stands for 1 kilometer in "real life."

Suppose a map has a scale of 1 centimeter to 500 meters. The distance between two locations on the map measures 10 centimeters. To determine the actual distance in meters, you can perform the following calculation:

$$\text{Distance traveled} = 10 \text{ cm} \times \frac{500 \text{ m}}{1 \text{ cm}} = 5{,}000 \text{ m}$$

A scale model may be bigger or smaller than the object it represents. For example, Figure 6 shows a model of the human immunodeficiency virus (HIV), which causes AIDS. Viruses are too small to see without a microscope. Therefore, the model is many times bigger than the actual virus.

Models may be built to different scales. For example, a scale model of the Golden Gate Bridge built at a scale of 1 centimeter to 1 kilometer could fit in the palm of your hand. The bridge at a scale of 1 centimeter to 1 meter would be about as long as a basketball court.

 **Reading Checkpoint** **What is a scale?**

Section 1 Assessment

S 7.7, E-LA: Reading: 7.1.0

Vocabulary Skill High-Use Academic Words
Complete the following sentence to show that you understand the meanings of *process* and *classifying*. Classifying is the process in which _____.

Reviewing Key Concepts

1. a. Listing Name five skills that are important in scientific thinking.
   b. Comparing and Contrasting How do observations differ from inferences?
   c. Classifying Is this statement an observation or an inference? *The cat must be ill.* Explain your reasoning.

Lab zone At-Home Activity

Something About Plants Take a walk through a park or garden with a family member. Make five qualitative observations and five quantitative observations about the plants you see. Then, make an inference based on your observations. Explain to your family member the difference between an observation and an inference.

The Study of Life

CALIFORNIA Standards Focus

S 7.5 The anatomy and physiology of plants and animals illustrate the complementary nature of structure and function.

S 7.6 Physical principles underlie biological structures and functions.

- How are the branches of life science related?
- What are some big ideas in life science?

Key Terms

- life science
- biology
- organism
- development
- structure
- function
- complementary

Lab zone Standards Warm-Up

How Is Structure Related to Function?

1. Study the photo of the bird and list its characteristics.
2. Next, study the photos of the three food items below.

Think It Over

Inferring Based on your observations, which of the food items do you think the bird feeds on? Explain your reasoning.

In a laboratory, detectives are solving a crime by comparing the genetic makeup of different suspects. On a beach, a scientist studies the nesting behavior of sea turtles. Deep in a tropical rain forest, another scientist discovers a new kind of beetle. In a hospital laboratory, doctors study a deadly form of bird flu. At a cancer research institute, a team of scientists develops new treatments for a rare form of cancer. What do all of these people have in common? All these people are working in the field of life science.

Life science is the study of living things. Another name for life science is biology. The word biology comes from two Greek words. *Bios* means "life" and *logos* means "reason" or "the study of." Thus **biology** is the study of life. Biologists are scientists who study living things.

Biologists study all kinds of living things. The general term for a living thing is an **organism**. An organism may be an animal, a plant, a fungus or a microbe.

Molecular biologists study the chemicals in cells.

Entomologists study insects.

Physiologists study the structure and function of organisms.

Ecologists study organisms in their environment.

FIGURE 7
Life Scientists at Work
You can find life scientists at work in such diverse places as forests, laboratories, zoos, and museums.

Go Online
SciLINKS™

For: Links on careers in life science
Visit: www.SciLinks.org
Web Code: cvn-1012

Branches of Life Science

Biologists can work outside or in a laboratory. They may work for universities, private companies, or government agencies. Biologists, like other scientists, usually work as part of a team studying a common topic.

Life science includes many different branches, or fields of study. Molecular biology, genetics, physiology, and ecology are just some fields of life science. Molecular biology is the study of the chemical building blocks of cells. Genetics is the study of how information about organisms is passed from parent to offspring. Physiology is the study of the structures and functions of organisms. Ecology is the study of how organisms interact with each other and with their surroundings. Other branches of life science include cell biology, plant biology, and microbiology. What do you think these fields involve?

🔵 **Though life science can be divided into branches, the different fields of study often overlap.** For example, understanding what controls plant development relies on concepts from molecular biology and plant biology. Progress in one field of life science often contributes to progress in another field.

Big Ideas in Life Science

Biologists investigate an incredible range of questions. But underlying all of their work are certain big ideas, or concepts. These big ideas connect the study of living things. It is helpful to keep these big ideas in mind as you study life science. As you read this textbook, notice how they come up again and again.

🔑 **The big ideas in life science include the following:**
- **Organisms are diverse, yet share similar characteristics.**
- **Groups of organisms change over time.**
- **The structure and function of organisms are complementary.**
- **Organisms operate on the same physical principles as the rest of the natural world.**

Diverse but Similar Living things come in a great variety of shapes and sizes, from microbes to giant redwood trees and blue whales. Although living things vary greatly, they have many basic similarities.

All organisms are made up of tiny building blocks called cells. Cells are far too small to be seen by the eye, but they carry out all the activities necessary for life. Some organisms are composed of just one cell. Others contain trillions.

The chemical composition of all living things is remarkably similar. Every living thing is made up mainly of water, a relatively simple compound. But organisms also contain highly complex chemicals. For example, most organisms contain DNA, the chemical that controls all the activities of the cell and allows organisms to pass information to their offspring.

All living things require energy. Plants are able to capture energy from sunlight. Other organisms must obtain energy by eating other living things.

Organisms can grow and develop. Growth is the process by which an organism becomes larger. **Development** is the process of change that causes an organism to become more complex during its lifetime. And finally, all living things reproduce, or produce more of their own kind.

 **Reading Checkpoint** How is development different from growth?

FIGURE 8
Diversity and Similarity of Life
This poison arrow frog and mushroom look very different. However, both are made of cells, use energy, grow, develop, and reproduce.

▲ Owl

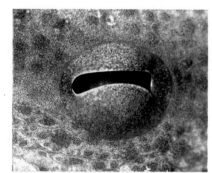
▲ Octopus

▲ Fly

FIGURE 9
Animal Eyes

Eyes come in many shapes, sizes, and, in some cases, numbers. Although each of these animals sees things differently, all of their eyes operate on similar physical principles. *Inferring How do you think the structure of each eye helps the organism to function?*

Change Over Time The characteristics of any group of organisms can change over time. The gradual process of change that occurs in groups of organisms is called evolution. Evolution differs from the growth and development that occurs in an individual organism's lifetime, such as when a tadpole becomes a frog. Evolution is a process that occurs over many generations, often over millions of years.

Complementary Structure and Function The form of each living thing is closely related to the way that it lives. In other words, the structure of an organism allows it to function. **Structure** is the way that an organism is put together as a whole. **Functions** are the processes that enable an organism to survive. The structure and function of an organism are **complementary,** or work together to meet the needs of the organism.

Look at the owl and fly eyes in Figure 9. Owls are adapted to life at night, when they actively hunt for food. An owl's large eyes allow it to see when there is little light. In contrast, flies see well in bright light. Flies have compound eyes, meaning that each eye is made up of thousands of smaller units. Compound eyes are very effective in detecting even the slightest movement—making flies very hard to catch!

Physical Principles Scientists once questioned whether living things operate on the same set of rules as the rest of the natural world. Did living things have unique qualities that could not be explained by chemistry or physics? But today scientists know that life follows the same rules, or principles, as the rest of nature.

For example, the principles of chemistry explain the processes that allow plants to capture the sun's energy. Chemical processes also explain how animals digest their food. And the rules of heredity are based on the chemical structure of DNA.

▲ Cat

▲ Lizard

▲ Spider

The principles of physics also help explain life processes. Consider, for example, the relationship between the physics of light and the way that eyes function. To understand how eyes function, scientists must know what light is and how light travels. Scientists can compare the structure of an eye to that of a camera. Like a camera, an eye uses a lens to focus light and form an image. The principles that allow a camera to take a picture also allow an eye to see.

Compare the variety of eyes in Figure 9. Although each of the animals may see slightly differently, all of the eyes operate on similar physical principles.

Section 2 Assessment

S 7.5, 7.6 E-LA: Reading: 7.2.0

Target Reading Skill Preview Text Structure When you took notes on Section 2, what question did you ask for the heading Change Over Time? What was your answer?

Reviewing Key Concepts

1. a. **Defining** What is life science?
   b. **Describing** List three branches of life science and describe what is studied in each.
   c. **Making Judgments** Your friend wants to be a plant biologist and says she only needs to take courses in plant biology. Why might it be a good idea for your friend to study other branches of life science as well?
2. a. **Listing** What are four big ideas in life science?
   b. **Comparing and Contrasting** What are some ways that a cat and a tree are similar? What are some ways they are different?

Lab zone **At-Home Activity**

It's Complementary Explain to a family member what "complementary structure and function" means. Then look through books or magazines for photos of organisms that illustrate this concept. Find five examples to show your family member. Describe how a structure on each of the organisms is adapted to its function.

Scientific Inquiry

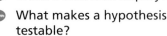
CALIFORNIA
Standards Focus

S 7.7.c Students will communicate the logical connection among hypotheses, science concepts, tests conducted, data collected, and conclusions drawn from the scientific evidence.

- What is scientific inquiry?
- What makes a hypothesis testable?

Key Terms

- scientific inquiry
- hypothesis
- variable
- controlled experiment
- manipulated variable
- responding variable
- control
- operational definition
- data
- communicating

A snowy tree cricket ▼

Lab zone Standards **Warm-Up**

What Can You Learn About Mealworms?

1. Study mealworms in a tray. Use a magnifying glass to see their structure more clearly.
2. Observe the mealworms' functions—for example, how they move or eat.

Think It Over
Posing Questions Write three questions you have about mealworms and their functions. How could you find out the answers?

"Chirp, chirp, chirp." It is one of the hottest nights of summer and your bedroom windows are wide open. On most nights, the quiet chirping of crickets gently lulls you to sleep, but not tonight. The noise from the crickets is almost deafening!

Why do all the crickets in your neighborhood seem determined to keep you awake tonight? Could the crickets be chirping more because of the heat? How could you find out?

As you lie awake, you are probably not thinking much about science. But, in fact, you are thinking just as a scientist would. You made observations—you heard the loud chirping of the crickets and felt the heat of the summer night. Your observations led you to infer that heat might cause increased chirping. You might even make a prediction: "If it's cooler tomorrow night, the crickets will be quieter."

The Scientific Process

You might not know it, but your questioning can be the start of **scientific inquiry.** Scientific inquiry **refers to the diverse ways in which scientists investigate the natural world and propose explanations based on the evidence they gather.** If you have ever tried to figure out why a plant has wilted, then you have used scientific inquiry. Similarly, you could use scientific inquiry to find out whether there is a relationship between the air temperature and crickets' chirping.

Posing Questions Scientific inquiry often begins with a problem or question about an observation. In the case of the crickets, your question might be: Does the air temperature affect the chirping of crickets? Of course, questions don't just come to you from nowhere. Instead, questions come from experiences that you have and from observations and inferences that you make. Curiosity plays a large role as well. Think of a time that you observed something unusual or unexpected. Chances are good that your curiosity sparked a number of questions.

Some questions cannot be investigated by scientific inquiry. Think about the difference between the two questions below.

- Does my dog eat more food than my cat?

- Which makes a better pet—a cat or a dog?

The first question is a scientific question because it can be answered by making observations and gathering evidence. For example, you could measure the amount of food your cat and dog each eat during a week. In contrast, the second question has to do with personal opinions or values. Scientific inquiry cannot answer questions about personal tastes or judgments.

Developing a Hypothesis How could you explain your observation of noisy crickets on that summer night? "Perhaps crickets chirp more when the temperature is higher," you think. In trying to answer the question, you are in fact developing a hypothesis. A **hypothesis** (plural: *hypotheses*) is a possible explanation for a set of observations or answer to a scientific question. In this case, your hypothesis would be that cricket chirping increases at higher air temperatures.

In science, a hypothesis must be testable. This means that researchers must be able to carry out investigations and gather evidence that will either support or disprove the hypothesis. Many trials will be needed before a hypothesis can be accepted as true.

 **Reading Checkpoint** What is a hypothesis?

Perhaps crickets chirp more when the temperature is higher.

FIGURE 10
Developing Hypotheses
A hypothesis is one possible way to explain a set of observations. **Developing Hypotheses** *Propose another hypothesis that could explain the observation that crickets seem to be noisier on some nights than others.*

Lab zone Skills Activity

Controlling Variables

Suppose you are designing an experiment to determine whether different varieties of apples contain the same number of seeds. What is your manipulated variable? What is your responding variable? What other variables would you need to control?

Designing an Experiment Hypotheses lead to predictions that can be tested. In this case, your prediction would be, *"If the temperature increases, crickets will chirp more frequently."*

To test your prediction, you will need to observe crickets at different air temperatures. All other **variables,** or factors that can change in an experiment, must be exactly the same. Other variables include the kind of crickets, the type of container you test them in, and the type of thermometer you use. By keeping all of these variables the same, you will know that any difference in cricket chirping must be due to temperature alone.

An experiment in which only one variable is manipulated at a time is called a **controlled experiment.** The one variable that is purposely changed in an experiment is called the **manipulated variable** (also called the independent variable). In your cricket experiment, the manipulated variable is the air temperature. The factor that may change in response to the manipulated variable is called the **responding variable** (also called the dependent variable). The responding variable here is the number of cricket chirps.

In life science, a controlled experiment often has a control. A **control** is a part of the experiment to which you can compare the results of the other tests. In the control, the conditions are the same except for the manipulated variable. For the cricket experiment, you would test your control crickets at a constant temperature. That way, you can better recognize the effects of increased temperature on chirping.

Another aspect of a well-designed experiment is having clear operational definitions. An **operational definition** is a statement that describes how to measure a variable or define a term. For example, in this experiment you would need to determine what sounds will count as a single "chirp."

 **Reading Checkpoint** What is a control?

FIGURE 11

A Controlled Experiment
In this controlled experiment, the experimental group crickets are tested at 15°C, 20°C, and 25°C. The students are using the same kinds of containers, leaves, thermometers, and crickets. The manipulated variable is temperature. The responding variable is cricket chirps per minute at each temperature.

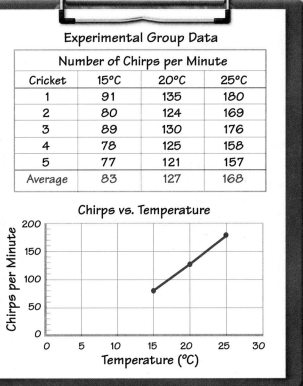

Experimental Group Data

Number of Chirps per Minute			
Cricket	15°C	20°C	25°C
1	91	135	180
2	80	124	169
3	89	130	176
4	78	125	158
5	77	121	157
Average	83	127	168

Chirps vs. Temperature

FIGURE 12
Collecting and Interpreting Data
A data table helps you organize the information you collect in an experiment. Graphing the data may reveal patterns.
Interpreting Data *Did all of the crickets chirp more at 25°C than at 20°C? Did you use the data table or the graph to answer this question?*

Collecting and Interpreting Data For your experiment, you need a data table in which to record your data. **Data** are the facts, figures, and other evidence gathered through observations. A data table is an organized way to collect and record observations. After the data have been collected, they need to be interpreted. A graph can help you interpret data. Graphs can reveal patterns or trends in data.

Drawing Conclusions A conclusion is a summary of what you have learned from an experiment. In drawing your conclusion, you should ask yourself whether the data support the hypothesis. You also need to consider whether you collected enough data. After reviewing the data, you decide that the evidence supports your original hypothesis. You conclude that cricket chirping does increase with temperature. It's no wonder that you have trouble sleeping on those warm summer nights!

Communicating An important part of scientific inquiry is communicating your results. **Communicating** is the sharing of ideas and experimental findings with others through writing and speaking. For example, scientists can give talks at scientific meetings and publish articles in journals and on the Internet. When scientists communicate their research, they describe the logical connections between their procedures and results. Other scientists can then repeat and build on their experiments.

FIGURE 13
Scientific Inquiry
There is no set path that a scientific inquiry must follow. Observations at each stage of the process may lead you to modify your hypothesis or experiment. Conclusions from one experiment often lead to new questions and experiments.

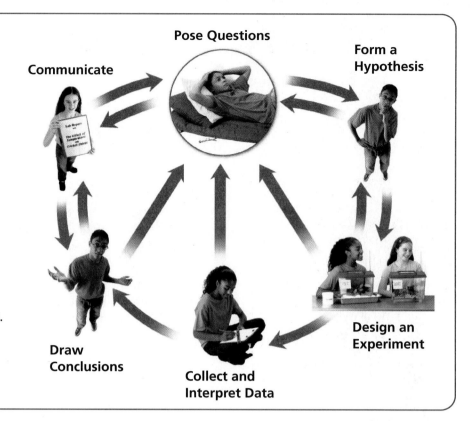

Pose Questions

Communicate

Form a Hypothesis

Design an Experiment

Collect and Interpret Data

Draw Conclusions

The Nature of Inquiry Scientific inquiry usually doesn't end once a set of experiments is done and results are communicated. Often, a scientific inquiry raises new questions, that lead to new hypotheses and experiments, as shown in Figure 13.

Section **3** **Assessment**

S 7.7.c, E-LA: Reading 7.1.0
Writing 7.2.5

Vocabulary Skill High-Use Academic Words Explain why *evidence* is an important part of scientific *research*.

Reviewing Key Concepts

1. a. **Defining** Define the term *scientific inquiry*.
   b. **Explaining** A friend claims that pea plants grow faster than corn plants. Could you investigate this idea through scientific inquiry? Explain.
   c. **Problem Solving** What kind of data would you need to collect to do this experiment?
2. a. **Reviewing** What is meant by saying that a hypothesis must be testable?
   b. **Developing Hypotheses** Every time you and your friend study for an exam while listening to classical music, both of you do well on the exam. What testable hypothesis can you develop from your observations?

Writing in Science

Summary You're going to a convention of cricket scientists from around the world. Write a paragraph describing the results of your cricket experiment. Include questions you'd like to ask other cricket scientists at the conference.

CALIFORNIA
Standards Focus

S 7.7 Scientific progress is made by asking meaningful questions and conducting careful investigations. As a basis for understanding this concept and addressing the content in the other three strands, students should develop their own questions and perform investigations.

- Why is preparation important when carrying out scientific investigations in the lab and in the field?
- What should you do if an accident occurs?

Standards Warm-Up

Lab zone

Where Is the Safety Equipment in Your School?

1. Look around your classroom or school for any safety-related equipment.
2. Draw a floor plan of the room or building and clearly label where each item is located.

Think It Over
Predicting Why is it important to know where safety equipment is located?

You and your family have just arrived at a mountain cabin for a vacation. The view of the mountaintops is beautiful, and the fresh scent of pine trees fills the air. In the distance, you can glimpse a lake through the pines.

You put on a bathing suit and head down the trail toward the lake. The sparkling, clear water looks inviting. You're tempted to jump in and swim. However, you wait for the rest of your family to join you. It isn't safe for a person to swim alone.

Safety During Investigations

Just as when you go swimming, you have to take steps to be safe during any scientific investigation. **Good preparation helps you conduct careful scientific investigations by planning for safety.** Do you know how to use lab equipment? What should you do if something goes wrong? Thinking about these questions ahead of time is an important part of being prepared.

Preparing for the Lab Preparing for a lab should begin the day before you will perform the lab. It is important to read through the procedure carefully and make sure you understand all the directions. Also, review the general safety guidelines in Appendix A, including those related to the specific equipment you will use. If anything is unclear, be prepared to ask your teacher about it before you begin the lab.

Go Online

SciLINKS NSTA

For: Links on laboratory safety
Visit: www.SciLinks.org
Web Code: scn-1624

Performing the Lab Whenever you perform a science lab, always follow your teacher's instructions and the textbook directions exactly. You should never try anything on your own without asking your teacher first. Keep your work area clean and organized. Also, do not rush through any of the steps. Finally, always show respect and courtesy to your teacher and classmates.

Labs and activities in this textbook include the safety symbols shown on the next page. These symbols alert you to possible dangers in performing the lab and remind you to work carefully. They also identify any safety equipment that you should use to protect yourself from potential hazards. The symbols are explained in detail in Appendix A. Make sure you are familiar with each safety symbol and what it means.

FIGURE 14
Safety in the Lab
Good preparation for an experiment helps you stay safe in the laboratory.
Observing *List three precautions each student is taking while performing the labs.*

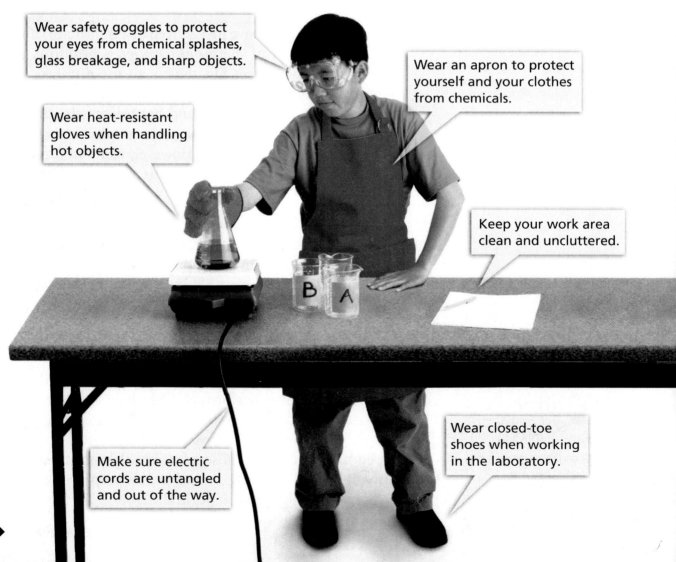

Wear safety goggles to protect your eyes from chemical splashes, glass breakage, and sharp objects.

Wear an apron to protect yourself and your clothes from chemicals.

Wear heat-resistant gloves when handling hot objects.

Keep your work area clean and uncluttered.

Make sure electric cords are untangled and out of the way.

Wear closed-toe shoes when working in the laboratory.

End-of-Lab Procedures When you have finished a lab, clean your work area. Turn off and unplug equipment and return it to its proper place. Dispose of any wastes as your teacher instructs you to. Finally, wash your hands thoroughly.

Safety in the Field You work in the "field" whenever you work outdoors—for example, in a forest, park, or schoolyard. Always tell an adult where you will be. Never carry out a field investigation alone. Ask an adult or classmate to go with you.

Possible safety hazards outdoors include such things as severe weather, traffic, wild animals, and poisonous plants. Planning ahead can help you avoid some hazards. For example, the weather report can alert you to severe weather. Use common sense to avoid any potentially dangerous situations.

Reading Checkpoint What should you do with equipment at the end of a lab?

Safety Symbols

	Safety Goggles
	Lab Apron
	Breakage
	Heat-Resistant Gloves
	Plastic Gloves
	Heating
	Flames
	No Flames
	Corrosive Chemical
	Poison
	Fumes
	Sharp Object
	Animal Safety
	Plant Safety
	Electric Shock
	Physical Safety
	Disposal
	Hand Washing
	General Safety Awareness

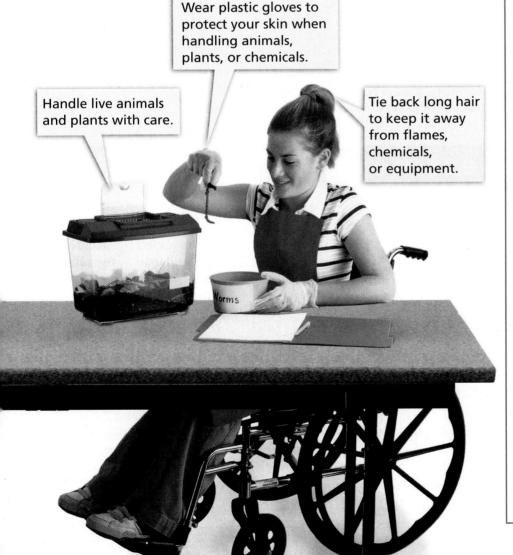

Wear plastic gloves to protect your skin when handling animals, plants, or chemicals.

Handle live animals and plants with care.

Tie back long hair to keep it away from flames, chemicals, or equipment.

In Case of Emergency

ALWAYS NOTIFY YOUR TEACHER IMMEDIATELY

Injury	What to Do
Burns	Immerse burns in cold water.
Cuts	Cover cuts with a clean dressing. Apply direct pressure to the wound to stop bleeding.
Spills on Skin	Flush the skin with large amounts of water.
Foreign Object in Eye	Flush the eye with large amounts of water. Seek medical attention.

FIGURE 15
First-Aid Tips
These first-aid tips can help guide your actions during emergency situations. Remember, always notify your teacher immediately if an accident occurs.

In Case of an Accident

Good preparation and careful work habits can go a long way toward making your lab experiences safe ones. But, at some point, an accident may occur. A classmate might accidentally knock over a beaker or a chemical might spill on your sleeve. Would you know what to do?

When any accident occurs, no matter how minor, notify your teacher immediately. Then, listen to your teacher's directions and carry them out quickly. Make sure you know the location and proper use of all the emergency equipment in your lab room. Knowing safety and first-aid procedures beforehand will prepare you to handle accidents properly. Figure 15 lists some first-aid procedures you should know.

Reading Checkpoint Why is knowing the location of emergency equipment important?

Section 4 Assessment

S 7.7, E-LA: Reading 7.2.0, Writing 7.2.0

Target Reading Skill Preview Text Structure Use your notes to help answer the questions below.

Reviewing Key Concepts

1. a. **Reviewing** Why is good preparation important in lab investigations?
   b. **Identifying** Identify two steps you should take to prepare for a lab.
   c. **Predicting** What might happen if you did not follow the steps you identified in Question (b)?

2. a. **Describing** What should you do immediately after any lab accident?
   b. **Applying Concepts** Your lab partner cuts herself and stops the bleeding with a tissue from her pocket. Did she follow the proper procedure? Explain.

   c. **Relating Cause and Effect** Explain how your partner might have prevented the accident if she had been more familiar with the safety symbols on page 25.

Writing in Science

Field Trip Safety Think of an outdoor area that you know, such as a park, field, or vacant lot, where you might observe wild plants. Write safety instructions that would help students prepare for a field trip to that place. You might add illustrations to help make the instructions clear.

Design Your Own Lab

Keeping Flowers Fresh

S 7.5, 7.7.c, 7.7.e

Problem

How can cut flowers stay fresher for a longer period of time?

Skills Focus

developing hypotheses, designing experiments, drawing conclusions

Suggested Materials

- plastic cups • cut flowers • spoon
- water • sugar

Design a Plan

1. Plants have structures that function in the transport of materials. You have just been given a bouquet of cut flowers. You remember once seeing a gardener put some sugar into the water in a vase before putting flowers in. You wonder if the sugar is a material that helps flowers stay fresh longer. Write a hypothesis for an experiment you could perform to answer your question.

2. Working with a partner, design a controlled experiment to test your hypothesis. Make a list of all of the variables you will need to control. Also decide what data you will need to collect. For example, you could count the number of petals each flower drops. Then write out a detailed experimental plan for your teacher to review.

3. If necessary, revise your plan according to your teacher's instructions. Then set up your experiment and begin collecting your data.

Analyze and Conclude

1. **Developing Hypotheses** What hypothesis did you decide to test? On what information or experience was your hypothesis based?

2. **Designing Experiments** What was the manipulated variable in the experiment you performed? What was the responding variable? What variables were kept constant?

3. **Graphing** Use the data you collected to create one or more graphs of your experimental results. (For more on creating graphs, see the Skills Handbook.) What patterns or trends do your graphs reveal?

4. **Drawing Conclusions** Based on your graphs, what conclusion can you draw about sugar and cut flowers? Do your results support your hypothesis and what you know about plant structure? Why or why not?

5. **Communicating** In a paragraph, describe which aspects of your experimental plan were difficult to carry out. Were any variables hard to control? Was it difficult to collect accurate data? What changes could you make to improve your experimental plan?

More to Explore

Make a list of some additional questions you would like to investigate about how to keep cut flowers fresh. Choose one of the questions and write a hypothesis for an experiment you could perform. Then design a controlled experiment to test your hypothesis. *Obtain your teacher's permission before carrying out your investigation.*

Study Guide

 The **BIG Idea** Scientific progress is made by asking meaningful questions and conducting careful investigations.

① Thinking Like a Scientist

 Key Concepts S 7.7

- Scientists use skills such as observing, inferring, predicting, classifying, and making models to learn more and make scientific progress.

Key Terms

science
observing
quantitative observation
qualitative observation
inferring
predicting
classifying
making models
scale model

② The Study of Life

Key Concepts S 7.5, 7.6

- Life science can be divided into branches; the different fields of study often overlap.

- The big ideas in life science include the following: Organisms are diverse, yet share similar characteristics. Groups of organisms change over time. The structure and function of organisms are complementary. Organisms operate on the same physical principles as the rest of the natural world.

Key Terms

life science
biology
organism
development
structure
function
complementary

③ Scientific Inquiry

Key Concepts S 7.7.c

- Scientific inquiry refers to the diverse ways in which scientists investigate the natural world and propose explanations based on the evidence they gather.

- In science, a hypothesis must be testable. This means that researchers must be able to carry out investigations and gather evidence that will either support or disprove the hypothesis.

Key Terms

scientific inquiry
hypothesis
variable
controlled experiment
manipulated variable
responding variable
control
operational definition
data
communicating

④ Safety in the Laboratory

Key Concepts S 7.7

- Good preparation helps you conduct careful scientific investigation by planning for safety.

- When any accident occurs, no matter how minor, notify your teacher immediately. Then, listen to your teacher's directions and carry them out quickly.

Review and Assessment

Target Reading Skill

To help you review part of Section 1, copy and complete the graphic organizer at the right.

Heading	Question	Answer
Developing a Hypothesis	a. _____?_____	b. _____?_____
	c. _____?_____	d. _____?_____

Reviewing Key Terms

Choose the letter of the best answer.

1. The process of change that occurs during an organism's life that produces a more complicated organism is called
   a. structure.
   b. function.
   c. development.
   d. variable.

2. When you note that a rabbit has white fur, you are making a
   a. quantitative observation.
   b. qualitative observation.
   c. prediction.
   d. model.

3. Music stores arrange CDs according to the type of music—rock, country, folk, and so on. This is an example of
   a. observation.
   b. inferring.
   c. posing questions.
   d. classifying.

4. A statement that describes how to measure a variable or define a term is a(n)
   a. controlled variable.
   b. manipulated variable.
   c. hypothesis.
   d. operational definition.

5. In labs in this book, which of the following indicates the danger of breakage?

   a.   b.

   c.   d.

Complete the following sentences so that your answers clearly explain the Key Terms.

6. Studying how the human body works and how different animals interact with one another are examples of topics in **life science,** which is _____ .

7. Obtaining oxygen is an example of a **function,** which is a process that _____ .

8. Noticing how much food is on your lunch tray is a **quantitative observation** because _____ .

9. Recording how many times your dog eats each day and how much he eats are examples of collecting **data,** which are _____ .

10. Giving a talk about the results of a scientific project is an example of **communicating** because _____ .

Writing in Science

Description Think about the ways in which the police who investigate crimes act like scientists. In a paragraph, describe the scientific skills that police use in their work.

Video Assessment

Discovery Channel School

What Is Science?

Review and Assessment

Checking Concepts

11. List five skills that a scientist uses to learn more about the world.

12. When you observe something, what are you doing?

13. How are models useful to scientists?

14. In your own words, explain what is meant by the statement: *Physical principles underlie biological structures and functions.*

15. What is a hypothesis? Why is it important to develop a scientific hypothesis that is testable?

16. In an experiment, why is it important to control all variables except one?

17. Identify three things that you should do to prepare for a lab.

Thinking Critically

18. **Applying Concepts** Describe how the structure of your hands are complementary to their functions.

19. **Comparing and Contrasting** Compare and contrast qualitative and quantitative observations.

20. **Inferring** Suppose you come home to the scene below. What can you infer happened while you were gone?

21. **Problem Solving** Suppose you would like to find out which brand of glue holds better. What variables would you need to control in your experiment?

Applying Skills

Use the data table below to answer Questions 22–26.

Three students conducted a controlled experiment to find out how walking and running affected their heart rates.

Effect of Activity on Heart Rate (in beats per minute)

Student	Heart Rate (at rest)	Heart Rate (walking)	Heart Rate (running)
1	70	90	115
2	72	80	100
3	80	100	120

22. **Controlling Variables** What is the manipulated variable in this experiment? What is the responding variable?

23. **Developing Hypotheses** What hypothesis might this experiment be testing?

24. **Predicting** Based on this experiment and what you know about exercising, predict how the students' heart rates would change while they are resting after a long run.

25. **Designing Experiments** Design a controlled experiment to determine which activity has more of an effect on a person's heart rate—jumping rope or doing push-ups.

26. **Drawing Conclusions** What do the data indicate about the increased physical activity and heart rate?

Lab zone Standards Investigation

Performance Assessment Create a poster that summarizes your experiment for the class. Your poster should include the question you tested, how you tested it, the data you collected, and what conclusion you drew from your experiment. What problems did you encounter while carrying out your experiment? Is additional testing necessary?

Choose the letter of the best answer.

1. During a lab, if you spill a chemical on your skin, you should
   A apply pressure to the area.
   B rub the chemical off with a clean tissue.
   C flush the skin with large amounts of water.
   D throw the chemical in a waste basket.   **S 7.7**

Use the table below to answer Questions 2–4.

Animals in a Field

Kind of Animal	Number of Animals	
	July	August
Grasshoppers	5,000	1,500
Birds	100	100
Spiders	200	500

2. Which statement accurately expresses what happened in the field between July and August?
   A The numbers of all the animals increased.
   B The number of grasshoppers increased.
   C The number of spiders decreased.
   D The number of birds stayed the same.
   S 7.7.c

3. Which of the following statements about the data is true?
   A In July, there were more grasshoppers than birds.
   B In August, there were more birds than spiders.
   C Between July and August, the number of grasshoppers increased by 500.
   D In both months, there were more spiders than grasshoppers.   **S 7.7.c**

4. Which of the following is a logical question that a scientist might pose based on the data in the table?
   A What killed off the spiders in the field?
   B Are spiders feeding on grasshoppers?
   C Do all birds fly south for the winter?
   D Are grasshoppers related to beetles?   **S 7.7**

5. Your brother has a cold and you think you will probably get a cold, too. Which of the following are you doing?
   A posing a question based on an inference
   B predicting based on an observation
   C making a model based on an observation
   D designing a controlled experiment
   S 7.7.c

6. Which of the following statements about structure and function in organisms is NOT true?
   A An organism's functions are the processes that enable it to survive.
   B An organism contains structures that are related to its functions.
   C All organisms have the same structure and function.
   D An organism needs energy to carry out its functions.
   S 7.5

Apply the BIG Idea

7. Read each question and explain whether it can be answered by conducting a scientific investigation.
   I. Can dogs see in the dark?
   II. How did pet dogs develop from wild dogs?
   III. Which type of dog is the most fun?
   IV. How does a dog's tail help it survive?

Select one question that can be investigated scientifically. State a hypothesis. Then describe how you might conduct a scientific investigation to test your hypothesis.   **S 7.7**

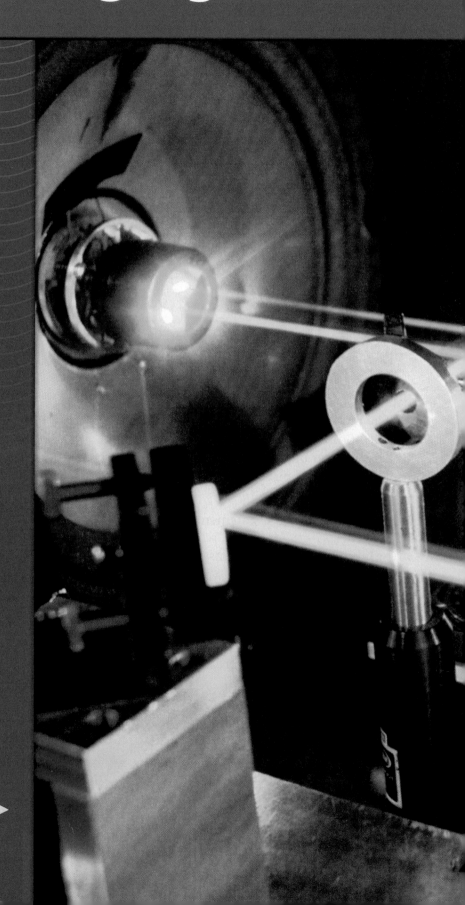

Chapter 2

Using Light

A laser produces a narrow beam of light. ▶

Focus on the
BIG Idea

S 7.6.b

How does light allow you to see?

Check What You Know

Suppose you aim a flashlight at a pair of colored light filters. The first filter is blue and the second one is red. When the light passes through the blue filter, it will emerge blue. But what happens when the blue light passes through the red filter?

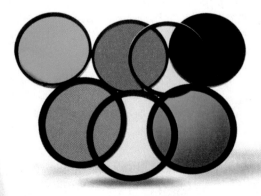

The images shown here represent some of the key terms in this chapter. You can use this vocabulary skill to help you understand the meaning of some key terms in this chapter.

Vocabulary Skill

Latin Word Origins

Many English words come from ancient Latin words. One example is the Latin word part *re-*, meaning "back" or "again." When you review for a chapter test, for example, you look <u>back</u> at the chapter or read it <u>again</u>. The table below shows Latin words that are sources for some key terms in this chapter.

Latin Word	Meaning of Latin Word	Key Term
flectere	to bend	**reflection** The bouncing back of something, such as light or sound, when it hits a surface
lux, lucere	to light	**translucent** Scattering light; allowing some, but not all, light to pass through
re-	back; again	**reflection** The bouncing back of something, such as light or sound, when it hits a surface
trans-	through; across	**transparent** Allowing light to pass through

Apply It!

1. Which key term in the chart comes from the two Latin words *flect* and *re*? How does the meaning of this key term involve both those Latin words?

2. What part of the word *translucent* lets you know that the word's meaning has something to do with light?

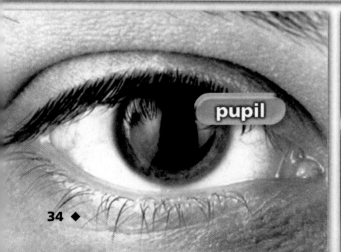

pupil

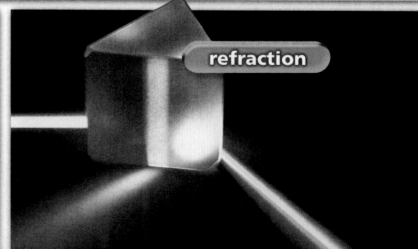

refraction

reflection

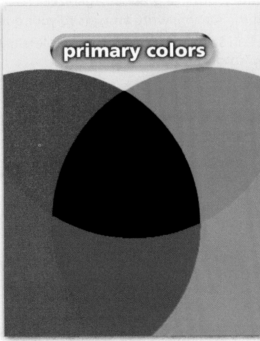
primary colors

electromagnetic radiation

microscope

Chapter 2 Vocabulary

Interactive Textbook

Build Science Vocabulary
Online
Visit: PHSchool.com
Web Code: cvj-1020

How to Read Science

 ## Preview Visuals

Before you read each chapter in your textbook, take time to preview the visuals. Visuals are photographs, graphs, tables, and illustrations. Visuals contain important information to help you understand what you read. Follow these steps to preview visuals.

- Look carefully at the visual.
- Read the title, the labels, and the caption.
- Ask yourself questions about the visual.
- Write your questions in a graphic organizer.
- As you read the section, write answers to your questions.

Preview Figure 2 in Section 1. Copy the incomplete graphic organizer below into your notebook.

Amplitude, Wavelength, and Frequency

Q. What is the subject of this illustration?

A. The basic properties of waves—amplitude, wavelength, and frequency

Q. What does the label Amplitude mean?

A.

Apply It!

1. What is the first question in the graphic organizer? Why is it good to ask this question when you preview any visual?

2. Add at least two questions about Figure 2 to your graphic organizer. As you read Section 1, answer the questions.

3. Before you read Section 2, preview Figure 8. Before you read Section 4, preview Figure 22. Before you read Section 5, preview Figure 25. For each of these visuals, make a graphic organizer with your questions. Answer the questions when you read the section.

S 7.6.d

Design and Build an Optical Instrument

You see reflections all the time—in shiny surfaces, windows, and mirrors. A camera can capture reflections on film. A telescope can capture reflected light with a curved mirror. Cameras and telescopes are optical instruments, devices that control light with mirrors or lenses. In this investigation, you will design and build your own optical instrument.

Your Goal

To design, build, and test an optical instrument that serves a specific purpose

Your optical instrument must

- be made of materials that are approved by your teacher
- include at least one mirror or one lens
- be built and used following the safety guidelines in Appendix A

Plan It!

Start by deciding on the purpose of your optical instrument and how you will use it. Sketch your design and choose the materials you will need. Then build and test your optical instrument. Finally, make a manual that describes and explains each part of the instrument.

Waves and the Electromagnetic Spectrum

CALIFORNIA
Standards Focus

S 7.6.a Students know visible light is a small band within a very broad electromagnetic spectrum.

- What causes waves?
- What are the basic properties of waves?
- What does an electromagnetic wave consist of?
- What are the waves of the electromagnetic spectrum?

Key Terms

- wave
- energy
- medium
- vibration
- crest
- trough
- amplitude
- wavelength
- frequency
- hertz
- electromagnetic wave
- electromagnetic radiation
- electromagnetic spectrum
- visible light

▼ A motorboat making waves

Lab zone Standards **Warm-Up**

What Is White Light?

1. Line a cardboard box with white paper. Hold a small triangular prism up to direct sunlight. **CAUTION:** *Do not look directly at the sun.*

2. Rotate the prism until the light coming out of the prism appears on the inside of the box as a wide band of colors. Describe the colors and their order.

3. Using colored pencils, draw a picture of what you see inside the box.

Think It Over

Forming Operational Definitions The term *spectrum* describes a range. How is this term related to what you just observed?

It was a long swim, but now you're resting on the swimming raft in the lake. You hear the water lapping gently against the raft as the sun warms your skin. Suddenly a motorboat zooms by. A few seconds later you're bobbing wildly up and down as the boat's waves hit the raft. Although the speedboat didn't touch the raft, its energy caused waves in the water. Then the waves moved the raft—and you!

You can see and feel the water waves when you're on a swimming raft. But did you know that many other kinds of waves affect you every day? Sound is a wave. Sunlight is a different kind of wave. Light, sound, and water waves may seem very different, but they all are waves. What is a wave?

FIGURE 1
Waves
You are being "showered" all the time by many types of waves.

Waves and Energy

A **wave** is a disturbance that transfers energy from place to place. In science, **energy** is defined as the ability to do work. To understand waves, think about the swimming raft. A wave that disturbs the surface of the water also will disturb the raft. The wave's energy lifts the heavy raft as the wave passes under it. But the disturbance caused by the wave is temporary. After the wave passes, the water is calm again and the raft stops bobbing.

What Carries Waves? Most kinds of waves need something to travel through. Water waves, for example, travel along the surface of the water. A wave can even travel along a rope. The material through which a wave travels is called a **medium.** Gases (such as air), liquids (such as water), and solids (such as rope), all act as mediums. Waves that require a medium through which to travel are called mechanical waves.

Some waves do not require a medium to travel through. Light can travel and carry energy through empty space. Waves that can travel without a medium are called electromagnetic waves.

How Do Waves Transfer Energy? Energy is required to make a wave. 🔑 **Mechanical waves are produced when a source of energy causes a medium to vibrate.** A **vibration** is a repeated back-and-forth or up-and-down motion. When a vibration moves through a medium, a wave results. When waves travel through a medium, they do not carry the medium with them. Why doesn't the medium travel along with the wave? All mediums are made of tiny particles. When a wave enters a medium, it transfers energy to the medium's particles. The particles bump into each other, passing the wave's energy along.

 **What is a vibration?**

Properties of Waves

Waves can carry a little energy or a lot. They can be short or long. All waves, however, share certain properties. ⊂⊃ **The basic properties of waves are amplitude, wavelength, frequency, and speed.**

Amplitude When you make a wave on a rope, the rope itself moves up and down or from side to side, perpendicular (at a 90° angle) to the direction in which the wave travels. The high point of a wave is called a **crest,** and the low point is called a **trough** (trawf). The distance the medium rises depends on the amplitude of the wave. **Amplitude** is the maximum distance that the particles of the medium carrying the wave move away from their rest positions. For example, the amplitude of a water wave is the maximum distance a water particle moves above or below the surface level of calm water. You can increase the amplitude of a wave in a rope by moving your hand up and down a greater distance. To do this, you have to use more energy. This energy is transferred to the rope. Thus, the more energy a wave has, the greater its amplitude.

FIGURE 2

Amplitude, Wavelength, and Frequency

The basic properties of all waves include amplitude, wavelength, and frequency. A wave moves the rope up and down in a direction perpendicular to the direction in which the wave travels.
Developing Hypotheses How could you increase the amplitude of a wave in a rope? How could you increase the frequency?

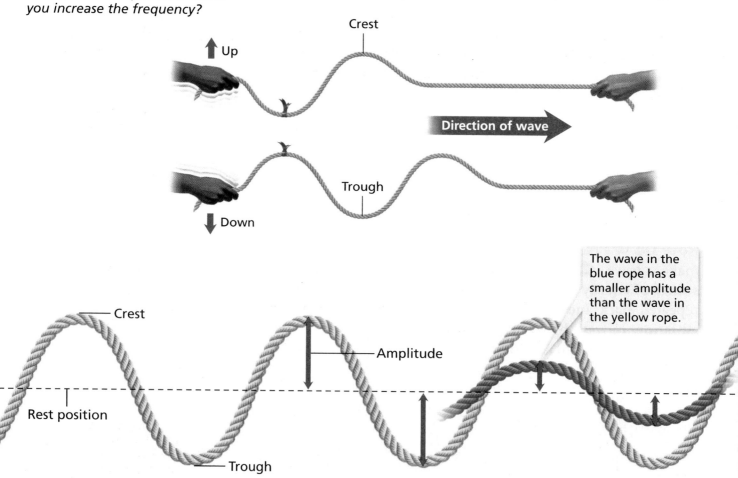

Crest

↑ Up

Direction of wave

Trough

↓ Down

The wave in the blue rope has a smaller amplitude than the wave in the yellow rope.

Crest

Amplitude

Rest position

Trough

Wavelength A wave travels a certain distance before it starts to repeat. The distance between two corresponding parts of a wave is its **wavelength.** You can find the wavelength of a wave by measuring the distance from crest to crest, as shown on Figure 2. Or you can measure from trough to trough.

Frequency Wave **frequency** is the number of complete waves that pass a given point in a certain amount of time. For example, if you make waves on a rope so that one wave passes by every second, the frequency is 1 wave per second. How can you increase the frequency? Simply move your hand up and down more quickly, perhaps two or three times per second. To decrease the frequency, move your hand up and down more slowly.

Frequency is measured in units called **hertz** (Hz). A wave that occurs every second has a frequency of 1 Hz. If two waves pass you every second, then the frequency of the wave is 2 per second, or 2 hertz. The hertz was named after Heinrich Hertz, the German scientist who discovered radio waves.

Speed Different waves can travel at different speeds. The speed of a wave is how far the wave travels in a given amount of time. If the medium that a wave travels through does not change, the speed of the wave is constant. The speed of a wave can be found by multiplying its frequency by its wavelength. Thus, you can increase the speed of a wave by increasing either the wavelength or the frequency.

Reading Checkpoint In what unit is the frequency of a wave measured?

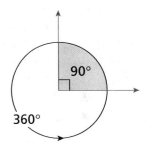

Math Skills

Angles
An angle is formed when two lines meet at a point. Angles are measured in degrees, indicated by the symbol °. A circle has 360 degrees. A right angle is an angle that contains 90 degrees. Two lines that meet at a point to form a 90° angle are said to be perpendicular to each other.

Practice Problems
1. Draw a circle on a piece of paper. How many right angles can you fit in the circle?
2. How many degrees do two right angles contain?

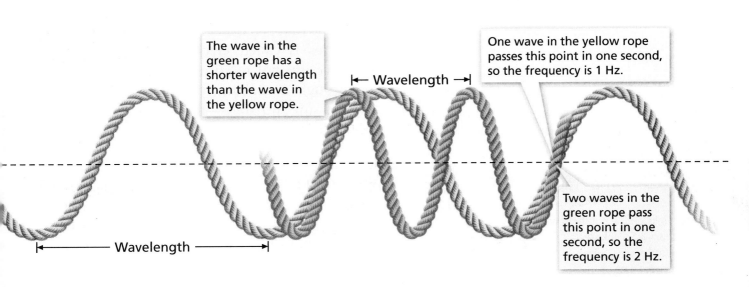

The wave in the green rope has a shorter wavelength than the wave in the yellow rope.

← Wavelength →

One wave in the yellow rope passes this point in one second, so the frequency is 1 Hz.

|← Wavelength →|

Two waves in the green rope pass this point in one second, so the frequency is 2 Hz.

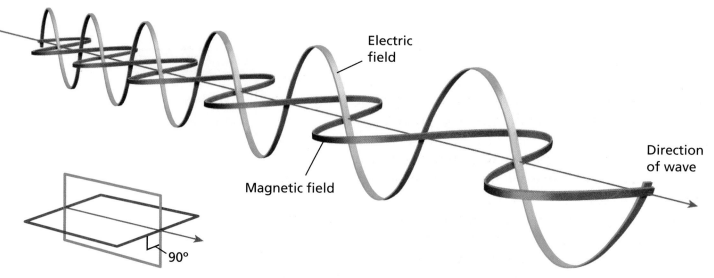

Electric field

Magnetic field

Direction of wave

90°

Fields are at right angles.

FIGURE 3
Electromagnetic Wave
In an electromagnetic wave, electric and magnetic fields vibrate at right angles to each other. *Interpreting Diagrams What is the angle between the fields?*

What Is an Electromagnetic Wave?

Waves in water and ropes have two things in common—they transfer energy and they also require a medium through which to travel. But electromagnetic waves can transfer energy without a medium. An **electromagnetic wave** transfers electrical and magnetic energy. **An electromagnetic wave consists of vibrating electric and magnetic fields that move through space at the speed of light.**

Producing Electromagnetic Waves Light and all other electromagnetic waves are produced by charged particles. Every charged particle has an electric field surrounding it. When a charged particle moves, it produces a magnetic field. When a charged particle changes its motion, its magnetic field changes. The changing magnetic field causes the electric field to change. When one field vibrates, so does the other. In this way, the two fields constantly cause each other to change. The result is an electromagnetic wave, as shown in Figure 3. Notice that the two fields vibrate at right angles to each other.

Energy The energy that is transferred through space by electromagnetic waves is called **electromagnetic radiation.** Electromagnetic waves do not require a medium, so they can transfer energy through a vacuum, or empty space. This is why you can see the sun and stars—their light reaches Earth through the vacuum of space.

Speed All electromagnetic waves travel at the same speed in a vacuum—about 300,000 kilometers per second. This speed is called the speed of light. At this speed, light from the sun takes about 8 minutes to travel the 150 million kilometers to Earth. When light waves travel through a medium such as air or water, however, they travel more slowly.

What Is the Electromagnetic Spectrum?

All electromagnetic waves travel at the same speed in a vacuum, but they have different wavelengths and different frequencies. As the wavelength decreases, the frequency increases. Waves with the longest wavelengths have the lowest frequencies. Waves with the shortest wavelengths have the highest frequencies. The amount of energy carried by an electromagnetic wave increases with frequency. The higher the frequency of a wave, the higher its energy.

The **electromagnetic spectrum** is the complete range of electromagnetic waves placed in order of increasing frequency. The full spectrum is shown in Figure 5. ⊂◗ **The electromagnetic spectrum is made up of radio waves, infrared rays, visible light, ultraviolet rays, X-rays, and gamma rays.** Electromagnetic waves that you can see are called **visible light.**

Radio Waves The electromagnetic waves with the longest wavelengths and lowest frequencies are radio waves. The very long wavelengths are used for broadcasting AM and FM radio and television signals.

Microwaves The radio waves with the shortest wavelengths and highest frequencies are microwaves. These waves are used in microwave ovens to heat your food, but they are also used in cellular phone communication and in radar systems.

Infrared Rays If you turn on a burner on an electric stove, you can feel it warm up before the heating element starts to glow. The invisible heat you feel is infrared radiation. Infrared rays are used in heat lamps.

 **Reading Checkpoint** What is the electromagnetic spectrum?

FIGURE 4
Radar Gun
Radio waves are used to find the speeds of moving vehicles.

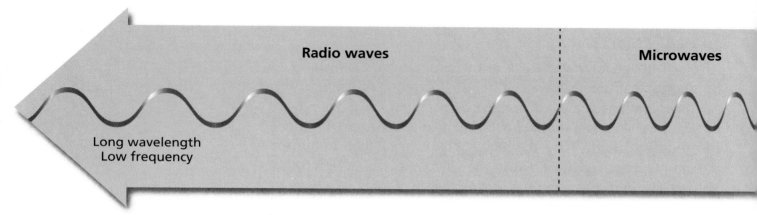

Radio waves

Microwaves

Long wavelength
Low frequency

FIGURE 5

The Electromagnetic Spectrum

The electromagnetic spectrum shows the range of different electromagnetic waves in order of increasing frequency and decreasing wavelength.
Interpreting Diagrams *Which electromagnetic waves have the longest wavelengths?*

Visible Light Visible light is a small band within a very broad electromagnetic spectrum. The wavelengths of visible light vary from 800 nanometers, or 0.0000008 m (red light) to 400 nanometers, or 0.0000004 m (violet light). The main colors of visible light in order from largest to smallest wavelength are red, orange, yellow, green, blue, indigo, and violet. They form a continuous spectrum.

Ultraviolet Rays Electromagnetic waves with wavelengths just shorter than those of visible light are called ultraviolet rays. They carry more energy than visible light. Small doses of ultraviolet rays are useful. For example, ultraviolet rays cause skin cells to produce vitamin D, which is needed for healthy bones and teeth. However, too much exposure to ultraviolet rays is dangerous. They can cause skin cancer and damage your eyes. If you apply sunblock and wear sunglasses that block ultraviolet rays, you can limit the damage caused by ultraviolet rays.

X-Rays Electromagnetic waves with wavelengths just shorter than those of ultraviolet rays are called X-rays. Because they have more energy than ultraviolet rays, they can penetrate most matter. But dense matter, such as bone or lead, absorbs them and does not allow them to pass through. Therefore, X-rays are used to make images of teeth and of bones inside the body. Too much exposure to X-rays, however, can lead to cancer.

Gamma Rays The electromagnetic waves with the shortest wavelengths and the greatest amount of energy are gamma rays. Gamma rays are the most penetrating of all the electromagnetic waves. They can be used to kill cancer cells inside the body.

 **Reading Checkpoint** What are the colors of visible light?

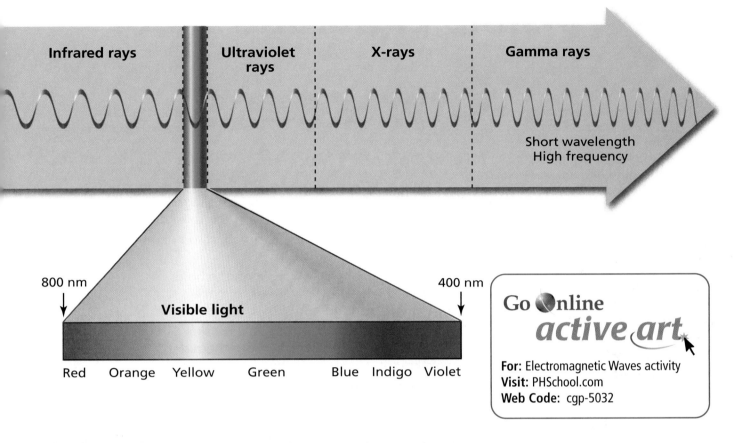

Infrared rays

Ultraviolet rays

X-rays

Gamma rays

Short wavelength
High frequency

800 nm

400 nm

Visible light

Red   Orange   Yellow   Green   Blue   Indigo   Violet

Go Online
active art

For: Electromagnetic Waves activity
Visit: PHSchool.com
Web Code: cgp-5032

Section 1 Assessment

S 7.6.a E-LA: Reading 7.2.0, Writing 7.2.1

> **Target Reading Skill** **Preview Visuals**
> Use your graphic organizer to help answer
> Question 2 below.

> **Reviewing Key Concepts**

1. a. **Identifying** What is a wave?
   b. **Explaining** How are mechanical waves produced?
   c. **Comparing and Contrasting** What is an example of a wave that requires a medium? What kind of wave can travel without a medium?
2. a. **Listing** What are four basic properties of waves?
   b. **Describing** Use a wave diagram to label the amplitude and wavelength of a wave. In a light wave, which of these properties tells you the color of the light?
   c. **Identifying** Which wave properties are distances? Which properties are measured relative to time?

3. a. **Identifying** What is an electromagnetic wave?
   b. **Explaining** Why can electromagnetic radiation travel through empty space?
4. a. **Listing** List the waves in the electromagnetic spectrum in order from longest wavelength to shortest wavelength. Make sure to include all the colors of visible light.
   b. **Explaining** Why are some electromagnetic waves harmful to you while others are not?
   c. **Classifying** List one or more types of electromagnetic waves that are useful for each of these purposes: cooking food, communication, seeing inside the body, curing diseases, reading a book, warming your hands.

Writing in Science

Firsthand Narrative Suppose you are a particle of water in a lake. Describe what happens to you when a motorboat passes by. Be sure to use words like *amplitude* and *crest* in your description.

Visible Light and Color

S 7.6.e Students know that white light is a mixture of many wavelengths (colors) and that retinal cells react differently to different wavelengths.

S 7.6.f Students know light can be reflected, refracted, transmitted, and absorbed by matter.

- How does visible light interact with an object?
- What determines the color of an opaque object?
- How is mixing pigments different from mixing colors of light?

Key Terms

- transparent
- translucent
- opaque
- primary colors
- secondary color
- complementary colors
- pigment

Lab zone Standards **Warm-Up**

How Do Colors Mix?

1. Cut a disk with a diameter of 10 cm out of white cardboard. Divide the disk into three equal-sized segments. Color one segment red, the next green, and the third blue.
2. Carefully punch two holes, 2 cm apart, on opposite sides of the center of the disk.
3. Thread a 1-m long string through the holes. Tie the ends of the string together to make a loop that passes through both holes.
4. With equal lengths of string on each side of the disk, tape the string in place. Turn the disk to wind up the string. Predict what color(s) you will see if the disk spins fast.
5. Spin the disk by pulling the loops to unwind the string.

Think It Over

Observing What color do you see as the wheel spins fast? Was your prediction correct?

It was hard work, but you are finally finished. You stand back to admire your work. Color is everywhere! The bright green grass rolls right up to the flower garden you just weeded. In the bright sunlight, you see patches of yellow daffodils, purple hyacinths, and red tulips. The sun's light allows you to see each color. But sunlight is white light. What makes each flower appear to be a different color?

Flowers in sunlight ▼

Visible Light

For you to see an object, light from the object has to reach your eye. An object can either be a primary source of light, meaning it emits, or gives off, its own light, or it can be a secondary source of light, meaning it reflects light from a primary source.

👁 **When light strikes an object, the light can be reflected, transmitted, or absorbed.** Think about a pair of sunglasses. If you hold the sunglasses in your hand, you can see light that reflects off the lenses. If you put the sunglasses on, you see light that is transmitted by the lenses. The lenses also absorb some light. That is why objects appear darker when seen through the lenses. Most materials can be classified as transparent, translucent, or opaque based on what happens to light that strikes the material.

Transparent Materials A **transparent** material transmits most of the light that strikes it. When light hits the particles of a transparent material, the particles absorb it but then reemit it, or send it back out, until the light finally passes through to the other side. However, if a transparent medium has impurities or imperfections in it, it can scatter some of the light so it doesn't reach your eye, similar to translucent materials.

Translucent Materials A **translucent** (trans LOO sunt) material scatters light as it passes through, just as smoke, fog, and clouds scatter light as it passes through the air. You can usually see something behind a translucent object, but the details are blurred. Wax paper and frosted glass like the middle glass in Figure 6 are translucent materials.

Opaque Materials An **opaque** (oh PAYK) material reflects or absorbs all of the light that strikes it. You cannot see through opaque materials because light cannot pass through them. You cannot see the straw through the white glass in Figure 6 because the glass is opaque.

Reading Checkpoint What happens when light strikes an opaque material?

FIGURE 6
Types of Materials
Different types of materials reflect, transmit, and absorb different amounts of light.
Comparing and Contrasting *How does a straw seen through transparent glass compare with a straw seen through translucent glass?*

Transparent   Translucent   Opaque

FIGURE 7

Colored Light

The color an apple appears to be depends on the color of the light that strikes it.
Applying Concepts *What color of light is reflected by a red apple?*

In red light, the apple appears red because it reflects the red light. But the leaves look black.

In green light, the apple appears black because no red light strikes it. But the leaves look green.

In blue light, both the apple and the leaves appear black.

Go Online

SciLINKS NSTA

For: Links on colors
Visit: www.SciLinks.org
Web Code: scn-1543

The Color of Objects

If you know how light interacts with objects, you can explain why objects such as flowers have different colors. The color and brightness of any object depends on the material the object is made of. The color and brightness of the light striking the object also affect the color of the object.

Color of Opaque Objects The color of an opaque object depends on the wavelengths of light that the object reflects. Every opaque object absorbs some wavelengths of light and reflects others. ☞ **The color of an opaque object is the color of the light it reflects.** For example, look at the apple shown at the top of Figure 7. The apple appears red because it reflects red wavelengths of light. The apple absorbs the other colors of light. The leaf looks green because it reflects green light and absorbs the other colors.

Objects can appear to be a different color if you view them in a different color of light. In red light, the apple appears red because there is red light for it to reflect. But the leaf appears black because there is no green light to reflect. In green light, the leaf looks green but the apple looks black. And in blue light, both the apple and the leaf look black.

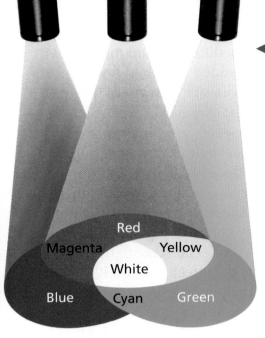

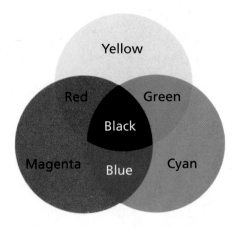

◀ **FIGURE 8**
Primary Colors of Light
The primary colors of light combine in equal amounts to form white light.

▲ **FIGURE 9**
Primary Colors of Pigments
Unlike the primary colors of light, the primary colors of pigments combine in equal amounts to form black.

Combining Colors

Color is used in painting, photography, theater lighting, and printing. People who work with color must learn how to produce a wide range of colors using just a few basic colors. Three colors that can combine to make any other color are called **primary colors.** Two primary colors combine in equal amounts to produce a **secondary color.**

Mixing Colors of Light The primary colors of light are red, green, and blue. ⬭ **When combined in equal amounts, the three primary colors of light produce white light.** If they are combined in different amounts, the primary colors can produce other colors. For example, red and green combine to form yellow light. Yellow is a secondary color of light because two primary colors produce it. The secondary colors of light are yellow (red + green), cyan (green + blue), and magenta (red + blue). Figure 8 shows the primary and secondary colors of light.

A primary and a secondary color can combine to make white light. Any two colors that combine to form white light are called **complementary colors.** Yellow and blue are complementary colors, as are cyan and red, and magenta and green.

Mixing Pigments How does a printer produce the many shades of colors you see in this textbook? Inks, paints, and dyes contain **pigments,** or colored substances that are used to color other materials. Pigments absorb some colors and reflect others. The color you see is the result of the colors that particular pigment reflects, as shown in Figure 9 .

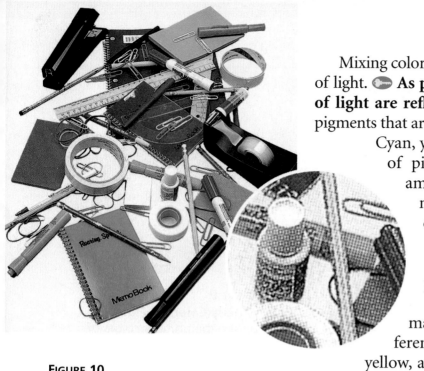

Mixing colors of pigments is different from mixing colors of light.  **As pigments are added together, fewer colors of light are reflected and more are absorbed.** The more pigments that are combined, the darker the mixture looks.

Cyan, yellow, and magenta are the primary colors of pigments. These colors combine in equal amounts to produce black. By combining pigments in varying amounts, you can produce many other colors. If you combine two primary colors of pigments, you get a secondary color. The secondary colors of pigments are red, green, and blue.

Look at the pictures in this book with a magnifying glass. You can see tiny dots of different colors of ink. The colors used are cyan, yellow, and magenta. Black ink is also used, so the printing process is called four-color printing.

FIGURE 10
The photograph shows a printed image, and the round insert shows an enlargement of it. Four-color printing uses the three primary colors of pigment, plus a very dark purple or black.

Reading Checkpoint **What colors are used in printing?**

Section 2 Assessment

S 7.6.e, 7.6.f, E-LA: Reading 7.1.2

Vocabulary Skill Latin Word Origins What does the Latin word part *trans* mean? What does *luc* mean? How do these Latin words help you understand what *translucent* means?

Reviewing Key Concepts

1. a. Identifying What three things may happen to the light that strikes an object?
   b. Applying Concepts What happens to light that strikes the following materials: clear plastic, aluminum foil, and tissue paper?
   c. Problem Solving Room-darkening window shades are used to keep sunlight out of a theater. What type of material should the shades be made of? Explain.
2. a. Reviewing What determines the color of an opaque object?
   b. Drawing Conclusions An actor's red shirt and blue pants both appear black. What color is the stage light shining on the actor?

3. a. Describing What are the primary colors of light? The primary colors of pigments?
   b. Comparing and Contrasting How does the result of mixing the primary colors of pigments compare to the result of mixing the primary colors of light?
   c. Interpreting Diagrams In Figure 9, which pair of colors combine to make blue?

Lab zone **At-Home Activity**

Color Mix See how many different shades of green you can make by mixing blue and yellow paint in different proportions. On white paper, paint a "spectrum" from yellow to green to blue. Show the results to your family. Then explain how magazine photos reproduce thousands of colors.

Changing Colors

S 7.6.e, 7.7.c

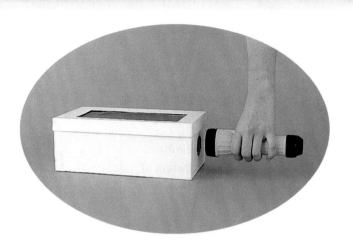

Problem

How do color filters affect the appearance of objects in white light?

Skills Focus

observing, inferring, predicting

Materials

- shoe box
- scissors
- flashlight
- removable tape
- red object
  (such as a ripe tomato)
- yellow object
  (such as a ripe lemon)
- blue object
  (such as blue construction paper)
- red, green, and blue cellophane, enough to cover the top of the shoe box

Procedure ✂

1. Carefully cut a large rectangular hole in the lid of the shoe box.

2. Carefully cut a small, round hole in the center of one of the ends of the shoe box.

3. Tape the red cellophane under the lid of the shoe box, covering the hole in the lid.

4. Place the objects in the box and put the lid on.

5. In a darkened room, shine the flashlight into the shoe box through the side hole. Note the apparent color of each object in the box.

6. Repeat Steps 3–5 using the other colors of cellophane.

Analyze and Conclude

1. **Observing** What did you see when you looked through the red cellophane? Explain why each object appeared as it did.

2. **Observing** What did you see when you looked through the blue cellophane? Explain.

3. **Inferring** What color(s) of light does each piece of cellophane allow through?

4. **Predicting** Predict what you would see under each piece of cellophane if you put a white object in the box. Test your prediction.

5. **Predicting** What do you think would happen if you viewed a red object through yellow cellophane? Draw a diagram to support your prediction. Then test your prediction.

6. **Communicating** Summarize your conclusions by drawing diagrams to show how each color filter affects white light. Write captions to explain your diagrams.

Design an Experiment

Do color filters work like pigments or like colors of light? Design an experiment to find out what happens if you shine a light through both a red and a green filter. *Obtain your teacher's permission before carrying out your investigation.*

Reflection and Refraction

CALIFORNIA
Standards Focus

S 7.6.c Students know light travels in straight lines if the medium it travels through does not change.

S 7.6.g Students know the angle of reflection of a light beam is equal to the angle of incidence.

- What does the law of reflection state?
- Why do light rays bend when they enter a new medium at an angle?
- What determines the types of images formed by convex and concave lenses?

Key Terms
- reflection
- law of reflection
- plane mirror
- image
- virtual image
- concave mirror
- optical axis
- focal point
- real image
- convex mirror
- refraction
- lens
- convex lens
- concave lens

Lab zone Standards Warm-Up

How Does a Ball Bounce?
1. Choose a spot at the base of a wall. From a distance of 1 m, roll a wet ball along the floor straight at the spot you choose. Watch the angle at which the ball bounces by looking at the path of moisture on the floor.
2. Wet the ball again. From a different position, roll the ball at the same spot, but at an angle to the wall. Again, observe the angle at which the ball bounces back.

Think It Over
Developing Hypotheses How do you think the angle at which the ball hits the wall is related to the angle at which the ball bounces back? Test your hypothesis.

You laugh as you and a friend move toward the curved mirror. First your reflections look tall and skinny. Then they become short and wide. At one point, your reflections disappear even though you are still in front of the mirror. Imagine what it would be like if this happened every time you tried to comb your hair in front of a mirror!

Funhouse Mirror ▶

Reflection

The reflection you see in a mirror depends on the surface. Light travels in straight lines if the medium it travels through does not change. But when a light beam encounters a shiny reflecting surface, it will bounce back.

If you did the Standards Warm-Up, you saw that the ball hit the wall and bounced back, or was reflected. When you look in a mirror, you use reflected light to see yourself. **Reflection** occurs when an object or wave bounces back off a surface through which it cannot pass.

All waves obey the **law of reflection.** To help you understand this law, look at Figure 11. In the photo, you see light reflected off the surface of the sunglasses. The diagram shows how the light waves travel to make the reflection. The arrow labeled *Incoming wave* represents a wave moving toward the surface at an angle. The arrow labeled *Reflected wave* represents the wave that bounces off the surface at an angle. The dashed line labeled *Normal* is drawn perpendicular to the surface at the point where the incoming wave strikes the surface. The angle of incidence is the angle between the incoming wave and the normal. The angle of reflection is the angle between the reflected wave and the normal line. ☞ **The law of reflection states that the angle of incidence equals the angle of reflection.**

FIGURE 11
Law of Reflection
The angle of incidence equals the angle of reflection. All waves obey this law, including the light waves reflected from these sunglasses.
Predicting *What happens to the angle of reflection if the angle of incidence increases?*

Reading Checkpoint What is reflection?

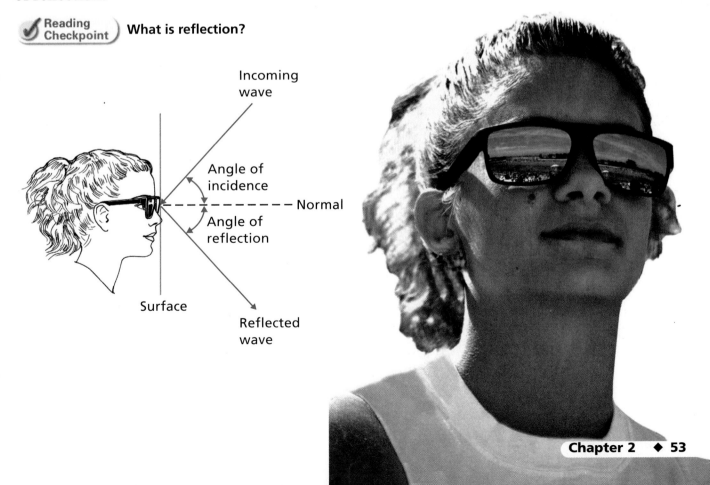

Incoming wave

Angle of incidence

Normal

Angle of reflection

Surface

Reflected wave

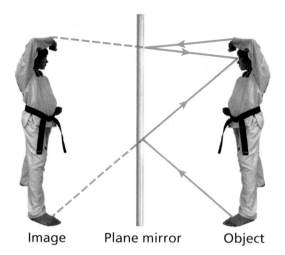

FIGURE 12
Image in a Plane Mirror
A plane mirror forms a virtual image. The reflected light rays appear to come from behind the mirror, where the image forms. **Observing** *Is the raised hand in the image a left hand or a right hand?*

Image   Plane mirror   Object

Mirrors

Did you look into a mirror this morning to comb your hair or brush your teeth? If you did, you probably used a plane mirror. The law of reflection explains the kind of images you see in different types of mirrors such as plane, concave, and convex mirrors.

Plane Mirrors A **plane mirror** is a flat sheet of glass that has a smooth, silver-colored coating on one side. When light strikes a mirror, the coating reflects the light. Because the coating is smooth, reflection occurs and a clear image forms. An **image** is a copy of an object formed by reflected or refracted rays of light.

The image you see in a plane mirror is a **virtual image**—an upright image that forms where light seems to come from. "Virtual" describes something that does not really exist. Your image appears to be behind the mirror, but you can't reach behind the mirror and touch it.

A plane mirror produces a virtual image that is upright and the same size as the object. But the image is not quite the same as the object. The left and right of the image are reversed. For example, when you look in a mirror, your right hand appears to be a left hand in the image.

Figure 12 shows how a plane mirror forms an image. Some light rays from the karate student strike the mirror and reflect toward his eye. Even though the rays are reflected, the student's brain treats them as if they had come from behind the mirror. The dashed lines show where the light rays appear to come from. Because the light appears to come from behind the mirror, this is where the student's image appears to be located.

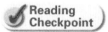 **Reading Checkpoint** **Where does an image in a plane mirror appear to be located?**

Concave Mirrors A mirror with a surface that curves inward like the inside of a bowl is a **concave mirror**. Figure 13 shows how a concave mirror can reflect parallel rays of light so that they meet at a point. Notice that the rays of light shown are parallel to the optical axis. The **optical axis** is an imaginary line that divides a mirror in half. The point at which rays parallel to the optical axis meet or converge is called the **focal point**. The location of the focal point depends on the shape of the mirror. The more curved the mirror is, the closer the focal point is to the mirror.

Concave mirrors can form either virtual images or real images. If an object is farther away from the mirror than the focal point, the reflected rays form a real image as shown in Figure 14. A **real image** forms when rays actually meet. But if the object is between the mirror and the focal point, the reflected rays form a virtual image behind the mirror. Virtual images formed by a concave mirror are always larger than the object.

FIGURE 13
Focal Point of a Concave Mirror
A concave mirror reflects rays of light parallel to the optical axis back through the focal point.

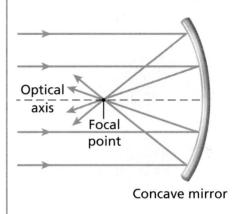

FIGURE 14
Images in Concave Mirrors
The type of image formed depends on the location of the object.
Interpreting Diagrams *When light rays actually meet, what kind of image is formed?*

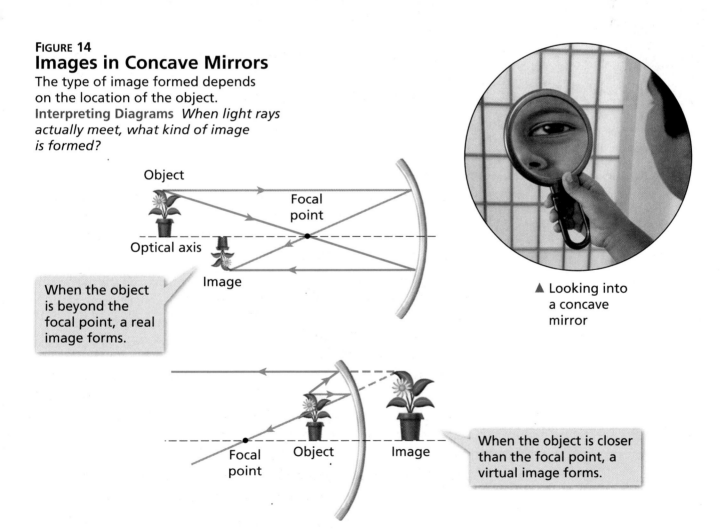

When the object is beyond the focal point, a real image forms.

▲ Looking into a concave mirror

When the object is closer than the focal point, a virtual image forms.

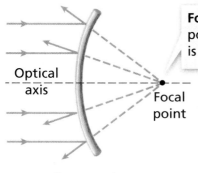

FIGURE 15
Images in Convex Mirrors
Light rays parallel to the optical axis reflect as if they came from the focal point behind the mirror. The image formed by a convex mirror is always virtual.
Making Generalizations *Describe the directions of the parallel rays reflected by a convex mirror.*

Looking into ▶ a convex mirror

Optical axis

Convex mirror

Focal Point The focal point of a convex mirror is behind the mirror.

Focal point

Image

Optical axis

Object

Focal point

Virtual Reduced Image No matter where the object is, the image is virtual, upright, and reduced.

Go **Online**
active art

For: Mirrors activity
Visit: PHSchool.com
Web Code: cgp-5042

Convex Mirrors A mirror with a surface that curves outward is called a **convex mirror.** Figure 15 shows how convex mirrors reflect parallel rays of light. The rays diverge but appear to come from a focal point behind the mirror. Because the rays never meet, images formed by convex mirrors are always virtual and smaller than the object. A convex mirror can never create a real image.

Perhaps you have seen this warning on a car mirror: "Objects in mirror are closer than they appear." Convex mirrors are used in cars as passenger-side mirrors. They are also used as security mirrors and safety mirrors in banks, grocery stores, parking garages, and offices. The advantage of a convex mirror is that it allows you to see a larger area than you can with a plane mirror. The disadvantage is that the image is reduced in size, so it appears to be farther away than it actually is.

 **Reading Checkpoint** **Where are convex mirrors typically used?**

Refraction

Light travels in straight lines if the medium it travels through does not change. If light enters a new medium, it might slow down or speed up, because the speed of light is different for different mediums. If light enters the new medium perpendicular to the boundary, it will keep moving in the same direction. But if it hits the boundary at an angle, it will also bend. This bending of light waves due to a change in speed is known as **refraction.**

Refraction in Different Mediums Some mediums cause light to bend more than others, as shown in Figure 16. **When light rays enter a medium at an angle, the change in speed causes the rays to bend, or change direction.** When light passes from air into water, the light slows down. Light slows down even more when it passes from water into glass. When light passes from glass back into air, the light speeds up. Light travels fastest in air, a little slower in water, and slower still in glass. Notice that the ray that leaves the glass is traveling in the same direction as it was before it entered the water.

Different densities within the same medium can cause refraction as well. For example, the air heated by a campfire can cause objects to appear to shimmer because the path of the light is not a straight line. Also, stars appear to twinkle because of variations in the density of Earth's atmosphere.

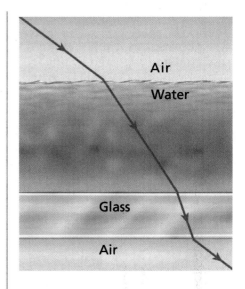

FIGURE 16
Refraction of Light
As light passes from a less dense medium into a more dense medium, it slows down and is refracted.

Math: Mathematical Reasoning 7.2.5

Math ▶ Analyzing Data

Bending Light

The index of refraction of a medium is a measure of how much light bends as it travels from air into the medium. The table shows the index of refraction of some common mediums.

1. **Interpreting Data** Which medium causes the greatest change in the direction of a light ray?

2. **Interpreting Data** Which tends to bend light more: solids or liquids?

3. **Predicting** Would light bend if it entered corn oil at an angle from glycerol? Explain.

Index of Refraction	
Medium	**Index of Refraction**
Air (gas)	1.00
Water (liquid)	1.33
Corn oil (liquid)	1.47
Glycerol (liquid)	1.47
Glass, crown (solid)	1.52
Sodium chloride (solid)	1.54
Diamond (solid)	2.42

Effects of Refraction

Effects of Refraction One pretty effect of refraction is the separation of visible light into its component colors by a prism. A prism does this because the angle of refraction is different for each color or wavelength of light. The longer the wavelength, the less the wave is bent by a prism. Red light, with the longest wavelength, is refracted the least. Violet light, with the shortest wavelength, is refracted the most. This difference in refraction causes white light to spread out into the colors of the spectrum—red, orange, yellow, green, blue, indigo, and violet.

The same process occurs in water droplets suspended in the air. When white light from the sun shines through the droplets, a rainbow may appear. The water droplets act like tiny prisms, refracting and reflecting the light and separating the colors.

You can also see the effects of refraction if you place a pencil in a glass of water, as shown in Figure 18. As you look at a pencil in a glass of water, the light coming from the pencil to your eye bends as it passes through three different mediums. The mediums are water, glass, and air. As the light passes from one medium to the next, it refracts.

 **Reading Checkpoint** **What causes a rainbow?**

FIGURE 18
Pencil in a Glass
The pencil appears broken because the light bends. As light from the pencil passes from water into glass, it slows down and is refracted. When the light passes from the glass into the air, it speeds up and is refracted again.

Lenses

When you look through a camera, a telescope, or a microscope, you use lenses. A **lens** is a curved piece of glass or other transparent material that refracts light. A lens forms an image by refracting light rays that pass through it. The type of image formed by a lens depends on the shape of the lens and the position of the object.

Convex Lenses A **convex lens** or magnifying glass is thicker in the center than at the edges. As light rays parallel to the optical axis pass through a convex lens, they converge. The rays meet at the focal point of the lens and continue to travel beyond. The distance from the lens to the focal point is called the focal length. The more curved the lens, the more it refracts light. A convex lens focuses rays of light.

An object's position relative to the focal point determines whether a convex lens forms a real image or a virtual image. Figure 19 shows that if the object is farther away than the focal point, the refracted rays form a real image on the other side of the lens. If the object is between the lens and the focal point, a virtual image forms on the same side of the lens as the object.

FIGURE 19
Images in Convex Lenses
The type of image formed by a convex lens depends on the object's position.

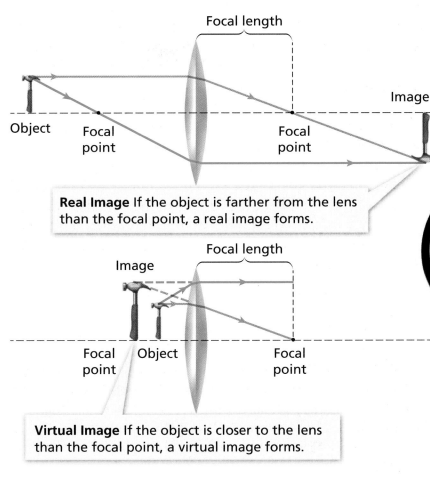

Real Image If the object is farther from the lens than the focal point, a real image forms.

Virtual Image If the object is closer to the lens than the focal point, a virtual image forms.

Lab zone Try This **Activity**

Making an Image

1. Hold a hand lens above a table that sits directly under a ceiling light. Lift the lens up until the sharpest image of the light is formed on the table. How high above the table are you holding the lens? That distance is called the focal length.

2. Now look through a lens above a printed page at a distance of less than the focal length. What do you see?

3. Move the lens until it is farther away from the printed page than the focal length. How does the print appear now?

Classifying What type of image do you see in each step?

FIGURE 20
Images in Concave Lenses

A concave lens produces virtual images that are upright and smaller than the object. **Interpreting Diagrams** *Why can a concave lens only form a virtual image?*

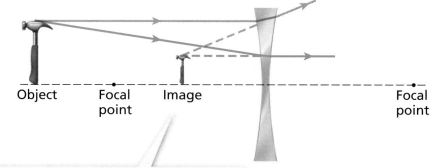

Virtual, Reduced Image Wherever the object is placed, a virtual image forms.

Object   Focal point   Image   Focal point

Go Online
active art

For: Lenses activity
Visit: PHSchool.com
Web Code: cgp-5042

Concave Lenses A **concave lens** is thinner in the center than at the edges. When light rays traveling parallel to the optical axis pass through a concave lens, they bend away, or diverge, from the optical axis and never meet. ◯ **A concave lens can produce only virtual images because parallel light rays passing through the lens never meet.**

Figure 20 shows how an image forms in a concave lens. The virtual image is located where the light rays appear to come from. The image is always upright and smaller than the object.

Reading Checkpoint **What is the shape of a concave lens?**

Section 3 Assessment

S 7.6.c, 7.6.g E-LA: Reading 7.1.2, Writing 7.2.1

Vocabulary Skill **Latin Word Origins** The Latin word *planus* means "flat." How does this Latin meaning help you remember what a plane mirror is?

Reviewing Key Concepts

1. **a. Defining** What is reflection?
   b. Identifying What does the law of reflection state?
   c. Predicting If a beam of light hits a plane mirror at a 30° angle, at what angle would it be reflected?
2. **a. Identifying** What is refraction?
   b. Relating Cause and Effect What causes light rays to bend when they enter a new medium at an angle?
   c. Predicting If a glass prism were placed in a medium such as water, would it separate white light into different colors? Explain.

3. **a. Defining** What is a lens?
   b. Comparing and Contrasting Describe the shapes of a concave lens and a convex lens.
   c. Interpreting Diagrams Use Figure 19 to explain how you can tell whether a convex lens will form a real or virtual image.

Writing in Science

Dialogue At a funhouse mirror, your younger brother notices he can make his image disappear as he walks toward the mirror. He asks you to explain, but your answer leads to more questions. Write the dialogue that might take place between you and your brother.

60 ◆

Looking at Images

S 7.6.d, 7.7.c

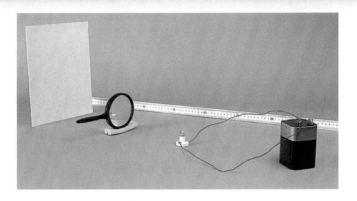

Problem

How does the distance between an object and a convex lens affect the image formed?

Skills Focus

controlling variables, interpreting data

Materials

- tape
- convex lens
- cardboard stand
- blank sheet of paper
- light bulb and socket
- clay, for holding the lens
- battery and wires
- meter stick
- centimeter ruler

Procedure

1. Tape the paper onto the cardboard stand.

2. Place a lit bulb more than 2 m from the paper. Use the lens to focus light from the bulb onto the paper. Measure the distance from the lens to the paper. This is the approximate focal length of the lens you are using.

3. Copy the data table into your notebook.

4. Now place the bulb more than twice the focal length away from the lens. Adjust the cardboard until the image is focused. Record the size of the image on the paper and note the orientation of the image. Record the distance from the bulb to the lens and from the lens to the cardboard.

5. Now, move the bulb so that it is just over one focal length away from the lens. Record the position and size of the image.

Analyze and Conclude

1. **Controlling Variables** Make a list of the variables in this experiment. Which variables did you keep constant? Which was the manipulated variable? Which were the responding variables?

2. **Observing** What happened to the position of the image as the bulb moved toward the lens?

3. **Interpreting Data** Was the image formed by the convex lens always enlarged? If not, under what conditions was the image reduced?

4. **Predicting** What would happen if you look through the lens at the bulb when it is closer to the lens than the focal point? Explain your prediction.

5. **Communicating** Write a paragraph explaining how the distance between an object and a convex lens affects the image formed. Use ray diagrams to help you summarize your results.

Design an Experiment

Design an experiment to study images formed by convex lenses with different thicknesses. How does the lens thickness affect the position and size of the images? *Obtain your teacher's permission before carrying out your investigation.*

Data Table			
Focal Length of Lens: ____ cm		Height of Bulb: ____ cm	
Distance From Bulb to Lens (cm)	Distance From Lens to Cardboard (cm)	Image Orientation (upright or upside down)	Image Size (height in cm)

Seeing Light

S 7.5.g Students know how to relate the structures of the eye and ear to their functions.

S 7.6.b Students know that for an object to be seen, light emitted by or scattered from it must be detected by the eye.

S 7.6.e Students know light is a mixture of many wavelengths (colors) and that retinal cells react differently to different wavelengths.

 How do you see objects?

 What types of lenses are used to correct vision problems?

Key Terms

- cornea
- pupil
- iris
- retina
- rods
- cones
- nearsighted
- farsighted

Lab zone Standards **Warm-Up**

How Does a Beam of Light Travel?

1. Punch a hole (about 0.5 cm in diameter) through four large index cards.
2. Use binder clips or modeling clay to stand each card upright so that the long side of the index card is on the tabletop. Space the cards about 10 cm apart, as shown in the photo. To line the holes up in a straight line, run a piece of string through them and pull it tight.
3. Place a flashlight in front of the card nearest you. Shut off all light except the flashlight. What do you see on the wall?
4. Move one of the cards sideways about 3 cm and repeat Step 3. Now what do you see on the wall?

Think It Over
Inferring Explain what happened in Step 4. What does this activity tell you about the path of light?

You return from a field trip to a nearby pond, carrying a bottle of water you collected. Carefully, you place a drop of water onto a slide and look through it using a microscope. At first, the image appears fuzzy. You turn the focus adjustment knobs. Suddenly the image becomes sharp. You are amazed to see a world of tiny creatures living in the drop of water!

In the next lesson, you will learn about optical tools that help scientists see things that are very small. Some of the tools are complex, with many parts that have to work together to produce a clear image. Just as you have to focus a microscope, your eye has to focus light for you to see clearly. In this lesson, you will learn how the many parts of your eye work together so you can see.

◀ Focusing light

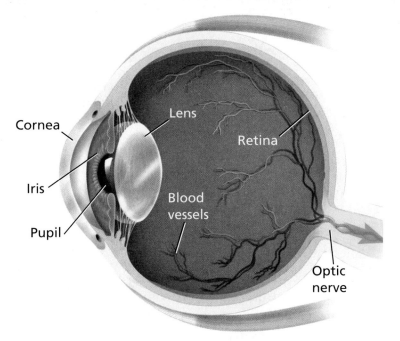

Cornea

Lens

Retina

Iris

Blood vessels

Pupil

Optic nerve

FIGURE 21
The Eye
Your eyes allow you to sense light. The pupil is the opening through which light enters the eye. In bright light, the pupil becomes smaller. In dim light, the pupil enlarges and allows more light to enter the eye. **Interpreting Diagrams** *What structure adjusts the size of the pupil?*

Vision

Your eyes sense light. The eye is a complex structure with many parts, as you can see in Figure 21. Each part plays a role in vision. 🔁 **When light from an object enters your eye, your eye sends a signal to your brain and you see the object.**

Light Enters the Eye Light enters the eye through the transparent front surface called the **cornea** (KAWR nee uh). The cornea protects the eye. It also acts as a lens to help focus light rays. Then, light enters the pupil, the part of the eye that looks black. The **pupil** is an opening through which light enters the inside of the eye. In dim light, the pupil becomes larger to allow in more light. In bright light, the pupil becomes smaller to allow in less light. The **iris** is a ring of muscle that contracts and expands to change the size of the pupil. The iris gives the eye its color. In most people the iris is brown; in others it is blue, green, or hazel.

An Image Forms After entering the pupil, the light passes through the lens. The lens bends light to form an upside-down image on the retina. The **retina** is a layer of cells that lines the inside of the eyeball.

The retina is made up of tiny, light-sensitive cells called rods and cones. **Rods** contain a pigment that responds to small amounts of light. **Cones** respond to color. They detect red light, green light, or blue light. Cones respond best in bright light. Rods and cones help change images on the retina into signals that travel to the brain along the optic nerve.

Pupil and Iris
The iris controls the size of the pupil, which determines how much light enters the eye.

Pupil

Iris

Dim Light The iris contracts, making the pupil large.

Bright Light The iris expands, making the pupil small.

Go Online
active art

For: Virtual Dissection of the Eye activity
Visit: PHSchool.com
Web Code: cvp-4153

 **Reading Checkpoint** Where does an image form in the eye?

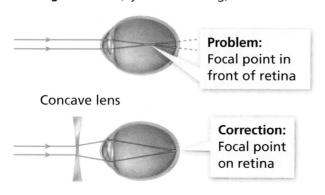

Nearsightedness (eyeball too long)

Problem:
Focal point in front of retina

Concave lens

Correction:
Focal point on retina

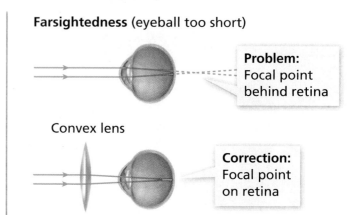

Farsightedness (eyeball too short)

Problem:
Focal point behind retina

Convex lens

Correction:
Focal point on retina

FIGURE 22
Correcting Vision

Nearsightedness and farsightedness are caused when the eyeball is too long or too short. Both can be corrected with lenses.

Correcting Vision If the eyeball is slightly too long or too short, the image on the retina is out of focus. Fortunately, wearing glasses or contact lenses can correct this type of vision problem. 🔑 **Concave lenses are used to correct nearsightedness. Convex lenses are used to correct farsightedness.**

A **nearsighted** person can see nearby things clearly, but objects at a distance are blurred. The eyeball is too long, so the lens focuses the image in front of the retina. To correct this, a concave lens in front of the eye spreads out light rays before they enter the eye. As a result, the image forms on the retina.

A **farsighted** person can see distant objects clearly, but nearby objects appear blurry. The eyeball is too short, so the image that falls on the retina is out of focus. A convex lens corrects this by bending light rays toward each other before they enter the eye. An image then focuses on the retina.

Section 4 Assessment

S 7.5.g, 7.6.b, 7.6.e, E-LA: Reading 7.2.0, Writing 7.2.1

🎯 **Target Reading Skill** Preview Visuals
Use a graphic organizer to answer Question 2.

🔑 **Reviewing Key Concepts**

1. **a. Listing** List the parts of the eye in the order in which light interacts with them.
   b. Explaining How is an image formed on the retina?
   c. Sequencing Events What happens to light after it strikes the retina?
2. **a. Reviewing** What types of lenses help correct vision problems?
   b. Describing Describe a nearsighted person's eye.

c. Comparing and Contrasting With uncorrected vision, where does an image form in a nearsighted person's eye? In a farsighted person's eye?

Writing in Science

Fictional Narrative Imagine that you meet an alien whose eyes work by seeing infrared light rather than visible light. Write a dialogue in which you explain to the alien the colors of light that you see.

Optical Tools

CALIFORNIA
Standards Focus

S 7.6.d Students know how simple lenses are used in a magnifying glass, the eye, a camera, a telescope, and a microscope.

🔑 How are lenses used in cameras, telescopes, and microscopes?

Key Terms
- camera
- telescope
- refracting telescope
- objective
- eyepiece
- reflecting telescope
- microscope
- electron microscope

Lab zone **Standards Warm-Up**

How Does a Pinhole Viewer Work?

1. Carefully use a pin to make a tiny hole in the center of the bottom of a paper cup.
2. Place a piece of wax paper over the open end of the cup. Hold the paper in place with a rubber band.
3. Turn off the room lights. Point the end of the cup with the hole in it at a bright window. **CAUTION:** *Do not look directly at the sun.*
4. Look at the image on the wax paper.

Think It Over
Classifying Describe the image you see. Is is upside down or right-side up? Is it smaller or larger than the actual object? What type of image is it?

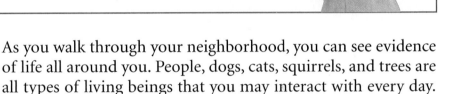

As you walk through your neighborhood, you can see evidence of life all around you. People, dogs, cats, squirrels, and trees are all types of living beings that you may interact with every day. But there is also life you can't see: tiny creatures that are not visible to the eye without help.

Since the 1600s, scientists have built many optical tools using lenses. Cameras allow them to record photographs of the objects they see. Telescopes help them see objects that are very far away. And microscopes help them see tiny nearby objects by magnifying them many times. Without a microscope, you couldn't see the detail in the water flea at the left. The water flea is only about 1 millimeter in size, not much bigger than the period at the end of this sentence.

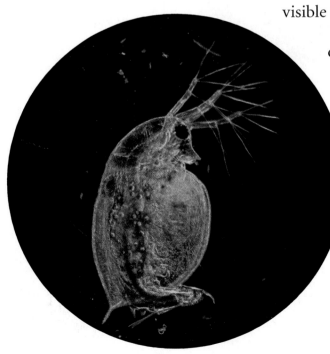

◀ **Image of a water flea taken with a microscope**

Cameras

A **camera** uses one or more lenses to focus light, and film to record an image. Figure 23 shows the structure of a camera. Light from an object travels to the camera and passes through the lens. **The lens of the camera focuses light to form a real, upside-down image on film in the back of the camera.** In many cameras, the lens automatically moves closer to or away from the film until the image is focused.

To take a photo, you press a button that briefly opens the shutter, a screen in front of the film. Opening the shutter allows light passing through the lens to hit the film. The diaphragm is a device with a hole called an aperture that can be made smaller or larger. The aperture can be adjusted in size to control the amount of light hitting the film, similar to how the iris controls the size of the pupil in your eye.

Reading Checkpoint What part of a camera controls the amount of light that enters the camera?

FIGURE 23
Camera
A camera uses a lens to project an image onto film. **Interpreting Diagrams** *What happens to each light ray as it passes through the lens?*

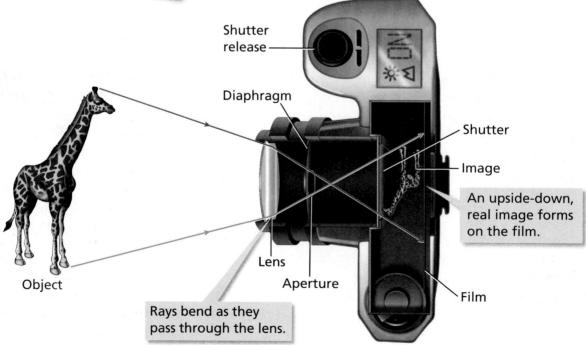

Shutter release

Diaphragm

Shutter

Image

An upside-down, real image forms on the film.

Object

Lens

Aperture

Film

Rays bend as they pass through the lens.

FIGURE 24
Refracting and Reflecting Telescopes

Both reflecting and refracting telescopes gather light from distant objects.

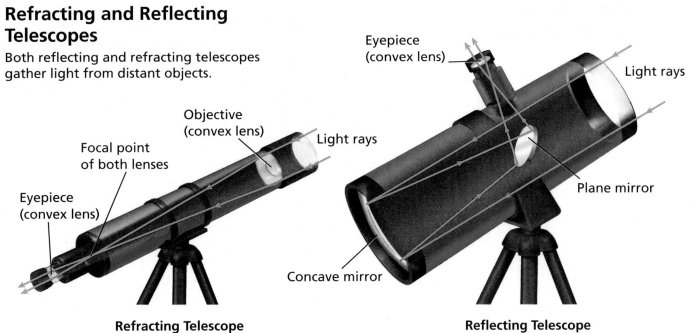

Refracting Telescope

Reflecting Telescope

Telescopes

Distant objects are difficult to see because light from them has spread out by the time it reaches your eyes. Your eyes are too small to gather much light. A **telescope** forms enlarged images of distant objects. 🔑 **Telescopes use combinations of lenses or mirrors to collect and focus light from distant objects.** The most common use of telescopes is to study objects in space. Binoculars, too, enable people to see distant objects. Unlike telescopes, binoculars have two eyepieces.

Figure 24 shows the two main types of telescopes: refracting telescopes and reflecting telescopes. A **refracting telescope** consists of two convex lenses, one at each end of a tube. The larger lens is called the objective. The **objective** gathers the light coming from an object and focuses the rays to form a real image. The lens close to your eye is called the eyepiece. The **eyepiece** magnifies the image so you can see it clearly. The image seen through the refracting telescope in Figure 24 is upside down.

A **reflecting telescope** uses a large concave mirror to gather light. The mirror collects light from distant objects and focuses the rays to form a real image. A small mirror inside the telescope reflects the image to the eyepiece. The images you see through a reflecting telescope are upside down, just like the images seen through a refracting telescope.

 **Reading Checkpoint** What are the objective and the eyepiece?

Lab zone **Try This Activity**

What a View!
You can use two hand lenses of different strengths to form an image.

1. Hold the stronger lens close to your eye.
2. Hold the other lens at arm's length.
3. Use your lens combination to view a distant object. **CAUTION:** *Do not look at the sun.* Adjust the distance of the farther lens until the image is clear.

Classifying What type of image do you see? What type of telescope is similar to this lens combination?

Sometimes your eyes need help in making detailed scientific observations. What is the correct optical tool to observe each of the following?

1. Birds at a bird feeder
2. Stars at night.
3. A sample of blood

Microscopes

To look at small, nearby objects you can use a microscope. A **microscope** is an optical tool that makes small objects look larger. You will use it when studying life science. ⬤ **A microscope uses a combination of lenses to form enlarged images of tiny objects.** Scientists today use two kinds of microscopes: light microscopes and electron microscopes.

For a microscope to be useful, it must combine two important properties—magnification and resolution.

Magnification Magnification is the ability to make things look larger than they are. The lenses in light microscopes magnify an object by bending the light that passes through them. Light passing through a convex lens converges. When this light hits the eye, the eye sees the object as larger than it really is.

Since light microscopes have more than one lens, they are also called compound microscopes. Light passes through a specimen and then through two lenses. The first lens, the objective, magnifies the object. Then a second lens, the eyepiece, further magnifies the enlarged image. The total magnification of the microscope is equal to the magnifications of the two lenses multiplied together. Figure 25 shows a hair follicle at two different magnifications, 18 times and 63 times its real size. You can learn more about using microscopes in Appendix B.

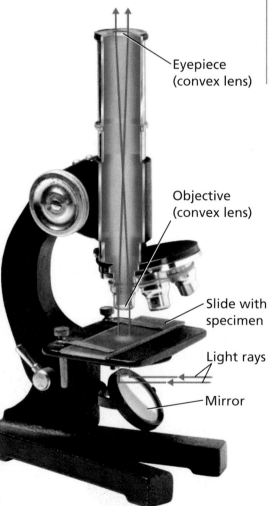

Eyepiece (convex lens)

Objective (convex lens)

Slide with specimen

Light rays

Mirror

FIGURE 25
Light Microscope
A compound microscope can change magnification. The two pictures of hair follicles were taken at different magnifications. **Inferring** *What is an advantage of higher magnification?*

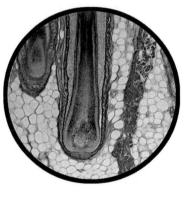

▲ **18 times actual size**

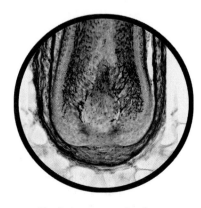

▲ **63 times actual size**

Resolution To create a useful image, a microscope must help you see individual parts clearly. The ability to clearly distinguish the individual parts of an object is called resolution. Resolution is another term for the sharpness of an image. For example, a newspaper photograph is really made up of a collection of small dots. If you put the photo under a microscope, you can see the separate dots because the microscope improves resolution.

Electron Microscopes The microscopes used by early researchers were all light microscopes. In the 1930s, scientists developed the **electron microscope**. Electron microscopes use a beam of tiny particles called electrons instead of light to produce a magnified image. Electron microscopes can take pictures of extremely small objects—much smaller than those that can be seen with light microscopes. The resolution of electron microscopes is much better than the resolution of light microscopes.

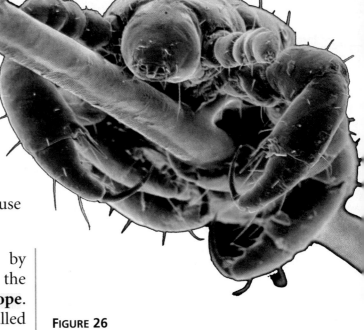

FIGURE 26
Electron Microscope Picture
A head louse clings to a human hair. This picture was taken with a scanning electron microscope. The louse has been magnified to more than 100 times its actual size.

Section 5 Assessment

S 7.6.d E-LA: Reading 7.2.0, Writing 7.2.4

Target Reading Skill Preview Visuals List three questions and answers that you wrote about Figure 25.

Reviewing Key Concepts

1. a. **Reviewing** How are lenses used in telescopes, microscopes, and cameras?
   b. **Comparing and Contrasting** Compare and contrast how images form in a refracting telescope, a reflecting telescope, and a microscope.
   c. **Classifying** A pair of binoculars has two lenses in each tube. Which type of optical instrument are the binoculars most similar to?
2. a. **Reviewing** What are the parts of a camera?
   b. **Comparing and Contrasting** How is the aperture of the camera like the pupil?
   c. **Explaining** Why does a camera need an aperture to control the amount of light hitting the film?

3. a. **Reviewing** What does a microscope enable people to do?
   b. **Defining** What is magnification?
   c. **Calculating** If one lens has a magnification of 10, and the other lens has a magnification of 50, what is the total magnification?
   d. **Comparing and Contrasting** Contrast the way light microscopes and electron microscopes magnify objects.

Writing in Science

Advertisement A company has asked you to write an advertisement for its new, easy-to-use camera. In the ad, the company wants you to describe the camera's features so that buyers will understand how the camera works. Be sure to mention the shutter, lens, diaphragm, and aperture.

The BIG Idea Light entering the eye is bent by the cornea and lens to form an image on the retina.

1 Waves and the Electromagnetic Spectrum

Key Concepts   S 7.6.a

- Mechanical waves are produced when a source of energy causes a medium to vibrate.
- The basic properties of waves are amplitude, wavelength, frequency, and speed.
- The electromagnetic spectrum is made up of radio waves, infrared rays, visible light, ultraviolet rays, X-rays, and gamma rays.

Key Terms

- wave • energy • medium • crest • trough
- amplitude • wavelength • frequency
- hertz • electromagnetic radiation
- electromagnetic spectrum • visible light

2 Visible Light and Color

Key Concepts   S 7.6.e, 7.6.f

- When light strikes an object, the light can be reflected, transmitted, or absorbed.
- The color of an opaque object is the color of the light it reflects.
- When combined in equal amounts, the three primary colors of light produce white light.
- As pigments are added together, fewer colors of light are reflected and more are absorbed.

Key Terms

- transparent • translucent • opaque
- primary colors • secondary color
- complementary colors • pigments

3 Reflection and Refraction

Key Concepts   S 7.6.c, 7.6g

- The law of reflection states that the angle of incidence equals the angle of reflection.
- When light rays enter a medium at an angle, the change in speed causes the rays to bend, or change direction.
- An object's position relative to the focal point determines whether a convex lens forms a real image or a virtual image.

- A concave lens can produce only virtual images because parallel light rays passing through the lens never meet.

Key Terms

- reflection • law of reflection • plane mirror
- image • virtual image • concave mirror
- optical axis • focal point • real image
- convex mirror • refraction • lens
- convex lens • concave lens

4 Seeing Light

Key Concepts   S 7.5.g, 7.6.b, 7.6.e

- When light from an object enters your eye, your eye sends a signal to your brain and you see the object.
- Concave lenses correct nearsightedness. Convex lenses correct farsightedness.

Key Terms

- cornea • pupil • iris • retina • rods
- cones • nearsighted • farsighted

5 Optical Tools

Key Concepts   S 7.6.d

- The camera lens camera focuses light to form a real, upside-down image on film in the back of the camera.
- Telescopes use combinations of lenses or mirrors to collect and focus light from distant objects.
- A microscope uses a combination of lenses to form enlarged images of tiny objects.

Key Terms

- camera • telescope • refracting telescope
- objective • eyepiece • reflecting telescope
- microscope • electron microscope

Review and Assessment

⟳ Target Reading Skill

Previewing Visuals Complete a graphic organizer for the illustration on Law of Reflection, Figure 11. Add more questions and answers to show that you understand the law of reflection.

Law of Reflection

Q. In your own words, what is the subject of this illustration?
A.   a. _____ ?
Q. What is the incoming wave?
A.   b. _____ ?
Q. How is the incoming wave different from the reflected wave?
A.   c. _____ ?

Reviewing Key Terms

Choose the letter of the best answer.

1. A wave transfers
   a. energy.   b. particles.
   c. water.   d. air.

2. Two complementary colors of light that can combine to form white light are
   a. red and green.
   b. green and cyan.
   c. cyan and yellow.
   d. yellow and blue.

3. A curved piece of glass or other transparent material that is used to refract light is a
   a. plane mirror.   b. concave mirror.
   c. convex mirror.   d. concave lens.

4. The opening through which light enters the inside of your eye is the
   a. cornea.   b. iris.
   c. pupil.   d. retina.

5. A device used to make objects that are far away appear closer is a(n)
   a. camera.
   b. telescope.
   c. microscope.
   d. electron microscope.

Complete the following sentences so that your answers clearly explain the key terms.

6. Visible light is a tiny part of the whole **electromagnetic spectrum,** which also includes _____ .

7. The colors in this textbook come from **pigments,** which are _____ .

8. If you look into a plane mirror, you see a **virtual image,** which is _____ .

9. The lens of the eye forms an image on the **retina,** which is _____ .

10. A **microscope** allows you to see something very small, because _____ .

Writing in Science

Persuasive Letter Write a short letter to your representative in Congress asking him or her to continue supporting telescopes in space. Include at least two advantages of space telescopes in your letter.

Video Assessment
Discovery Channel School
Light

Review and Assessment

Checking Concepts

11. How can you measure the amplitude of a wave?

12. How do you know that electromagnetic waves can travel through a vacuum?

13. Explain why the energy of infrared waves is greater than the energy of radio waves.

14. Which color of light has the longest wavelength? The shortest wavelength?

15. Describe transparent, translucent, and opaque materials. Give an example of each.

16. Why do you see the petals of a rose as red and the leaves as green?

17. Sketch the optical axis and focal point(s) of a concave lens and a convex lens.

18. Describe real and virtual images. How can each type of image be formed by mirrors?

19. Which parts of the eye help you see colors?

20. How are lenses used in a microscope?

Thinking Critically

Use the illustration to answer Question 21.

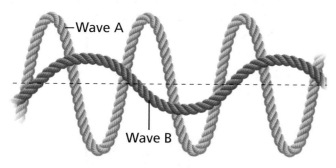

—Wave A

Wave B

21. **Comparing and Contrasting** The waves shown travel at the same speed.
    a. Which wave has the higher frequency?
    b. Which has the longer wavelength?
    c. Which has the greater amplitude?

22. **Applying Concepts** Suppose ripples move from one side of a lake to the other. Does the water move across the lake? Explain.

23. **Applying Concepts** Why is it hard to see on a foggy day?

24. **Applying Concepts** Can a plane mirror produce a real image? Explain.

25. **Comparing and Contrasting** How are convex and concave mirrors alike? How are they different?

26. **Comparing and Contrasting** How is a nearsighted person's sight similar to a farsighted person's? How is it different?

27. **Problem Solving** A telescope produces an upside-down image. How could you modify the telescope so the image is upright?

28. **Comparing and Contrasting** How is a microscope similar to a convex lens used as a magnifying lens? How is it different?

Applying Skills

Use the illustration to answer Questions 29–31.

29. **Explaining** What colors of visible light are absorbed by the red apple?

30. **Predicting** In green light, what color would the red apple appear?

31. **Drawing Conclusions** Why do we use ceiling lights that give off white light?

Lab zone Standards Investigation

Performance Assessment Demonstrate your optical instrument to your class. Explain how your instrument works and how it can be used. Use diagrams that show how the mirrors or lenses in your instrument reflect or refract light.

S 7.1

Focus on the
BIG Idea

What is the structure of a cell?

Check What You Know

You hear that a pinch of soil may contain millions of organisms. What optical tools would you use to see these organisms and to study their structure?

Build Science Vocabulary

The images shown here represent some of the Key Terms in this chapter. You can use this vocabulary skill to help you understand the meaning of some Key Terms in this chapter.

Vocabulary Skill

Prefixes

Words can sometimes be divided into parts. A root is the part of the word that carries the basic meaning. A prefix is a word part that is placed in front of the root to change the word's meaning. In the word *multicellular*, for example, *-cellular* is the root and *multi-* is the prefix. The prefix *multi-* means "many." *Multicellular* means "having many cells."

The prefixes below will help you understand some Key Terms.

Prefix	Meaning	Example Word
chlor-	green	**chloroplast** A cellular structure that captures energy from sunlight
cyto-	cell	**cytoskeleton** The framework inside a cell
multi-	many	**multicellular** Having many cells
uni-	one	**unicellular** Having one cell

Apply It!

1. A **chloroplast** is a structure in plant cells. What color do you think a chloroplast is?

2. What clue within the word **cytoplasm** lets you know that the word has something to do with cells?

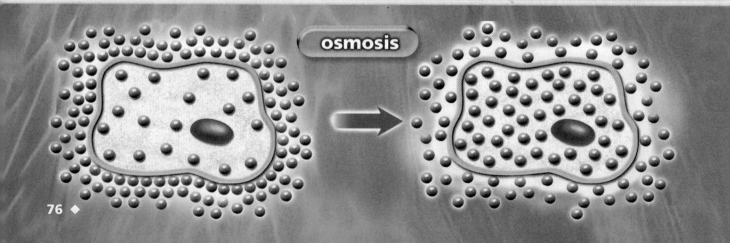

osmosis

compound

Water   Carbon Dioxide

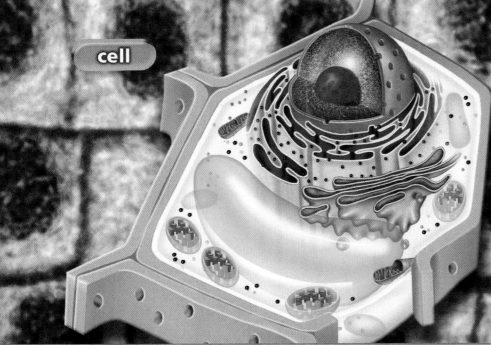

cell

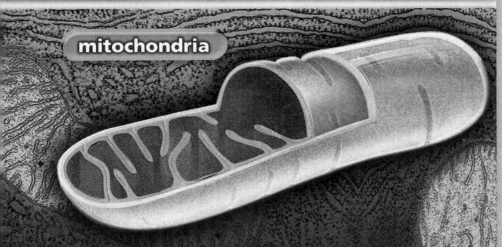

mitochondria

Chapter 3 Vocabulary

Section 1 (page 80)

cell	tissue
cell theory	organ
unicellular	organ system
multicellular	

Section 2 (page 88)

organelle	endoplasmic reticulum
cell wall	
cytoskeleton	ribosome
cell membrane	Golgi body
nucleus	chloroplast
cytoplasm	vacuole
mitochondria	lysosome

Section 3 (page 97)

element	enzyme
compound	lipid
carbohydrate	nucleic acid
protein	DNA
amino acid	RNA

Section 4 (page 102)

selectively permeable
diffusion
osmosis
passive transport
active transport

Interactive Textbook

Build Science Vocabulary
Online
Visit: PHSchool.com
Web Code: cvj-1030

How to Read Science

 ## Identify Main Ideas

The main idea in a section or paragraph is the most important—or biggest—idea. Sometimes the main idea is stated directly. Other times you have to figure it out on your own. Be sure to look at any headings. Headings can help you identify main ideas.

The details in a paragraph or section support the main idea. Details are often specific facts and examples.

Look for the main idea and details in the paragraph below.

What Are Cells? Cells are the basic units of structure and function in living things. Cells form the parts of an organism. The structure of a living thing is determined by the variety of ways in which its cells are put together. Cells carry out all the basic functions or processess of life in an organism, such as getting oxygen and food and getting rid of wastes.

Apply It!

Copy the graphic organizer below in your notebook. Complete it by writing the main idea of the paragraph in the box at the top. Then add two important details.

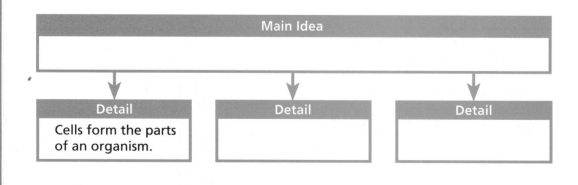

Main Idea

Detail	Detail	Detail
Cells form the parts of an organism.		

Standards Investigation

Egg-speriment With a Cell

In this chapter, you'll learn that all living things are made of cells—sometimes just one cell, sometimes trillions! You can study an everyday object that can serve as a model of a cell: an uncooked egg.

Your Goal

To observe how various materials enter or leave the cells of organisms, using an egg as a model of a typical cell

To complete this investigation, you will

- observe what happens when you soak an uncooked egg in vinegar, then in water, food coloring, salt water, and finally in a liquid of your choice
- measure the circumference of the egg every day, and graph your results
- explain the changes that you observe in your egg
- follow the safety guidelines in Appendix A

Plan It!

Predict what might happen when you put an uncooked egg in vinegar for two days. How might other liquids affect an egg? Find a place where you can leave your egg undisturbed. Then begin your egg-speriment!

1

Discovering Cells

CALIFORNIA
Standards Focus

S 7.1 All living organisms are composed of cells, from just one to many trillions, whose details usually are visible only through a microscope.

- What are cells?
- How did the invention of the microscope contribute to knowledge about living things?
- What is the cell theory?
- How are the cells of multicellular organisms organized?

Key Terms
- cell
- cell theory
- unicellular
- multicellular
- tissue
- organ
- organ system

Lab zone Standards Warm-Up

Is Seeing Believing?

1. ✂ Cut a black-and-white photograph out of a page in a newspaper. With only your eyes, closely examine the photo. Record your observations.

2. Examine the same photo with a hand lens. Again, record your observations.

3. Place the photo on the stage of a microscope. Use the clips to hold the photo in place. Shine a light down on the photo. Focus the microscope on part of the photo. (See Appendix B for instructions on using the microscope.) Record your observations.

Think It Over

Observing What did you see in the photo with the hand lens and microscope that you could not see with only your eyes? Which tool is a better choice for studying a tiny object?

A forest is filled with an amazing variety of living things. Some are easy to see, but you have to look closely to find others. If you look carefully at the floor of a forest, you can often find spots of bright color. A beautiful pink coral fungus grows beneath tall trees. Beside the pink fungus, a tiny red newt perches on a fallen leaf.

What do you think a fungus, a tree, and a red newt have in common? They are all living things, or organisms. And, like all organisms, they are made of cells.

FIGURE 1
Newt and Coral Fungus
All living things are made of cells, including this pink fungus and the red newt that perches next to it.

An Overview of Cells

Cells are the basic units of structure and function in living things. This means that **cells** form the parts of an organism and carry out all of an organism's processes, or functions.

Cells and Structure When you describe the structure of an object, you describe what it is made of and how its parts are put together. The structures of many buildings, for example, are determined by the way in which bricks, steel beams, and other materials are arranged. The structures of living things are determined by the amazing variety of ways in which cells are put together. A red newt's cells, for example, form a body with a head and four legs.

Cells and Function The functions of an organism include obtaining oxygen, getting rid of wastes, obtaining food, and growing. Cells are involved in all these functions. For example, cells in your digestive system absorb food. The food provides your body with energy and materials needed for growth.

Cells function similarly in all organisms. Regardless of the organism they are a part of, cells carry out the basic processes of life in similar ways.

Size of Cells Cells are so small that they are measured in units call micrometers (μm). One micrometer is one millionth of a meter. Each one of your red blood cells is about 7 micrometers across. Figure 2 shows human skin cells. To give you an idea of their size, one square centimeter of your skin's surface contains more than 100,000 cells. No matter how closely you look with your eyes alone, you won't be able to see the individual cells in your skin. Cells are usually visible only through a microscope.

 **Reading Checkpoint** What are some functions that cells perform in living things?

First Observations of Cells

Until the late 1600s, no one knew cells existed because there was no way to see them. Around 1590, the invention of the microscope enabled people to look at very small objects. The invention of the microscope made it possible for people to discover and learn about cells. As people built more advanced microscopes, it was possible to discover more about cells. Two early contributors to the understanding of cells were Robert Hooke and Anton van Leeuwenhoek (LAY vun hook). Both built their own microscopes.

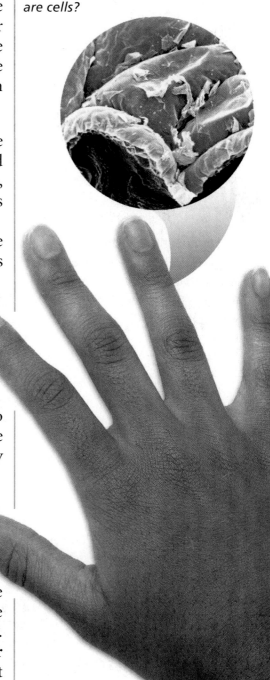

FIGURE 2
Skin Cells
Your skin is made of cells such as these. **Applying Concepts** *What are cells?*

Robert Hooke One of the first people to observe cells was the English scientist and inventor Robert Hooke. Hooke built his own compound microscope, which was one of the best microscopes of his time. In 1663, Hooke used his microscope to observe the structure of a thin slice of cork. Cork, the bark of the cork oak tree, is made up of cells that are no longer alive. To Hooke, the empty spaces in the cork looked like tiny rectangular rooms. Therefore, Hooke called the empty spaces *cells,* which is a word meaning "small rooms."

Hooke described his observations this way: "These pores, or cells, were not very deep, but consisted of a great many little boxes. . . ." What most amazed Hooke was how many cells the cork contained. He calculated that in a cubic inch there were about twelve hundred million cells—a number he described as "almost incredible."

• Tech & Design in History •

The Microscope: Improvements Over Time

The microscope made the discovery of cells possible. Microscopes have improved in many ways over the last 400 years.

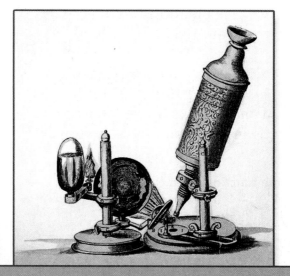

1590 First Compound Microscope
Dutch eyeglass makers Zacharias and Hans Janssen made one of the first compound microscopes. It was a tube with a lens at each end.

1660 Hooke's Compound Microscope
Robert Hooke's compound microscope included an oil lamp for lighting. A lens focuses light from the flame onto the specimen.

1674 Leeuwenhoek's Simple Microscope
Although Anton van Leeuwenhoek's simple microscope used only one tiny lens, it could magnify a specimen up to 266 times.

1500	1600	1700

Anton van Leeuwenhoek At about the same time that Robert Hooke made his discovery, Anton van Leeuwenhoek also began to observe tiny objects with microscopes. Leeuwenhoek was a Dutch businessman who sold cloth. In his spare time, he built simple microscopes.

Leeuwenhoek looked at drops of lake water, scrapings from teeth and gums, and water from rain gutters. In many materials, Leeuwenhoek was surprised to find a variety of tiny organisms. Leeuwenhoek noted that many of these tiny organisms moved. Some whirled, some hopped, and some shot through water like fast fish. He called these moving organisms *animalcules* (an ih MAL kyoolz), meaning "little animals."

✔ **Reading Checkpoint** Which type of microscope—simple or compound—did Leeuwenhoek make and use?

Writing in Science

Research and Write Find out more about one of the microscopes. Then write an advertisement for it that might appear in a popular science magazine. Be creative. Emphasize the microscope's usefulness or describe the wonders that can be seen with it.

1965 Scanning Electron Microscope (SEM)
An SEM sends electrons over the surface of a specimen, rather than through it. The result is a three-dimensional image of the specimen's surface. SEMs can magnify a specimen up to 150,000 times.

1981 Scanning Tunneling Microscope (STM)
An STM measures electrons that leak, or "tunnel," from the surface of a specimen. STMs can magnify a specimen up to 1,000,000 times.

1886 Modern Compound Light Microscope
German scientists Ernst Abbé and Carl Zeiss made a compound light microscope with complex lenses that greatly improved the image. A mirror focuses light up through the specimen. Modern compound microscopes can effectively magnify a specimen up to 1,000 times.

1933 Transmission Electron Microscope (TEM)
German physicist Ernst Ruska created the first electron microscope. TEMs send electrons through a very thinly sliced specimen. TEMs can magnify a specimen up to 500,000 times.

1800   1900   2000

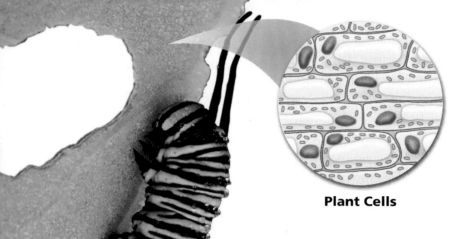

FIGURE 3
Monarch and Milkweed
The monarch butterfly caterpillar and the milkweed leaf that the caterpillar nibbles on are both made of cells. **Applying Concepts** *Where do the cells of the caterpillar and leaf come from?*

Plant Cells

Animal Cells

Development of the Cell Theory

Leeuwenhoek's exciting discoveries caught the attention of other researchers. Many other people began to use microscopes to discover what secrets they could learn about cells.

Schleiden, Schwann, and Virchow Three German scientists made especially important contributions to knowledge about cells. These scientists were Matthias Schleiden (SHLY dun), Theodor Schwann, and Rudolf Virchow (FUR koh). In 1838, Schleiden concluded that all plants are made of cells. He based this conclusion on his own research and on the research of others before him. The next year, Theodor Schwann concluded that all animals are also made up of cells. Thus, stated Schwann, all living things are made up of cells.

Schleiden and Schwann had made an important discovery about living things. However, they didn't explain where cells came from. Until their time, most people thought that living things could come from nonliving matter. In 1855, Virchow proposed that new cells are formed only from cells that already exist. "All cells come from cells," wrote Virchow.

What the Cell Theory Says Schleiden, Schwann, Virchow, and others helped develop the cell theory. The **cell theory** is a widely accepted explanation of the relationship between cells and living things. The cell theory states the following:

- **All living things are composed of cells.**

- **Cells are the basic units of structure and function in living things.**

- **All cells are produced from other cells.**

The cell theory holds true for all living things, no matter how big or how small. Since cells are common to all living things, they can provide information about the functions that living things perform. Because all cells come from other cells, scientists can study cells to learn about growth and reproduction.

Go Online
SciLINKS NSTA

For: Links on cell theory
Visit: www.SciLinks.org
Web Code: scn-0311

Unicellular and Multicellular

Organisms may be composed of only one cell or many trillions of cells. **Unicellular,** or single-celled, organisms include bacteria (bak TIHR ee uh), the most numerous organisms on Earth. **Multicellular** organisms are composed of many cells.

🔑 In multicellular organisms, cells are often organized into tissues, organs, and organ systems. A **tissue** is a group of similar cells that work together to perform a specific function. For example, your brain is mostly made up of nervous tissue, which consists of nerve cells. An **organ,** such as your brain, is made up of different kinds of tissues that work together. In addition to nervous tissue, your brain contains other kinds of tissue that support and protect it. Your brain is part of your nervous system, an organ system that directs body activities and processes. An **organ system** is a group of organs that work together to perform a major function.

Unicellular

Multicellular

FIGURE 4
Cellular Organization
This dog is multicellular. The bacteria that live naturally on its teeth are unicellular. Each green sphere is a bacterial cell.

 **Reading Checkpoint**   **What is an organ?**

Section 1 Assessment

S 7.1 E-LA: Reading 7.1.2, Writing 7.2.4

Vocabulary Skill **Prefixes** Complete the following sentences with Key Terms.
Because bacteria each have only one cell, they are _____ organisms.
Animals have many cells. Therefore, animals are _____ organisms.

🔑 Reviewing Key Concepts

1. a. **Defining** Define *structure* and *function*.
   b. **Explaining** Explain this statement: Cells are the basic units of structure and function in organisms.
   c. **Applying Concepts** In what important function are the cells in your eyes involved?
2. a. **Reviewing** What does a microscope enable people to do?
   b. **Summarizing** Summarize Hooke's observations of cork under a microscope.
   c. **Relating Cause and Effect** Why would Hooke's discovery have been impossible without a microscope?
3. a. **Listing** What does the cell theory state?
   b. **Explaining** What did Virchow contribute to the cell theory?
   c. **Applying Concepts** Use Virchow's ideas to explain why plastic plants are not alive.
4. a. **Reviewing** How do multicellular organisms differ from unicellular organisms?
   b. **Explaining** What is the relationship among cells, tissues, and organs?
   c. **Inferring** Would a tissue or an organ have more kinds of specialized cells? Explain.

Writing in Science

Writing an Award Speech Suppose you are a member of a scientific society that is giving an award to one of the early cell scientists. Choose the scientist, and write a speech that you might give at the award ceremony. Be sure to describe the scientist's accomplishments.

Design and Build a Microscope

S 7.6.d, 7.7.a

Problem

How can you design and build a compound microscope?

Design Skills

building a prototype, evaluating design constraints

Materials

- book
- 2 dual magnifying glasses, each with one high-power and one low-power lens
- metric ruler
- 2 cardboard tubes from paper towels, or black construction paper
- tape

Procedure

PART 1 Research and Investigate

1. Work with a partner. Using only your eyes, examine words in a book. Then use the high-power lens to examine the same words. In your notebook, contrast what you saw with and without the magnifying lens.

2. Hold the high-power lens about 5–6 cm above the words in the book. When you look at the words through the lens, they will look blurry.

3. Keep the high-power lens about 5–6 cm above the words. Hold the low-power lens above the high-power lens, as shown in the photograph on the right.

4. Move the low-power lens up and down until the image is in focus and upside down. (*Hint:* You may have to move the high-power lens up or down slightly too.)

5. Once the image is in focus, experiment with raising and lowering both lenses. Your goal is to produce the highest magnification while keeping the image in clear focus.

6. When the image is in focus at the position of highest magnification, have your lab partner measure and record the distance between the book and the high-power lens. Your lab partner should also measure and record the distance between the two lenses.

7. Write a description of how the magnified words viewed through two lenses compares with the words seen without magnification.

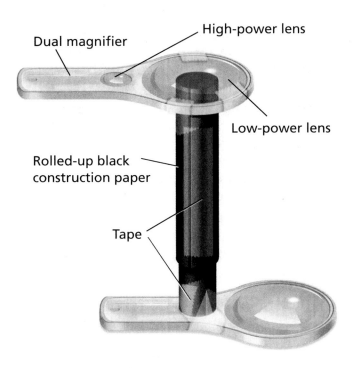

High-power lens

Dual magnifier

Low-power lens

Rolled-up black
construction paper

Tape

PART 2 Design and Build

8. Based on what you learned in Part 1, work with a partner to design your own two-lens (compound) microscope. Your microscope should
   - consist of one high-power lens and one low-power lens, each attached to a tube of paper or rolled-up cardboard
   - allow one tube to fit snugly inside the other tube so the distance between the two lenses can be easily adjusted
   - focus to produce a clear, enlarged, upside-down image of the object
   - be made from dual magnifying glasses, cardboard tubes, and tape

9. Sketch your design on a sheet of paper. Obtain your teacher's approval for your design. Then construct your microscope.

PART 3 Evaluate and Redesign

10. Test your microscope by examining printed words or a printed photograph. Then, examine other objects such as a leaf or your skin. Record your observations. Did your microscope meet the criteria listed in Step 8?

11. Examine microscopes made by other students. Based on your tests and your examination of other microscopes, list ways you could improve your microscope.

Analyze and Conclude

1. **Observing** Compare the images you observed using one lens with the image from two lenses.

2. **Evaluating** When you used two lenses, how did moving the top lens up and down affect the image? What was the effect of moving the bottom lens up and down?

3. **Building a Prototype** Describe how you built your microscope and explain why you built it that way.

4. **Evaluating the Impact on Society** Describe some of the ways that microscopes have aided scientists in their work.

5. **Making Judgments** Suppose you had to observe the movement of an ant's legs as the ant moved across the ground. You can use a single magnifying glass or the tool you just constructed. Which would you select? Why?

Communicate

Imagine it is 1675. Write an explanation that will convince scientists to use your new microscope rather than the single-lens variety used by Leeuwenhoek. Describe how your microscope makes the details of organisms more visible.

Looking Inside Cells

S 7.1.b Students know the characteristics that distinguish plant cells from animal cells, including chloroplasts and cell walls.

S 7.1.c Students know that the nucleus is the repository for genetic information in plant and animal cells.

- What role do the cell wall and cell membrane play in the cell?
- What is the role of the nucleus in the cell?
- What organelles are found in the cytoplasm and what are their functions?
- How do cells differ?

Key Terms
- organelle
- cell wall
- cytoskeleton
- cell membrane
- nucleus
- cytoplasm
- mitochondria
- endoplasmic reticulum
- ribosome
- Golgi body
- chloroplast
- vacuole
- lysosome

Lab zone **Standards Warm-Up**

How Large Are Cells?

1. Look at the organism in the photo. The organism is an amoeba (uh MEE buh), a large single-celled organism. This type of amoeba is about 1 mm long.
2. Multiply your height in meters by 1,000 to get your height in millimeters. How many amoebas would you have to stack end-to-end to equal your height?
3. Many of the cells in your body are about 0.01 mm long—one hundredth the size of an amoeba. How many body cells would you have to stack end-to-end to equal your height?

Think It Over

Inferring Look at a metric ruler to see how small 1 mm is. Now imagine a distance one one-hundredth as long, or 0.01 mm. Why can't you see your body's cells without a microscope?

Nasturtiums brighten up many gardens with green leaves and colorful flowers. How do nasturtiums carry out all the functions necessary to stay alive? To answer this question, you will take an imaginary journey into the cell of a nasturtium leaf. You will observe some of the structures found in plant cells. You will also learn some differences between plant and animal cells.

As you will discover on your journey, there are even smaller structures inside a cell, called organelles. **Organelles** carry out specific functions within the cell. Just as your stomach, lungs, and heart have different functions in your body, each organelle has a different function within the cell. Now, hop aboard your imaginary ship and sail into a typical plant cell. As you travel through the plant cell, refer to Figure 6. And be sure to note the differences between plant and animal cells.

Nasturtiums ▶

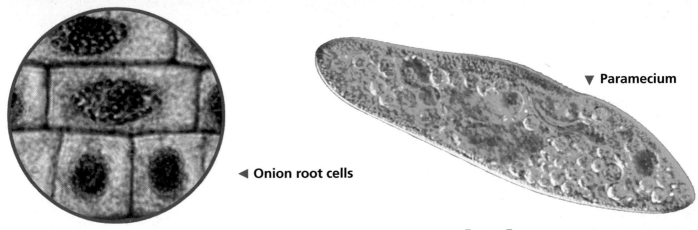

◄ Onion root cells

▼ Paramecium

Enter the Cell

Your ship doesn't have an easy time getting inside the plant cell. It has to pass through the cell wall and the cell membrane.

Cell Wall The **cell wall** is a rigid layer of nonliving material that surrounds the cells of plants and some other organisms. 🔑 **A cell wall helps to protect and support the cell.** In plants, the cell wall is made mostly of a strong material called cellulose. Although the cell wall is tough, many materials, including water and oxygen, can pass through easily.

Unlike plant cells, the cells of animals and many single-celled organisms do not have cell walls. Instead, a protein "framework" inside the cell called a **cytoskeleton** gives the cells their shape.

Cell Membrane After passing through the cell wall, the next barrier you must cross is the **cell membrane.** All cells have cell membranes. The cell membrane forms the outside boundary that separates the cell from its environment. In cells with cell walls, the cell membrane is located just inside the cell wall. In other cells, the cell membrane forms the outside boundary that separates the cell from its environment.

🔑 **The cell membrane controls what substances come into and out of a cell.** Everything the cell needs, from food to oxygen, enters the cell through the cell membrane. For a cell to survive, the cell membrane must allow these materials to pass in and out. Harmful waste products leave the cell through the cell membrane. The cell membrane also prevents harmful materials from entering the cell. In a sense, the cell membrane is like a window screen. The screen allows air to enter and leave a room, but it keeps insects out. Fortunately, on this trip, your ship can slip through.

 **Reading Checkpoint** Do animal cells contain cell walls?

FIGURE 5
Cell Wall and Cell Membrane
The onion root cells have both a cell wall and a cell membrane. The single-celled paramecium has only a cell membrane, but it is dense and tough.
Interpreting Photographs *What shape do the cell walls give to the onion root cells?*

Video Field Trip
Discovery Channel School
Cell Structure and Function

FIGURE 6
Plant and Animal Cells

These illustrations show typical structures found in plant and animal cells. **Comparing and Contrasting** *Identify one structure found in plant cells but not animal cells.*

Endoplasmic Reticulum
This network of passageways carries materials from one part of the cell to another.

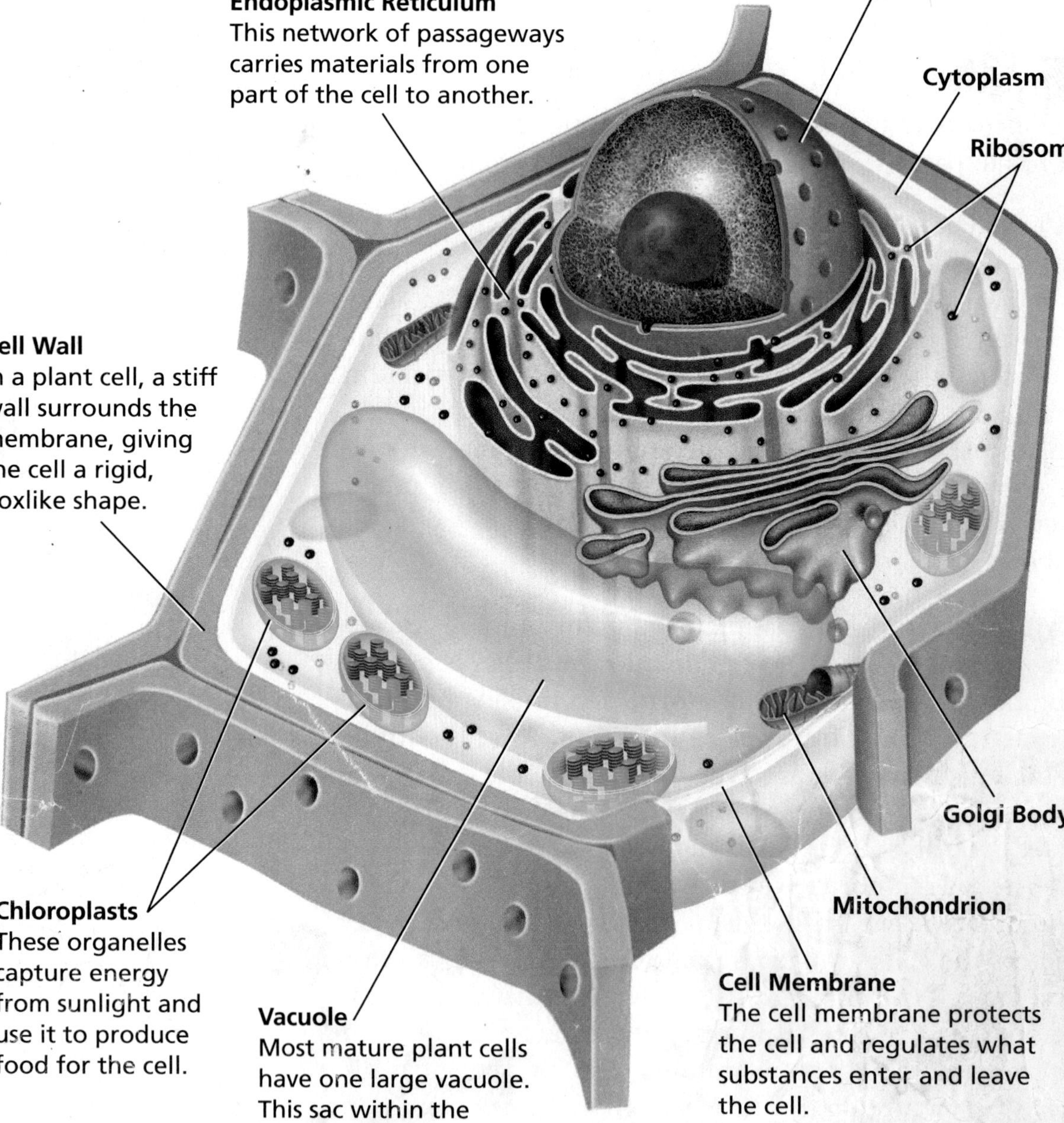

Nucleus
The nucleus directs all of the cell's activities, including reproduction.

Cytoplasm

Ribosomes

Cell Wall
In a plant cell, a stiff wall surrounds the membrane, giving the cell a rigid, boxlike shape.

Chloroplasts
These organelles capture energy from sunlight and use it to produce food for the cell.

Vacuole
Most mature plant cells have one large vacuole. This sac within the cytoplasm stores water, food, waste products, and other materials.

Golgi Body

Mitochondrion

Cell Membrane
The cell membrane protects the cell and regulates what substances enter and leave the cell.

Plant Cell

Cytoplasm
The cytoplasm includes a gel-like fluid in which many different organelles are found.

Ribosomes
These small structures function as factories to produce proteins. Ribosomes may be attached to the endoplasmic reticulum, or they may float in the cytoplasm.

Nucleus
The nucleus directs all of the cell's activities, including reproduction.

Mitochondria
Most of the cell's energy is produced within these rod-shaped organelles.

Endoplasmic Reticulum

Golgi Body
The Golgi bodies receive materials from the endoplasmic reticulum and send them to other parts of the cell. They also release materials outside the cell.

Lysosomes
These small organelles contain chemicals that break down food particles and worn-out cell parts.

Vacuole
Some animal cells have vacuoles that store food, water, waste, and other materials.

Cell Membrane
The cell membrane protects the cell and regulates what substances enter and leave the cell.

Animal Cell

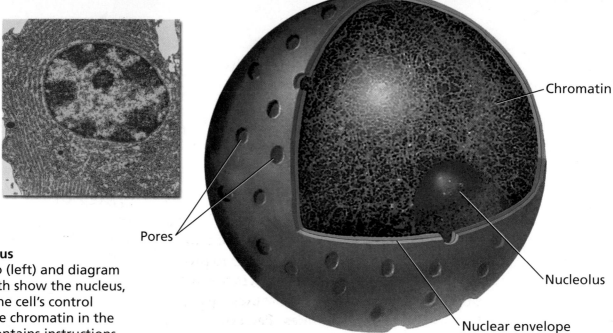

FIGURE 7
The Nucleus
The photo (left) and diagram (right) both show the nucleus, which is the cell's control center. The chromatin in the nucleus contains instructions for carrying out the cell's activities.

Sail on to the Nucleus

As you sail inside the cell, a large, oval structure comes into view. This structure, called the **nucleus** (NOO klee us), acts as the control center of the cell. **The nucleus is the cell's control center, directing all of the cell's activities.**

Nuclear Envelope Notice in Figure 7 that the nucleus is surrounded by a membrane called the nuclear envelope. Just as a mailing envelope protects the letter inside it, the nuclear envelope protects the nucleus. Materials pass in and out of the nucleus through pores in the nuclear envelope. So aim for that pore just ahead and carefully glide into the nucleus.

Chromatin You might wonder how the nucleus "knows" how to direct the cell. The answer lies in those thin strands floating directly ahead in the nucleus. These strands, called chromatin, contain genetic material, the instructions for directing the cell's functions. For example, the instructions in the chromatin ensure that leaf cells grow and divide to form more leaf cells. You can think of the nucleus as a repository for genetic information in cells. A repository is a storage area.

Nucleolus As you prepare to leave the nucleus, you spot a small object floating by. This structure, a nucleolus, is where ribosomes are made. Ribosomes are the organelles where proteins are produced. Proteins are important chemicals in cells.

 **Reading Checkpoint** **Where in the nucleus is genetic material found?**

Lab zone Try This **Activity**

Gelatin Cell

Make your own model of a cell.

1. Dissolve a packet of colorless gelatin in warm water. Pour the gelatin into a rectangular pan (for a plant cell) or a round pan (for an animal cell).

2. Choose different materials that resemble each of the cell structures found in the cell you are modeling. Insert these materials into the gelatin before it begins to solidify.

Making Models On a sheet of paper, develop a key that identifies each cell structure in your model. Describe the function of each structure.

Organelles in the Cytoplasm

As you leave the nucleus, you find yourself in the **cytoplasm,** the region between the cell membrane and the nucleus. Your ship floats in a clear, thick, gel-like fluid. The fluid in the cytoplasm is constantly moving, so your ship does not need to propel itself. ⊙ **In the cytoplasm are many organelles, including mitochondria, endoplasmic reticulum, ribosomes, Golgi bodies, chloroplasts, vacuoles, and lysosomes. Each of these organelles has specific functions in the cell.**

Mitochondria Suddenly, rod-shaped structures loom ahead. These organelles are **mitochondria** (my tuh KAHN dree uh) (singular *mitochondrion*). Mitochondria are known as the "powerhouses" of the cell because they convert energy in food molecules to energy the cell can use to carry out its functions. Figure 8 shows a mitochondrion up close.

Endoplasmic Reticulum As you sail farther into the cytoplasm, you find yourself in a maze of passageways called the **endoplasmic reticulum** (en duh PLAZ mik rih TIK yuh lum). The endoplasmic reticulum's passageways help form proteins and other materials. They also carry material throughout the cell.

Ribosomes Attached to some surfaces of the endoplasmic reticulum are small, grainlike bodies called **ribosomes.** Other ribosomes float in the cytoplasm. Ribosomes function as factories to produce proteins. Some newly made proteins are released through the wall of the endoplasmic reticulum. From the interior of the endoplasmic reticulum, the proteins will be transported to the Golgi bodies.

FIGURE 9
Endoplasmic Reticulum
The endoplasmic reticulum is similar to the system of hallways in a building. Proteins and other materials move throughout the cell by way of the endoplasmic reticulum. The spots on this organelle are ribosomes, which produce proteins.

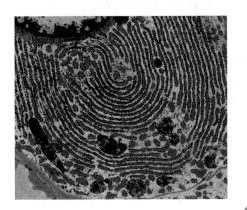

Ribosomes

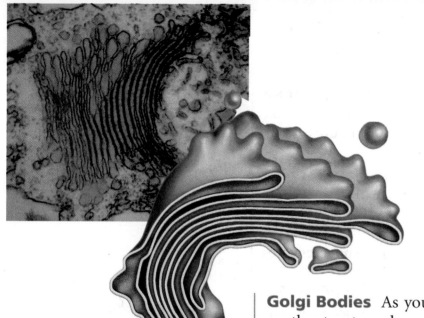

FIGURE 10
A Golgi Body
Golgi bodies are organelles that transport materials.

Golgi Bodies As you leave the endoplasmic reticulum, you see the structure shown in Figure 10. It looks like flattened sacs and tubes. This structure, called a **Golgi body,** can be thought of as the cell's mail room. Golgi bodies receive proteins and other newly formed materials from the endoplasmic reticulum. They then package and distribute materials to other parts of the cell. Golgi bodies also release materials outside the cell.

Chloroplasts Have you noticed the many large green structures floating in the cytoplasm? Only the cells of plants and some other organisms have these green organelles called **chloroplasts** (KLAWR uh plasts). Chloroplasts capture energy from sunlight and use it to produce food. Chloroplasts make leaves green.

Vacuoles Steer past the chloroplasts and head for that large, water-filled sac, called a **vacuole** (VAK yoo ohl), floating in the cytoplasm. Vacuoles are the storage areas of cells. Most plant cells have one large, central vacuole. Vacuoles store food and other materials needed by the cell. Vacuoles can also store waste products. Animal cells do not have central vacuoles. However, some animal cells have smaller storage organelles.

Lysosomes Your journey through the cell is almost over. Before you leave, take another look around you. If you carefully swing your ship around the vacuole, you may be lucky enough to see a lysosome. **Lysosomes** (LY suh sohms) are small, round structures containing chemicals that break down certain materials in the cell. Some chemicals break down large food particles into smaller ones. Lysosomes also break down old cell parts and release the substances so they can be used again. In this sense, you can think of lysosomes as the cell's cleanup crew.

Reading Checkpoint What organelle captures the energy of sunlight and uses it to make food for the cell?

Lab zone **Try This Activity**

Comparing Cells

Observe the characteristics of plant and animal cells.

1. Obtain a prepared slide of plant cells from your teacher. Examine these cells under the low-power and high-power lenses of a microscope.

2. Draw a picture of what you see.

3. Repeat Steps 1 and 2 with a prepared slide of animal cells.

Observing How are plant and animal cells alike? How are they different?

Cell Diversity

You just had a tour of a typical leaf cell. But actually, there's a lot of variety in cells—both within individual organisms and across different organisms. **The variety of structure in cells reflects differences in cell function.**

Cells come in many shapes. Look at the nerve cell and red blood cells in Figure 11. Notice the long, fingerlike extensions of the nerve cell. These extensions help transmit information from one part of your body to another. Red blood cells carry oxygen throughout your body. Their flattened shape enables them to fit through tiny blood vessels.

Some cells contain certain organelles but not others. For example, not all plant cells have chloroplasts. Since root cells grow underground away from sunlight, they have no need for chloroplasts. Cells may also have more of a particular kind of organelle. For example, cells that actively produce proteins, such as liver cells, contain many ribosomes. Each human liver cell has millions of ribosomes.

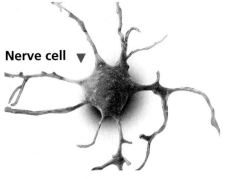

Nerve cell ▼

Red blood cells in a blood vessel ▼

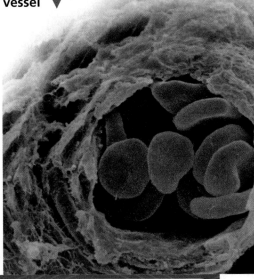

FIGURE 11 Specialized Cells
Nerve cells carry information throughout the human body. Red blood cells carry oxygen. *Developing Hypotheses How do the shapes of these cells help them function?*

Section 2 Assessment

S 7.1.b, 7.7.c, E-LA: Reading 7.1.2, Writing 7.2.0

Vocabulary Skill Prefixes The Key Term *endoplasmic reticulum* begins with the prefix *endo-*, which means "in" or "within." Within what part of a cell is the endoplasmic reticulum located?

Reviewing Key Concepts

1. **a. Comparing and Contrasting** Compare the functions of the cell wall and the cell membrane in plant and animal cells.
   b. Inferring How does cellulose help with the function of the cell wall?
2. **a. Identifying** What is the key function of the nucleus?
   b. Describing Which structure inside the nucleus is involved in this function?
   c. Predicting Suppose a dye for staining cells stains the region where ribosomes are made. What would you expect to see inside the stained cell's nucleus?

3. **a. Identifying** Identify the functions of ribosomes and Golgi bodies.
   b. Describing Describe the characteristics of the endoplasmic reticulum.
   c. Applying Concepts How are the functions of ribosomes, Golgi bodies, and the endoplasmic reticulum related?
4. **a. Listing** What are two ways cells can differ?
   b. Applying Concepts Which organelles might you expect to see in large quantities in cells that actively release proteins outside the cell?

Writing in Science

Writing a Description Write a paragraph describing a typical animal cell. Your paragraph should include all the structures generally found in animal cells and a brief explanation of the functions of those structures.

Sizing Up a Cell

 S 7.1.b, 7.7.d

Problem

How can you build a scale model showing the relative sizes of plant cell organelles?

Skills Focus

calculating, making models

Materials

• various materials provided by your teacher

Procedure

1. The table below gives the approximate sizes of structures in a typical plant cell. Copy the table into your notebook.

2. Convert the size of each structure using the scale one centimeter to one micrometer (1 cm : 1 μm). For example, at this scale, a model of a plant cell that is 150 μm long would be 150 cm long.

$$\text{Length of model} = 150\,\mu\text{m} \times \frac{1\ \text{cm}}{1\,\mu\text{m}} = 150\ \text{cm}$$

Record your calculations in the third column.

3. Then, calculate the size of each structure at a scale of 10 cm : 1 μm. Fill in your calculations in the correct column.

4. Now select a scale you would like to use for your model. Calculate the sizes of structures for a cell model built according to the scale you selected. Record your calculations.

5. With your lab partner, choose four cell structures that would be practical to model. Discuss the possible materials you can use.

6. Sketch your design on a sheet of paper. Obtain your teacher's approval for your design. Then construct your model.

Analyze and Conclude

1. **Calculating** A plant cell model has been built using the scale one meter to one micrometer. How large would a ribosome with a diameter of 0.02 micrometer be in this model?

2. **Making Models** What scale did you choose to use for your model? Why? What problems did you encounter in building your model?

3. **Drawing Conclusions** Based on your calculations in this lab, why would it be difficult to include all the structures of a cell in a scale model the size of a shoebox?

4. **Communicating** You are designing a giant scale model of a cell for a museum exhibit. The museum is able to provide unlimited space and construction materials for your project. Write a memo to your construction team explaining what factors to keep in mind while building a giant cell to scale.

Cell Structure	Actual Size	1 cm : 1 μm	10 cm : 1 μm	Your Scale (___:___)
Plant cell	150 μm (length); 100 μm (width)	150 cm ; 100 cm	1,500 cm ; 1,000 cm	
Nucleus	6.5–10 μm (diameter)			
Vacuole	130 μm (length); 80 μm (width)			
Chloroplast	5–10 μm (length); 2–3 μm (width)			
Mitochondrion	3–5 μm (length); 0.5–1 μm (width)			
Ribosome	0.017–0.023 μm (diameter)			

Chemical Compounds in Cells

CALIFORNIA
Standards Focus

S 7.1.a Students know cells function similarly in all living organisms.

- What are elements and compounds?

- How is water important to the function of cells?

- What are the functions of carbohydrates, lipids, proteins, and nucleic acids?

Key Terms

- element
- compound
- carbohydrate
- lipid
- protein
- amino acid
- enzyme
- nucleic acid
- DNA
- RNA

Lab zone Standards **Warm-Up**

What Is a Compound?

1. Your teacher will provide you with containers filled with various substances. All of the substances are chemical compounds.

2. Examine each substance. Read the label on each container to learn what each substance is made of.

Think It Over

Forming Operational Definitions Chemical compounds are important to the structure and function of all cells. Write a definition of what you think a chemical compound is.

Cells and organelles are very small, but you are surrounded by particles even smaller than cells! Air is made up of trillions of these tiny particles. They bump into your skin, hide in the folds of your clothes, and whoosh into your nose every time your take a breath. In fact, you and the world around you, including the cells in your body and all other organisms, are composed of tiny particles. Some of these particles are elements, and others are compounds. One reason why cells function similarly in all organisms is that cells consists of, use, and produce many identical compounds.

Elements and Compounds

You may not realize it, but air is a mixture of gases. These gases include both elements and compounds. Three gases in the air are oxygen, nitrogen, and carbon dioxide.

Elements Oxygen and nitrogen are examples of **elements.** An element is any substance that cannot be broken down into simpler substances. The smallest unit of an element is called an atom. An element is made up of only one kind of atom. The elements found in living things include carbon, hydrogen, oxygen, nitrogen, phosphorus, and sulfur.

Go Online

SC*i*LINKS™ NSTA

For: Links on proteins
Visit: www.SciLinks.org
Web Code: scn-0313

Compounds Carbon dioxide is a **compound** made up of the elements carbon and oxygen. ⊙ **When two or more elements combine chemically, they form a compound.** Most elements in living things occur in the form of compounds. The smallest unit of many compounds is a molecule. A molecule of carbon dioxide consists of one carbon atom and two oxygen atoms.

The Compound Called Water Like carbon dioxide, water is a compound. Each water molecule is made up of two hydrogen atoms and one oxygen atom. Water makes up about two thirds of your body. Water plays many important roles in cells. Water dissolves chemicals that cells need. ⊙ **Most chemical reactions within cells could not take place without water.** For example, without water, plants would not be able to convert the energy captured by chloroplasts into food. Water also helps cells keep their size and shape. In fact, a cell without water would be like a balloon without air. In addition, because water changes temperature so slowly, it helps keep the temperature of cells from changing rapidly.

Inorganic and Organic Compounds Water is an example of an inorganic compound. An inorganic compound does not contain the element carbon. Sodium chloride, or table salt, is another inorganic compound.

Many compounds in living things contain the element carbon. Most compounds that contain carbon are called organic compounds. ⊙ **Carbohydrates, lipids, proteins, and nucleic acids are important groups of organic compounds in living things.** These organic compounds play important roles in the function of cells.

FIGURE 12
Molecules and Compounds
Water is a chemical compound. So is carbon dioxide, which is found in the gas bubbles.
Applying Concepts *What is a compound?*

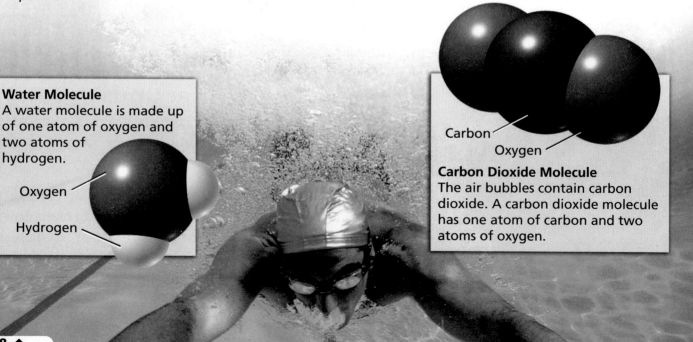

Water Molecule
A water molecule is made up of one atom of oxygen and two atoms of hydrogen.

Oxygen

Hydrogen

Carbon

Oxygen

Carbon Dioxide Molecule
The air bubbles contain carbon dioxide. A carbon dioxide molecule has one atom of carbon and two atoms of oxygen.

Carbohydrates

A **carbohydrate** is an energy-rich organic compound made of the elements carbon, hydrogen, and oxygen. Sugars and starches are examples of carbohydrates.

Sugars are produced during the food-making process that takes place in plants. Foods such as fruits and some vegetables have a high sugar content. Sugar molecules can combine, forming large molecules called starches, or complex carbohydrates. Plant cells store excess energy in molecules of starch. Many foods that come from plants contain starch. These foods include potatoes, pasta, rice, and bread. When you eat these foods, your body breaks down the starch into glucose, a sugar that your cells can use for energy.

🔑 **In addition to providing energy for the cell, carbohydrates are important components of some cell parts.** For example, the cellulose found in the cell walls of plants is a type of carbohydrate. Carbohydrates are also found in cell membranes.

Lipids

Have you ever seen a cook trim the fat from a piece of meat before cooking it? The cook is trimming away a lipid. Fats, oils, and waxes are all lipids. Like carbohydrates, **lipids** are energy-rich organic compounds made of carbon, hydrogen, and oxygen. Lipids contain even more energy than carbohydrates. Cells store energy in lipids for later use. For example, during winter, a dormant bear lives on the energy stored in fat within its cells. 🔑 **In addition to their function as an energy source, lipids also make up most of the cell membrane.**

 Reading Checkpoint What are the kinds of lipids?

FIGURE 13
Starch
These potatoes contain a large amount of starch. Starch is a carbohydrate. The blue grains in the close-up are starch granules in a potato. The grains have been colored blue to make them easier to see.

FIGURE 14
Lipids
Olive oil, which comes from olives such as those shown here, is made mostly of lipids.
Making Generalizations
What elements are lipids composed of?

Chapter 3 ◆ 99

Math Analyzing Data

Compounds in Bacteria and Mammals

Do all cells contain the same amounts of carbohydrates, lipids, proteins, and nucleic acids? The graph compares the percentages of different compounds in a bacterial cell and a mammal cell.

1. **Reading Graphs** What do the red bars represent? What do the blue bars represent?

2. **Interpreting Data** Which kind of compound—proteins or nucleic acids—makes up the larger percentage of a mammal cell?

3. **Drawing Conclusions** In general, how do a bacterial cell and a mammal cell compare in their chemical composition?

Comparing Compounds in Cells

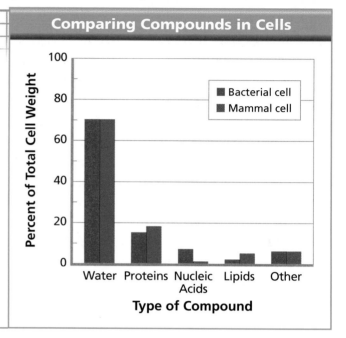

Proteins

What do a bird's feathers, a spider's web, and your fingernails have in common? All of these substances are made mainly of proteins. **Proteins** are large organic molecules made of carbon, hydrogen, oxygen, nitrogen, and, in some cases, sulfur. Foods that are high in protein include meat, eggs, fish, nuts, and beans.

Structure of Proteins Protein molecules are made up of smaller molecules called **amino acids.** Although there are only 20 common amino acids, cells can combine them in different ways to form thousands of different proteins. The kinds of amino acids and the order in which they link together determine the type of protein that forms. You can think of the 20 amino acids as being like the 26 letters of the alphabet. Those 26 letters can form thousands of words. The letters you use and their order determine the words you form.

Functions of Proteins Much of the structure of cells is made up of proteins. Proteins form parts of cell membranes. Proteins also make up many of the organelles within the cell.

The proteins known as enzymes perform important functions in the chemical reactions that take place in cells. An **enzyme** is a type of protein that speeds up a chemical reaction in a living thing. Without enzymes, many chemical reactions that are necessary for life would either take too long or not occur at all. For example, enzymes in your saliva speed up the digestion of food by breaking down starches into sugars in your mouth.

Nucleic Acids

Nucleic acids are very long organic molecules made of carbon, oxygen, hydrogen, nitrogen, and phosphorus. 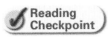 **Nucleic acids contain the instructions that cells need to carry out all the functions of life.**

There are two kinds of nucleic acids. Deoxyribonucleic acid (dee ahk see ry boh noo KLEE ik), or **DNA,** is the genetic material that carries information about an organism and is passed from parent to offspring. The information in DNA is also used to direct all of the cell's functions. Most of the DNA in a cell is found in the chromatin in the nucleus.

Ribonucleic acid (ry boh noo KLEE ik), or **RNA,** plays an important role in the production of proteins. RNA is found in the cytoplasm as well as in the nucleus.

Reading Checkpoint What are the two kinds of nucleic acids? What are their functions?

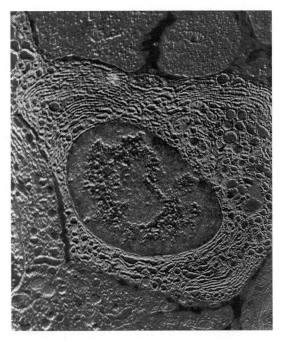

FIGURE 15
DNA in the Nucleus
A cell's nucleus (colored purple) contains most of the cell's DNA in its chromatin (colored red and yellow).

Section 3 Assessment

S 7.1.a, E-LA: Reading 7.2.0

Target Reading Skill Identify Main Ideas Reread the text following the heading Structure of Proteins. What sentence expresses the main idea of this paragraph?

Reviewing Key Concepts

1. **a. Defining** What is a compound?
   b. Classifying What is one inorganic compound vital for chemical reactions in cells? What are four groups of organic compounds important to living things?

2. **a. Reviewing** What three important functions does water perform in cells?
   b. Relating Cause and Effect Suppose a cell is seriously deprived of water. How might this lack of water affect the cell's enzymes? Explain.

3. **a. Reviewing** Which of the four types of organic compounds serve as an energy source for cells?
   b. Classifying Which of the four types of organic molecules contain the element nitrogen?
   c. Inferring An organic compound contains only the elements carbon, hydrogen, and oxygen. Could this compound be a carbohydrate? Could it be a protein? Explain.

Lab zone At-Home Activity

Compounds in Food With family members, look at the "Nutrition Facts" labels on a variety of food products. Identify foods that contain large amounts of the following organic compounds: carbohydrates, proteins, and fats. Discuss with your family what elements make up each of these compounds and what roles they play in cells and in your body.

The Cell in Its Environment

CALIFORNIA
Standards Focus

S 7.1.a Students know cells function similarly in all living organisms.

- How do most small molecules cross the cell membrane?
- Why is osmosis important to cells?
- What is the difference between passive transport and active transport?

Key Terms
- selectively permeable
- diffusion
- osmosis
- passive transport
- active transport

Lab zone **Standards Warm-Up**

How Do Molecules Move?

1. Stand with your classmates in locations that are evenly spaced throughout the classroom.
2. Your teacher will spray an air freshener into the room. When you first smell the air freshener, raise your hand.
3. Note how long it takes for other students to smell the scent.

Think It Over
Developing Hypotheses How was each student's distance from the teacher related to when he or she smelled the air freshener? Develop a hypothesis about why this pattern occurred.

As darkness fell, the knight urged his horse toward the castle. The weary knight longed for the safety of the castle, with its thick walls of stone and strong metal gates. The castle's gate-keeper opened the gates and slowly lowered the drawbridge. The horse clopped across the bridge, and the knight sighed with relief. Home at last!

Like ancient castles, cells have structures that protect their contents from the world outside. All cells are surrounded by a cell membrane that separates the cell from the outside environment. The cell membrane is **selectively permeable,** which means that some substances can pass through the membrane while others cannot.

Cells, like castles, must let things enter and leave. All cells must let in needed materials, such as oxygen and food molecules. In contrast, waste materials must move out of cells. Oxygen, food molecules, waste products, and many useful cell products must pass through the cell membrane.

Diffusion

Substances that can move into and out of a cell do so by one of three methods: diffusion, osmosis, or active transport. **Diffusion is the main method by which small molecules move across the cell membrane.** Diffusion (dih FYOO zhun) is the process by which molecules move from an area of higher concentration to an area of lower concentration. The concentration of a substance is the amount of the substance in a given volume. For example, suppose you dissolve 1 gram of sugar in 1 liter of water. The concentration of the sugar solution is 1 gram per liter.

If you did the Standards Warm-Up activity, you observed diffusion in action. The area where the air freshener was sprayed had many molecules of freshener. The molecules gradually moved from this area of higher concentration to the other parts of the classroom, where there were fewer molecules of freshener—and thus a lower concentration.

What Causes Diffusion? Molecules are always moving. As they move, the molecules bump into one another. The more molecules there are in an area, the more collisions there will be. Collisions cause molecules to push away from one another. Over time, the molecules of a substance will continue to spread out. Eventually, they will be spread evenly throughout the area.

Ratios

The concentration of a solution can be expressed as a ratio. A ratio compares two numbers. It tells you how much you have of one item in comparison to another. For example, suppose you dissolve 5 g of sugar in 1 L of water. You can express the concentration of the solution in ratio form as

5 g : 1 L

This can also be written

5 g/L

Practice Problem Suppose you dissolve 7 g of salt in 1 L of water. Express the concentration of the solution as a ratio.

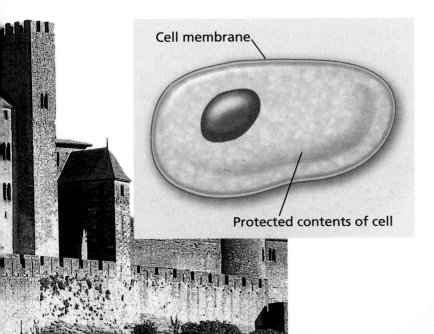

Cell membrane

Protected contents of cell

FIGURE 16
A Selective Barrier
The walls of a castle protected the inhabitants within, and the castle gatekeeper allowed only certain people to pass through. Similarly, the cell membrane protects the contents of the cell and helps control the materials that enter and leave.

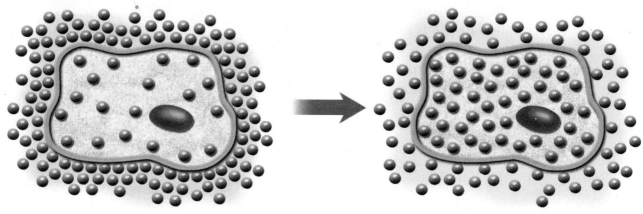

Before Diffusion
There is a higher concentration of oxygen molecules outside the cell than inside the cell.

After Diffusion
The concentration of oxygen molecules is the same outside and inside the cell.

FIGURE 17
Diffusion in Action
Molecules move by diffusion from an area of higher concentration to an area of lower concentration. *Predicting What would happen if the concentration of oxygen molecules outside the cell was lower than inside the cell?*

For: More on cellular transport
Visit: PHSchool.com
Web Code: ced-3014

Diffusion of Oxygen Have you ever used a microscope to observe one-celled organisms in pond water? These organisms obtain the oxygen they need to survive from the water around them. Luckily for them, there are many more molecules of oxygen in the water outside the cell than there are inside the cell. In other words, there is a higher concentration of oxygen molecules in the water than inside the cell. Remember that the cell membrane is permeable to oxygen molecules. The oxygen molecules diffuse from the area of higher concentration—the pond water—through the cell membrane to the area of lower concentration—the inside of the cell.

 **Reading Checkpoint** By what process do small molecules move into cells?

Osmosis

Like oxygen, water passes easily into and out of cells through the cell membrane. **Osmosis** is the diffusion of water molecules through a selectively permeable membrane. **Because cells cannot function properly without adequate water, many cellular processes depend on osmosis.**

Osmosis and Diffusion Remember that molecules tend to move from an area of higher concentration to an area of lower concentration. In osmosis, water molecules move by diffusion from an area where they are highly concentrated through the cell membrane to an area where they are less concentrated.

Effects of Osmosis Osmosis can have important consequences for the cell. Look at Figure 18 to see the effect of osmosis on cells. In Figure 18A, a red blood cell is bathed in a solution in which the concentration of water is the same as it is inside the cell. This is the normal shape of a red blood cell.

Contrast this shape to the cell in Figure 18B. The red blood cell is floating in water that contains a lot of salt. The concentration of water molecules outside the cell is lower than the concentration of water molecules inside the cell. This difference in concentration occurs because the salt takes up space in the salt water. Therefore, there are fewer water molecules in the salt water outside the cell compared to the water inside the cell. As a result, water moves out of the cell by osmosis. When water moves out, the cell shrinks.

In Figure 18C, the red blood cell is floating in water that contains a very small amount of salt. The water inside the cell contains more salt than the solution outside the cell. Thus, the concentration of water outside the cell is greater than it is inside the cell. The water moves into the cell, causing it to swell.

Reading Checkpoint How is osmosis related to diffusion?

Lab zone Try This **Activity**

Osmosis in Action

1. Use water to prepare a wet-mount slide of *Elodea* (a freshwater plant).
2. Observe the leaf cells at low magnification and record your observations.
3. Increase the magnification and record what you see.
4. Place a drop of 10% salt solution on one edge of the coverslip.
5. Place a small piece of paper towel on the opposite edge of the coverslip to draw the salt solution under the coverslip.
6. Repeat steps 2 and 3.

Inferring What role did osmosis play in the changes you observed?

FIGURE 18

Effects of Osmosis on Cells

In osmosis, water diffuses through a selectively permeable membrane.

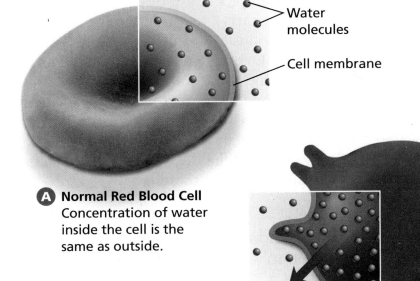

Water molecules

Cell membrane

Ⓐ **Normal Red Blood Cell**
Concentration of water inside the cell is the same as outside.

Ⓑ **Low Water Concentration Outside Cell**
Water moves out of the cell during osmosis.

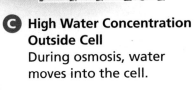

Ⓒ **High Water Concentration Outside Cell**
During osmosis, water moves into the cell.

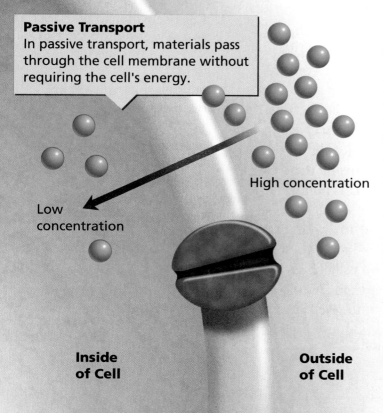

Passive Transport
In passive transport, materials pass through the cell membrane without requiring the cell's energy.

High concentration

Low concentration

Inside of Cell

Outside of Cell

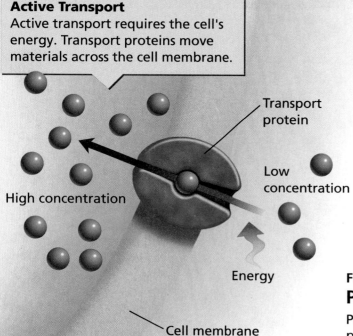

Active Transport
Active transport requires the cell's energy. Transport proteins move materials across the cell membrane.

High concentration

Transport protein

Low concentration

Energy

Cell membrane

Active Transport

If you have ever ridden a bicycle down a long hill, you know that it doesn't take any of your energy to go fast. But you do have to use some of your energy to pedal back up the hill. For a cell, moving materials through the cell membrane by diffusion and osmosis is like cycling downhill. These processes do not require the cell to use its own energy. The movement of dissolved materials through a cell membrane without using cellular energy is called **passive transport.**

What if a cell needs to take in a substance that is present in a higher concentration inside the cell than outside? The cell would have to move the molecules in the opposite direction than they naturally move by diffusion. Cells can do this, but they have to use energy—just as you would use energy to pedal back up the hill. **Active transport** is the movement of materials through a cell membrane using cellular energy. ⟳ **Active transport requires the cell to use its own energy, while passive transport does not.**

Transport Proteins Cells have several ways of moving materials by active transport. In one method, transport proteins in the cell membrane "pick up" molecules outside the cell and carry them in, using energy. Figure 19 illustrates this process. Transport proteins also carry molecules out of cells in a similar way. Some substances that are carried into and out of cells in this way include calcium, potassium, and sodium.

A cell membrane may contain many transport proteins. Each transport protein can carry a specific substance.

FIGURE 19
Passive and Active Transport
Passive and active transport are two processes by which materials pass through the cell membrane.
Interpreting Diagrams *What is the function of a transport protein?*

Transport by Engulfing Figure 20 shows another method of active transport. First, the cell membrane surrounds and engulfs, or encloses, a particle. Once the particle is engulfed, the cell membrane wraps around the particle and forms a vacuole within the cell. The cell must use energy in this process.

Why Cells Are Small As you know, most cells are so small that you cannot see them without a microscope. Have you ever wondered why cells are so small? One reason is related to how materials move into and out of cells.

As a cell's size increases, more of its cytoplasm is located farther from the cell membrane. Once a molecule enters a cell, it is carried to its destination by a stream of moving cytoplasm, somewhat like the way currents in the ocean move a raft. But in a very large cell, the streams of cytoplasm must travel farther to bring materials to all parts of the cell. It would take much longer for a molecule to reach the center of a very large cell than it would in a small cell. Likewise, it would take a long time for wastes to be removed. If a cell grew too large, it could not function well enough to survive.

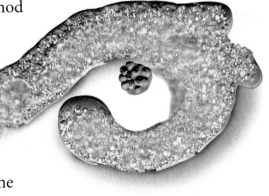

FIGURE 20
Amoeba Engulfing Food
This single-celled amoeba is surrounding a smaller organism. The amoeba will engulf the organism and use it for food. Engulfing is a form of active transport.

 **Reading Checkpoint** What prevents cells from growing very large?

Section 4 Assessment

S 7.1.a, E-LA: Reading 7.2.0

Target Reading Skill **Identify Main Ideas** Reread the text following the heading Osmosis. What is the main idea of the text under this heading?

Reviewing Key Concepts

1. a. **Defining** What is diffusion?
   b. **Relating Cause and Effect** Use diffusion to explain what happens when you drop a sugar cube into a mug of hot tea.
2. a. **Defining** What is osmosis?
   b. **Describing** Describe how water molecules move through the cell membrane during osmosis.
   c. **Applying Concepts** A selectively permeable membrane separates solutions A and B. The concentration of water molecules in Solution B is higher than that in Solution A. Describe how the water molecules will move.

3. a. **Comparing and Contrasting** How is active transport different from passive transport?
   b. **Reviewing** What are transport proteins?
   c. **Explaining** Explain why transport proteins require energy to function in active transport.

Math Practice

A scientist dissolves 60 g of sugar in 3 L of water.

4. **Calculating a Concentration** Calculate the concentration of the solution in grams per liter.
5. **Ratios** Express the concentration as a ratio.

Chapter 3 Study Guide

 The **BIG Idea**   Cells are the basic building blocks of all living things. All cells have similar structures and carry out similar functions.

① Discovering Cells

Key Concepts   S 7.1

- Cells are the basic units of structure and function in living things.
- The invention of the microscope enabled people to discover and learn about cells.
- The cell theory states the following: All living things are composed of cells. Cells are the basic units of structure and function in living things. All cells are produced from other cells.
- In multicellular organisms, cells are often organized into tissues, organs, and organ systems.

Key Terms

cell   tissue
cell theory   organ
unicellular   organ system
multicellular

② Looking Inside Cells

Key Concepts   S 7.1.b, 7.1.c

- A cell wall helps to protect and support a plant cell.
- The cell membrane controls what substances come into and out of a cell.
- The nucleus directs the cell's activities.
- In the cytoplasm are many organelles, including mitochondria, endoplasmic reticulum, ribosomes, Golgi bodies, chloroplasts, vacuoles, and lysosomes. Each of these organelles has specific functions in the cell.
- The variety among cells reflects differences in structure and function.

Key Terms

organelle   endoplasmic
cell wall   reticulum
cytoskeleton   ribosome
cell membrane   Golgi body
nucleus   chloroplast
cytoplasm   vacuole
mitochondria   lysosome

③ Chemical Compounds in Cells

Key Concepts   S 7.1.a

- An element is any substance that cannot be broken down into simpler substances. When two or more elements combine chemically, they form a compound.
- Most chemical reactions within cells could not take place without water.
- Carbohydrates, lipids, proteins, and nucleic acids are important groups of organic compounds in living things. Carbohydrates provide energy for the cell and are important components of some cell parts.
- Lipids function as an energy source and make up most of the cell membrane.
- The proteins known as enzymes perform important functions in the chemical reactions that take place in cells.
- Nucleic acids contain the instructions that cells need to carry out all the functions of life.

Key Terms

element   enzyme
compound   lipid
carbohydrate   nucleic acid
protein   DNA
amino acid   RNA

④ The Cell in Its Environment

Key Concepts   S 7.1.a

- Diffusion is the main method by which small molecules move across the cell membrane.
- Osmosis is important because cells cannot function properly without adequate water.
- Active transport requires the cell to use energy, while passive transport does not.

Key Terms

selectively permeable   passive transport
diffusion   active transport
osmosis

Review and Assessment

Go Online
PHSchool.com

For: Self-Assessment
Visit: PHSchool.com
Web Code: cva-1030

Target Reading Skill

Identifying Main Ideas To review part of Section 3, reread the text following the heading The Compound Called Water. Copy the graphic organizer at right. Complete the graphic organizer by supplying details that support the main idea.

Main Idea

Most chemical reactions within cells could not take place without water.

Detail a. _____ ?

Detail b. _____ ?

Detail c. _____ ?

Reviewing Key Terms

Choose the letter of the best answer.

1. All living things are composed of
   a. blood.
   b. chloroplasts.
   c. vacuoles.
   d. cells.

2. In plant and animal cells, the control center of the cell is the
   a. chloroplast.
   b. cytoplasm.
   c. nucleus.
   d. Golgi body.

3. A storage compartment of the cell is the
   a. cell wall.
   b. lysosome.
   c. endoplasmic reticulum.
   d. vacuole.

4. Starch is an example of a
   a. nucleic acid.
   b. protein.
   c. lipid.
   d. carbohydrate.

5. The process by which water moves across a cell membrane is called
   a. osmosis.
   b. active transport.
   c. organelle.
   d. resolution.

Complete the following sentences so that your answers clearly explain the Key Terms.

6. The **nucleus** can direct the cell's activities because it contains _____ .

7. **Mitochondria** are "powerhouses" of the cell because _____ .

8. Water is an example of a **compound,** which is _____ .

9. Saliva in your mouth is an example of an **enzyme** because _____ .

10. Oxygen molecules enter a cell by **diffusion,** which is _____ .

Writing in Science

Dialogue A dialogue is a conversation. Write a dialogue that might have taken place between Schleiden and Schwann. The scientists should discuss their observations and conclusions.

Video Assessment
Discovery Channel School
Cell Structure and Function

Review and Assessment

Checking Concepts

11. What role did the microscope play in the development of the cell theory?

12. Describe the function of the cell wall.

13. Explain the difference between elements and compounds.

14. How are enzymes important to living things?

15. What are the functions of DNA and RNA?

16. Why is water important in the cell?

17. What is diffusion? What function does diffusion have in the cell?

18. Explain the relationship between cell size and the movement of materials into and out of cells.

Thinking Critically

19. **Applying Concepts** Do the cells below come from a plant or an animal? Explain your answer.

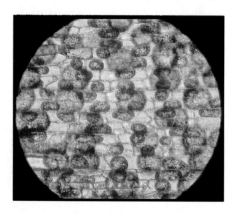

20. **Problem Solving** A cell is actively producing a protein to be released outside the cell. Sequence the following organelles in the order that the protein will travel: Golgi bodies, ribosomes, endoplasmic reticulum.

21. **Predicting** Suppose a cell did not have a supply of amino acids and could not produce them. What effect might this have on the cell?

22. **Comparing and Contrasting** Explain how active transport is different from osmosis.

Math Practice

23. **Ratios** A solution consists of 24 g of table salt dissolved in 2 L of water. Express the concentration of salt in the form of a ratio.

24. **Ratios** What is the concentration of a sugar solution that contains 8 g sugar dissolved in 500 mL of water? Express your answer in the form of a ratio.

Applying Skills

Use the diagrams to answer Questions 25–27.

A scientist watered the plant in Figure A with salt water. After 30 minutes, the plant looked as you see it in Figure B.

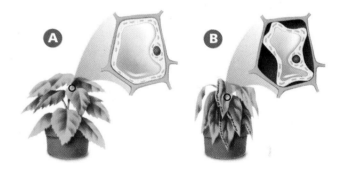

25. **Observing** How did the plant cells change after the plant was watered?

26. **Inferring** Describe a process that would lead to the changes in the plant cells.

27. **Developing Hypotheses** Suppose the scientist were to water the plant in B with fresh (unsalted) water. Develop a hypothesis about what would happen to the plant. Explain your hypothesis.

Lab zone Standards Investigation

Performance Assessment Bring in your egg, graph, and any diagrams you made. As a class, discuss your results and conclusions. Then, as a group, try to answer these questions: What happened to the eggshell? What process took place at each stage of the experiment?

Choose the letter of the best answer.

1. A reasonable estimate for the size of a cell's nucleus is
   A 0.006 mm.
   B 6 mm.
   C 0.006 m.
   D 6 m.   **S 7.1.a**

2. Which of the following statements is not true according to the cell theory?
   A All plants and animals are made of cells.
   B Cells are the basic unit of structure in organisms.
   C Only some cells come from other cells.
   D All cells come from other cells.   **S 7.1**

Use the table below and your knowledge of science to answer Question 3.

Comparing the Cells of Three Organisms			
Organism	Cell Wall	Cell Membrane	Chloroplasts
1	No	Yes	Yes
2	Yes	Yes	No
3	No	Yes	No

3. Which organism is most likely an animal?
   A Organism 1
   B Organism 2
   C Organism 3
   D None of the organisms is an animal. **S 7.1.b**

4. Which of the following statements about a cell's membrane is true?
   A Only small molecules can pass through the membrane.
   B Only water molecules can pass through the membrane.
   C Only food molecules can pass through the membrane.
   D Some substances can pass through the membrane while others cannot.   **S 7.5**

5. A tissue in an animal produces and releases chemicals that are used by cells throughout the animal's body. Cells in that tissue probably have a larger than normal number of
   A lysosomes.
   B mitochondria.
   C Golgi bodies.
   D nuclei.   **S 7.1.b**

Use the diagram below and your knowledge of science to answer Questions 6 and 7.

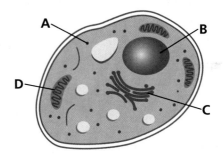

6. Which organelle contains instructions for directing the cell's functions?
   A A
   B B
   C C
   D D   **S 7.1.c**

7. In which organelle is food energy converted to energy that the cell can use?
   A A
   B B
   C C
   D D   **S 7.1.d**

🔑 Apply the
BIG Idea

8. How are plant and animal cells similar? How are they different? Make a list of the different organelles in each cell. Explain how each organelle is vital to the life and function of a plant or animal.   **S 7.5**

Cell Processes and Energy

CALIFORNIA
Standards Preview

S 7.1 All living organisms are composed of cells, from just one to many trillions, whose details usually are visible only through a microscope. As a basis for understanding this concept:

d. Students know that mitochondria liberate energy for the work that cells do and that chloroplasts capture sunlight energy for photosynthesis.

e. Students know cells divide to increase their numbers through a process of mitosis, which results in two daughter cells with identical sets of chromosomes.

f. Students know that as multicellular organisms develop, their cells differentiate.

S 7.2 A typical cell of any organism contains genetic instructions that specify its traits. Those traits may be modified by environmental influences. As a basis for understanding this concept:

e. Students know DNA (deoxyribonucleic acid) is the genetic material of living organisms and is located in the chromosomes of each cell.

Sunlight on these maple leaves powers ▶ the process of photosynthesis.

S 7.1.d

Focus on the
BIG Idea

How do cells obtain the energy they need to carry out all their functions?

Check What You Know

Hummingbirds feed on the nectar produced by flowers. Nectar is a sweet liquid composed largely of carbohydrates. What does nectar provide for the cells of the hummingbird?

Build Science Vocabulary

The images shown here represent some of the key terms in this chapter. You can use this vocabulary skill to help you understand the meaning of some key terms in this chapter.

Greek Word Origins

Many English science words come from ancient Greek words. One example is the word *photograph.* The first part of *photograph* comes from the Greek word *photos,* which means "light." The second part comes from *graphos,* which means "written" or "recorded." A photograph is a picture recorded by using light.

The table below shows three Greek words that are sources of some key terms in this chapter. (Recall from Chapter 3 that prefixes are word parts placed at the beginning of a root word to change its meaning.)

Greek Word	Meaning of Greek Word	Key Term
auto-	self	**autotroph** An organism that makes food for itself
hetero-	other, different	**heterotroph** An organism that depends on other organisms for food
kinesis	motion	**cytokinesis** During cell division, the process in which a cell's cytoplasm divides and organelles move into the two new cells that form

Apply It!

The Greek word *trophe* means "food." What two key terms in the table come from this Greek word? How does the meaning of each of these words put two Greek words together?

fermentation

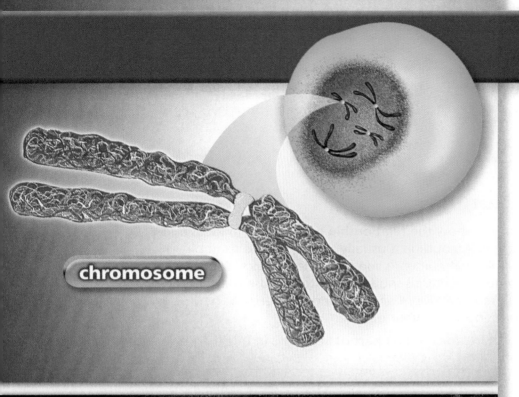

chromosome

stomata

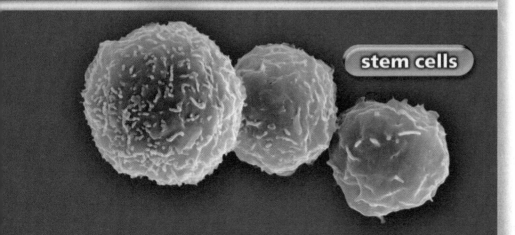

stem cells

Interactive Textbook

Build Science Vocabulary
Online
Visit: PHSchool.com
Web Code: cvj-1040

How to Read Science

Create Outlines

In an outline, you show the relationship between main ideas and supporting ideas. An outline is usually set up like the example shown below. Roman numerals show the main topics. Capital letters and regular numerals show the subtopics. Use the chapter's headings, subheadings, Key Concepts, and Key Terms to help you decide what to include in your outline.

Look at the outline for the first part of Section 2 in this chapter.

> Respiration
> I. What Is Respiration?
> A. Respiration—process by which cells get energy from glucose
> B. During respiration, cells
>   1. Break down simple food molecules such as sugar
>   2. Release the energy in the molecules
> C. Storing and Releasing Energy
>   1. Photosynthesis—plants capture sunlight's energy, store as carbohydrates
>   2. Respiration—plants use stored energy by breaking down carbohydrates

Apply It!

1. What is the one main topic in the partial outline above? How do you indicate main topics in an outline?
2. How many subtopics appear under **B** in the outline above? What are these subtopics?

When you read Section 2, complete the outline above. Also make an outline of Section 4.

Standards Investigation

S 7.1.d

Shine On!

Every morning when the sun rises, tiny living factories start a manufacturing process called photosynthesis. The power they use is sunlight. In this investigation, you will study how light affects one familiar group of photosynthesizers—plants.

Your Goal

To determine how different lighting conditions affect the health and growth of plants

To complete the investigation, you will

- write up a plan to grow plants under different lighting conditions
- care for your plants daily, and keep careful records of their health and growth for three weeks
- graph your data, and draw conclusions about the effect of light on plant growth
- follow the safety guidelines in Appendix A

Plan It!

Brainstorm with classmates to answer these questions: What different light conditions might you test? What plants will you use? How will you measure health and growth? How can you be sure your results are due to the light conditions? Write up your plan and submit it to your teacher.

Photosynthesis

S 7.1.d Students know that mitochondria liberate energy for the work that cells do and that chloroplasts capture sunlight energy for photosynthesis.

🔑 How does the sun supply living things with the energy they need?

🔑 What happens during the process of photosynthesis?

Key Terms
- photosynthesis
- autotroph
- heterotroph
- pigment
- chlorophyll
- stomata

Lab zone Standards **Warm-Up**

Where Does the Energy Come From?

1. Obtain a solar-powered calculator that does not use batteries. Place the calculator in direct light.
2. Cover the solar cells with your finger. Note how your action affects the number display.
3. Uncover the solar cells. What happens to the number display?
4. Now cover all but one of the solar cells. How does that affect the number display?

Think It Over
Inferring From your observations, what can you infer about the energy that powers the calculator?

On a plain in Africa, a herd of zebras peacefully eat the grass. But watch out—the zebras' grazing will soon be harshly interrupted. A group of lions is about to attack the herd. The lions will kill one of the zebras and eat it.

Both the zebras and the lions use the food they eat to obtain energy. Every living thing needs energy. All cells need energy to carry out their functions, such as making proteins and transporting substances into and out of the cell. The zebra's meat supplies the lion's cells with the energy they need, just as the grass provides the zebra's cells with energy. But plants and certain other organisms, such as algae and some bacteria, obtain their energy in a different way. These organisms use the energy in sunlight to make their own food.

The sun is the source of energy for most living things.

Plants such as grass use energy from the sun to make their own food.

The zebra obtains energy by eating grass.

The lion obtains energy by feeding on the zebra.

FIGURE 1
Energy From the Sun
The sun supplies energy for most living things, directly or indirectly.
Relating Cause and Effect *How does sunlight provide food for the zebra?*

Sources of Energy

The process by which a cell captures energy in sunlight and uses it to make food is called **photosynthesis** (foh toh SIN thuh sis). The term *photosynthesis* comes from the Greek words *photo*, which means "light," and *synthesis*, which means "putting together."

🔑 **Nearly all living things obtain energy either directly or indirectly from the energy of sunlight captured during photosynthesis.** Grass obtains energy directly from sunlight, because it makes its own food during photosynthesis. When the zebra eats the grass, it gets energy that has been stored in the grass. Similarly, the lion obtains energy stored in the zebra. The zebra and lion both obtain the sun's energy indirectly, from the energy that the grass obtained through photosynthesis.

Plants manufacture their own food through the process of photosynthesis. An organism that makes its own food is called an **autotroph** (AWT oh trohf). An organism that cannot make its own food, including animals such as the zebra and the lion, is called a **heterotroph** (HET ur oh trohf). Many heterotrophs obtain food by eating other organisms. Some heterotrophs, such as fungi, absorb their food from other organisms.

 Reading Checkpoint **What are autotrophs?**

FIGURE 2
Autotrophs and Heterotrophs
Grass, which makes its own food during photosynthesis, is an autotroph. Zebras and lions are heterotrophs, because they cannot make their own food.

Go Online
active art

For: The Photosynthesis Process
Visit: PHSchool.com
Web Code: cep-1042

The Two Stages of Photosynthesis

Photosynthesis is a complex process. 🔑 **During photosynthesis, plants and some other organisms use energy from the sun to convert carbon dioxide and water into oxygen and sugars.** The process of photosynthesis is shown in Figure 3. You can think of photosynthesis as taking place in two stages: capturing the sun's energy and producing sugars. You're probably familiar with many two-stage processes. To make a cake, for example, the first stage is to combine the ingredients to make the batter. The second stage is to bake the batter. To get the desired result—the cake—both stages must occur in the correct order.

Stage 1: Capturing the Sun's Energy The first stage of photosynthesis involves capturing the energy in sunlight. In plants, this energy-capturing process occurs mostly in the leaves. Recall that chloroplasts are green organelles inside plant cells. The green color comes from **pigments,** colored chemical compounds that absorb light. The main photosynthetic pigment in chloroplasts is **chlorophyll** (KLAWR uh fil).

Chlorophyll functions in a manner similar to that of the solar "cells" in a solar-powered calculator. Solar cells capture the energy in light and use it to power the calculator. Similarly, chlorophyll captures light energy and uses it to power the second stage of photosynthesis.

FIGURE 3
Two Stages of Photosynthesis

Photosynthesis has two stages, as shown in the diagram.
Interpreting Diagrams *Which stage requires light?*

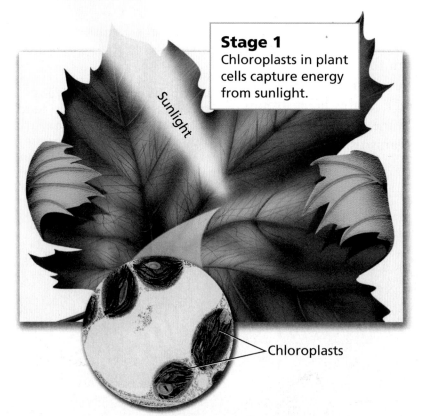

Stage 1
Chloroplasts in plant cells capture energy from sunlight.

Sunlight

Chloroplasts

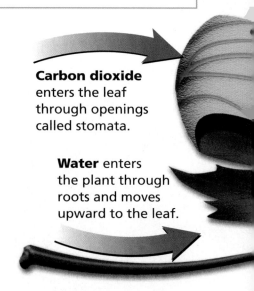

Stage 2
The captured light energy is used to produce sugars and oxygen from water and carbon dioxide.

Carbon dioxide enters the leaf through openings called stomata.

Water enters the plant through roots and moves upward to the leaf.

Stage 2: Using Energy to Make Food In the next stage of photosynthesis, the cell uses the captured energy to produce sugars. The cell needs two raw materials for this stage: water (H_2O) and carbon dioxide (CO_2). In plants, the roots absorb water from the soil. The water then moves up through the plant's stem to the leaves. Carbon dioxide is one of the gases in the air. Carbon dioxide enters the plant through small openings on the undersides of the leaves called **stomata** (STOH muh tuh) (singular *stoma*). Once in the leaves, the water and carbon dioxide move into the chloroplasts.

Inside the chloroplasts, the water and carbon dioxide undergo a complex series of chemical reactions. The reactions are powered by the energy captured in the first stage. These reactions produce chemicals as products. One product is a sugar that has six carbon atoms. Six-carbon sugars have the chemical formula $C_6H_{12}O_6$. Recall that sugars are a type of carbohydrate. Cells can use the energy in the sugar to carry out important cell functions.

The other product of photosynthesis is oxygen (O_2), which exits the leaf through the stomata. In fact, almost all the oxygen in Earth's atmosphere was produced by living things through the process of photosynthesis.

Reading Checkpoint What makes plants green?

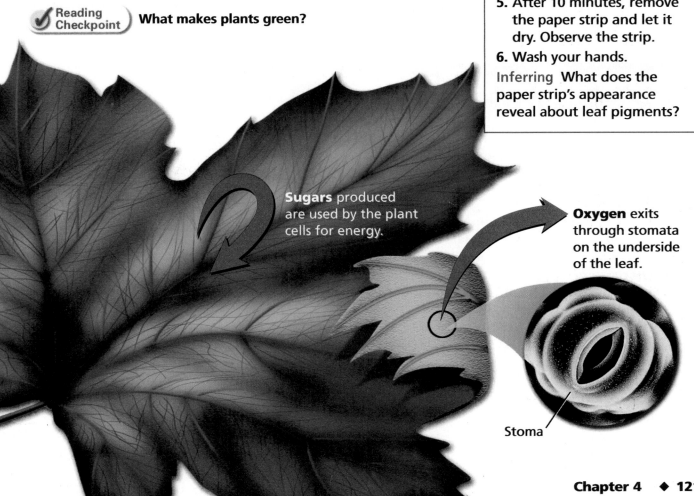

Sugars produced are used by the plant cells for energy.

Oxygen exits through stomata on the underside of the leaf.

Stoma

The Photosynthesis Equation The events of photosynthesis can be summed up by the following chemical equation:

$$6\ CO_2 \quad + \quad 6\ H_2O \quad \xrightarrow{\text{light energy}} \quad C_6H_{12}O_6 + 6\ O_2$$

carbon dioxide   water   a sugar   oxygen

Notice that the raw materials—six molecules of carbon dioxide and six molecules of water—are on the left side of the equation. The products—one molecule of a sugar and six molecules of oxygen—are on the right side of the equation. An arrow, which you can read as "yields," connects the raw materials to the products. Light energy, which is necessary for the chemical reaction to occur, is written above the arrow.

What happens to the sugar produced in photosynthesis? Plant cells use some of the sugar for food. The cells break down the sugar molecules to release the energy they contain. This energy can then be used to carry out the plant's functions. Some sugar molecules are converted into other compounds, such as cellulose. Other sugar molecules may be stored in the plant's cells for later use. When you eat food from plants, such as potatoes or carrots, you are eating the plant's stored energy.

FIGURE 4
Stored Energy
When you eat a carrot, you obtain energy stored during photosynthesis.

Reading Checkpoint In the photosynthesis equation, what does the arrow mean?

Section 1 Assessment

S 7.1.d, E-LA: Reading 7.1.2, Writing 7.2.0

Build Science Vocabulary Greek Word Origins
What clue in the Key Term **photosynthesis** lets you know that the term has something to do with light?

Reviewing Key Concepts

1. **a.** Reviewing Why do living things need energy?
   b. Explaining How do plants obtain energy?
   c. Applying Concepts An insect eats a leaf. Explain how the insect depends on the sun for energy.
2. **a.** Reviewing What chemical equation sums up the events of photosynthesis?
   b. Comparing and Contrasting What are the substances needed for photosynthesis? What substances are produced during photosynthesis?
   c. Making Generalizations Would you expect a plant to produce more oxygen on a cloudy day or a sunny day? Explain.

Writing in Science

Job Qualifications When people apply for jobs, they must describe their qualifications for the job. Suppose that you are a leaf, and that you are applying for a job in a photosynthesis factory. Write a paragraph in which you summarize your qualifications for the job of photosynthesis. Your paragraph should include the following words: *chloroplasts, chlorophyll, light, energy, water, carbon dioxide,* and *stomata.*

Respiration

S 7.1.d Students know that mitochondria liberate energy for the work that cells do and that chloroplasts capture sunlight energy for photosynthesis.

- What events occur during respiration?
- What is fermentation?

Key Terms

- respiration
- fermentation

Lab zone Standards **Warm-Up**

What Is a Product of Respiration?

1. 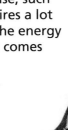 Put on your goggles. Fill two test tubes half full of warm water. Add 5 mL of sugar to one of the test tubes. Put the tubes in a test-tube rack.

2. Add 0.5 mL of dried yeast (a single-celled organism) to each tube. Stir the contents of each tube with a straw. Place a stopper snugly in the top of each tube.

3. Observe any changes that occur in the two test tubes over the next 10 to 15 minutes.

Think It Over

Observing What changes occurred in each test tube? How can you account for any differences that you observed?

You and your friend have been hiking all morning. You look for a flat rock to sit on, so you can eat lunch. The steepest part of the trail is ahead. You'll need a lot of energy to get to the top of the mountain. That energy will come from food.

Before food can provide your body with energy, it must pass through your digestive system. There, the food is broken down into small molecules. These molecules can then pass into your bloodstream. Next, the molecules travel through the bloodstream to the cells of your body. Inside the cells, the energy in the molecules is released. In this section, you'll learn how your body's cells obtain energy from the food you eat.

FIGURE 5
Energy
Vigorous exercise, such as hiking, requires a lot of energy. All the energy your body uses comes from food.

FIGURE 6
Energy From Respiration
All organisms need energy to live. The leopard frog uses energy to leap great distances. Although the mushrooms don't move, they still need energy to grow and reproduce.

What Is Respiration?

After you eat a meal, your body converts some of the food into glucose, a type of sugar. **Respiration** is the process by which cells obtain energy from glucose. **During respiration, cells break down simple food molecules such as sugar and release the energy they contain.** Because living things need a continuous supply of energy, the cells of all living things carry out respiration continuously. Plant cells, as well as animal cells, respire.

Storing and Releasing Energy Energy stored in cells is something like money you put in a savings account in a bank. When you want to buy something, you withdraw some of the money. Cells store and use energy in a similar way. During photosynthesis, plants capture the energy from sunlight and "save" it in the form of carbohydrates, including sugars and starches. Similarly, when you eat a meal, you add to your body's energy savings account. When cells need energy, they "withdraw" it by breaking down the carbohydrates in the process of respiration.

Breathing and Respiration The term *respiration* has two meanings. You have probably used it to mean "breathing," that is, moving air in and out of your lungs. To avoid confusion, the respiration process that takes place inside cells is sometimes called *cellular respiration*. The two meanings of the term *respiration* do point out a connection, however. Breathing brings oxygen, which is usually necessary for cellular respiration, into your lungs.

 **Reading Checkpoint** What is respiration?

The Two Stages of Respiration Like photosynthesis, respiration is a two-stage process. Figure 7 shows these two stages. The first stage takes place in the cytoplasm. There, molecules of glucose are broken down into smaller molecules. Oxygen is not involved, and only a small amount of energy is released.

The second stage of respiration takes place in the mitochondria. There, the small molecules are broken down into even smaller molecules. These chemical reactions require oxygen, and they release a great deal of energy. This is why the mitochondria are sometimes called the "powerhouses" of the cell. The energy liberated, or released, by mitochondria is still stored in the form of chemical energy. But now it is stored in molecules that are readily used by the cell.

Two other products of respiration are carbon dioxide and water. The carbon dioxide diffuses out of the cell. In most animals, the carbon dioxide and some water leave the body during exhalation. Thus, when you breathe in, you take in oxygen—a raw material for respiration. When you breathe out, you release carbon dioxide and water—products of respiration.

The Respiration Equation Although respiration occurs in a series of complex steps, the overall process can be summarized in the following equation:

$$C_6H_{12}O_6 \ + \ 6\,O_2 \ \longrightarrow \ 6\,CO_2 \ + \ 6\,H_2O \ + \ energy$$

sugar   oxygen   carbon dioxide   water

Notice that the raw materials for respiration are sugar and oxygen. Plants and other organisms that undergo photosynthesis make their own sugar. The glucose in the cells of animals and other organisms comes from food they eat. The oxygen comes from the air or water surrounding the organism.

FIGURE 7
Two Stages of Respiration
Respiration, like photosynthesis, takes place in two stages. Note that energy is released in both stages.
Interpreting Diagrams *In which stage of respiration is oxygen used?*

Stage 1 In the cytoplasm, glucose is broken down into smaller molecules. A small amount of energy is released.

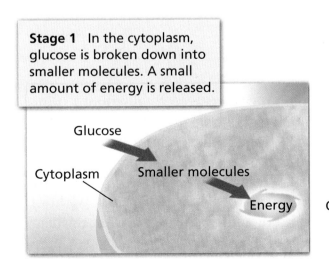

Stage 2 In the mitochondria, the smaller molecules combine with oxygen to produce water and carbon dioxide. This reaction releases a large amount of energy.

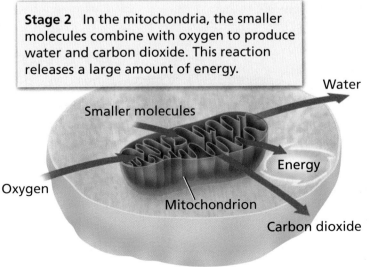

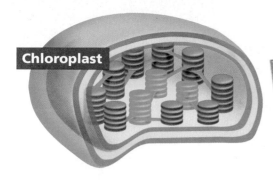

Chloroplast

Photosynthesis
During photosynthesis, plants use carbon dioxide and release oxygen.

$$6\ CO_2 + 6\ H_2O \longrightarrow C_6H_{12}O_6 + 6\ O_2$$

Sugar and Oxygen

Respiration
During respiration, organisms use oxygen and release carbon dioxide.

$$C_6H_{12}O_6 + 6\ O_2 \longrightarrow 6\ CO_2 + 6\ H_2O$$

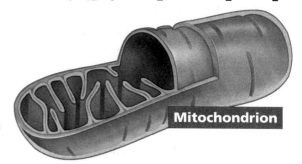

Mitochondrion

Carbon Dioxide and Water

FIGURE 8
Photosynthesis and Respiration
You can think of photosynthesis and respiration as opposite processes.
Comparing and Contrasting
Which process uses oxygen? Which uses carbon dioxide?

Comparing Photosynthesis and Respiration Can you notice anything familiar about the equation for respiration? You are quite right if you said it is the opposite of the equation for photosynthesis. This is an important point. During photosynthesis, carbon dioxide and water are used to produce sugars and oxygen. During respiration, the sugar glucose and oxygen are used to produce carbon dioxide and water. Photosynthesis and respiration can be thought of as opposite processes.

Together, these two processes form a cycle that keeps the levels of oxygen and carbon dioxide fairly constant in Earth's atmosphere. As you can see in Figure 8, living things use both gases over and over again.

 **Reading Checkpoint** Which process—photosynthesis or respiration—produces water?

Fermentation

Some cells are able to obtain energy from food without using oxygen. For example, some single-celled organisms live where there is no oxygen, such as deep in the ocean or in the mud of lakes or swamps. These organisms obtain their energy through **fermentation,** an energy-releasing process that does not require oxygen. ⬤ **Fermentation provides energy for cells without using oxygen.** The amount of energy released from each sugar molecule during fermentation, however, is much lower than the amount released during respiration.

Alcoholic Fermentation One type of fermentation occurs when yeast and some other single-celled organisms break down sugars. This process is sometimes called alcoholic fermentation because alcohol is one of the products. The other products are carbon dioxide and a small amount of energy.

The products of alcoholic fermentation are important to bakers and brewers. The carbon dioxide produced by yeast creates air pockets in bread dough, causing it to rise. Carbon dioxide is also the source of bubbles in alcoholic drinks such as beer and sparkling wine.

Lactic Acid Fermentation Another type of fermentation takes place at times in your body. You've probably felt its effects. Think of a time when you ran as fast as you could for as long as you could. Your leg muscles were pushing hard against the ground, and you were breathing quickly.

No matter how hard you breathed, your muscle cells used up the oxygen faster than it could be replaced. Because your cells lacked oxygen, fermentation occurred. The fermentation supplied your cells with energy. One product of this type of fermentation is an acid known as lactic acid. When lactic acid builds up, you feel a painful sensation in your muscles. Your muscles feel weak and sore.

FIGURE 9
Lactic Acid Fermentation
When an athlete's muscles run out of oxygen, lactic acid fermentation supplies the cells with energy.

 **Reading Checkpoint** **Which kind of fermentation is important to bakers?**

Section 2 Assessment

S 7.1.d, E-LA: Reading 7.2.4

Target Reading Skill Create Outlines Use your completed outline to help answer the questions below.

Reviewing Key Concepts

1. a. Reviewing What happens during respiration?
   b. Reviewing What is the equation for respiration?
   c. Comparing and Contrasting Compare the equations for respiration and photosynthesis.
   d. Relating Cause and Effect Explain why cellular respiration adds carbon dioxide to the atmosphere, but photosynthesis does not.

2. a. Identifying What is the process in which cells obtain energy without using oxygen?
   b. Inferring How would athletes be affected if this process could not take place?
   c. Predicting Is this process more likely to occur during a short run or a long walk? Explain your answer.

Lab zone **At-Home Activity**

Make Bread With an adult family member, follow a recipe in a cookbook to make a loaf of bread using yeast. Explain to your family the cellular process that causes the dough to rise. After you bake the bread, observe a slice and look for evidence that fermentation occurred.

Exhaling Carbon Dioxide

S 7.1.d, 7.7

Problem

Is there a relationship between exercise and the amount of carbon dioxide you exhale?

Skills Focus

predicting, controlling variables

Materials

- 2 250-mL beakers
- bromthymol blue solution (0.1% solution), 30 mL
- 2 straws
- stopwatch or watch with second hand
- graduated cylinder, 25 mL
- paper towels

Procedure

PART 1 Testing for Carbon Dioxide

1. Label one beaker "Beaker 1" and the other beaker "Beaker 2." Beaker 1 will be the control in the experiment.

2. Bromthymol blue can be used to test for the presence of carbon dioxide. To see how this works, fill each beaker with 15 mL of bromthymol solution. **CAUTION:** *Bromthymol blue can stain skin and clothing. Avoid spilling or splashing it on yourself.*

3. Note and record the color of the solution in both beakers.

4. Place a straw in Beaker 2. Gently blow through the straw into the solution until the solution changes color. **CAUTION:** *Use the straw to breathe out only. Do not suck the solution back through the straw.* Your partner should begin timing when you first blow through the straw and stop as soon as the solution changes color. Record the time that has elapsed.

PART 2 Exercise and Carbon Dioxide

5. In Part 1 you timed the change of color without exercising first. Predict how long it will take the solution to change color if you conduct the test after you exercise. Design an experiment to test your prediction. Be sure to include a plan for recording your results and steps to review your results.

6. Write down the steps of your experiment and get your teacher's approval. Then, conduct your experiment. **CAUTION:** *Do not over-exert yourself. If you have a medical condition that limits your ability to exercise, do not take part in the exercise portion of this experiment.*

Analyze and Conclude

1. **Measuring** How long did it take for the solution to change color the first time you did the test (without exercising)?

2. **Drawing Conclusions** How did exercising affect the amount of time it took for the solution to change color?

3. **Predicting** What was your prediction in Step 5 based upon? Was your prediction accurate?

4. **Controlling Variables** In Part 2, what variables did you need to control? Explain how you controlled those variables.

5. **Communicating** Write a paragraph that relates the results of your experiment to the process of cellular respiration. Be sure to explain how increased cellular activity affects carbon dioxide output.

More to Explore

Some plants grow in water. If you added bromthymol blue to the water, do you think it would turn color? *(Hint:* What might happen to the carbon dioxide that the plants produce during respiration?)

Cell Division

CALIFORNIA
Standards Focus

S 7.1.e Students know cells divide to increase their numbers through a process of mitosis, which results in two daughter cells with identical sets of chromosomes.

S 7.2.e Students know DNA (deoxyribonucleic acid) is the genetic material of living organisms and is located in the chromosomes of each cell.

What events take place during the three stages of the cell cycle?

How does the structure of DNA help account for the way in which DNA copies itself?

Key Terms

- cell cycle
- interphase
- replication
- mitosis
- chromosome
- cytokinesis

Lab zone **Standards Warm-Up**

What Are the Yeast Cells Doing?

1. Use a plastic dropper to transfer some yeast cells from a yeast culture to a microscope slide. Your teacher has prepared the slide by drying methylene blue stain onto it. Add a coverslip and place the slide under a microscope.

2. Examine the cells on the slide. Use low power first, then high power. Look for what appears to be two cells attached to each other. One cell may be larger than the other. Draw what you see.

Think It Over

Developing Hypotheses What process do you think the "double cells" are undergoing? Develop a hypothesis that might explain what you see.

In the early autumn, many local fairs run pumpkin contests. Proud growers enter their largest pumpkins, hoping to win a prize. The pumpkin below has a mass greater than 600 kilograms! This giant pumpkin began as a structure inside a small flower. How did the pumpkin grow so big?

A pumpkin grows in size by increasing both the size and the number of its cells. A single cell grows and then divides, forming two cells. Then two cells grow and divide, forming four, and so on. This process of cell growth and division does not occur only in pumpkins, though. In fact, many cells in your body are dividing as you read this page.

◀ **Prize-winning pumpkin**

Stage 1: Interphase

How do little pigs get to be big pigs? Their cells grow and divide, over and over. The regular sequence of growth and division that cells undergo is known as the **cell cycle.** During the cell cycle, a cell grows, prepares for division, and divides into two new cells, which are called "daughter cells." Each of the daughter cells then begins the cell cycle again. You can see details of the cell cycle in Figure 12. Notice that the cell cycle is divided into three main stages: interphase, mitosis, and cytokinesis.

The first stage of the cell cycle is called **interphase.** Interphase is the period before cell division. ⬅ **During interphase, the cell grows, makes a copy of its DNA, and prepares to divide into two cells.**

Growing During the first part of interphase, the cell grows to its full size and produces structures it needs. For example, the cell makes new ribosomes and produces enzymes. Copies are made of both mitochondria and chloroplasts.

Copying DNA In the next part of interphase, the cell makes an exact copy of the DNA in its nucleus in a process called **replication.** Recall that DNA is found in the thin strands of chromatin in the nucleus. During interphase, the chromatin appears as a dense mass within a clearly defined nucleus.

DNA holds all the information that the cell needs to carry out its functions. Replication of DNA is very important, since each daughter cell must have a complete set of DNA to survive. At the end of DNA replication, the cell contains two identical sets of DNA. You will learn the details of DNA replication later in this section.

Preparing for Division Once the DNA has replicated, preparation for cell division begins. The cell produces structures that it will use to divide into two new cells. At the end of interphase, the cell is ready to divide.

Lab zone Try This **Activity**

Modeling Mitosis

Refer to Figure 12 as you carry out this activity.

1. Construct a model of a cell that has four chromosomes. Use a piece of construction paper to represent the cell. Use different-colored pipe cleaners to represent the chromosomes. Make sure that the chromosomes look like double rods.

2. Position the chromosomes in the cell where they would be during prophase.

3. Repeat Step 2 for metaphase, anaphase, and telophase.

Making Models How did the model help you understand the events of mitosis?

Stage 2: Mitosis

Once interphase is complete, the second stage of the cell cycle begins. **Mitosis** (my TOH sis) is the stage during which the cell's nucleus divides into two new nuclei. ⊜ **During mitosis, one copy of the DNA is distributed into each of the two daughter cells.**

Scientists divide mitosis into four parts, or phases: prophase, metaphase, anaphase, and telophase. During prophase, the threadlike chromatin in the nucleus condenses to form double-rod structures called **chromosomes** (KROH muh sohmz). Each chromosome has two rods because the cell's DNA has replicated, and each rod in a chromosome is an exact copy of the other. Each identical rod in a chromosome is called a chromatid. Notice in Figure 11 that the two chromatids are held together by a structure called a centromere.

As the cell progresses through metaphase, anaphase, and telophase, the chromatids separate from each other and move to opposite ends of the cell. Then two nuclear envelopes form around the new chromosomes at the two ends of the cell.

FIGURE 10
Bigger Pig, More Cells
The mother pig has more cells in her body than her small piglets.

FIGURE 11
Chromosomes
During mitosis, the chromatin condenses to form chromosomes. Each chromosome consists of two identical rods, or chromatids.
Applying Concepts *During which phase of mitosis do the chromosomes form?*

Chromosomes ▼

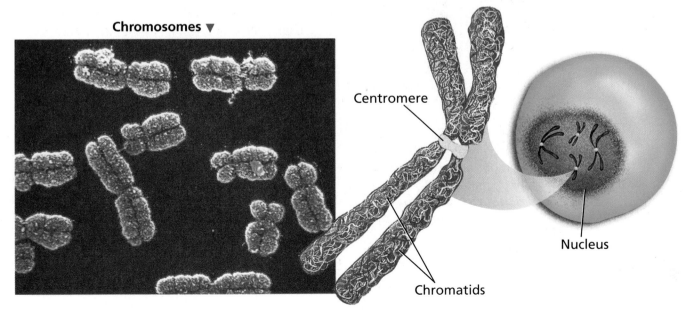

Centromere

Chromatids

Nucleus

FIGURE 12

The Cell Cycle

Cells undergo an orderly sequence of events as they grow and divide. The sequence shown here is a typical cell cycle in an animal cell. **Comparing and Contrasting** *Compare the location of the chromosomes during metaphase and anaphase.*

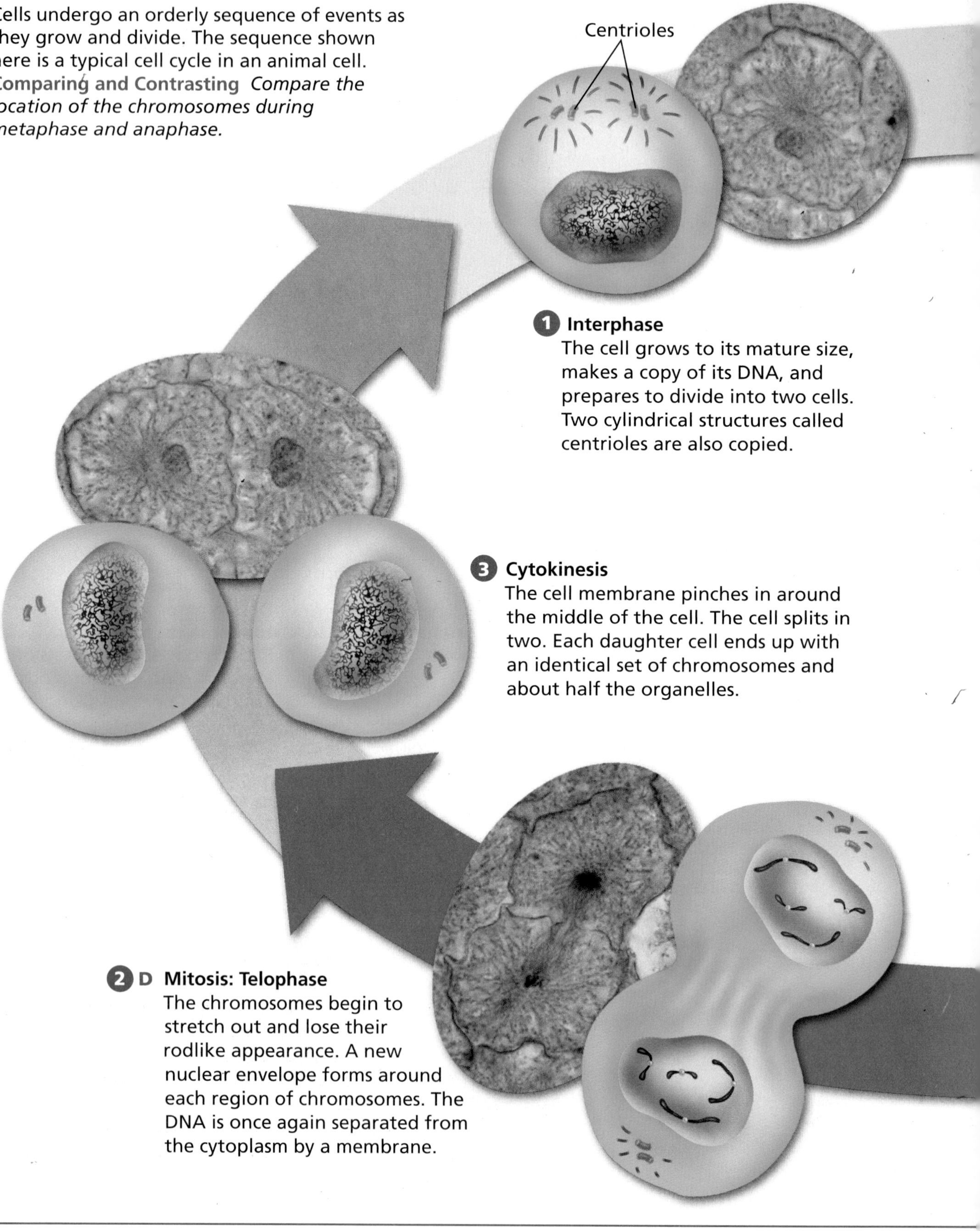

Centrioles

1 Interphase
The cell grows to its mature size, makes a copy of its DNA, and prepares to divide into two cells. Two cylindrical structures called centrioles are also copied.

3 Cytokinesis
The cell membrane pinches in around the middle of the cell. The cell splits in two. Each daughter cell ends up with an identical set of chromosomes and about half the organelles.

2 D Mitosis: Telophase
The chromosomes begin to stretch out and lose their rodlike appearance. A new nuclear envelope forms around each region of chromosomes. The DNA is once again separated from the cytoplasm by a membrane.

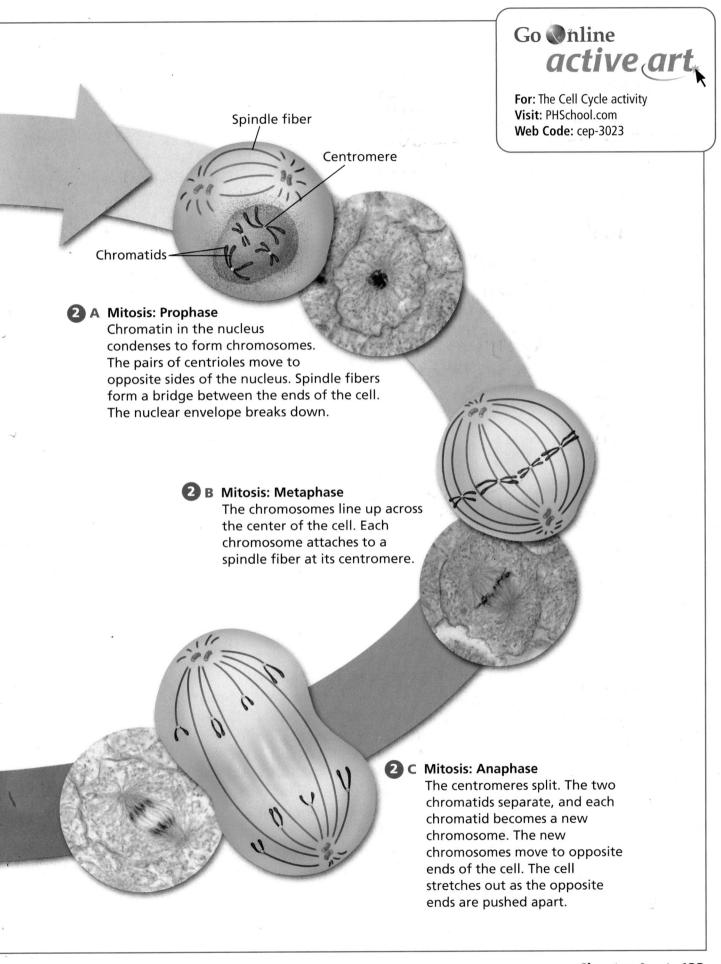

Spindle fiber

Centromere

Chromatids

2 A Mitosis: Prophase
Chromatin in the nucleus
condenses to form chromosomes.
The pairs of centrioles move to
opposite sides of the nucleus. Spindle fibers
form a bridge between the ends of the cell.
The nuclear envelope breaks down.

2 B Mitosis: Metaphase
The chromosomes line up across
the center of the cell. Each
chromosome attaches to a
spindle fiber at its centromere.

2 C Mitosis: Anaphase
The centromeres split. The two
chromatids separate, and each
chromatid becomes a new
chromosome. The new
chromosomes move to opposite
ends of the cell. The cell
stretches out as the opposite
ends are pushed apart.

Math ▸ Analyzing Data

Length of the Cell Cycle

How long does it take for a cell to go through one cell cycle? It all depends on the cell. A human liver cell, for example, completes one cell cycle in about 22 hours, as shown in the graph. Study the graph and then answer the following questions.

1. **Reading Graphs** What do the three curved arrows outside the circle represent?

2. **Reading Graphs** In what stage of the cell cycle is the wedge representing growth?

3. **Interpreting Data** In human liver cells, how long does it take DNA replication to occur?

4. **Drawing Conclusions** In human liver cells, what stage in the cell cycle takes the longest time?

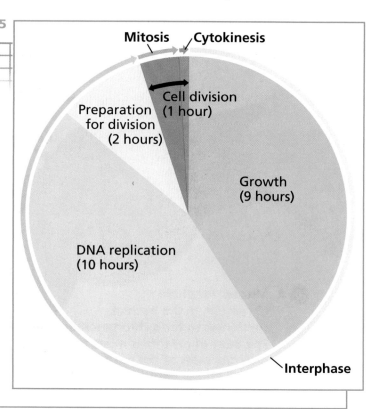

Mitosis   Cytokinesis

Cell division (1 hour)

Preparation for division (2 hours)

Growth (9 hours)

DNA replication (10 hours)

Interphase

Stage 3: Cytokinesis

The final stage of the cell cycle, which is called **cytokinesis** (sy toh kih NEE sis), completes the process of cell division. 🔑 **During cytokinesis, the cytoplasm divides. The organelles are distributed into each of the two new cells.** Cytokinesis usually starts at about the same time as telophase. When cytokinesis is complete, two new cells, or daughter cells, have formed. Each daughter cell has the same number of chromosomes as the original parent cell. At the end of cytokinesis, each cell enters interphase, and the cycle begins again.

Cytokinesis in Animal Cells During cytokinesis in animal cells, the cell membrane squeezes together around the middle of the cell. The cytoplasm pinches into two cells. Each daughter cell gets about half of the organelles.

Cytokinesis in Plant Cells Cytokinesis is somewhat different in plant cells. A plant cell's rigid cell wall cannot squeeze together in the same way that a cell membrane can. Instead, a structure called a cell plate forms across the middle of the cell. The cell plate gradually develops into new cell membranes between the two daughter cells. New cell walls then form around the cell membranes.

FIGURE 13
Cytokinesis in Plant Cells
During cytokinesis in plant cells, a cell plate forms between the two new nuclei.
Applying Concepts *What is the function of the cell plate?*

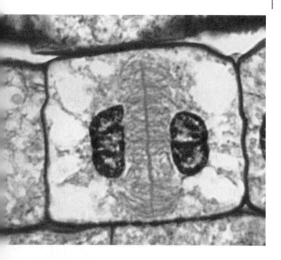

 **Reading Checkpoint** **During what phase of mitosis does cytokinesis begin?**

Structure and Replication of DNA

DNA replication ensures that each daughter cell will have the genetic information it needs to carry out its activities. Before scientists could understand how DNA replicates, they had to know its structure. In 1952, Rosalind Franklin used an X-ray method to photograph DNA molecules. Her photographs helped James Watson and Francis Crick figure out the structure of DNA in 1953.

The Structure of DNA If you were to unravel a chromosome, you would find that the DNA strands are wound tightly around proteins. The proteins help support the chromosome's structure. Notice in Figure 14 that the strands of the DNA molecule look like a twisted ladder. The two sides of the DNA ladder are made up of molecules of a sugar called deoxyribose, alternating with molecules known as phosphates.

Each rung is made up of a pair of molecules called nitrogen bases. Nitrogen bases are molecules that contain the element nitrogen and other elements. DNA has four kinds of nitrogen bases: adenine (AD uh neen), thymine (THY meen), guanine (GWAH neen), and cytosine (SY tuh seen). The capital letters A, T, G, and C are used to represent the four bases.

The bases on one side of the ladder pair with the bases on the other side. Adenine (A) only pairs with thymine (T), while guanine (G) only pairs with cytosine (C). This pairing pattern is the key to understanding how DNA replication occurs.

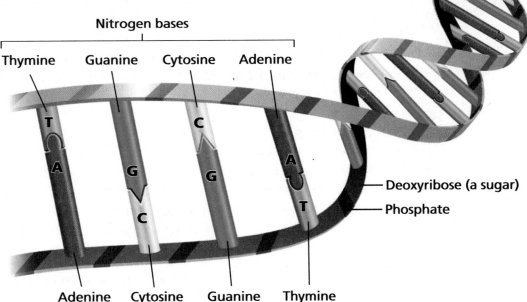

Proteins

FIGURE 14
The Structure of DNA
The DNA molecule, supported by proteins, is shaped like a twisted ladder.

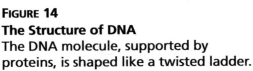

Nitrogen bases

Thymine   Guanine   Cytosine   Adenine

T   C

A   G   G   A

C   T

Deoxyribose (a sugar)
Phosphate

Adenine   Cytosine   Guanine   Thymine

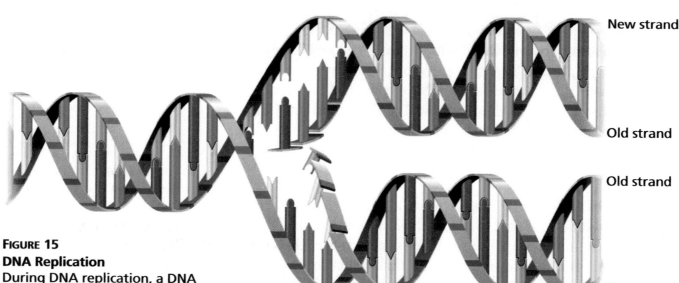

New strand

Old strand

Old strand

New strand

FIGURE 15
DNA Replication
During DNA replication, a DNA molecule "unzips" between its paired bases. New bases pair with the bases on each old strand. As a result, two identical DNA strands form.

The Replication Process DNA replication begins when the two sides of the DNA molecule unwind and separate, somewhat like a zipper unzipping. As you can see in Figure 15, the molecule separates between the paired nitrogen bases.

Next, nitrogen bases that are floating in the nucleus pair up with the bases on each half of the DNA molecule. **Because of the way in which the nitrogen bases pair with one another, the order of the bases in each new DNA molecule exactly matches the order in the original DNA molecule.** Adenine always pairs with thymine, while guanine always pairs with cytosine. Once the new bases are attached, two new DNA molecules are formed.

 **Reading Checkpoint** During DNA replication, which base pairs with guanine?

Section 3 Assessment

S 7.1.e, 7.2.e E-LA: Reading 7.1.2, Writing 7.2.0

Build Science Vocabulary Greek Word Origins The Greek word *kinesis* means "motion." During cytokinesis, what motion occurs?

Reviewing Key Concepts

1. a. Reviewing What are the three stages of the cell cycle?
   b. Summarizing Summarize what happens to chromosomes during the stage of the cell cycle in which the nucleus divides. Include the terms *prophase, metaphase, anaphase,* and *telophase*.
   c. Interpreting Diagrams Look at Figure 12. What is the role of spindle fibers during cell division?

2. a. Listing List the nitrogen bases in DNA.
   b. Describing Describe how the nitrogen bases pair in a DNA molecule.
   c. Inferring One section of a strand of DNA has the base sequence AGATTC. What is the base sequence on the other strand?

Writing in Science

Writing Instructions Imagine that you work in a factory where cells are manufactured. Write instructions for newly forming cells on how to carry out cytokinesis. Provide instructions for both plant and animal cells.

Multiplying by Dividing

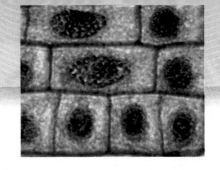

 S 7.1.e, 7.7.a

Problem

How long do the stages of the cell cycle take?

Skills Focus

observing, calculating

Materials

- microscope
- colored pencils
- calculator (optional)
- prepared slides of onion root tip cells undergoing cell division

Procedure

1. Place the slide on the stage of a microscope. Use low power to locate a cell in interphase. Then switch to high power, and make a labeled drawing of the cell. **CAUTION:** *Slides and coverslips break easily. Do not allow the objective to touch the slide. If the slide breaks, notify your teacher. Do not touch broken glass.*

2. Repeat Step 1 to find cells in prophase, metaphase, anaphase, and telophase. Then copy the data table into your notebook.

3. Return to low power. Find an area of the slide with many cells undergoing cell division. Switch to the magnification that lets you see about 50 cells at once (for example, 100 ×).

4. Examine the cells row by row, and count the cells that are in interphase. Record that number in the data table under *First Sample*.

5. Examine the cells row by row four more times to count the cells in prophase, metaphase, anaphase, and telophase. Record the results.

6. Move to a new area on the slide. Repeat Steps 3–5 and record your counts in the column labeled *Second Sample*.

7. Fill in the column labeled *Total Number* by adding the numbers across each row in your data table.

8. Add the totals for the five stages to find the total number of cells counted.

Analyze and Conclude

1. **Observing** Based on your observations, did the root tissue have a high rate or low rate of growth? Explain. Which stage of the cell cycle did you observe most often?

2. **Calculating** The cell cycle for onion root tips takes about 720 minutes (12 hours). Use your data and the formula below to find the number of minutes each stage takes.

$$\text{Time for each stage} = \frac{\text{Number of cells at each stage}}{\text{Total number of cells counted}} \times 720 \text{ min}$$

3. **Communicating** Use the data to compare the amount of time spent in mitosis with the total time for the whole cell cycle. Write your answer in the form of a paragraph.

More to Explore

Examine prepared slides of animal cells undergoing cell division. Use drawings and descriptions to compare plant and animal mitosis.

Data Table			
Stage of Cell Cycle	First Sample	Second Sample	Total Number
Interphase			
Mitosis:			
Prophase			
Metaphase			
Anaphase			
Telophase			
Total number of cells counted			

Cell Differentiation

S 7.1.f Students know that as multicellular organisms develop, their cells differentiate.

- What is differentiation?
- What factors influence how and when cells differentiate within different organisms?

Key Terms
- differentiation
- stem cell

Lab zone Standards Warm-Up

How Is It Different?

A   B   C   D

1. Study the photos above of a growing bean plant.
2. Write your observations about how the plant changes in structure in each stage of its development.

Think It Over
Forming Operational Definitions As the plant grows, its cells divide and undergo a process called differentiation. Based on your observations, what does differentiation mean?

You have learned that the cell theory states that living things are made of cells. Some living things are single-celled, or unicellular, organisms. Other living things are multicellular. They consist of many kinds of cells that differ from one another. The cell theory also says that cells are produced from other cells. When a cell divides by mitosis, it produces two daughter cells with identical sets of chromosomes. So how do cells in multicellular organisms become different from one another?

Differentiation

Cell division alone cannot explain the development of new structures. If cells only divided, the result would merely be a big ball of identical cells. Instead, cells differentiate. **Differentiation** is the process by which cells change in structure and become capable of carrying out specialized functions. As cells differentiate, they become different from one another. They also form groups made of other, similarly specialized cells. These groups then form tissues and organs.

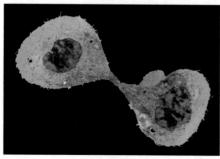

A skin cell undergoes mitosis. ▼

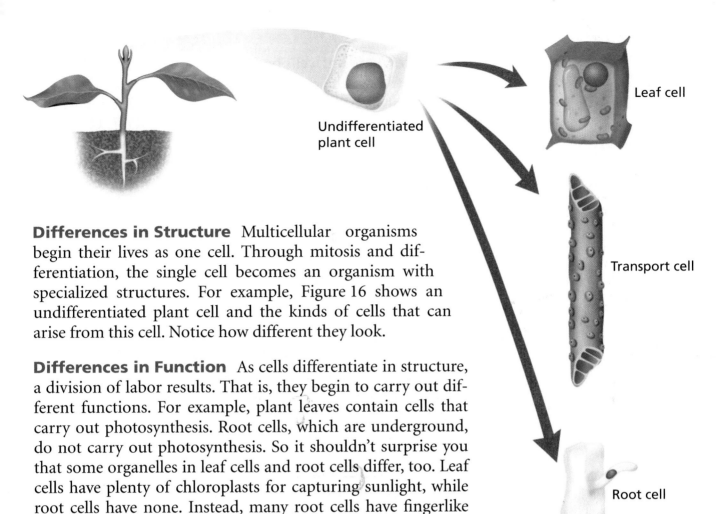

Differences in Structure Multicellular organisms begin their lives as one cell. Through mitosis and differentiation, the single cell becomes an organism with specialized structures. For example, Figure 16 shows an undifferentiated plant cell and the kinds of cells that can arise from this cell. Notice how different they look.

Differences in Function As cells differentiate in structure, a division of labor results. That is, they begin to carry out different functions. For example, plant leaves contain cells that carry out photosynthesis. Root cells, which are underground, do not carry out photosynthesis. So it shouldn't surprise you that some organelles in leaf cells and root cells differ, too. Leaf cells have plenty of chloroplasts for capturing sunlight, while root cells have none. Instead, many root cells have fingerlike projections that reach into the soil. These structures increase the amount of water the root cells can absorb from the soil.

Tissues, Organs, and Systems When cells differentiate, they also become organized. At first, they group into tissues. Such cells work together, carrying out specific functions. For example, muscle cells in animals become organized into long strands of muscle tissue that can move legs or arms. Groups of tissues can combine to form organs, such as the roots of a plant or the stomach of an animal. Systems, such as the digestive system, begin to function as organs and tissues work together.

Increasingly Specialized Cells As development continues, more fine-grained differentiation occurs. For example, the retina in your eye consists of two types of cells that are sensitive to light. Rod cells function in dim light but cannot detect color. Cone cells detect color, but require brighter light to function. The cells of your retina differentiated early in your development. Rods and cones differentiated later.

FIGURE 16
Specialized Cells
Plants have undifferentiated cells in their stems and roots that can give rise to different kinds of cells. *Inferring Can photosynthesis take place in a root cell? Why or why not?*

 Reading Checkpoint **What is the result of cell differentiation?**

How Cells Differentiate

During development, cells become fixed—or set—in how they will differentiate. The instructions that determine what will happen to a cell are coded in the DNA in its nucleus. Differentiation occurs when certain sections of DNA are turned off. The active DNA then guides how the cell develops. **Once a cell's future has been determined, when and how much it changes depends on its DNA, its function, and the type of organism.** Some cells differentiate completely during development. Others do not change until later in the life of an organism.

Cell Differentiation Among Animals Did you know that a lizard that loses its tail can grow a new one? Many adult animals, such as insects and some crustaceans and reptiles, can grow a limb or a tail to replace a lost one. Cells at the point of injury can differentiate, forming new muscle, bone, blood, and nerves.

The replacement of lost body parts in lizards and some other animals does not occur in humans. Once human cells differentiate, they usually lose the ability to become other types of cells. A blood cell cannot change into a skin cell, for instance. However, humans do produce certain cells—called **stem cells**—that can differentiate throughout life. Stem cells exist all around the body. These cells can respond to specific needs in the body by becoming specialized. For example, your body needs a constant supply of new blood cells to replace older cells. Every day, stem cells produce a steady supply of blood cells. These include red cells that carry oxygen, white cells that fight infection, and other cells needed in the blood.

Reading Checkpoint What kind of cells can stem cells produce in the human body?

FIGURE 17

A Source of Blood Cells

Different types of blood cells can form when stem cells undergo differentiation.
Observing *How do the structures of red blood cells and white blood cells differ?*

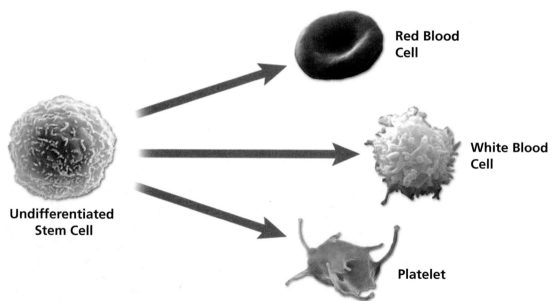

Red Blood Cell

White Blood Cell

Platelet

Undifferentiated Stem Cell

African violet plant

The leaf is cut and transferred to soil.

Cell differentiation leads to new root and leaf tissues.

Cell Differentiation in Plants Cells differentiate in developing plants much the same way they do in animals. Differentiated cells become grouped into the tissues that make up the roots, stems, and leaves. Cells also continue to differentiate further within each kind of organ. For example, some cells in the stem become specialized as the tubes that transport food and water through the plant.

Many plants have the ability to grow throughout their lives. This growth happens because certain cells in the roots and stems of plants are not fixed in their development. These cells can undergo rapid cell division and differentiation, increasing the size of the roots and stems. It can also lead to the growth of new roots, stems, and leaves. For example, if a leaf of an African violet plant is cut off and put into soil or water, its stem will begin to grow roots! Eventually, more cells will differentiate into root cells and stem cells, and a new plant grows. Gardeners use this technique to create many plants from one original plant.

FIGURE 18
A New Plant
The stem of a leaf from an African violet plant gives rise to the structures of a new plant.

Section 4 Assessment

S 7.1.f, E-LA: Reading 7.2.4

Target Reading Skill Create Outlines
Use your completed outline to help answer the questions below.

Reviewing Key Concepts

1. a. **Describing** What happens to cells when they undergo differentiation?
   b. **Explaining** How does differentiation lead to tissues and organs in a developing organism?
   c. **Applying Concepts** How does the phrase *division of labor* relate to differentiation?
2. a. **Identifying** Name two factors that affect how and when cells differentiate.
   b. **Relating Cause and Effect** What stimulates human stem cells to differentiate into specialized blood cells?

c. **Comparing and Contrasting** How does the ability of cells to differentiate in humans compare to the ability in plants?

Lab zone At-Home **Activity**

Model Differences Use a ball of clay to represent a single cell. Divide the "cell" into two smaller ones, and then again into four. Fashion each "cell" into a different shape. Then divide each shape in two, and reshape the new pieces to look like the shape they came from. Explain to a family member how your clay models represent cell differentiation in a developing organism.

The BIG Idea Cells obtain energy through the processes of photosynthesis and respiration, which are carried out by chloroplasts and mitochondria.

① Photosynthesis

Key Concepts   S 7.1.d

- Nearly all living things obtain energy either directly or indirectly from the energy of sunlight captured during photosynthesis.

- During photosynthesis, plants and some other organisms use energy from the sun to convert carbon dioxide and water into oxygen and sugars.

- The equation for photosynthesis is:

$$6\,CO_2 + 6\,H_2O \xrightarrow{\text{light energy}} C_6H_{12}O_6 + 6\,O_2$$

Key Terms

photosynthesis	pigment
autotroph	chlorophyll
heterotroph	stomata

② Respiration

Key Concepts   S 7.1.d

- During respiration, cells break down simple food molecules such as sugar and release the energy they contain.

- The respiration equation is:

$$C_6H_{12}O_6 + 6\,O_2 \longrightarrow 6\,CO_2 + 6\,H_2O + \text{energy}$$

- Fermentation provides energy for cells without using oxygen.

Key Terms

respiration   fermentation

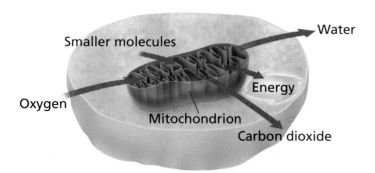

Smaller molecules

Water

Oxygen

Energy

Mitochondrion

Carbon dioxide

③ Cell Division

Key Concepts   S 7.1.e, 7.2.e

- During interphase, the cell grows, makes a copy of its DNA, and prepares to divide into two cells.

- During mitosis, one copy of the DNA is distributed into each of the two daughter cells.

- During cytokinesis, the cytoplasm divides. The organelles are distributed into each of the two new cells.

- Because of the way in which the nitrogen bases pair with one another, the order of the bases in each new DNA molecule exactly matches the order in the original DNA molecule.

Key Terms

cell cycle
interphase
replication
mitosis
chromosome
cytokinesis

④ Cell Differentiation

Key Concepts   S 7.1.f

- As cells differentiate, they become different from one another. They also form groups made of other, similarly specialized cells. These groups then form tissues and organs.

- Once a cell's future has been determined, when and how much it changes depends on the cell's function and the type of organism.

Key Terms

differentiation
stem cell

Review and Assessment

Target Reading Skill

Create Outlines To help review the structure and replication of DNA, fill in details under **A** and **B** in the partially completed outline at right.

> **I. Structure and Replication of DNA**
>   A. Structure of DNA
>
>
>
>   B. Replication of DNA

Reviewing Key Terms

Choose the letter of the best answer.

1. The organelle in which photosynthesis takes place is the
   a. mitochondrion.
   b. chloroplast.
   c. chlorophyll.
   d. nucleus.

2. What process produces carbon dioxide?
   a. photosynthesis
   b. replication
   c. mutation
   d. respiration

3. The process in which a cell makes an exact copy of its DNA is called
   a. fermentation.
   b. respiration.
   c. replication.
   d. reproduction.

4. The stage of the cell cycle when a spindle forms is called
   a. interphase.   b. prophase.
   c. metaphase.   d. anaphase.

5. Which of the following is a result of differentiation?
   a. An organism grows larger.
   b. Cells in an embryo increase in number.
   c. Cells in an embryo become different from one another.
   d. An organism reproduces.

Complete the following sentences so that your answers clearly explain the key terms.

6. Chlorophyll is a type of **pigment,** which is _____ .

7. A lion is a **heterotroph,** a type of organism that _____ .

8. Organisms that live in the mud of swamps obtain their energy through **fermentation,** which is _____ .

9. **Cytokinesis** is the stage of the cell cycle in which _____ .

10. Both red blood cells and white blood cells can be produced in the body by **stem cells** because _____ .

Review and Assessment

Checking Concepts

11. Briefly explain what happens to energy from the sun during photosynthesis.

12. Why do organisms need to carry out the process of respiration?

13. How are respiration and fermentation similar? How are these processes different?

14. Explain why cell division is a vital process for organisms.

15. Describe what happens during interphase.

16. How do the events in the cell cycle ensure that the genetic information in the daughter cells will be identical to that of the parent cell?

17. How are stem cells different from other cells in an adult animal?

Thinking Critically

18. **Predicting** Suppose a volcano threw so much ash into the air that it blocked most of the sunlight that usually strikes Earth. How might this affect the ability of animals to obtain the energy they need to live?

19. **Comparing and Contrasting** Explain the relationship between the processes of breathing and cellular respiration.

20. **Relating Cause and Effect** Do plant cells need to carry out respiration? Explain.

21. **Inferring** The diagram below shows part of one strand of a DNA molecule. What would the bases on the other strand be?

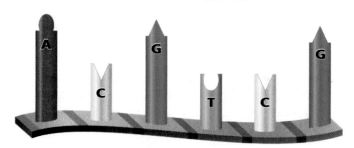

22. **Making Generalizations** Why is cell differentiation a necessary process in a developing multicellular organism?

Applying Skills

Use the table below to answer Questions 23–26.

Percentages of Nitrogen Bases in the DNA of Various Organisms

Nitrogen Base	Human	Wheat	E. coli Bacterium
Adenine	30%	27%	24%
Guanine	20%	23%	26%
Thymine	30%	27%	24%
Cytosine	20%	23%	26%

23. **Graphing** For each organism, draw a bar graph to show the percentages of each nitrogen base in its DNA.

24. **Interpreting Data** What is the relationship between the amounts of adenine and thymine in the DNA of each organism? What is the relationship between the amounts of guanine and cytosine?

25. **Inferring** Based on your answer to Question 24, what can you infer about the structure of DNA in these three organisms?

26. **Applying Concepts** Suppose cytosine made up 28% of the nitrogen bases in an organism. What percentage of the organism's nitrogen bases should be thymine? Explain.

Standards Investigation

Performance Assessment Bring in your plants, recorded observations, and graphs to share with the class. Be prepared to describe your experimental plan and explain your results. How well did you follow your experimental plan? What did you learn about photosynthesis and light from the experiment you performed?

Choose the letter of the best answer.

1. Which of the following statements is true?
   A Plants cannot respire because they have no mitochondria.
   B Photosynthesis produces carbon dioxide.
   C Animals cannot photosynthesize.
   D Only plants photosynthesize and only animals respire. S 7.1.d

2. Which of the following nitrogen base pairs can be found in DNA?
   A A-G   B T-C
   C G-T   D A-T   S 7.2.e

3. Which stage of mitosis is represented by the following cell?

   A interphase
   B anaphase
   C telophase
   D metaphase   S 7.1.e

4. Which of the following statements about differentiated cells is false?
   A They look different but have the same functions.
   B They look different and have different functions.
   C They become grouped with similar cells, forming tissues.
   D They make up the tissues and organs of multicellular organisms. S 7.1.f

5. Which statement best describes chromosomes?
   A They carry out respiration.
   B They consist mostly of the pigment chlorophyll.
   C They consist of tightly coiled strands of DNA and proteins.
   D Their structure is only visible during interphase. S 7.2.e

Use the table below to answer Questions 6 and 7.

Effect of Temperature on Length of Onion Cell Cycle	
Temperature (°C)	Length of Cell Cycle (hours)
10	54.6
15	29.8
20	18.8
25	13.3

6. A scientist performed an experiment to determine the effect of temperature on the length of the cell cycle. On the basis of the data in the table above, how long would the cell cycle last at a temperature of 5°C?
   A less than 13.3 hours
   B more than 54.6 hours
   C between 29.8 and 54.6 hours
   D about 20 hours
                                              S 7.1.e

7. The data in the table above show that
   A cells divide faster when the temperature is decreased.
   B cells divide faster when the temperature is increased.
   C the length of the cell cycle is not affected by temperature.
   D the length of the cell cycle is inherited.
                                              S 7.1.e

Apply the
BIG Idea

8. Compare and contrast the raw materials and products of photosynthesis with those of respiration. Then explain how the two processes are connected. S 7.1.d

Introduction to Life Science
Unit 1 Review

Chapter 1
What Is Life Science?
🔑 The BIG Idea

Scientific progress is made by asking meaningful questions and conducting careful investigations.

🔑 What skills do scientists use to learn about the world?
🔑 What are some big ideas in life science?
🔑 What is scientific inquiry?
🔑 Why is preparation important when carrying out scientific investigations in the lab and in the field?

Chapter 2
Using Light
🔑 The BIG Idea

Light entering the eye is bent by the cornea and lens to form an image on the retina.

🔑 What are the basic properties of waves?
🔑 How does visible light help you see?
🔑 What determines the color of an opaque object?
🔑 What determines the types of images formed by convex and concave lenses?

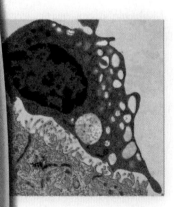

Chapter 3
Cell Structure and Function
🔑 The BIG Idea

Cells are the basic building blocks of all living things. All cells have similar structures and carry out similar functions.

🔑 What is the cell theory?
🔑 What organelles are found in the cytoplasm, and what are their functions?
🔑 How is water important to the function of cells?
🔑 How do most small molecules cross the cell membrane?

Chapter 4
Cell Processes and Energy
🔑 The BIG Idea

Cells obtain energy through the processes of respiration and photosynthesis, which are carried out by mitochondria and chloroplasts.

🔑 What happens during the process of photosynthesis?
🔑 What events take place during the three stages of the cell cycle?
🔑 What factors influence how and when cells differentiate within different organisms?

Unit 1 Assessment

Emily wanted to learn more about cells. She cut a paper-thin leaf from a freshwater plant and used it to prepare a microscope slide. Then she used a cotton swab to get some cells from the inside of her cheek. She used the cheek cells to prepare another slide. Next, she used a chemical to stain the cells so they would be easier to see.

Unfortunately, the slides got mixed up before they could be labeled. Emily used a microscope to see if she could determine which slide held plant cells and which held cheek cells. She observed the structures in cells from each slide and drew diagrams to show what she observed. She noted that the cells on one slide had cell walls, while the cells on the other did not. She observed mitochondria in both samples and chloroplasts in one sample. She also noted that some of the cells with cell walls had chromosomes in their nuclei.

Drawing of
slide A

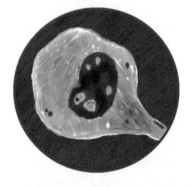

Drawing of
slide B

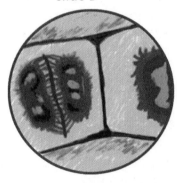

1. **Which is an example of a scientific model?** *(Chapter 1)*
   a. microscope slides
   b. the microscope
   c. diagrams of cells
   d. mitochondria

2. **What forms the enlarged images produced by a microscope?** *(Chapter 2)*
   a. lenses
   b. the pupil of the eye
   c. mirrors
   d. slides

3. **Which of the following would be found in plant cells but not in cheek cells?** *(Chapter 3)*
   a. cell walls   b. chromosomes
   c. mitochondria   d. nuclei

4. **Where in plant cells does photosynthesis occur?** *(Chapter 4)*
   a. cell wall   b. chloroplasts
   c. mitochondria   d. nuclei

5. **Summary** Does the Slide A drawing represent plant or cheek cells? How do you know? What process do Emily's observations of chromosomes provide evidence for? Explain why chromosomes were not visible in all the cells on that slide.

Genetics: The Science of Heredity

These puppies and their mother ▶ resemble each other in many ways.

Focus on the
BIG Idea

S 7.2

How are traits passed from parents to offspring?

Check What You Know

In a litter of puppies, some of the puppies have a black and white coat, and others have a red and white coat. What can you infer about how their parents look? What can you infer about the parents' DNA?

Build Science Vocabulary

The images shown here represent some of the Key Terms in this chapter. You can use this vocabulary skill to help you understand the meaning of some Key Terms in this Chapter.

Use Suffixes

A suffix is a word part that is added to the end of a word to change its meaning. For example, the suffix *-tion* means "process of." If you add the suffix *-tion* to the verb *produce*, you get the noun *production*. *Production* means "the process of making."

The table below lists some common suffixes and their meanings.

Suffix	Meaning of Suffix	Example and Meaning of Example
-ance, -ence	state of; quality of	**importance** State of being important
-ant, -ent	inclined to; likely to	**dependent** Likely to rely on something or someone else
-ity	state of; quality of	**simplicity** State of being simple or easy
-tion	process of; state of	**production** Process of making

Apply It!

1. What is the suffix in the word *dominant?* If the verb *dominate* means "to have control over," what do you think *dominant* means? What does *dominance* probably mean?

2. The word *probable* means "likely to happen." What does *probability* mean?

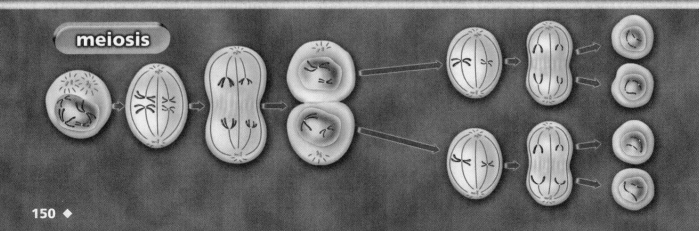

meiosis

mutation

BB

B   B

bb   Bb   Bb

b

b   Bb   Bb

Punnett square

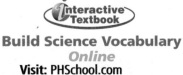

fertilization

Chapter 5
Vocabulary

interactive Textbook

Build Science Vocabulary
Online
Visit: PHSchool.com
Web Code: cvj-2050

How to Read Science

Take Notes

When you take notes, you write the important ideas in the textbook in shortened form.

- Use a red or blue heading as the title of your notes.
- In the left column, write questions about the text that follows the heading.
- Write the answers in the right column.
- Write a summary statement that expresses the main idea.

See the sample notes below, which are notes on part of Section 3.

Questions	Notes: Chromosomes and Inheritance
Where did Sutton find evidence that chromosomes were important in inheritance?	In grasshopper cells—body cells have 24 chromosomes, sex cells only 12.
What happens to chromosomes after fertilization?	Chromosomes form pairs. One chromosome in each pair comes from each parent.
Where are genes?	On chromosomes
	<u>Summary Statement:</u> The chromosome theory of inheritance says that parents pass genes to their offspring on chromosomes.

Apply It!

Review the notes in the right column.

1. What is one important idea found in the notes?
2. What question in the left column helps you recall the idea?

Finish these notes as you read Section 3. Also take notes on all of Section 4.

S 7.2.b

All in the Family

Did you ever wonder why some offspring resemble their parents while others do not? In this chapter, you'll learn how offspring come to have traits similar to those of their parents. You'll create a family of "paper pets" to explore how traits pass from parents to offspring.

Your Goal

To create a "paper pet" that will be crossed with a classmate's pet, and to determine what traits the offspring will have

To complete this investigation successfully, you must

- create your own unique paper pet with five different traits
- cross your pet with another pet to produce six offspring
- determine what traits the offspring will have, and explain how they came to have those traits
- follow the safety guidelines in Appendix A

Plan It!

Cut out your pet from either blue or yellow construction paper. Choose other traits for your pet from this list:

- square eyes or round eyes
- oval nose or triangular nose
- pointed teeth or square teeth

Then create your pet using materials of your choice.

Mendel's Work

S 7.2.d Students know plant and animal cells contain many thousands of different genes and typically have two copies of every gene. The two copies (or alleles) of the gene may or may not be identical, and one may be dominant in determining the phenotype while the other is recessive.

 What were the results of Mendel's experiments, or crosses?

 What controls the inheritance of traits in organisms?

Key Terms

- heredity
- trait
- genetics
- fertilization
- purebred
- gene
- alleles
- dominant allele
- recessive allele
- hybrid

Lab zone **Standards Warm-Up**

What Does the Father Look Like?

1. Observe the colors of the kitten in the photo. Record the kitten's coat colors and pattern. Include as many details as you can.

2. Observe the mother cat in the photo. Record her coat color and pattern.

Think It Over

Inferring Based on your observations, describe what you think the kitten's father might look like. Identify the evidence on which you based your inference.

In the mid-nineteenth century, a priest named Gregor Mendel tended a garden in a central European monastery. Mendel's experiments in that peaceful garden would one day revolutionize the study of heredity. **Heredity** is the passing of physical characteristics from parents to offspring.

Mendel wondered why different pea plants had different characteristics. Some pea plants grew tall, while others were short. Some plants produced green seeds, while others had yellow seeds. Each different form of a characteristic, such as stem height or seed color, is called a **trait.** Mendel observed that the pea plants' traits were often similar to those of their parents. Sometimes, however, the plants had different traits from those of their parents.

Mendel experimented with thousands of pea plants to understand the process of heredity. Today, Mendel's discoveries form the foundation of **genetics,** the scientific study of heredity.

Gregor ▶ Mendel

Mendel's Experiments

Figure 1 shows a pea plant's flower. The flower's petals surround the pistil and the stamens. The pistil produces female sex cells, or eggs. The stamens produce pollen, which contains the male sex cells, or sperm. A new organism begins to form when egg and sperm join in the process called **fertilization.** Before fertilization can happen in pea plants, pollen must reach the pistil of a pea flower. This process is called pollination.

Pea plants are usually self-pollinating. In self-pollination, pollen from a flower lands on the pistil of the same flower. Mendel developed a method by which he cross-pollinated, or "crossed," pea plants. To cross two plants, he removed pollen from a flower on one plant. He then brushed the pollen onto a flower on a second plant.

Crossing Pea Plants What could you do to study the inheritance of traits in pea plants? Mendel decided to cross plants with contrasting traits—for example, tall plants and short plants. He started his experiments with true-breeding, or purebred plants. A **purebred** organism is the offspring of many generations that have the same trait. For example, purebred short pea plants always come from short parent plants.

FIGURE 1
Crossing Pea Plants
Gregor Mendel crossed pea plants that had different traits. The illustrations show how he did this. **Interpreting Diagrams** *How did Mendel prevent self-pollination?*

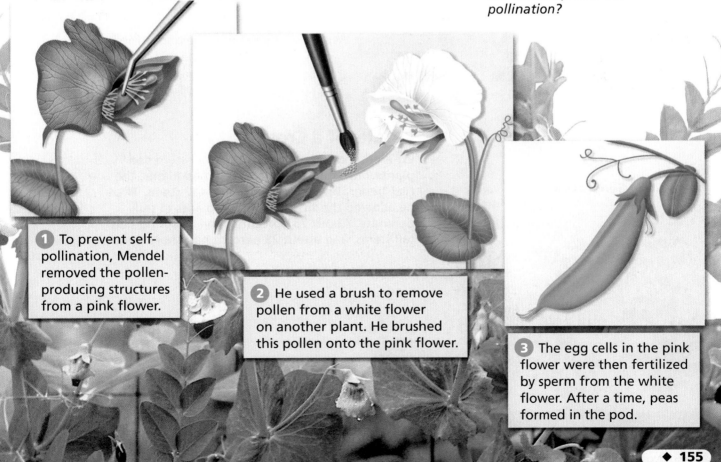

1 To prevent self-pollination, Mendel removed the pollen-producing structures from a pink flower.

2 He used a brush to remove pollen from a white flower on another plant. He brushed this pollen onto the pink flower.

3 The egg cells in the pink flower were then fertilized by sperm from the white flower. After a time, peas formed in the pod.

◆ 155

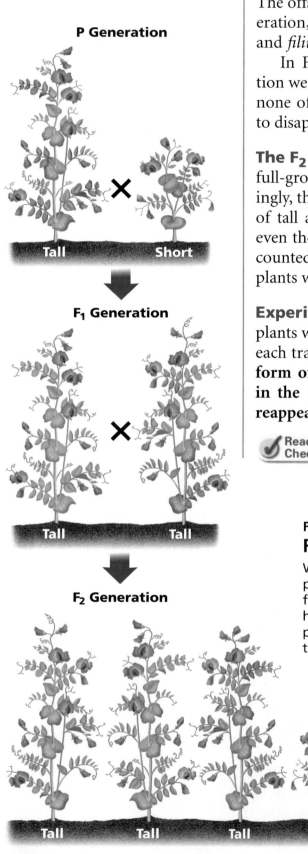

P Generation

Tall   Short

F₁ Generation

Tall   Tall

F₂ Generation

Tall   Tall   Tall   Short

The F₁ Offspring In one experiment, Mendel crossed pure-bred tall plants with purebred short plants. Scientists today call these parent plants the parental generation, or P generation. The offspring from this cross are the first filial (FIL ee ul) generation, or the F₁ generation. The word *filial* comes from *filia* and *filius*, the Latin words for "daughter" and "son."

In Figure 2, notice that all the offspring in the F₁ generation were tall. Even though one of the parent plants was short, none of the offspring were short. The shortness trait seemed to disappear!

The F₂ Offspring When the plants in the F₁ generation were full-grown, Mendel allowed them to self-pollinate. Surprisingly, the plants in the F₂ (second filial) generation were a mix of tall and short plants. The shortness trait had reappeared, even though none of the F₁ parent plants were short. Mendel counted the tall and short plants. About three fourths of the plants were tall, while one fourth were short.

Experiments With Other Traits Mendel also crossed pea plants with other contrasting traits. Compare the two forms of each trait in Figure 3. **In all of Mendel's crosses, only one form of the trait appeared in the F₁ generation. However, in the F₂ generation, the "lost" form of the trait always reappeared in about one fourth of the plants.**

> **Reading Checkpoint**   What did Mendel observe about the F₂ plants?

FIGURE 2
Results of a Cross
When Mendel crossed purebred tall-stemmed plants with purebred short-stemmed plants, the first-generation offspring all had tall stems. Then he allowed the first-generation plants to self-pollinate. About 75 percent of the offspring had tall stems, and about 25 percent had short stems.

Genetics of Pea Plants							
Traits	Seed Shape	Seed Color	Seed Coat Color	Pod Shape	Pod Color	Flower Position	Stem Height
Controlled by Dominant Allele	Round	Yellow	Gray	Smooth	Green	Side	Tall
Controlled by Recessive Allele	Wrinkled	Green	White	Pinched	Yellow	End	Short

Dominant and Recessive Alleles

Mendel reached several conclusions on the basis of his experimental results. He reasoned that individual factors, or sets of genetic "information," must control the inheritance of traits in peas. The factors that control each trait exist in pairs. The female parent contributes one factor, while the male parent contributes the other factor. Finally, one factor in a pair can mask, or hide, the other factor. The tallness factor, for example, masked the shortness factor.

Genes and Alleles Today, scientists use the word **gene** for the factors that control a trait. **Alleles** (uh LEELZ) are the different forms of a gene. The gene that controls stem height in peas, for example, has one allele for tall stems and one allele for short stems. Each pea plant inherits two alleles from its parents—one allele from the egg and the other from the sperm. A pea plant may inherit two alleles for tall stems, two alleles for short stems, or one of each.

🔑 An organism's traits are determined by the alleles it inherits from its parents. Some alleles are dominant, while other alleles are recessive. A **dominant allele** is one whose trait always shows up in the organism when the allele is present. A **recessive allele,** on the other hand, is hidden whenever the dominant allele is present. A trait controlled by a recessive allele will only show up if the organism does not have the dominant allele. Figure 3 shows dominant and recessive alleles in Mendel's crosses.

FIGURE 3
Mendel studied several traits in pea plants.
Interpreting Diagrams *Is yellow seed color controlled by a dominant allele or a recessive allele?*

Lab zone Skills Activity

Predicting

In fruit flies, long wings are dominant over short wings. A scientist crossed a purebred long-winged male fruit fly with a purebred short-winged female. Predict the wing length of the F_1 offspring. If the scientist crossed a hybrid male F_1 fruit fly with a hybrid F_1 female, what would their offspring probably be like?

In pea plants, the allele for tall stems is dominant over the allele for short stems. Pea plants with one allele for tall stems and one allele for short stems will be tall. The allele for tall stems masks the allele for short stems. Only pea plants that inherit two recessive alleles for short stems will be short.

Alleles in Mendel's Crosses In Mendel's cross for stem height, the purebred tall plants in the P generation had two alleles for tall stems. The purebred short plants had two alleles for short stems. The F_1 plants each inherited an allele for tall stems from the tall parent and an allele for short stems from the short parent. Therefore, each F_1 plant had one allele for tall stems and one for short stems. The F_1 plants are called hybrids. A **hybrid** (HY brid) organism has two different alleles for a trait. All the F_1 plants are tall because the dominant allele for tall stems masks the recessive allele for short stems.

When Mendel crossed the F_1 plants, some of the offspring in the F_2 generation inherited two dominant alleles for tall stems. These plants were tall. Other F_2 plants inherited one dominant allele for tall stems and one recessive allele for short stems. These plants were also tall. The rest of the F_2 plants inherited two recessive alleles for short stems. These plants were short.

Symbols for Alleles Geneticists use letters to represent alleles. A dominant allele is represented by a capital letter. For example, the allele for tall stems is represented by T. A recessive allele is represented by the lowercase version of the letter. So, the allele for short stems would be represented by t. When a plant inherits two dominant alleles for tall stems, its alleles are written as TT. When a plant inherits two recessive alleles for short stems, its alleles are written as tt. When a plant inherits one allele for tall stems and one allele for short stems, its alleles are written as Tt.

FIGURE 4
Black Fur, White Fur
In rabbits, the allele for black fur is dominant over the allele for white fur. **Inferring** *What combination of alleles must the white rabbit have?*

Significance of Mendel's Contribution Mendel's work eventually changed scientists' ideas about heredity. Before Mendel, most people thought that genetic information could be blended to produce new traits. They thought that traits could be blended to form a combined version, the same way red and white paint can be mixed to make pink paint. According to this incorrect model, if a tall plant and a short plant were crossed, the offspring would all have medium height.

However, when Mendel crossed purebred tall and purebred short pea plants, the offspring were all tall. Mendel's experiments demonstrated that parents' traits do not simply blend in the offspring. Instead, traits are determined by individual, separate alleles inherited from each parent. Some of these alleles are recessive. If a trait is determined by a recessive allele, the trait can seem to disappear in the offspring.

Unfortunately, the importance of Mendel's discovery was not recognized during his lifetime. Then, in 1900, three different scientists rediscovered Mendel's work. These scientists quickly recognized the importance of Mendel's ideas. Because of his work, Mendel is often called the Father of Genetics.

 **Reading Checkpoint** If an allele is represented by a capital letter, what does this indicate?

FIGURE 5
The Mendel Medal
Every year, to honor the memory of Gregor Mendel, an outstanding scientist is awarded the Mendel Medal.

Section 1 Assessment

S 7.2.d, E-LA: Reading 7.1.2

Vocabulary Skill Suffixes In the key term *fertilization*, what does the suffix *-tion* mean?

Reviewing Key Concepts

1. a. **Identifying** In Mendel's cross for stem height, what contrasting traits did the pea plants in the P generation exhibit?
   b. **Explaining** What trait or traits did the plants in the F_1 generation exhibit? When you think of the traits of the parent plants, why is this result surprising?
   c. **Comparing and Contrasting** Contrast the offspring in the F_1 generation to the offspring in the F_2 generation. What did the differences in the F_1 and F_2 offspring show Mendel?

2. a. **Defining** What is a dominant allele? What is a recessive allele?

   b. **Relating Cause and Effect** Explain how dominant and recessive alleles for the trait of stem height determine whether a pea plant will be tall or short.
   c. **Applying Concepts** Can a short pea plant ever be a hybrid for the trait of stem height? Why or why not? As part of your explanation, write the letters that represent the alleles for stem height of a short pea plant.

Lab zone At-Home Activity

Gardens and Heredity Some gardeners save the seeds produced by flowers and plant them in the spring. If there are gardeners in your family, ask them how closely the plants that grow from these seeds resemble the parent plants. Are the offspring's traits ever different from those of the parents?

Lab zone — Skills Lab

Take a Class Survey

S 7.2.d

Problem

Are traits controlled by dominant alleles more common than traits controlled by recessive alleles?

Skills Focus

developing hypotheses, interpreting data

Materials

• mirror (optional)

Procedure

PART 1 Dominant and Recessive Alleles

1. Write a hypothesis reflecting your ideas about the problem. Then copy the data table.

2. For each of the traits listed in the data table, work with a partner to determine which trait you have. Circle that trait in your data table.

3. Count the number of students in your class who have each trait. Record that number in your data table. Also record the total number of students.

PART 2 Are Your Traits Unique?

4. Look at the circle of traits on the opposite page. All the traits in your data table appear in the circle. Place the eraser end of your pencil on the trait in the small central circle that applies to you—either free ear lobes or attached ear lobes.

5. Look at the two traits touching the space your eraser is on. Move your eraser onto the next description that applies to you. Continue using your eraser to trace your traits until you reach a number on the outside rim of the circle. Share that number with your classmates.

Analyze and Conclude

1. **Observing** The traits listed under Trait 1 in the data table are controlled by dominant alleles. The traits listed under Trait 2 are controlled by recessive alleles. Which traits controlled by dominant alleles were shown by a majority of students? Which traits controlled by recessive alleles were shown by a majority of students?

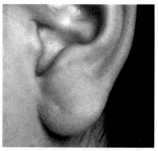
Free ear lobe

Widow's peak

Cleft chin

Dimple

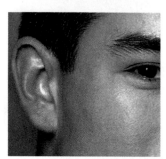
Attached ear lobe

No widow's peak

No cleft chin

No dimple

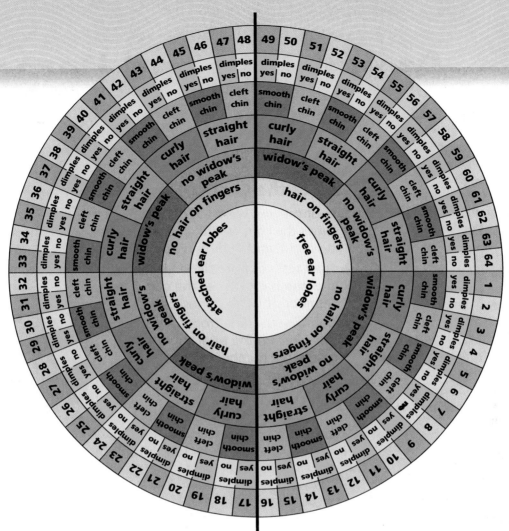

2. **Interpreting Data** How many students ended up on the same number on the circle of traits? How many students were the only ones to have their number? What do the results suggest about each person's combination of traits?

3. **Developing Hypotheses** Do your data support the hypothesis you proposed in Step 1? Write an answer with examples.

4. **Communicating** Based on your observation of traits in this lab, write a paragraph explaining why people look so different from one another.

Design an Experiment

Do people who are related to each other show more genetic similarity than unrelated people? Write a hypothesis. Then design an experiment to test your hypothesis. *Obtain your teacher's permission before carrying out your investigation.*

Data Table				
Total Number of Students_____				
	Trait 1	Number	Trait 2	Number
A	Free ear lobes		Attached ear lobes	
B	Hair on fingers		No hair on fingers	
C	Widow's peak		No widow's peak	
D	Curly hair		Straight hair	
E	Cleft chin		Smooth chin	
F	Smile dimples		No smile dimples	

Probability and Heredity

CALIFORNIA
Standards Focus

S 7.2.d Students know plant and animal cells contain many thousands of different genes and typically have two copies of every gene. The two copies (or alleles) of the gene may or may not be identical, and one may be dominant in determining the phenotype while the other is recessive.

- What is probability and how does it help explain the results of genetic crosses?
- What is meant by genotype and phenotype?
- What is codominance?

Key Terms

- probability
- Punnett square
- phenotype
- genotype
- homozygous
- heterozygous
- codominance

Lab zone Standards **Warm-Up**

What's the Chance?

1. Suppose you were to toss a coin 20 times. Predict how many times the coin would land with heads up and how many times it would land with tails up.

2. Now test your prediction by tossing a coin 20 times. Record the number of times the coin lands with heads up and the number of times it lands with tails up.

3. Combine the data from the entire class. Record the total number of tosses, the number of heads, and the number of tails.

Think It Over

Predicting How did your results in Step 2 compare to your prediction? How can you account for any differences between your results and the class results?

Go Online

SC LINKS NSTA

For: Links on probability and genetics
Visit: www.SciLinks.org
Web Code: scn-0332

On a brisk fall afternoon, the stands are packed with cheering football fans. Today is the big game between North Shore and South Shore high schools, and it's almost time for the kickoff. Suddenly, the crowd becomes silent, as the referee is about to toss a coin. The outcome of the coin toss will decide which team kicks the ball and which receives it. The captain of the visiting North Shore team says "heads." If the coin lands with heads up, North Shore High wins the toss and the right to decide whether to kick or receive the ball.

What is the chance that North Shore High will win the coin toss? To answer this question, you need to understand the principles of probability.

Principles of Probability

If you did the Standards Warm-Up activity, you used the principles of **probability** to predict the results of a particular event. In this case, the event was the toss of a coin. **Probability is a number that describes how likely it is that a certain event will occur.**

Mathematics of Probability Each time you toss a coin, there are two possible ways that the coin can land—heads up or tails up. Each of these two events is equally likely to occur. In mathematical terms, you can say that the probability that a tossed coin will land with heads up is 1 in 2. There is also a 1 in 2 probability that the coin will land with tails up. A 1 in 2 probability can also be expressed as the fraction $\frac{1}{2}$ or as a percent—50 percent.

The laws of probability predict what is likely to occur, not necessarily what will occur. If you tossed a coin 20 times, you might expect it to land with heads up 10 times and with tails up 10 times. However, you might not get these results. You might get 11 heads and 9 tails, or 8 heads and 12 tails. The more tosses you make, the closer your actual results will be to the results predicted by probability.

Independence of Events When you toss a coin more than once, the results of one toss do not affect the results of the next toss. Each event occurs independently. For example, suppose you toss a coin five times and it lands with heads up each time. What is the probability that it will land with heads up on the next toss? Because the coin landed heads up on the previous five tosses, you might think that it would be likely to land heads up on the next toss. However, this is not the case. The probability of the coin landing heads up on the next toss is still 1 in 2, or 50 percent. The results of the first five tosses do not affect the result of the sixth toss.

 **What is probability?**

Percentage

One way you can express a probability is as a percentage. A percentage (%) is a number compared to 100. For example, 50% means 50 out of 100.

Suppose that 3 out of 5 tossed coins landed with heads up. Here's how you can calculate what percent of the coins landed with heads up.

1. Write the comparison as a fraction.

$$3 \text{ out of } 5 = \frac{3}{5}$$

2. Multiply the fraction by 100% to express it as a percentage.

$$\frac{3}{5} \times \frac{100\%}{1} = 60\%$$

Practice Problem Suppose 3 out of 12 coins landed with tails up. How can you express this as a percent?

FIGURE 6
A Coin Toss
The result of a coin toss can be explained by probability.

◆ **163**

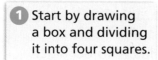

1 Start by drawing a box and dividing it into four squares.

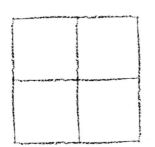

2 Write the male parent's alleles along the top of the square and the female parent's alleles along the left side.

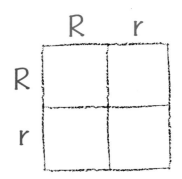

FIGURE 7

How to Make a Punnett Square

The diagrams show how to make a Punnett square. In this cross, both parents are heterozygous for the trait of seed shape. *R* represents the dominant round allele, and *r* represents the recessive wrinkled allele.

Coin Crosses

Here's how you can use coins to model Mendel's cross between two *Tt* pea plants.

1. Place a small piece of masking tape on each side of two coins.

2. Write a *T* (for tall) on one side of each coin and a *t* (for short) on the other.

3. Toss both coins together 20 times. Record the letter combinations that you obtain from each toss.

Interpreting Data How many of the offspring would be tall plants? (*Hint:* What different letter combinations would result in a tall plant?) How many would be short? Convert your results to percentages. Then compare your results to Mendel's.

Probability and Genetics

How is probability related to genetics? To answer this question, think back to Mendel's experiments with peas. Remember that Mendel carefully counted the offspring from every cross that he carried out. When Mendel crossed two plants that were hybrid for stem height (Tt), three fourths of the F_1 plants had tall stems. One fourth of the plants had short stems.

Each time Mendel repeated the cross, he obtained similar results. Mendel realized that the mathematical principles of probability applied to his work. He could say that the probability of such a cross producing a tall plant was 3 in 4. The probability of producing a short plant was 1 in 4. Mendel was the first scientist to recognize that the principles of probability can be used to predict the results of genetic crosses.

Punnett Squares A tool that can help you understand how the laws of probability apply to genetics is called a Punnett square. A **Punnett square** is a chart that shows all the possible combinations of alleles that can result from a genetic cross. Geneticists use Punnett squares to show all the possible outcomes of a genetic cross, and to determine the probability of a particular outcome.

Figure 7 shows how to construct a Punnett square. In this case, the Punnett square shows a cross between two hybrid pea plants with round seeds (Rr). The allele for round seeds (R) is dominant over the allele for wrinkled seeds (r). Each parent can pass either of its alleles, R or r, to its offspring. The boxes in the Punnett square represent the possible combinations of alleles that the offspring can inherit.

 **Reading Checkpoint** What is a Punnett square?

3 Copy the female parent's alleles into the boxes to their right.

4 Copy the male parent's alleles into the boxes beneath them.

5 The completed Punnett square shows all the possible allele combinations in the offspring.

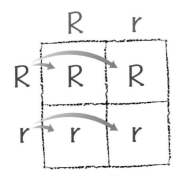

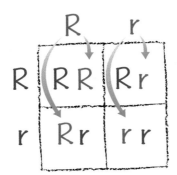

	R	r
R	RR	Rr
r	Rr	rr

Using a Punnett Square You can use a Punnett square to calculate the probability that offspring with a certain combination of alleles will result. 🔑 **In a genetic cross, the allele that each parent will pass on to its offspring is based on probability.** The completed Punnett square in Figure 7 shows four possible combinations of alleles. The probability that an offspring will be *RR* is 1 in 4, or 25 percent. The probability that an offspring will be *rr* is also 1 in 4, or 25 percent. Notice, however, that the *Rr* allele combination appears in two boxes in the Punnett square. This is because there are two possible ways in which this combination can occur. So the probability that an offspring will be *Rr* is 2 in 4, or 50 percent.

When Mendel crossed hybrid plants with round seeds, he discovered that about three fourths of the plants (75 percent) had round seeds. The remaining one fourth of the plants (25 percent) produced wrinkled seeds. Plants with the *RR* allele combination would produce round seeds. So too would those plants with the *Rr* allele combination. Remember that the dominant allele masks the recessive allele. Only those plants with the *rr* allele combination would have wrinkled seeds.

Predicting Probabilities You can use a Punnett square to predict probabilities. For example, Figure 8 shows a cross between a purebred black guinea pig and a purebred white guinea pig. The allele for black fur is dominant over the allele for white fur. Notice that only one allele combination is possible in the offspring—*Bb*. All of the offspring will inherit the dominant allele for black fur. Because of this, all of the offspring will have black fur. There is a 100 percent probability that the offspring will have black fur.

FIGURE 8
Guinea Pig Punnett Square
This Punnett square shows a cross between a black guinea pig (*BB*) and a white guinea pig (*bb*).
Calculating *What is the probability that an offspring will have white fur?*

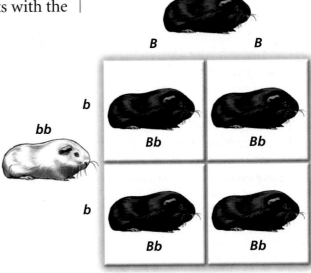

Math Analyzing Data

What Are the Genotypes?

Mendel allowed several F₁ pea plants with yellow seeds to self-pollinate. The graph shows the approximate numbers of the F₂ offspring with yellow seeds and with green seeds.

1. **Reading Graphs** How many F₂ offspring had yellow seeds? How many had green seeds?

2. **Calculating** Use the information in the graph to calculate the total number of offspring that resulted from this cross. Then calculate the percentage of the offspring with yellow peas, and the percentage with green peas.

3. **Inferring** Use the answers to Question 2 to infer the probable genotypes of the parent plants. (*Hint:* Construct Punnett squares with the possible genotypes of the parents.)

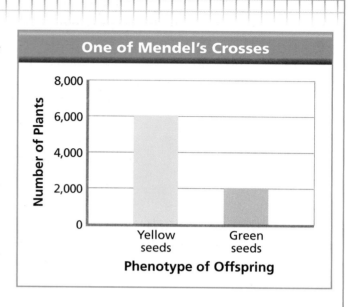

One of Mendel's Crosses

Number of Plants / Phenotype of Offspring

Phenotypes and Genotypes

Two terms that geneticists use are **phenotype** (FEE noh typ) and **genotype** (JEN uh typ). **An organism's phenotype is its physical appearance, or visible traits. An organism's genotype is its genetic makeup, or allele combinations.**

To understand the difference between phenotype and genotype, look at Figure 9. The allele for smooth pea pods (S) is dominant over the allele for pinched pea pods (s). All of the plants with at least one dominant allele have the same phenotype—they all produce smooth pods. However, the plants can have two different genotypes—SS or Ss. If you were to look at the plants with smooth pods, you would not be able to tell the difference between those with the SS genotype and those with the Ss genotype. The plants with pinched pods, on the other hand, would all have the same phenotype—pinched pods—as well as the same genotype—ss.

Geneticists use two additional terms to describe genotypes. An organism that has two identical alleles for a trait is said to be **homozygous** (hoh moh ZY gus) for that trait. A smooth-pod plant that has the alleles SS and a pinched-pod plant with the alleles ss are both homozygous. An organism that has two different alleles for a trait is **heterozygous** (het ur oh ZY gus). A smooth-pod plant with the alleles Ss is heterozygous. Mendel used the term *hybrid* to describe heterozygous pea plants.

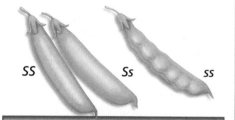

Phenotypes and Genotypes	
Phenotype	**Genotype**
Smooth pods	SS
Smooth pods	Ss
Pinched pods	ss

FIGURE 9
The phenotype of an organism is its physical appearance. Its genotype is its genetic makeup. **Interpreting Tables** *How many genotypes are there for the smooth-pod phenotype?*

Codominance

For all of the traits that Mendel studied, one allele was dominant while the other was recessive. This is not always the case. For some alleles, an inheritance pattern called **codominance** exists. ⊙ **In codominance, the alleles are neither dominant nor recessive. As a result, both alleles are expressed in the offspring.**

Look at Figure 10. Mendel's principle of dominant and recessive alleles does not explain why the heterozygous chickens have both black and white feathers. The alleles for feather color are codominant—neither dominant nor recessive. As you can see, neither allele is masked in the heterozygous chickens. Notice also that the codominant alleles are written as capital letters with superscripts—F^B for black feathers and F^W for white feathers. As the Punnett square shows, heterozygous chickens have the $F^B F^W$ allele combination.

 **Reading Checkpoint** How are the symbols for codominant alleles written?

FIGURE 10
Codominance
The offspring of the cross in this Punnett square will have both black and white feathers. **Classifying** *Will the offspring be heterozygous or homozygous? Explain your answer.*

Section 2 Assessment

S 7.2.d, E-LA: Reading 7.1.2

Vocabulary Skill **Suffixes** Use the meanings of the suffixes *-ant* and *-ance* to contrast the meanings of *codominant* and *codominance*.

⊙ **Reviewing Key Concepts**

1. **a. Reviewing** What is probability?
   b. Explaining If you know the parents' alleles for a trait, how can you use a Punnett square to predict the probable genotypes of the offspring?
   c. Predicting A pea plant with round seeds has the genotype *Rr*. You cross this plant with a wrinkled-seed plant, genotype *rr*. What is the probability that the offspring will have wrinkled seeds? (Use a Punnett square.)

2. **a. Defining** Define *genotype* and *phenotype*.
   b. Relating Cause and Effect Explain how two organisms can have the same phenotype but different genotypes. Give an example.
   c. Applying Concepts A pea plant has a tall stem. What are its possible genotypes?

3. **a. Explaining** What is codominance? Give an example of codominant alleles and explain why they are codominant.
   b. Applying Concepts What is the phenotype of a chicken with the genotype $F^B F^W$?

Math Practice

4. **Ratios** A scientist crossed a tall pea plant with a short pea plant. Of the offspring, 13 were tall and 12 were short. Write the ratio of each phenotype to the total number of offspring. Express the ratios as fractions.

5. **Percentage** Use the fractions to calculate the percentage of the offspring that were tall and the percentage that were short.

Make the Right Call!  S 7.2.d

Problem

How can you predict the possible results of genetic crosses?

Skills Focus

making models, interpreting data

Materials

• 2 small paper bags   • marking pen
• 3 blue marbles   • 3 white marbles

Procedure

1. Label one bag "Bag 1, Female Parent." Label the other bag "Bag 2, Male Parent." Then read over Part 1, Part 2, and Part 3 of this lab. Write a prediction about the kinds of offspring you expect from each cross.

PART 1   Crossing Two Homozygous Parents

2. Copy the data table and label it *Data Table 1*. Then place two blue marbles in Bag 1. This pair of marbles represents the female parent's alleles. Use the letter *B* to represent the dominant allele for blue color.

3. Place two white marbles in Bag 2. Use the letter *b* to represent the recessive allele for white color.

4. For Trial 1, remove one marble from Bag 1 without looking in the bag. Record the result in your data table. Return the marble to the bag. Again, without looking in the bag, remove one marble from Bag 2. Record the result in your data table. Return the marble to the bag.

5. In the column labeled Offspring's Alleles, write *BB* if you removed two blue marbles, *bb* if you removed two white marbles, or *Bb* if you removed one blue marble and one white marble.

6. Repeat Steps 4 and 5 nine more times.

PART 2   Crossing Homozygous and Heterozygous Parents

7. Place two blue marbles in Bag 1. Place one white marble and one blue marble in Bag 2. Copy the data table again, and label it *Data Table 2*.

8. Repeat Steps 4 and 5 ten times.

Data Table			
Number _____			
Trial	Allele From Bag 1 (Female Parent)	Allele From Bag 2 (Male Parent)	Offspring's Alleles
1			
2			
3			
4			
5			
6			

PART 3 Crossing Two Heterozygous Parents

9. Place one blue marble and one white marble in Bag 1. Place one blue marble and one white marble in Bag 2. Copy the data table again and label it *Data Table 3*.

10. Repeat Steps 4 and 5 ten times.

Analyze and Conclude

1. **Making Models** Make a Punnett square for each of the crosses you modeled in Part 1, Part 2, and Part 3.

2. **Interpreting Data** According to your results in Part 1, how many different kinds of offspring are possible when the homozygous parents (*BB* and *bb*) are crossed? Do the results you obtained using the marble model agree with the results shown by a Punnett square?

3. **Predicting** According to your results in Part 2, what percentage of offspring are likely to be homozygous when a homozygous parent (*BB*) and a heterozygous parent (*Bb*) are crossed? What percentage of offspring are likely to be heterozygous? Does the model agree with the results shown by a Punnett square?

4. **Making Models** According to your results in Part 3, what different kinds of offspring are possible when two heterozygous parents (*Bb* × *Bb*) are crossed? What percentage of each type of offspring are likely to be produced? Does the model agree with the results of a Punnett square?

5. **Inferring** For Part 3, if you did 100 trials instead of 10 trials, would your results be closer to the results shown in a Punnett square? Explain.

6. **Communicating** In a paragraph, explain how the marble model compares with a Punnett square. How are the two methods alike? How are they different?

More to Explore

In peas, the allele for yellow seeds (*Y*) is dominant over the allele for green seeds (*y*). What possible crosses do you think could produce a heterozygous plant with yellow seeds (*Yy*)? Use the marble model and Punnett squares to test your predictions.

The Cell and Inheritance

CALIFORNIA
Standards Focus

S 7.2.b Students know sexual reproduction produces offspring that inherit half their genes from each parent.

- What role do chromosomes play in inheritance?
- What events occur during meiosis?
- What is the relationship between chromosomes and genes?

Key Term

- sexual reproduction
- diploid
- meiosis

Which Chromosome Is Which?

Mendel did not know about chromosomes or their role in genetics. Today we know that genes are located on chromosomes.

1. Label two craft sticks with the letter *A*. The craft sticks represent a pair of chromosomes in the female parent. Turn the sticks face down on a piece of paper.
2. Label two more craft sticks with the letter *a*. These represent a pair of chromosomes in the male parent. Turn the sticks face down on another piece of paper.
3. Turn over one craft stick "chromosome" from each piece of paper. Move both sticks to a third piece of paper. These represent a pair of chromosomes in the offspring. Note the allele combination that the offspring received.

Think It Over
Making Models Use this model to explain how chromosomes are involved in the inheritance of alleles.

Mendel's work showed that genes exist. But scientists in the early twentieth century did not know what structures in cells contained genes. The search for the answer to this puzzle is something like a mystery story. The story could be called "The Clue in the Grasshopper's Cells."

In 1903, Walter Sutton, an American geneticist, was studying the cells of grasshoppers. He wanted to understand how sex cells (sperm and egg) form. Sutton focused on the movement of chromosomes during the formation of sex cells. Sex cells form during sexual reproduction. In **sexual reproduction,** genetic material from two parents combines to produce a new organism, which differs from both parents. Sutton hypothesized that chromosomes were the key to understanding how offspring have traits similar to those of their parents.

FIGURE 11
Sex Cells
The large egg is a female sex cell, and the smaller sperm is a male sex cell.

Sperm ▼

Egg ▶

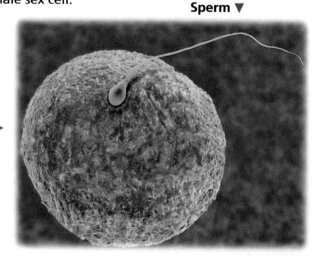

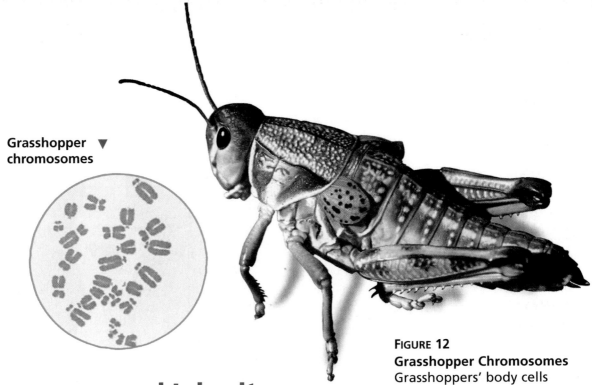

Grasshopper ▼
chromosomes

FIGURE 12
Grasshopper Chromosomes
Grasshoppers' body cells
have twice the number of
chromosomes as their sex cells.
Applying Concepts *What is the
function of chromosomes?*

Chromosomes and Inheritance

Sutton needed evidence to support his hypothesis that chromosomes were important in the inheritance of traits. He found that evidence in grasshoppers' cells. The body cells of a grasshopper have 24 chromosomes. To his surprise, Sutton found that the grasshopper's sex cells have only 12 chromosomes. In other words, a grasshopper's sex cells have exactly half the number of chromosomes found in its body cells.

Chromosome Pairs Sutton observed what happened when a sperm cell and an egg cell joined during fertilization. The fertilized egg that formed was diploid. A **diploid** cell contains two sets of chromosomes, one set from each parent. The fertilized grasshopper egg had 24 chromosomes, or 12 pairs. One chromosome in each pair came from each parent. As result, the grasshopper offspring had exactly the same number of chromosomes in its cells as did each of its parents.

Genes on Chromosomes Recall that alleles are different forms of a gene. From the results of Mendel's work, Sutton knew that alleles exist in pairs in an organism. One allele in a pair comes from the organism's female parent and the other allele comes from the male parent. Sutton realized that paired alleles were carried on paired chromosomes. Sutton's idea came to be known as the chromosome theory of inheritance. ⊂ **According to the chromosome theory of inheritance, genes are carried from parents to their offspring on chromosomes.**

 **Reading Checkpoint** What is the relationship between alleles and chromosomes?

FIGURE 13
Meiosis

During meiosis, a cell produces sex cells with half the number of chromosomes. **Interpreting Diagrams** *What happens before meiosis?*

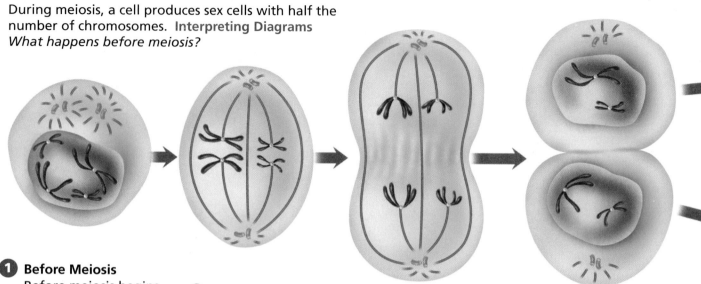

1 Before Meiosis
Before meiosis begins, every chromosome in the parent cell is copied. Centromeres hold the two chromatids together.

2 Meiosis I
A The chromosome pairs line up in the center of the cell.

B The pairs separate and move to opposite ends of the cell.

C Two cells form, each with half the number of chromosomes. Each chromosome still has two chromatids.

Meiosis

How do sex cells end up with half the number of chromosomes as body cells? To answer this question, you need to understand the events that occur during meiosis. **Meiosis** (my OH sis) is the process by which the number of chromosomes is reduced by half to form sex cells—sperm and eggs.

What Happens During Meiosis You can trace the events of meiosis in Figure 13. In this example, each parent cell has four chromosomes arranged in two pairs. **During meiosis, the chromosome pairs separate and are distributed to two different cells. The resulting sex cells have only half as many chromosomes as the other cells in the organism.** The sex cells in Figure 13 end up with only two chromosomes each—half the number found in the parent cell. Each sex cell has one chromosome from each original pair.

When sex cells combine to form an organism, each sex cell contributes half the normal number of chromosomes. Thus, the offspring gets the normal number of chromosomes—half from each parent.

Go Online
SciLINKS
NSTA

For: Links on meiosis
Visit: www.SciLinks.org
Web Code: scn-0333

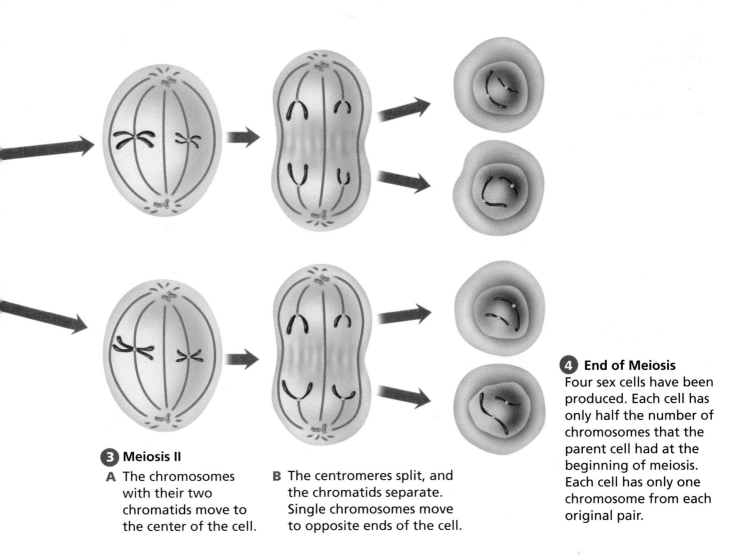

③ Meiosis II

A The chromosomes with their two chromatids move to the center of the cell.

B The centromeres split, and the chromatids separate. Single chromosomes move to opposite ends of the cell.

④ End of Meiosis
Four sex cells have been produced. Each cell has only half the number of chromosomes that the parent cell had at the beginning of meiosis. Each cell has only one chromosome from each original pair.

Meiosis and Punnett Squares A Punnett square is actually a way to show the events that occur at meiosis. When the chromosome pairs separate and go into two different sex cells, so do the alleles carried on each chromosome. One allele from each pair goes to each sex cell.

In Figure 14, you can see how the Punnett square accounts for the separation of alleles during meiosis. As shown across the top of the Punnett square, half of the sperm cells from the male parent will receive the chromosome with the *T* allele. The other half of the sperm cells will receive the chromosome with the *t* allele. In this example, the same is true for the egg cells from the female parent, as shown down the left side of the Punnett square. Depending on which sperm cell combines with which egg cell, one of the allele combinations shown in the boxes will result.

FIGURE 14
Meiosis Punnett Square
Suppose both parents are heterozygous for the trait of stem height. The Punnett square shows the possible allele combinations after fertilization.

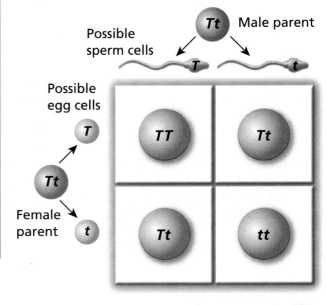

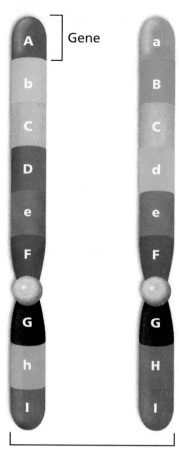

Gene

Chromosome pair

A Lineup of Genes

Each human body cell contains 23 chromosome pairs, or 46 chromosomes. **Chromosomes are made up of many genes joined together like beads on a string.** Plant and animal chromosomes contain many thousands of genes. Although you have only 23 pairs of chromosomes, your body cells each contain about 35,000 genes. Each gene controls a trait.

In Figure 15, one chromosome in the pair came from the female parent. The other chromosome came from the male parent. There are usually two copies of every gene. The genes are lined up in the same order on both chromosomes. However, the alleles for some of the genes might be different. For example, the organism has the *A* allele on one chromosome and the *a* allele on the other. As you can see, this organism is heterozygous for some traits and homozygous for others.

FIGURE 15
Genes on Chromosomes
The chromosomes in a pair may have different alleles for some genes and the same alleles for others. **Classifying** *For which genes is this organism homozygous? For which genes is it heterozygous?*

Section 3 Assessment

S 7.2.b, E-LA: Reading 7.2.0, Writing 7.2.0

Target Reading Skill Take Notes Use your notes to help answer the questions below.

Reviewing Key Concepts

1. **a. Comparing and Contrasting** According to Sutton's observations, how does the number of chromosomes in a grasshopper's body cells compare to the number in its sex cells?
   b. Describing Describe what happens to the number of chromosomes when two grasshopper sex cells join in fertilization.
   c. Explaining How do Sutton's observations about chromosome number support the chromosome theory of inheritance?

2. **a. Defining** What is meiosis?
   b. Interpreting Diagrams Briefly describe meiosis I and meiosis II. Refer to Figure 13.
   c. Sequencing Use the events of meiosis to explain why a sex cell normally does not receive both chromosomes from a pair.

3. **a. Describing** How are genes arranged on a chromosome?
   b. Comparing and Contrasting How does the order of genes in one member of a chromosome pair compare to the order of genes on the other chromosome?

Writing in Science

Newspaper Interview You are a newspaper reporter in the early 1900s. You want to interview Walter Sutton about his work with chromosomes. Write three questions you would like to ask Sutton. Then, for each question, write answers that Sutton might have given.

Genes, DNA, and Proteins

S 7.1.a Students know cells function similarly in all living organisms.

- What forms the genetic code?
- How does a cell produce proteins?
- How can mutations affect an organism?

Key Terms
- messenger RNA
- transfer RNA
- mutation

Lab zone Standards **Warm-Up**

Can You Crack the Code?

1. Use the Morse code in the chart to decode the question in the message below. The letters are separated by slash marks.

•――/•••••/•/•―•/•/•―•/•―•/
•/――•/•/―•/•/•••/•―••/――
/―•―•/•―/―/•/―••/

2. Write your answer to the question in Morse code.

3. Exchange your coded answer with a partner. Then decode your partner's answer.

Think It Over
Forming Operational Definitions
Based on your results from this activity, write a definition of the word *code*. Then compare your definition to one in a dictionary.

A •–	N –•
B –•••	O –––
C –•–•	P •––•
D –••	Q ––•–
E •	R •–•
F ••–•	S •••
G ––•	T –
H ••••	U ••–
I ••	V •••–
J •–––	W •––
K –•–	X –••–
L •–••	Y –•––
M ––	Z ––••

The white kangaroo in the photograph below was born at the San Francisco zoo. The young kangaroo beside her is her offspring. Notice that the offspring's coat is much darker—the natural coat color for eastern grey kangaroos. White kangaroos are extremely rare. Why was the mother born with such an uncommon phenotype? To answer this question, you need to know how the genes on a chromosome determine an organism's inherited traits.

◀ **A white kangaroo and her offspring**

The Genetic Code

The main function of genes is to control the production of proteins in an organism's cells. Many proteins serve as enzymes that control chemical reactions in the cell. Proteins also help to determine the size, shape, color, and many other traits of an organism.

Genes and DNA In Figure 16, you can see the relationship between chromosomes and DNA. Notice that a DNA molecule is made up of four different nitrogen bases—adenine (A), thymine (T), guanine (G), and cytosine (C). These bases form the rungs of the DNA "ladder."

A gene is a section of a DNA molecule that contains the information to code for one specific protein. A gene is made up of a series of bases in a row. The bases in a gene are arranged in a specific order—for example, ATGACGTAC. A single gene on a chromosome may contain anywhere from several hundred to a million or more of these bases. Each gene is located at a specific place on a chromosome.

Order of the Bases A gene contains the code that determines the structure of a protein. **The order of the nitrogen bases along a gene forms a genetic code that specifies what type of protein will be produced.** Remember that proteins are long-chain molecules made of individual amino acids. In the genetic code, a group of three DNA bases codes for one specific amino acid. For example, the base sequence CGT (cytosine-guanine-thymine) always codes for the amino acid alanine. The order of the three-base code units determines the order in which amino acids are put together to form a protein.

FIGURE 16
The DNA Code
Chromosomes are made of DNA. Each chromosome contains thousands of genes. The sequence of bases in a gene forms a code that tells the cell what protein to produce. Interpreting Diagrams *Where in the cell are chromosomes located?*

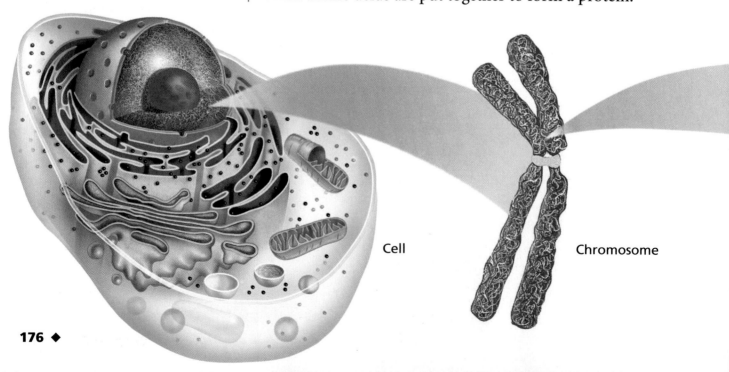

Cell

Chromosome

How Cells Make Proteins

The production of proteins in cells is called protein synthesis. 🔑 **During protein synthesis, the cell uses information from a gene on a chromosome to produce a specific protein.** Protein synthesis takes place on the ribosomes in the cytoplasm of a cell. As you know, the cytoplasm is outside the nucleus. The chromosomes, however, are found inside the nucleus. How, then, does the information needed to produce proteins get out of the nucleus and into the cytoplasm?

The Role of RNA Before protein synthesis can take place, a "messenger" must first carry the genetic code from the DNA inside the nucleus into the cytoplasm. This genetic messenger is called ribonucleic acid, or RNA.

Although RNA is similar to DNA, the two molecules differ in some important ways. Unlike DNA, which has two strands, RNA has only one strand. RNA also contains a different sugar molecule from the sugar found in DNA. Another difference between DNA and RNA is in their nitrogen bases. Like DNA, RNA contains adenine, guanine, and cytosine. However, instead of thymine, RNA contains uracil (YOOR uh sil).

Types of RNA There are several types of RNA involved in protein synthesis. **Messenger RNA** copies the coded message from the DNA in the nucleus, and carries the message to the ribosome in the cytoplasm. Another type of RNA, called **transfer RNA,** carries amino acids to the ribosome and adds them to the growing protein.

 **Reading Checkpoint** **How is RNA different from DNA?**

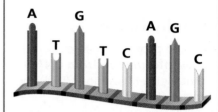
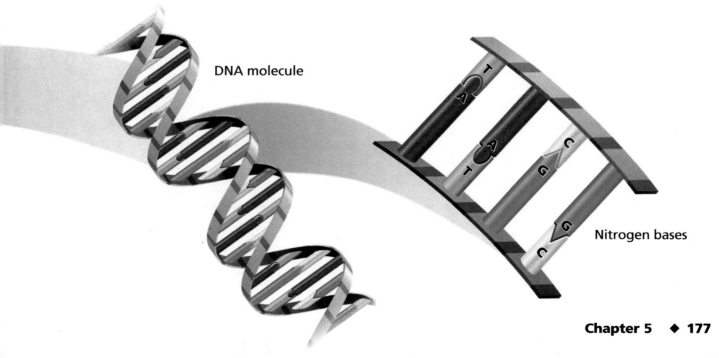

DNA molecule

Nitrogen bases

Translating the Code The process of protein synthesis is shown in Figure 17. Look at the illustration as you read the following steps.

1️⃣ The first step is for a DNA molecule to "unzip" between its base pairs. Then one of the strands of DNA directs the production of a strand of messenger RNA. To form the RNA strand, RNA bases pair up with the DNA bases. The process is similar to the process in which DNA replicates. Cytosine always pairs with guanine. However, uracil—not thymine— pairs with adenine.

2️⃣ The messenger RNA then leaves the nucleus and enters the cytoplasm. In the cytoplasm, messenger RNA attaches to a ribosome. On the ribosome, the messenger RNA provides the code for the protein molecule that will form. During protein synthesis, the ribosome moves along the messenger RNA strand.

FIGURE 17
Protein Synthesis
To make proteins, messenger RNA copies information from DNA in the nucleus. Messenger RNA and transfer RNA then use this information to produce proteins.
Interpreting Diagrams *In which organelle of the cell are proteins manufactured?*

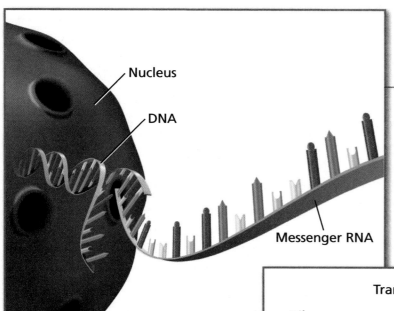

Nucleus

DNA

Messenger RNA

1 Messenger RNA Production
In the nucleus, a DNA molecule serves as a "pattern" for making messenger RNA. The DNA molecule "unzips" between base pairs. RNA bases match up along one of the DNA strands. The genetic information in the DNA is transferred to the messenger RNA strand.

2 Messenger RNA Attaches to a Ribosome
When the messenger RNA enters the cytoplasm, it attaches to a ribosome, where production of the protein chain begins. The ribosome moves along the messenger RNA strand.

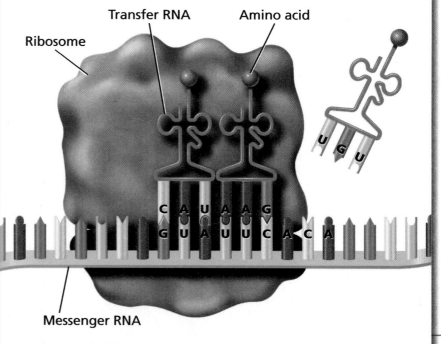

Transfer RNA   Amino acid

Ribosome

Messenger RNA

C A U A A G
G U A U U C A C A

U G U

3 Molecules of transfer RNA attach to the messenger RNA. The bases on the transfer RNA "read" the message by pairing up three-letter codes to bases on the messenger RNA. For example, you can see that a molecule of transfer RNA with the bases AAG pairs with the bases UUC on the messenger RNA. The molecules of transfer RNA carry specific amino acids. The amino acids link in a chain. The order of the amino acids in the chain is determined by the order of the three-letter codes on the messenger RNA.

4 The protein molecule grows longer as each transfer RNA molecule puts the amino acid it is carrying along the growing protein chain. Once an amino acid is added to the protein chain, the transfer RNA is released into the cytoplasm and can pick up another amino acid. Each transfer RNA molecule always picks up the same kind of amino acid.

 **Reading Checkpoint**   **What is the function of transfer RNA?**

Go Online
active art

For: Protein Synthesis activity
Visit: PHSchool.com
Web Code: cep-3034

3 Transfer RNA Attaches to Messenger RNA
Transfer RNA molecules carry specific amino acids to the ribosome. There they "read" the message in messenger RNA by matching up with three-letter codes of bases. The protein chain grows as each amino acid is attached.

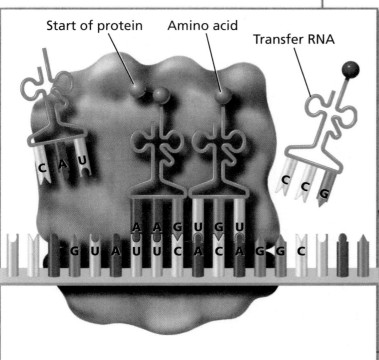

Growing protein

Start of protein   Amino acid   Transfer RNA

4 Protein Production Continues
The protein chain continues to grow until the ribosome reaches a three-letter code that acts as a stop sign. The ribosome then releases the completed protein.

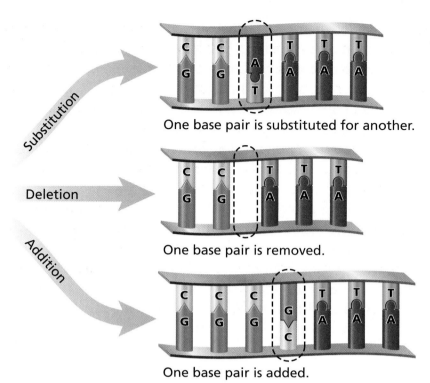

One base pair is substituted for another.

Deletion

One base pair is removed.

Addition

One base pair is added.

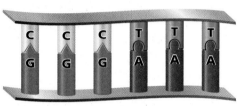

Original DNA sequence

FIGURE 18
Mutations in Genes
The illustration shows three types of mutations that can occur in genes.
Comparing and Contrasting *How are these mutations different from the mutations that occur when chromosomes do not separate during meiosis?*

Mutations

Suppose that a mistake occurred in one gene of a chromosome. Instead of the base A, for example, the DNA molecule might have the base G. Such a mistake is one type of mutation that can occur in a cell's hereditary material. A **mutation** is any change in a gene or chromosome. ⊙ **Mutations can cause a cell to produce an incorrect protein during protein synthesis. As a result, the organism's trait, or phenotype, may be different from what it normally would have been.** In fact, the term *mutation* comes from a Latin word that means "change."

If a mutation occurs in a body cell, such as a skin cell, the mutation will not be passed on to the organism's offspring. If, however, a mutation occurs in a sex cell, the mutation can be passed on to an offspring and affect the offspring's phenotype.

Types of Mutations Some mutations are the result of small changes in an organism's hereditary material. For example, a single base may be substituted for another, or one or more bases may be removed from a section of DNA. This type of mutation can occur during the DNA replication process. Other mutations may occur when chromosomes don't separate correctly during meiosis. When this type of mutation occurs, a cell can end up with too many or too few chromosomes. The cell could also end up with extra segments of chromosomes.

Video Field Trip

Discovery Channel School
Genetics: The Science of Heredity

Effects of Mutations Because mutations can introduce changes in an organism, they can be a source of genetic variety. Some mutations are harmful to an organism. A few mutations, however, are helpful, and others are neither harmful nor helpful. A mutation is harmful to an organism if it reduces the organism's chance for survival and reproduction.

Whether a mutation is harmful or not depends partly on the organism's environment. The mutation that led to the production of a white kangaroo would probably be harmful to an organism in the wild. The kangaroo's white color would make it more visible, and thus easier for predators to find. However, a white kangaroo in a zoo has the same chance for survival as a brown kangaroo. In a zoo, the mutation neither helps nor harms the kangaroo.

Helpful mutations, on the other hand, improve an organism's chances for survival and reproduction. Antibiotic resistance in bacteria is an example. Antibiotics are chemicals that kill bacteria. Gene mutations have enabled some kinds of bacteria to become resistant to certain antibiotics—that is, the antibiotics do not kill the bacteria that have the mutations. The mutations have improved the bacteria's ability to survive and reproduce.

FIGURE 19
Six-Toed Cat
Because of a mutation in one of its ancestors, this cat has six toes on each front paw.

✓ Reading Checkpoint **What are two types of mutations?**

Section **4** **Assessment**

S 7.1.a E-LA: Reading 7.2.0, Writing 7.2.0

Target Reading Skill Take Notes Use your notes to help answer the questions below.

Reviewing Key Concepts

1. a. **Explaining** What is the relationship between a gene, a DNA molecule, and a protein?
   b. **Relating Cause and Effect** How does a DNA molecule determine the structure of a specific protein?
   c. **Inferring** The DNA base sequence GGG codes for the amino acid proline. Could this same base sequence code for a different amino acid? Why or why not?
2. a. **Listing** List the sequence of events that happens during protein synthesis.
   b. **Describing** What is messenger RNA? Describe how it performs its function.

   c. **Inferring** Does transfer RNA perform its function in the nucleus or cytoplasm? Explain.
3. a. **Reviewing** How does a mutation in a gene affect the order of DNA bases?
   b. **Relating Cause and Effect** How can a mutation in a gene cause a change in an organism's phenotype?

Writing in Science

Compare/Contrast Paragraph Write a paragraph comparing and contrasting gene mutations and chromosome mutations. In your paragraph, explain what the two types of mutations are, and how they are similar and different.

The **BIG Idea**   **Organisms produced by sexual reproduction inherit half their DNA from each parent. The new combination of DNA determines an organism's traits.**

① Mendel's Work

Key Concepts   S 7.2.d

- In all of Mendel's crosses, only one form of the trait appeared in the F_1 generation. However, in the F_2 generation, the "lost" form of the trait reappeared in about one fourth of the plants.

- An organism's traits are controlled by the alleles it inherits from its parents. Some alleles are dominant, while other alleles are recessive.

Key Terms

heredity	alleles
trait	dominant allele
genetics	recessive allele
fertilization	hybrid
purebred	
gene	

② Probability and Heredity

Key Concepts   S 7.2.d

- Probability is the likelihood that a particular event will occur.

- In a genetic cross, the allele that each parent will pass on to its offspring is based on probability.

- An organism's phenotype is its physical appearance, or visible traits. An organism's genotype is its genetic makeup, or allele combinations.

- In codominance, the alleles are neither dominant nor recessive. As a result, both alleles are expressed in the offspring.

Key Terms

probability
Punnett square
phenotype
genotype
homozygous
heterozygous
codominance

③ The Cell and Inheritance

Key Concepts   S 7.2.b

- According to the chromosome theory of inheritance, genes are carried from parents to their offspring on chromosomes.

- During meiosis, the chromosome pairs separate and are distributed to two different cells. The resulting sex cells have half as many chromosomes as the other cells in the organism.

- Chromosomes are made up of many genes joined together like beads on a string.

Key Term

sexual reproduction
diploid
meiosis

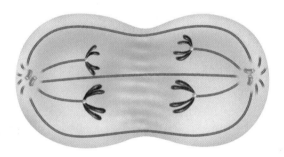

④ Genes, DNA, and Proteins

Key Concepts   S 7.1.a

- The order of the nitrogen bases along a gene forms a genetic code that specifies what type of protein will be produced.

- During protein synthesis, the cell uses information from a gene on a chromosome to produce a specific protein.

- Mutations can cause a cell to produce an incorrect protein during protein synthesis. As a result, the organism's trait, or phenotype, may be different from what it normally would have been.

Key Terms

messenger RNA	transfer RNA
mutation	

Review and Assessment

Target Reading Skill

Take Notes To help review Section 2, take notes on the text that follows the heading Principles of Probability (pages 162–163). The notes have been started for you as shown at the right.

Questions	Notes: Principles of Probability
What is probability?	Probability is a number that descibes how likely it is that an event will occur.
What are three ways of expressing the probability that a coin will land heads up?	

Reviewing Key Terms

Choose the letter of the best answer.

1. The different forms of a gene are called
   a. alleles.
   b. chromosomes.
   c. phenotypes.
   d. genotypes.

2. The likelihood that a particular event will occur is called
   a. mutation.
   b. Punnett square.
   c. probability.
   d. recessive.

3. An organism with two identical alleles for a trait is
   a. heterozygous.
   b. homozygous.
   c. recessive.
   d. dominant.

4. The process by which the number of chromosomes is reduced by half to form sperm and eggs is called
   a. hybrid.
   b. mitosis.
   c. meiosis.
   d. purebred.

5. During protein synthesis, which of the following provides a code from DNA in the nucleus?
   a. amino acid
   b. transfer RNA
   c. guanine
   d. messenger RNA

Complete the following sentences so that the second part further explains the first part.

6. Round seed shape in peas is an example of a trait controlled by a **dominant allele** because _____.

7. An organism with a genotype of *Hh* is a **hybrid** because _____.

8. The results of a genetic cross can be shown in a **Punnett square,** which is _____.

9. Having dimples is an example of a **phenotype,** which is _____.

10. The deletion of a base pair of DNA during meiosis is an example of a **mutation** because _____.

Writing in Science

Science Article You are a science reporter for a newspaper. Write an article about gene mutations. Explain what a mutation is and what determines whether it is helpful or harmful.

Video Assessment

Discovery Channel School
Genetics: The Science of Heredity

Review and Assessment

Checking Concepts

11. Describe what happened when Mendel crossed purebred tall pea plants with purebred short pea plants.

12. You toss a coin five times and it lands heads up each time. What is the probability that it will land heads up on the sixth toss? Explain.

13. In guinea pigs, the allele for black fur (*B*) is dominant over the allele for white fur (*b*). In a cross between a heterozygous black guinea pig (*Bb*) and a homozygous white guinea pig (*bb*), what is the probability that an offspring will have white fur? Use a Punnett square to answer the question.

14. Describe the role of transfer RNA in protein synthesis.

15. How can mutations affect protein synthesis?

Thinking Critically

16. **Applying Concepts** In rabbits, the allele for a spotted coat is dominant over the allele for a solid-colored coat. A spotted rabbit was crossed with a solid-colored rabbit. The offspring all had spotted coats. What are the probable genotypes of the parents? Explain.

17. **Interpreting Diagrams** The diagram below shows a chromosome pair. For which genes is the organism heterozygous?

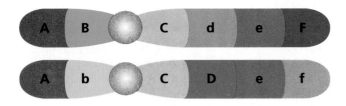

18. **Predicting** A new mutation in mice causes the coat to be twice as thick as normal. In what environments would this mutation be helpful? Why?

19. **Applying Concepts** If the body cells have 12 chromosomes, how many will the sex cells have?

20. **Relating Cause and Effect** Why are mutations that occur in an organism's body cells not passed on to its offspring?

Math Practice

21. **Percentage** A garden has 80 pea plants. Of the plants, 20 have short stems and 60 have tall stems. What percentage of the plants have short stems? What percentage have tall stems?

Applying Skills

Use the information in the table to answer Questions 22–24.

In peas, the allele for green pods (G) is dominant over the allele for yellow pods (g). The table shows the phenotypes of offspring produced from a cross of two plants with green pods.

Phenotype	Number of Offspring
Green pods	27
Yellow pods	9

22. **Calculating Percent** Calculate what percent of the offspring produce green pods. Calculate what percent have yellow pods.

23. **Inferring** What is the genotype of the offspring with yellow pods? What are the possible genotypes of the offspring with green pods?

24. **Drawing Conclusions** What are the genotypes of the parents? How do you know?

Lab zone Standards Investigation

Performance Assessment Finalize your display of your pet's family. Be prepared to discuss the inheritance patterns in your pet's family. Examine your classmates' exhibits. See which offspring look most like, and least like, their parents. Can you find any offspring that "break the laws" of inheritance?

Choose the letter of the best answer.

1. Which of the following is the first step in the formation of sex cells in an organism that has eight chromosomes?
   A The two chromatids of each chromosome separate.
   B Chromosome pairs line up next to each other in the center of the cell.
   C The DNA in the eight chromosomes is copied.
   D The chromatids move apart, producing cells with four chromosomes each.

   S 7.2.b

An organism contains two chromosomes with the genes shown.

2. Which of the following most likely represents the genotypes of each parent?
   A Father: Aa CC
      Mother: BB dd
   B Father: Aa Cc
      Mother: BB dd
   C Father: AA BB CC dd
      Mother: aa BB cc dd
   D Father: AA BB CC dd
      Mother: AA bb cc DD

   S 7.2.d

3. Which of the following events begins the process of protein synthesis?
   A Messenger RNA enters the cytoplasm and attaches to a ribosome.
   B The coded message in DNA is copied when a molecule of messenger RNA is formed.
   C The protein chain grows until a stop code is reached.
   D Transfer RNA molecules carrying amino acids attach to messenger RNA.

   S 7.1.a

Use the Punnett square below to answer Questions 4–6.

The Punnett square below shows a cross between two pea plants, each with round seeds.

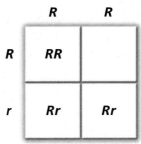

4. The missing genotype in the empty square is correctly written as
   A Rr.
   B rR.
   C rr.
   D RR.
   S 7.2.d

5. Which statement is true about the cross shown in the Punnett square?
   A Both parents are heterozygous for the trait.
   B Both parents are homozygous for the trait.
   C One parent is heterozygous and the other is homozygous for the trait.
   D The trait is controlled by codominant alleles.
   S 7.2.d

6. What percentage of the offspring of this cross will produce round seeds?
   A 0%
   B 25%
   C 50%
   D 100%
   S 7.2.d

7. A section of DNA has the base sequence GCTTAA. The corresponding messenger RNA made from this strand will have the base sequence
   A GCTTAA.
   B CGAAUU.
   C CGAATT.
   D UUTTCG.
   S 7.1.a

Apply the
BIG Idea

8. Summarize the stages of meiosis.   **S 7.2.b**

The members of this family resemble one another because they share some alleles. ▶

S 7.2

Focus on the
BIG Idea

How are traits inherited in people?

Check What You Know

Suppose you have a friend who doesn't have freckles. Both of her biological parents have freckles. The allele for freckles is dominant. What can you infer about the genotype of your friend's parents? Explain your answer.

The images shown here represent some of the Key Terms in this chapter. You can use this vocabulary skill to help you understand the meaning of some Key Terms in this chapter.

Vocabulary Skill

High-Use Academic Words

High-use academic words are words that are used frequently in classrooms. You and your teachers use these words when you discuss the subjects you study. Look for the words in the table below as you read this chapter.

Word	Definition	Example Sentence
normal (NAWR muhl) p. 200	*adj.* Usual, typical, expected	Its normal to feel nervous a bout going to a new school.
structure (STRUK chur) p. 200	*n.* The way in which parts of something are connected	You have learned the basic structure of plant and animal cells.
affect (uh FEKT) p. 198	*v.* To influence; to produce a change in	Scientists are looking for ways to treat diseases that affect people.
technique (tek NEEK) p. 206	*n.* A special way of doing something, a method, a procedure	There are special techniques for balancing on a skateboard.

Apply It!

Choose the word that best completes each sentence.

1. People's diets can _____ their health.

2. Doctors have developed a new _____ for doing heart surgery.

3. A(n) _____ body temperature in a human is about 37°C.

hybridization

X =

clone

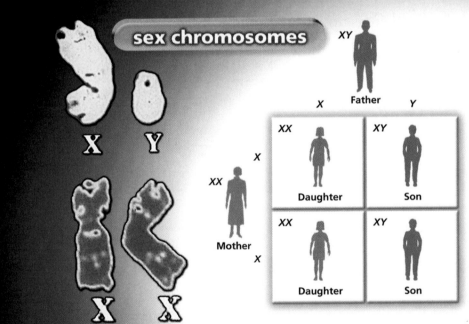

sex chromosomes

X   Y

XY   Father   Y

X

XX Mother

X

XX | X | Y
Daughter | Son
XX | XX | XY
Daughter | Son

X   X

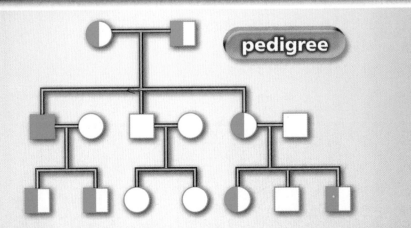

pedigree

Interactive Textbook
Build Science Vocabulary
Online
Visit: PHSchool.com
Web Code: cvj-2060

How to Read Science

 ## Identify Main Ideas

The main idea in a paragraph or section is the most important—or biggest—idea. Sometimes the main idea is stated directly in a sentence. Other times you have to figure it out on your own. The boldfaced Key Concept statements can help you identify main ideas.

The details in a paragraph or section support the main idea. Details are usually specific facts and examples that help readers understand the main idea.

Look for the main idea and details in the paragraph below.

> In human inheritance, there is not always a one-to-one relationship between gene and trait. For example, some traits, such as blood type, are controlled by genes with more than two alleles. Other traits, such as height, are controlled by many genes that act together to produce the trait.

After you have read the paragraph, copy the graphic organizer below. Complete it by filling in the main idea and missing detail.

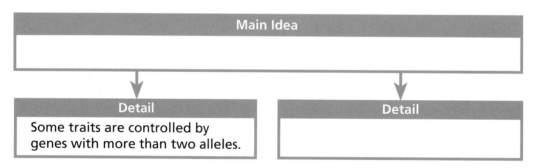

Main Idea

Detail	Detail
Some traits are controlled by genes with more than two alleles.	

Apply It!

Use your graphic organizer to answer the following questions.

1. What is the main idea of the paragraph?
2. What details support the main idea?

S 7.2.d

Teach Others About a Trait

People inherit alleles for traits from their parents. Some traits, such as keen eyesight, are beneficial. Other traits, such as colorblindness, can present challenges. In this investigation, you will design a display to help teach younger children about a genetically inherited trait. You and your group will need to research the inheritance pattern of your selected trait.

Your Goal

To design and build an educational tool or display about genetically inherited traits that can be used to educate young children

The display you create should

- illustrate how the trait is inherited and whom it can affect

- explain whether the trait is dominant, recessive, or codominant

- contain an interactive question and answer section that includes a way of predicting the probability that a person will inherit the trait

- stand by itself and be easy to set up

Plan It!

Begin by choosing a trait and researching its inheritance pattern. Then determine how the display will look and the materials you need. Determine what is the best method to make the display interactive. Plan to test your display on a younger audience to assess their understanding and then revise your design.

Human Inheritance

S 7.2 A typical cell of any organism contains genetic instructions that specify its traits. Those traits may be modified by environmental influences.

7.2.c. Students know an inherited trait can be determined by one or more genes.

- What are some patterns of inheritance in humans?
- What are the functions of the sex chromosomes?
- What is the relationship between genes and the environment?

Key Terms
- multiple alleles
- sex chromosomes
- sex-linked gene
- carrier

Lab zone Standards **Warm-Up**

How Tall Is Tall?

1. Choose a partner. Measure each other's height to the nearest 5 centimeters. Record your measurements on the chalkboard.
2. Create a bar graph showing the number of students at each height. Plot the heights on the horizontal axis and the number of students on the vertical axis.

Think It Over
Inferring Do you think height in humans is controlled by a single gene, as it is in peas? Explain your answer.

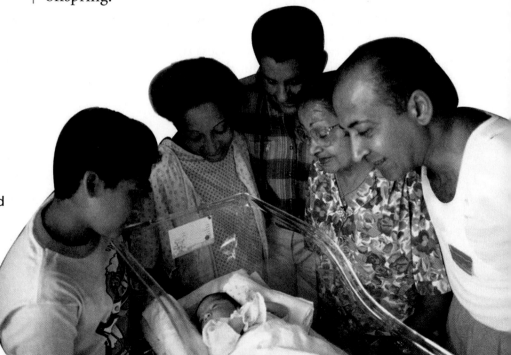

The arrival of a baby is a happy event. Eagerly, the parents and grandparents gather around to admire the newborn baby. "Don't you think she looks like her father?" "Yes, but she has her mother's eyes."

When a baby is born, the parents, their families, and their friends try to determine whom the baby resembles. Chances are good that the baby will look a little bit like both parents. That is because both parents pass alleles for traits on to their offspring.

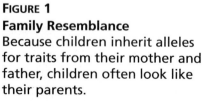

FIGURE 1
Family Resemblance
Because children inherit alleles for traits from their mother and father, children often look like their parents.

Patterns of Human Inheritance

When Mendel experimented with peas, he studied traits that were controlled by genes with one dominant allele and one recessive allele. The inheritance of traits is rarely this simple. A single gene can have more than two alleles, or more than one gene can be involved. Sometimes, a single gene can affect more than one trait. Or, all of a gene's effects may not be visible or even known. Because patterns of inheritance can be complicated, there is not always a one-to-one correspondence between trait and gene.

In this section, you will learn about some patterns of human inheritance. 🔑 **Some human traits are controlled by single genes with two alleles, and others by single genes with multiple alleles. Still other traits are controlled by many genes that act together.**

Single Genes With Two Alleles Several human traits are controlled by a single gene with one dominant allele and one recessive allele. These human traits have two distinctly different phenotypes, or physical appearances.

Whether your earlobes are free or attached is a trait controlled by a single gene with two alleles. A widow's peak is another. A widow's peak is a hairline that comes to a point in the middle of the forehead. The allele for a widow's peak is dominant over the allele for a straight hairline. The Punnett square in Figure 2 illustrates a cross between two parents who are heterozygous for a widow's peak. Notice that each child has a 3 in 4, or 75 percent, probability of having a widow's peak. There is only a 1 in 4, or 25 percent, probability that a child will have a straight hairline. When Mendel crossed peas that were heterozygous for a trait, he obtained similar percentages in the offspring.

FIGURE 2
Widow's Peak Punnett Square
This Punnett square shows a cross between two parents with widow's peaks.
Interpreting Diagrams *What are the possible genotypes of the offspring? What percentage of the offspring will have each genotype?*

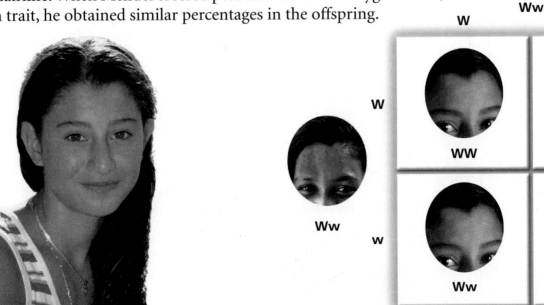

FIGURE 3
Inheritance of Blood Type
Blood type is determined by a single gene with three alleles. This chart shows which combinations of alleles result in each blood type.

Alleles of Blood Types	
Blood Type	**Combination of Alleles**
A	$I^A I^A$ or $I^A i$
B	$I^B I^B$ or $I^B i$
AB	$I^A I^B$
O	ii

Single Genes With Multiple Alleles Some human traits are controlled by a single gene that has more than two alleles. Such a gene is said to have **multiple alleles**—three or more forms of a gene that code for a single trait. Even though a gene may have multiple alleles, a person can carry only two of those alleles. This is because chromosomes exist in pairs. Each chromosome in a pair carries only one allele for each gene.

Human blood type is controlled by a gene with multiple alleles, as shown in Figure 3. There are four main blood types—A, B, AB, and O. Three alleles control the inheritance of blood types. The alleles for blood types A and B are codominant. The allele for blood type A is written as I^A. The allele for blood type B is written I^B. The allele for blood type O—written i—is recessive. Recall that when two codominant alleles are inherited, neither allele is masked. A person who inherits an I^A allele from one parent and an I^B allele from the other parent will have type AB blood. Only people who inherit two i alleles have type O blood.

Traits Controlled by Many Genes If you completed the Standards Warm-Up activity, you saw that height in humans has more than two distinct phenotypes. In fact, there is an enormous variety of phenotypes for height. Some human traits show a large number of phenotypes because the traits are controlled by many genes. The genes act together as a group to produce a single trait. At least four genes control height in humans, so there are many possible combinations of genes and alleles. Skin, eye, and hair color are other human traits that are controlled by multiple genes.

 **Reading Checkpoint** **Why do some traits exhibit a large number of phenotypes?**

FIGURE 4
Many Phenotypes
Skin color in humans is determined by three or more genes. Different combinations of alleles for each of the genes result in a wide range of possible skin colors.

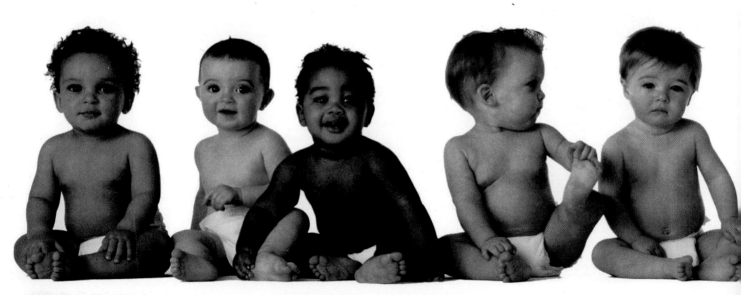

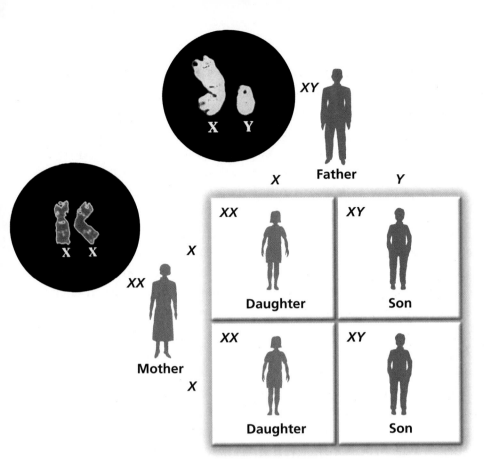

FIGURE 5
Male or Female?
As this Punnett square shows, there is a 50 percent probability that a child will be a girl and a 50 percent probability that a child will be a boy.
Interpreting Diagrams *What sex will the child be if a sperm with a Y chromosome fertilizes an egg?*

The Sex Chromosomes

The **sex chromosomes** are one of the 23 pairs of chromosomes in each body cell. ⬤ **The sex chromosomes carry genes that determine whether a person is male or female. They also carry genes that determine other traits.**

Girl or Boy? The sex chromosomes are the only chromosome pair that do not always match. If you are a girl, your two sex chromosomes match. The two chromosomes are called X chromosomes. If you are a boy, your sex chromosomes do not match. One of them is an X chromosome, and the other is a Y chromosome. The Y chromosome is much smaller than the X chromosome, as you can see in Figure 5.

Sex Chromosomes and Fertilization What happens to the sex chromosomes when egg and sperm cells form? Since both of a female's sex chromosomes are X chromosomes, all eggs carry one X chromosome. Males, however, have two different sex chromosomes. Therefore, half of a male's sperm cells carry an X chromosome, while half carry a Y chromosome.

When a sperm cell with an X chromosome fertilizes an egg, the egg has two X chromosomes. The fertilized egg will develop into a girl. When a sperm with a Y chromosome fertilizes an egg, the egg has one X chromosome and one Y chromosome. The fertilized egg will develop into a boy.

Sex-Linked Genes The genes for some human traits are carried on the sex chromosomes. Genes on the X and Y chromosomes are often called **sex-linked genes** because their alleles are passed from parent to child on a sex chromosome. Traits controlled by sex-linked genes are called sex-linked traits. One sex-linked trait is red-green colorblindness. A person with this trait cannot distinguish between red and green.

Recall that females have two X chromosomes, whereas males have one X chromosome and one Y chromosome. Unlike most chromosome pairs, the X and Y chromosomes have different genes. Most of the genes on the X chromosome are not on the Y chromosome. Therefore, an allele on an X chromosome may have no corresponding allele on a Y chromosome.

Like other genes, sex-linked genes can have dominant and recessive alleles. In females, a dominant allele on one X chromosome will mask a recessive allele on the other X chromosome. But in males, there is usually no matching allele on the Y chromosome to mask the allele on the X chromosome. As a result, any allele on the X chromosome—even a recessive allele—will produce the trait in a male who inherits it. Because males have only one X chromosome, males are much more likely than females to have a sex-linked trait that is controlled by a recessive allele.

FIGURE 6
Colorblindness
The lower photo shows how a red barn and green fields look to a person with red-green colorblindness.

Normal vision
▼

Red-green colorblind vision
▼

Inheritance of Colorblindness Colorblindness is a trait controlled by a recessive allele on the X chromosome. Many more males than females have red-green colorblindness. You can understand why this is the case by examining the Punnett square in Figure 7. Both parents in this example have normal color vision. Notice, however, that the mother is a carrier of colorblindness. A **carrier** is a person who has one recessive allele for a trait and one dominant allele. A carrier of a trait controlled by a recessive allele does not have the trait. However, the carrier can pass the recessive allele on to his or her offspring. In the case of sex-linked traits, only females can be carriers.

As you can see in Figure 7, there is a 25 percent probability that this couple will have a colorblind child. Notice that none of the couple's daughters will be colorblind. On the other hand, the sons have a 50 percent probability of being colorblind. For a female to be colorblind, she must inherit two recessive alleles for colorblindness, one from each parent. A male needs to inherit only one recessive allele. This is because there is no gene for color vision on the Y chromosome. Thus, there is no allele that could mask the recessive allele on the X chromosome.

 **Reading Checkpoint** **What is the sex of a person who is a carrier for colorblindness?**

Lab zone **Try This Activity**

Seeing Red
In this activity, you will take a simple test to see if you have red-green colorblindness. Take a look at the diagram below. What do you see? Can you see an eye among the dots? If you do not see the eye, you cannot distinguish between red and green.

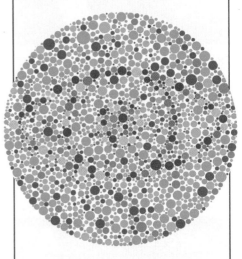

Inferring Based on the results of the test, what is your genotype for this trait?

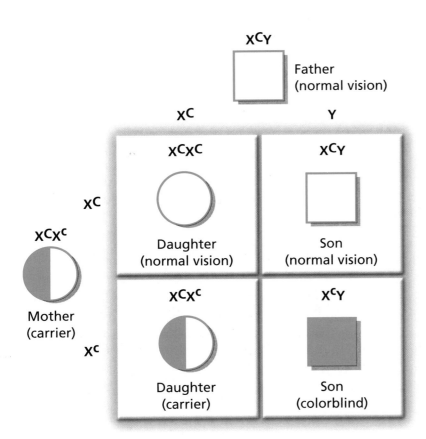

FIGURE 7
Colorblindness Punnett Square
Red-green colorblindness is a sex-linked trait. A girl who receives only one recessive allele (written X^c) for red-green colorblindness will not have the trait. However, a boy who receives one recessive allele will be colorblind.
Applying Concepts *What allele combination would a daughter need to inherit to be colorblind?*

FIGURE 8
Heredity and Environment
When a person plays a violin, genetically determined traits such as muscle coordination interact with environmental factors such as time spent in practice.

The Effect of Environment

In humans and other organisms, the effects of genes are often influenced by an organism's surroundings—the environment. 🔑 **Many of an organism's characteristics are determined by an interaction between genes and the environment.**

You have learned that several genes work together to help determine human height. However, people's heights are also influenced by their environments. For example, people's diets can affect their height. A diet lacking in protein, certain minerals, or certain vitamins can prevent a person from growing as tall as might be possible.

Environmental factors can also affect human skills, such as playing a musical instrument. For example, physical traits such as muscle coordination and a good sense of hearing will help a musician play well. But the musician also needs instruction on how to play the instrument. Musical instruction is an environmental factor.

 **Reading Checkpoint** How can environmental factors affect a person's height?

Section 1 Assessment

S 7.2, 7.2.c, E-LA: Reading 7.2.0, Writing 7.2.0

🎯 **Target Reading Skill** Identify Main Ideas Read the text following the heading Girl or Boy (page 195). Identify the main idea and two supporting details.

🔑 **Reviewing Key Concepts**

1. a. **Identifying** Identify three patterns of inheritance in humans. Give an example of a trait that follows each pattern.
   b. **Summarizing** How many human blood types are there? Summarize how blood type is inherited.
   c. **Drawing Conclusions** Aaron has blood type O. Can either of his parents have blood type AB? Explain your answer.
2. a. **Reviewing** What are the functions of the sex chromosomes?
   b. **Comparing and Contrasting** Contrast the sex chromosomes found in human females and human males.

   c. **Relating Cause and Effect** Explain how red-green colorblindness is inherited. Why is the condition more common in males than in females?
3. a. **Reviewing** Are a person's characteristics determined only by genes? Explain.
   b. **Applying Concepts** Explain what factors might work together to enable a great soccer player to kick a ball a long distance.

Writing in Science

Heredity and Environment Think of an ability you admire, such as painting, dancing, snowboarding, or playing games skillfully. Write a paragraph explaining how genes and the environment might work together to enable a person to develop this ability.

Human Genetic Disorders

S 7.2.d Students know plant and animal cells contain many thousands of different genes and typically have two copies of every gene. The two copies (or alleles) of the gene may or may not be identical, and one may be dominant in determining the phenotype while the other is recessive.

🔑 What are two major causes of genetic disorders in humans?

🔑 How do geneticists trace the inheritance of traits?

🔑 How are genetic disorders diagnosed and treated?

Key Terms
- genetic disorder
- pedigree
- karyotype

Lab zone Standards **Warm-Up**

How Many Chromosomes?
The photo at right shows the chromosomes from a cell of a person with Down syndrome, a genetic disorder. The chromosomes have been sorted into pairs.

1. Count the number of chromosomes in the photo.
2. How does the number of chromosomes compare to the usual number of chromosomes in human cells?

Think It Over
Inferring How do you think a cell could have ended up with this number of chromosomes? (*Hint:* Think about the events that occur during meiosis.)

The air inside the stadium was hot and still. The crowd cheered loudly as the runners approached the starting blocks. At the crack of the starter's gun, the runners sprinted down the track. Seconds later, the race was over. The runners, bursting with pride, hugged each other and their coaches. These athletes were running in the Special Olympics, a competition for people with disabilities. Many of the athletes who compete in the Special Olympics have disabilities that result from genetic disorders. A **genetic disorder** is an abnormal condition that a person inherits through genes or chromosomes.

◀ **Runners in the Special Olympics**

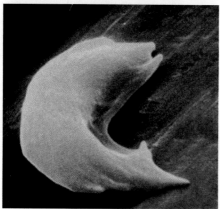

FIGURE 9
Sickle-Cell Disease
Normally, red blood cells are shaped like round disks (top). In a person with sickle-cell disease, red blood cells can become sickle-shaped (bottom).

Lab zone Skills **Activity**

Predicting
A man has sickle-cell disease. His wife does not have the disease, but is heterozygous for the sickle-cell trait. Predict the probability that their child will have sickle-cell disease. (*Hint:* Construct a Punnett square.)

Causes of Genetic Disorders

Recall that a person normally inherits two copies of a gene, one from each parent. But sometimes a person inherits an abnormal version of a gene that can lead to a disorder. (It is not accurate to say that someone has a *gene* for a disorder. Instead, a person has an *allele* for the trait.)

👄 **Some genetic disorders are caused by changes in the DNA of genes. Other disorders are caused by changes in the overall structure or number of chromosomes.** Common genetic disorders include cystic fibrosis, sickle-cell disease, hemophilia, and Down syndrome.

Cystic Fibrosis Cystic fibrosis is a disorder in which the body produces abnormally thick mucus in the lungs and intestines. The thick mucus fills the lungs, making it hard for the affected person to breathe. Cystic fibrosis is caused by a recessive allele on one chromosome. The recessive allele is the result of a mutation in which three bases are removed from a DNA molecule.

Sickle-Cell Disease Sickle-cell disease affects hemoglobin, a protein in red blood cells that carries oxygen. When oxygen concentrations are low, the red blood cells of people with the disease have an unusual sickle shape. Sickle-shaped red blood cells clog blood vessels and cannot carry as much oxygen as normal cells. The allele for the sickle-cell trait is codominant with the normal allele. A person with two sickle-cell alleles will have the disease. A person with one sickle-cell allele will produce both normal hemoglobin and abnormal hemoglobin. This person usually will not have symptoms of the disease.

Hemophilia Hemophilia is a sex-linked disorder in which a person's blood clots very slowly or not at all. People with the disorder do not produce one of the proteins needed for normal blood clotting. The danger of internal bleeding from small bumps and bruises is very high. Hemophilia is caused by a recessive allele on the X chromosome.

Down Syndrome In Down syndrome, a person's cells have an extra copy of chromosome 21. In other words, instead of a pair of chromosomes, a person with Down syndrome has three of that chromosome. Down syndrome most often occurs when chromosomes fail to separate properly during meiosis. People with Down syndrome have some degree of mental retardation.

 **Reading Checkpoint** How is the DNA in the sickle-cell allele different from the normal allele?

Pedigrees

Imagine that you are a geneticist who is interested in tracing the occurrence of a genetic disorder through several generations of a family. What would you do? 🔑 **One important tool that geneticists use to trace the inheritance of traits in humans is a pedigree.** A **pedigree** is a chart or "family tree" that tracks which members of a family have a particular trait.

The trait in a pedigree can be an ordinary trait, such as a widow's peak, or a genetic disorder, such as cystic fibrosis. Figure 10 shows a pedigree for albinism, a condition in which a person's skin, hair, and eyes lack normal coloring.

Go Online

active art

For: Pedigree activity
Visit: PHSchool.com
Web Code: cep-3042

FIGURE 10
A Pedigree
The father in the photograph has albinism. The pedigree shows the inheritance of the allele for albinism in three generations of a family. **Interpreting Diagrams** *Where is an albino male shown in the pedigree?*

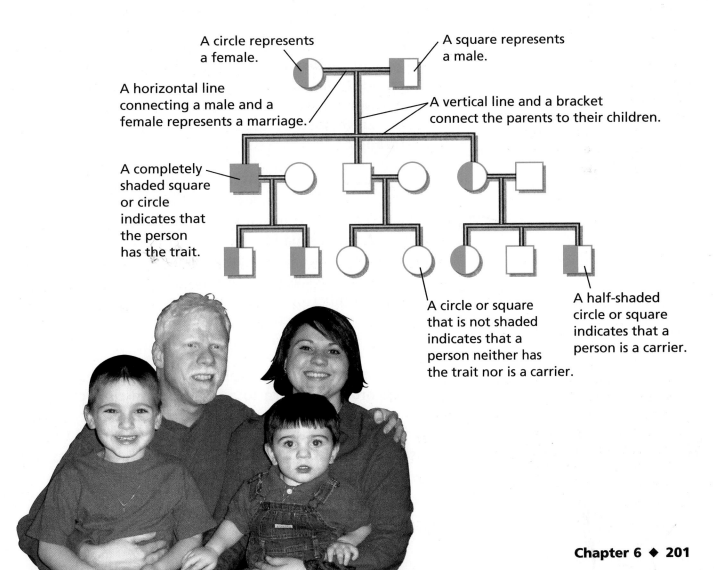

A circle represents a female.

A square represents a male.

A horizontal line connecting a male and a female represents a marriage.

A vertical line and a bracket connect the parents to their children.

A completely shaded square or circle indicates that the person has the trait.

A circle or square that is not shaded indicates that a person neither has the trait nor is a carrier.

A half-shaded circle or square indicates that a person is a carrier.

Figure 11
Living With Hemophilia

With proper care, people with hemophilia can manage their disorder. **Interpreting Diagrams** *In the pedigree, how many people have hemophilia?*

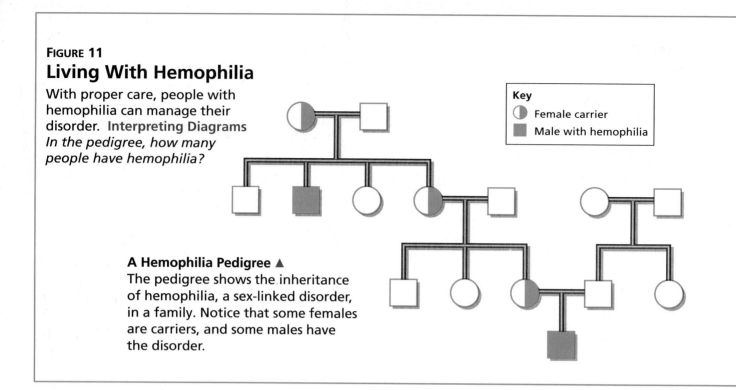

Key
◖ Female carrier
■ Male with hemophilia

A Hemophilia Pedigree ▲
The pedigree shows the inheritance of hemophilia, a sex-linked disorder, in a family. Notice that some females are carriers, and some males have the disorder.

Managing Genetic Disorders

Years ago, doctors had only Punnett squares and pedigrees to help them predict whether a child might have a genetic disorder. ⊸ **Today, doctors use tools such as karyotypes to help diagnose genetic disorders. People with genetic disorders are helped through medical care, education, job training, and other methods.**

Karyotypes To detect chromosomal disorders such as Down syndrome, a doctor examines the chromosomes from a person's cells. The doctor uses a karyotype to examine the chromosomes. A **karyotype** (KA ree uh typ) is a picture of all the chromosomes in a cell. The chromosomes in a karyotype are arranged in pairs. A karyotype can reveal whether a person has the correct number of chromosomes in his or her cells. The Standards Warm-Up activity on page 199 shows a karyotype from a girl with Down syndrome.

Genetic Counseling A couple that has a family history of a genetic disorder may turn to a genetic counselor for advice. Genetic counselors help couples understand their chances of having a child with a particular genetic disorder. Genetic counselors use tools such as karyotypes, pedigree charts, and Punnett squares to help them in their work.

 **Reading Checkpoint** **What do genetic counselors do?**

Physical Therapy ▶ Trained medical workers help hemophilia patients cope with their disorder. Here, a boy receives physical therapy.

Sports ▶ A boy with hemophilia learns how to play golf. The disorder does not stop people from living active lives.

Dealing With Genetic Disorders People with genetic disorders face serious challenges, but help is available. Modifying an affected person's environment—for example, through medicine, diet, or education—can help manage some disorders. People with sickle-cell disease take folic acid, a vitamin, to help their bodies make red blood cells. Through education and job training, adults with Down syndrome can find work in many places. Fortunately, most genetic disorders do not prevent people from living active, productive lives.

Section 2 Assessment

S 7.2.d, E-LA: Reading 7.1.0, Writing 7.2.0

Vocabulary Skill High-Use Academic Words
Use the words *effect* and *normal* to explain the relationship between hemophilia and blood-clotting.

Reviewing Key Concepts

1. a. **Identifying** Identify the two major causes of genetic disorders in humans.
   b. **Explaining** Which of those two major causes is responsible for Down syndrome?
   c. **Describing** How are the cells of a person with Down syndrome different from those of a person without the disorder?
2. a. **Defining** What is a pedigree?
   b. **Inferring** Why are pedigrees helpful in understanding genetic disorders?
   c. **Applying Concepts** Sam has hemophilia. Sam's brother, mother, and father do not have hemophilia. Draw a pedigree showing who has the disorder and who is a carrier.
3. a. **Reviewing** What is a karyotype?
   b. **Inferring** Would a karyotype reveal the presence of sickle-cell disease? Why or why not?

Writing in Science

Creating a Web Site Create an imaginary Web site to inform the public about genetic disorders. Write a description of one disorder for the Web site.

Family Puzzle  S 7.2.d

Problem

A husband and wife want to understand the probability that their children might inherit cystic fibrosis. How can you use the information in the box labeled Case Study to predict the probability?

Skills Focus

interpreting data, predicting

Materials

• 12 index cards   • scissors   • marker

Procedure

1. Read the Case Study. In your notebook, draw a pedigree that shows all the family members. Use circles to represent the females, and squares to represent the males. Shade in the circles or squares representing the individuals who have cystic fibrosis.

2. You know that cystic fibrosis is controlled by a recessive allele. To help you figure out Joshua and Bella's family pattern, create a set of cards to represent the alleles. Cut each of six index cards into four smaller cards. On 12 of the small cards, write *N* to represent the dominant normal allele. On the other 12 small cards, write *n* for the recessive allele.

Case Study: Joshua and Bella

• Joshua and Bella have a son named Ian. Ian has been diagnosed with cystic fibrosis.

• Joshua and Bella are both healthy.

• Bella's parents are both healthy.

• Joshua's parents are both healthy.

• Joshua's sister, Sara, has cystic fibrosis.

3. Begin by using the cards to represent Ian's alleles. Since he has cystic fibrosis, what alleles must he have? Write in this genotype next to the pedigree symbol for Ian.

4. Joshua's sister, Sara, also has cystic fibrosis. What alleles does she have? Write in this genotype next to the pedigree symbol that represents Sara.

5. Now use the cards to figure out what genotypes Joshua and Bella must have. Write their genotypes next to their symbols in the pedigree.

6. Work with the cards to figure out the genotypes of all other family members. Fill in each person's genotype next to his or her symbol in the pedigree. If more than one genotype is possible, write in both genotypes.

Analyze and Conclude

1. **Interpreting Data** What were the possible genotypes of Joshua's parents? What were the genotypes of Bella's parents?

2. **Predicting** Joshua also has a brother. What is the probability that he has cystic fibrosis? Explain.

3. **Communicating** Imagine that you are a genetic counselor. A couple asks why you need information about many generations of their families to draw conclusions about a hereditary condition. Write an explanation you can give to them.

More to Explore

Review the pedigree that you just studied. What data suggest that the traits are not sex-linked? Explain.

Advances in Genetics

S 7.2.b Framework Mitochondria DNA is derived solely from the mother, making possible the tracing of heritage from grandmothers to grandchildren with great certainty.

S 7.2.e Students know DNA (deoxyribonucleic acid) is the genetic material of living organisms and is located in the chromosomes of each cell.

🔑 What are three ways of producing organisms with desired traits?

🔑 What are two applications of DNA technology in human genetics?

Key Terms

- selective breeding
- inbreeding
- hybridization
- clone
- genetic engineering
- gene therapy
- genome

Lab zone Standards **Warm-Up**

What Do Fingerprints Reveal?

1. Label a sheet of paper with your name. Then roll one of your fingers from side to side on an ink pad. Make a fingerprint by carefully rolling your inked finger on the paper.
2. Divide into groups. Each group should choose one member to use the same finger to make a second fingerprint on a sheet of paper. Leave the paper unlabeled.
3. Exchange your group's fingerprints with those from another group. Compare each labeled fingerprint with the fingerprint on the unlabeled paper. Decide whose fingerprint it is.
4. Wash your hands after completing this activity.

Think It Over

Inferring Why are fingerprints used to identify people? Would it be useful if DNA could be used to identify organisms?

Would you like to have your picture taken with a 9,000-year-old family member? Adrian Targett, a history teacher in the village of Cheddar in England, has actually done that. All that's left of his ancient relative, known as "Cheddar Man," is a skeleton. The skeleton was discovered in a cave near the village. DNA analysis indicates that Targett and Cheddar Man are relatives.

Like your fingerprints, your DNA is different from everyone else's. Because of advances in genetics, DNA evidence can show many things, such as family relationships.

FIGURE 12
Distant Relatives
Adrian Targett visits his distant relative, Cheddar Man. Unfortunately, Cheddar Man cannot respond to questions about life 9,000 years ago.

FIGURE 13
Inbreeding
Turkeys such as the one with white feathers were developed by inbreeding. Breeders started with wild turkeys.

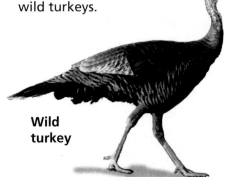

Wild turkey

Domestic turkey

Selective Breeding

Genetic techniques have enabled people to produce organisms with desirable traits. ☞ **Selective breeding, cloning, and genetic engineering are three methods for developing organisms with desirable traits.**

The process of selecting organisms with desired traits to be parents of the next generation is called **selective breeding**. Thousands of years ago, in what is now Mexico, the food that we call corn was developed in this way. Every year, farmers saved seeds from the healthiest plants that produced the best food. In the spring, they planted those seeds. By repeating this process over and over, farmers developed plants that produced better corn. People have used selective breeding with many different plants and animals. Two selective breeding techniques are inbreeding and hybridization.

Inbreeding The technique of **inbreeding** involves crossing two individuals that have similar characteristics. For example, suppose a male and a female turkey are both plump and grow quickly. Their offspring will probably also have those desirable qualities. Inbred organisms have alleles that are very similar to those of their parents.

Inbred organisms are genetically very similar. Therefore, inbreeding increases the probability that organisms may inherit alleles that lead to genetic disorders. For example, inherited hip problems are common in many breeds of dogs.

Hybridization In **hybridization** (hy brid ih ZAY shun), breeders cross two genetically different individuals. The hybrid organism that results is bred to have the best traits from both parents. For example, a farmer might cross corn that produces many kernels with corn that is resistant to disease. The result might be a hybrid corn plant with both of the desired traits.

✓ **Reading Checkpoint** What is the goal of hybridization?

FIGURE 14
Hybridization
McIntosh and Red Delicious apples were crossed to produce Empire apples.
Applying Concepts *What desirable traits might breeders have been trying to produce?*

McIntosh   **Red Delicious**   **Empire**

Math ▶ Analyzing Data

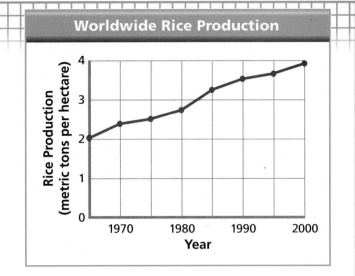

Worldwide Rice Production

Changing Rice Production

The graph shows how worldwide rice production changed between 1965 and 2000. New, hybrid varieties of rice plants are one factor that has affected the amount of rice produced.

1. **Reading Graphs** According to the graph, how did rice production change between 1965 and 2000?

2. **Reading Graphs** How many metric tons of rice per hectare were produced in 1965? How many were produced in 2000?

3. **Calculating** Calculate the difference between rice production in 1965 and 2000.

4. **Developing Hypotheses** What factors besides new varieties of plants might help account for the difference in rice production between 1965 and 2000?

Cloning

For some organisms, a technique called cloning can be used to produce offspring with desired traits. A **clone** is an organism that has exactly the same genes as the organism from which it was produced. It isn't hard to clone some kinds of plants, such as an African violet. Just cut a stem from one plant, and put the stem in soil. Water it, and soon you will have a whole new plant. The new plant is genetically identical to the plant from which the stem was cut.

Researchers have also cloned animals such as sheep and pigs. The methods for cloning these animals are complex. They involve taking the nucleus of an animal's body cell and using that nucleus to produce a new animal.

Video Field Trip
Discovery Channel School
Modern Genetics

 **Reading Checkpoint** How can a clone of a plant be produced?

FIGURE 15
Cloned Goats
These goats were produced by cloning.

Genetic Engineering

Geneticists have developed another powerful technique for producing organisms with desired traits. In this process, called **genetic engineering,** genes from one organism are transferred into the DNA of another organism. Genetic engineering can produce medicines and improve food crops.

Genetic Engineering in Bacteria One type of genetically engineered bacteria produces a protein called insulin. Injections of insulin are needed by many people with diabetes. Bacteria have a single DNA molecule in the cytoplasm. Some bacterial cells also contain small circular pieces of DNA called plasmids. In Figure 16, you can see how scientists insert the DNA for a human gene into the plasmid of a bacterium.

FIGURE 16
Genetic Engineering

Scientists use genetic engineering to create bacterial cells that produce important human proteins such as insulin.
Interpreting Diagrams *How does a human insulin gene become part of a plasmid?*

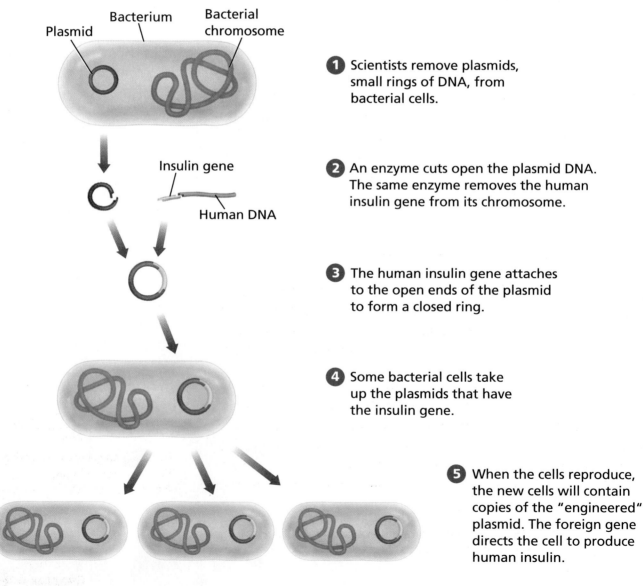

Plasmid **Bacterium** **Bacterial chromosome**

Insulin gene

Human DNA

1 Scientists remove plasmids, small rings of DNA, from bacterial cells.

2 An enzyme cuts open the plasmid DNA. The same enzyme removes the human insulin gene from its chromosome.

3 The human insulin gene attaches to the open ends of the plasmid to form a closed ring.

4 Some bacterial cells take up the plasmids that have the insulin gene.

5 When the cells reproduce, the new cells will contain copies of the "engineered" plasmid. The foreign gene directs the cell to produce human insulin.

Normal
zebra danio ▲

Genetically ▶
engineered
zebra danio

FIGURE 17
Genetically Engineered Fish
The bright red zebra danios are
the result of genetic engineering.

Once the gene is inserted into the plasmid, the bacterial cell and all its offspring will contain this human gene. As a result, the bacteria produce the protein that the human gene codes for—in this case, insulin. Because bacteria reproduce quickly, large amounts of insulin can be produced in a short time.

Genetic Engineering in Other Organisms Scientists can also use genetic engineering techniques to insert genes into animals. For example, human genes can be inserted into the cells of cows. The cows then produce the human protein for which the gene codes in their milk. Scientists have used this technique to produce the blood clotting protein needed by people with hemophilia.

Genes have also been inserted into the cells of plants, such as tomatoes and rice. Some of the genes enable the plants to survive in cold temperatures or in poor soil. Other genetically engineered crops can resist insect pests.

Gene Therapy Someday it may be possible to use genetic engineering to correct some genetic disorders in humans. This process, called **gene therapy,** will involve inserting copies of a gene directly into a person's cells. For example, doctors may be able to treat hemophilia by replacing the defective allele on the X chromosome. The person's blood would then clot normally.

Concerns About Genetic Engineering Some people are concerned about the long-term effects of genetic engineering. For example, some people think that genetically engineered crops may not be entirely safe. People fear that these crops may harm the environment or cause health problems in humans. To address such concerns, scientists are trying to learn more about the effects of genetic engineering.

For: Links on genetic engineering
Visit: www.SciLinks.org
Web Code: scn-0343

 **Reading Checkpoint** **How do genetic engineering techniques enable scientists to produce clotting proteins?**

FIGURE 18
The Human Genome Project
Scientists on the Human Genome
Project continue to study
human DNA.

Learning About Human Genetics

🔑 **Applications of DNA technology include studying the human genome in detail and identifying people.**

The Human Genome Project A **genome** is all the DNA in one cell of an organism. The main goal of a project called the Human Genome Project has been to identify the DNA sequence of every gene in the human genome. Scientists have learned that the DNA of humans has at least 30,000 genes. The average gene has about 3,000 bases. Scientists now know the DNA sequence of nearly every human gene.

DNA Fingerprinting DNA technology can also identify people and show whether people are related. Nuclear DNA from a person's cells is broken down into small pieces, or fragments. Selected fragments are used to produce a pattern called a DNA fingerprint. Except for identical twins, no two people have exactly the same DNA fingerprint.

Scientists can also use mitochondrial DNA to determine a person's identity. Mitochondria contain their own DNA, which is inherited from the mother through the egg cell. This means that a child has virtually the same mitochondrial DNA as his or her mother. By analyzing mitochondrial DNA, it is possible to trace inheritance from grandmothers to grandchildren with great certainty. For example, mitochondrial DNA was used to establish the relationship between Cheddar Man and his descendant.

Section 3 Assessment

S 7.2.b Framework, 7.2.e
E-LA: Reading 7.1.0

Vocabulary Skill High-Use Academic Words
What is hybridization? Use the word *technique* in your answer.

🔑 **Reviewing Key Concepts**

1. **a. Listing** List three methods that scientists can use to develop organisms with desirable traits.
   b. Describing Briefly describe each method.
   c. Applying Concepts Which method would be the best way of producing a plant similar to the one you already have? Explain.
2. **a. Reviewing** What are two applications of DNA technology?
   b. Making Judgments Do you think DNA fingerprinting would be useful in solving crimes? Explain your reasoning.

Lab zone At-Home Activity

Food and Selective Breeding Go to a grocery store with a family member. Discuss how fruits and vegetables have been produced by selective breeding. Choose a fruit or vegetable, and identify the traits that make it valuable.

Skills Lab

Guilty or Innocent?

S 7.2.e

Problem

A crime scene may contain hair, skin, or blood from a criminal. These materials all contain DNA that can be used to make a DNA fingerprint. A DNA fingerprint, which consists of a series of bands, is something like a bar code. How can a DNA fingerprint identify individuals?

Skills Focus

drawing conclusions, inferring

Materials

• 4–6 bar codes   • hand lens

Procedure

1. Look at the photograph of DNA band patterns shown at right. Each person's DNA produces a unique pattern of these bands.

2. Now look at the Universal Product Code, also called a bar code, shown below the DNA bands. A bar code can be used as a model of a DNA band pattern. Compare the bar code with the DNA bands to see what they have in common. Record your observations.

3. Suppose that a burglary has taken place, and you're the detective leading the investigation. Your teacher will give you a bar code that represents DNA from blood found at the crime scene. You arrange to have DNA samples taken from several suspects. Write a sentence describing what you will look for as you try to match each suspect's DNA to the DNA sample from the crime scene.

4. You will now be given bar codes representing DNA samples taken from the suspects. Compare those bar codes with the bar code that represents DNA from the crime scene.

5. Use your comparisons to determine whether any of the suspects was present at the crime scene.

Analyze and Conclude

1. **Drawing Conclusions** Based on your findings, were any of the suspects present at the crime scene? Support your conclusion with specific evidence.

2. **Inferring** Why do people's DNA patterns differ so greatly?

3. **Drawing Conclusions** How would your conclusions be affected if you learned that the suspect whose DNA matched the evidence had an identical twin?

4. **Communicating** Suppose you are a defense lawyer. DNA evidence indicates that the bloodstain at the scene of a crime belongs to your client. Do you think this DNA evidence should be enough to convict your client? Write a speech you might give to the jury in defense of your client.

More to Explore

Do you think the DNA fingerprints of a parent and a child would show any similarities? Explain your thinking.

DNA Fingerprinting

What do you have that no one else has? Unless you are an identical twin, your DNA is unique. Because one person's DNA is like no one else's, it can be used to produce genetic "fingerprints." These fingerprints can tie a person to the scene of a crime. They can prevent the wrong person from going to jail. They can also be used to identify skeletal remains. Today, soldiers and sailors give blood and saliva samples so their DNA fingerprints can be saved. Like the identification tags that soldiers wear, DNA records can be used to identify the bodies of unknown soldiers or civilians.

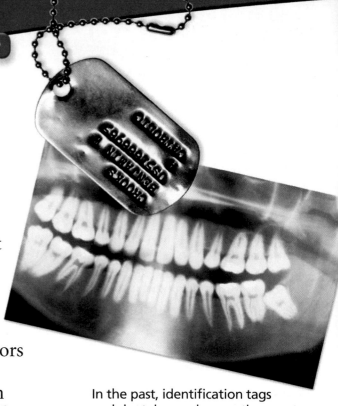

In the past, identification tags and dental records were the main methods for identifying skeletal remains.

T T C G A A T T C G A A T T C T G A A T T C T A G A A T T C G A A

T T C G | A A T T C G | A A T T C T G | A A T T C T A G | A A T T C G A A

4 bases   **6 bases**   **7 bases**   **8 bases**   **8 bases**

This enzyme cuts the DNA every time it encounters the DNA sequence GAATTC.

❶ After a sample of DNA is extracted from the body, an enzyme cuts the DNA strand into several smaller pieces.

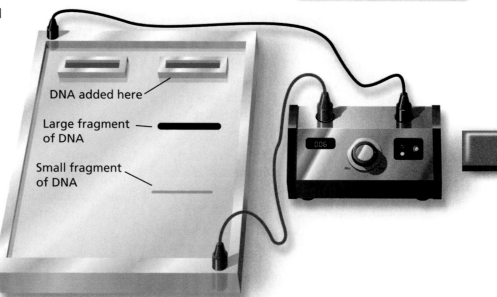

DNA added here

Large fragment of DNA

Small fragment of DNA

❷ The cut-up DNA fragments are loaded into a gel that uses electric current to separate fragments. Larger fragments of DNA move through the gel more slowly than the smaller fragments.

Analyzing DNA

In one method of DNA analysis, DNA from saliva, blood, bones, teeth, or other fluids or tissues is taken from cells. Special enzymes are added to cut the DNA into small pieces. Selected pieces are put into a machine that runs an electric current through the DNA and sorts the pieces by size. The DNA then gets stained and photographed. When developed, a unique banded pattern, similar to a product bar code, is revealed. The pattern can be compared to other samples of DNA to determine a match.

Limitations of DNA Fingerprinting

Like all technology, DNA fingerprinting has its limitations. DNA is very fragile and the films produced can be difficult to read if the DNA samples are old. In rare instances, DNA from the people testing the samples can become mixed in with the test samples and produce inaccurate results. DNA testing is also time consuming and expensive.

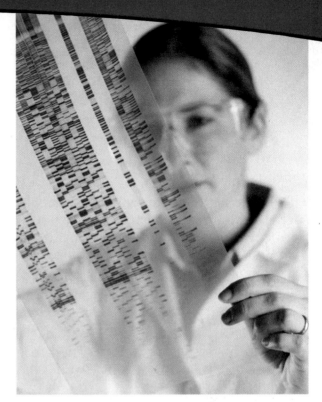

▲ **Scientist reading a DNA fingerprint**

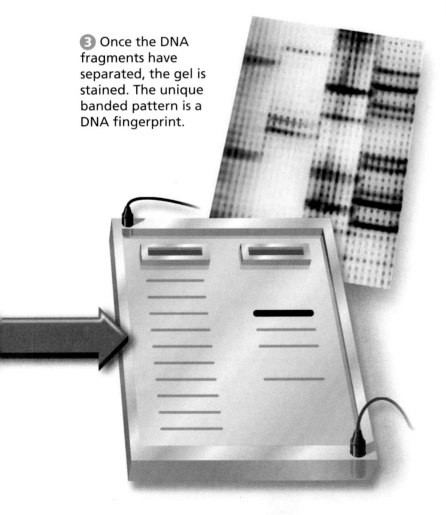

❸ Once the DNA fragments have separated, the gel is stained. The unique banded pattern is a DNA fingerprint.

Weigh the Impact

1. Identify the Need
Make a list of at least five situations in which DNA fingerprinting could be useful.

2. Research
Research the situations you listed in Question 1 to find out if DNA analysis is or can be used in each.

3. Write
Choose one application of DNA analysis and write one or two paragraphs to explain when the application can be used.

For: More on DNA fingerprinting
Visit: PHSchool.com
Web Code: ceh-3040

The BIG Idea A person's traits depend on which alleles are inherited from each parent, how those alleles work together, and environmental factors.

① Human Inheritance

Key Concepts S 7.2, 7.2.c

- Some human traits are controlled by single genes with two alleles, and others by single genes with multiple alleles. Still other traits are controlled by many genes that act together.

- The sex chromosomes carry genes that determine whether a person is male or female. They also carry genes that determine other traits.

- Many of an organism's characteristics are determined by an interaction between genes and the environment.

Key Terms
multiple alleles
sex chromosomes
sex-linked gene
carrier

② Human Genetic Disorders

Key Concepts S 7.2.d

- Some genetic disorders are caused by mutations in the DNA of genes. Other disorders are caused by changes in the overall structure or number of chromosomes.

- One important tool that geneticists use to trace the inheritance of traits in humans is a pedigree.

- Today doctors use tools such as karyotypes to help detect genetic disorders. People with genetic disorders are helped through medical care, education, job training, and other methods.

Key Terms
genetic disorder
pedigree
karyotype

③ Advances in Genetics

Key Concepts S 7.b Framework, 7.2.e

- Selective breeding, cloning, and genetic engineering are three methods for developing organisms with desirable traits.

- Applications of DNA technology include studying the human genome in detail and identifying people.

Key Terms
selective breeding
inbreeding
hybridization
clone
genetic engineering
gene therapy
genome

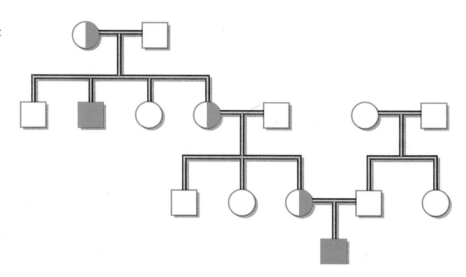

Review and Assessment

Go Online
PHSchool.com

For: Self-Assessment
Visit: PHSchool.com
Web Code: cva-2060

Target Reading Skill

Identifying Main Ideas Reread the three paragraphs following the heading The Effect of Environment, page 198. In a graphic organizer like the one at right, identify the main idea and supply the second detail.

Main Idea

a. _____ ?

Detail

Both genes and diet affect height.

Detail

b. _____ ?

Reviewing Key Terms

Choose the letter of the best answer.

1. A gene that is carried on the X or Y chromosome is called a
   a. carrier.
   b. sex-linked gene.
   c. sex chromosome.
   d. clone.

2. An abnormal condition that a person inherits through genes or chromosomes is called a
   a. karyotype.
   b. pedigree.
   c. multiple allele.
   d. genetic disorder.

3. Which of the following would most likely be used to diagnose Down syndrome?
   a. a karyotype
   b. a pedigree
   c. a blood-clotting test
   d. a Punnett square

4. Inserting a human gene into a bacterial plasmid is an example of
   a. inbreeding.
   b. selective breeding.
   c. DNA fingerprinting.
   d. genetic engineering.

5. An organism that has the same genes as the organism from which it was produced is called a
   a. clone.
   b. hybrid.
   c. genome.
   d. pedigree.

Complete the following sentences so that your answers clearly explain the Key Terms.

6. In humans, the X and Y chromosomes are **sex chromosomes,** which determine the _____ .

7. A person that has an extra copy of chromosome 21 is an example of someone with a **genetic disorder** because _____ .

8. Selecting and growing only the healthiest corn plants every season is an example of **selective breeding,** a process in which _____ .

9. **Inbreeding** produces organisms that are genetically very similar because _____ .

10. Modifying bacteria to produce human insulin is an example of **genetic engineering,** a process in which _____ .

Writing in Science

Fact Sheet You are a scientist in a cloning lab. Write a fact sheet that explains what the process of cloning involves. Describe at least one example.

Video Assessment
Discovery Channel School
Modern Genetics

Review and Assessment

Checking Concepts

11. Explain why there are a wide variety of phenotypes for skin color in humans.

12. Traits controlled by recessive alleles on the X chromosome are more common in males than in females. Explain why.

13. What is sickle-cell disease? How is this disorder inherited?

14. What is a pedigree? How do geneticists use pedigrees?

15. Describe two ways in which people with genetic disorders can be helped.

16. Explain how a horse breeder might use selective breeding to produce horses that have golden coats.

17. Describe how gene therapy might be used in the future to treat a person with hemophilia.

18. What is the Human Genome Project?

Thinking Critically

19. **Problem Solving** A woman with normal color vision has a colorblind daughter. What are the genotypes and phenotypes of both parents?

20. **Calculating** If a mother is a carrier of hemophilia and the father does not have hemophilia, what is the probability that their son will have the trait? Explain your answer.

21. **Interpreting Diagrams** The allele for cystic fibrosis is recessive. Identify which members of the family in the pedigree have cystic fibrosis and which are carriers.

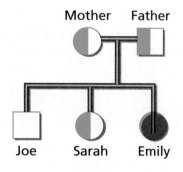

Mother   Father

Joe   Sarah   Emily

Applying Skills

Use the Punnett square to answer Questions 22–24.

The Punnett square below shows how muscular dystrophy, a sex-linked recessive disorder, is inherited.

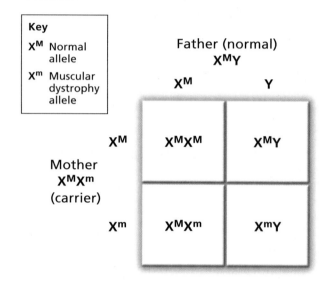

22. **Interpreting Data** What is the probability that a daughter of these parents will have muscular dystrophy? Explain your answer.

23. **Interpreting Data** What is the probability that a son of these parents will have muscular dystrophy? Explain your answer.

24. **Inferring** Is it possible for a woman to have muscular dystrophy? Why or why not?

Lab zone Standards Investigation

Performance Assessment Present your display board to your class. Highlight important facts about the genetic trait you selected. Discuss the innovative designs you incorporated into the display board. In your presentation, highlight the interactive part of your investigation.

Choose the letter of the best answer.

1. To produce a human protein through genetic engineering, scientists use
   A a bacterial gene inserted into a human chromosome.
   B a human gene inserted into a plasmid.
   C a bacterial gene inserted into a plasmid.
   D a human gene inserted into a human chromosome.   **S 7.2.e**

2. Down syndrome is an example of a genetic disorder in which
   A one DNA base has been added.
   B one DNA base has been deleted.
   C one chromosome is substituted for another.
   D an extra chromosome is added to a pair.   **S 7.2.d**

3. The Punnett square shows the probability that the children of this couple will inherit hemophilia.

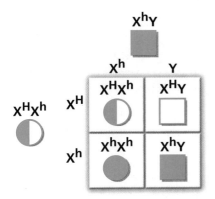

   Which of the following statements best describes the pattern of inheritance in this family?
   A All the sons will have hemophilia.
   B All the daughters will have hemophilia.
   C 50% of daughters and 50% of sons will have hemophilia.
   D 25% of all children will have hemophilia.   **S 7.2.b**

4. Height in humans is an example of a trait that is controlled by
   A a single gene with two alleles.
   B a single gene with multiple alleles.
   C many genes.
   D environmental factors only.   **S 7.2.c**

Use the pedigree to answer Questions 5–6.

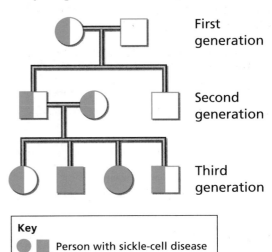

First generation

Second generation

Third generation

Key	
● ■	Person with sickle-cell disease
◐ ◻	Carrier of sickle-cell disease

5. How many people in the second generation have sickle-cell disease?
   A none
   B one person
   C two people
   D three people   **S 7.2.d**

6. Which statement is true about the third generation in the pedigree?
   A No one has sickle-cell disease.
   B Everyone has sickle-cell disease.
   C Everyone has at least one allele for sickle-cell disease.
   D No one has any alleles for sickle-cell disease.   **S 7.2.d**

🔑 Apply the BIG Idea

7. Identical twin boys were separated at birth and raised by different families. One boy is tall and is an outstanding soccer player. The other boy is shorter and not very athletic, but he is a good musician. Which of the boys' characteristics were influenced by genetics? Which were influenced by environment?   **S 7.2.c**

Chapter

7

Changes Over Time

Darwin observed Sally light-foot crabs and iguanas on the Galápagos Islands. ▶

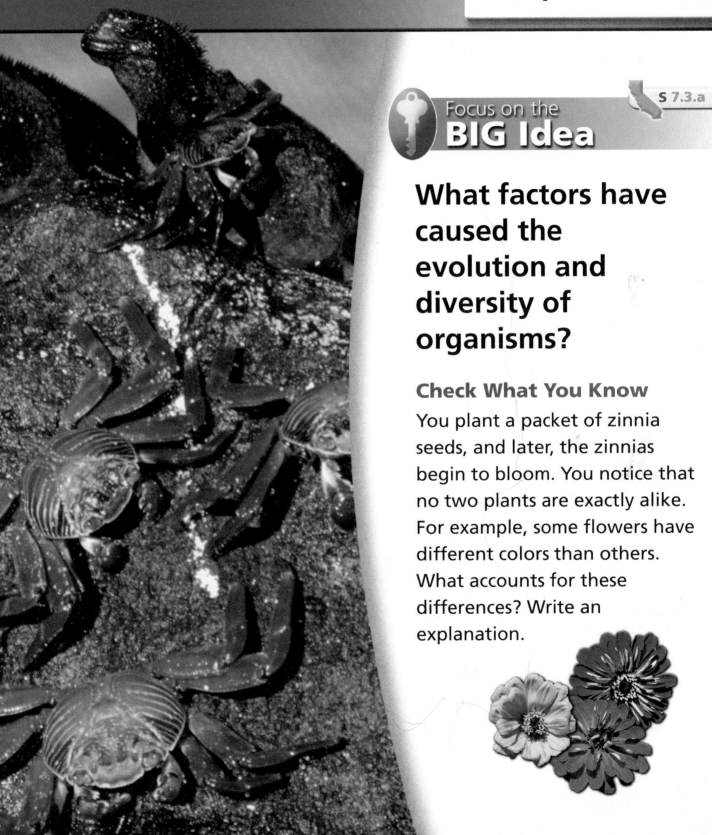

Focus on the
BIG Idea

S 7.3.a

What factors have caused the evolution and diversity of organisms?

Check What You Know

You plant a packet of zinnia seeds, and later, the zinnias begin to bloom. You notice that no two plants are exactly alike. For example, some flowers have different colors than others. What accounts for these differences? Write an explanation.

Build Science Vocabulary

The images shown here represent some of the key terms in this chapter. You can use this vocabulary skill to help you understand the meaning of some key terms in this chapter.

Vocabulary Skill

Identify Multiple Meanings

Some words, such as *theory* and *cast,* have different meanings in science and in everyday use. Look at the different meanings of *theory* and *cast* in the graphic below.

Word	Everyday Meaning	Scientific Meaning
theory	*n.* A guess; an idea of how or why something might happen **Example:** Emily has a <u>theory</u> that basketball is harder to play than baseball.	*n.* A well-tested concept that explains a wide range of observations **Example:** The cell <u>theory</u> says that all organisms are made of cells.
cast	*n.* A device that protects a broken bone by preventing it from moving **Example:** Tim's broken elbow has healed, so the <u>cast</u> can be removed.	*n.* A type of fossil that forms when a mold becomes filled with minerals **Example:** The <u>cast</u> of the foot print shows that the extinct animal had five toes.

Apply It!

In the sentences below, identify which meaning of the word *theory* was used—the everyday meaning or the scientific meaning.

1. The <u>theory</u> of evolution explains how organisms have changed over time.

2. Do you have a <u>theory</u> about why Sarah is a vegetarian?

eukaryotes

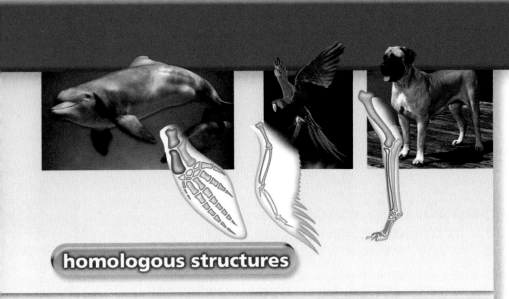

homologous structures

adaptation

extinct

Chapter 7 Vocabulary

interactive Textbook

Build Science Vocabulary
Online
Visit: PHSchool.com
Web Code: cvj-2070

How to Read Science

Identify Supporting Evidence

Scientific theories are always supported by a great deal of evidence. Evidence consists of facts that can be confirmed by testing or observation. A huge amount of evidence supports the theory of evolution. Section 2 of this chapter identifies and explains this evidence. Look at the incomplete graphic organizer below. Notice that fossils provide one kind of evidence.

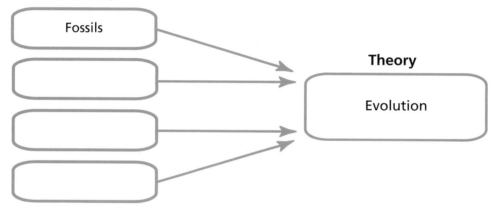

Evidence

Fossils

Theory

Evolution

Apply It!

Copy the incomplete graphic organizer into your notebook. As you read Section 2, fill in the missing spaces with other kinds of evidence that support the theory of evolution.

Standards Investigation

S 7.3.c

Extinction and Fossils

During the long history of life on Earth, many organisms have become extinct. Scientists have been able to learn a lot about many of these organisms because of the fossils they left behind. In this investigation, you will learn about an extinct organism whose fossils have been discovered in California.

Your Goal

To choose an extinct organism whose fossils have been discovered in California, and to research and present information about that organism

To complete this project you must

- research an extinct organism whose fossils have been found in California
- identify the environment that the organism probably lived in
- describe what may have led to the organism's extinction
- create a way of displaying your findings to the class
- follow the safety guidelines in Appendix A

Plan It!

Begin by choosing an extinct organism whose fossils have been discovered in California. Then find the information you need about the organism. Natural history museums and the Internet are good sources for identifying fossils found in California and for finding answers to your questions. Finally, decide how you will present that information to your class. Some possibilities include posters, booklets, and three-dimensional displays.

Fossil of a grazing ground sloth found in the La Brea tar pits ▶

Darwin's Theory

CALIFORNIA
Standards Focus

S 7.3.a Students know both genetic variation and environmental factors are causes of evolution and diversity of organisms.

S 7.3.b Students know the reasoning used by Charles Darwin in reaching his conclusion that natural selection is the mechanism of evolution.

🔑 What important observations did Darwin make on his voyage?

🔑 How did Darwin account for the diversity of species and the differences between similar species?

🔑 How does natural selection lead to evolution?

Key Terms
- species
- fossil
- adaptation
- evolution
- scientific theory
- natural selection
- variation

Lab zone Standards Warm-Up

How Do Living Things Vary?

1. Use a ruler to measure the length and width of 10 sunflower seeds. Record each measurement.
2. Now use a hand lens to carefully examine each seed. Record each seed's shape, color, and number of stripes.

Think It Over

Classifying In what ways are the seeds in your sample different from one another? In what ways are they similar? How could you group the seeds based on their similarities and differences?

In December 1831, the British ship HMS *Beagle* set sail from England on a five-year trip around the world. On board was a 22-year-old named Charles Darwin. Darwin eventually became the ship's naturalist—a person who studies the natural world. His job was to learn as much as he could about the living things he saw on the voyage. Darwin observed plants and animals he had never seen before. He wondered why they were so different from those in England. Darwin's observations led him to develop one of the most important scientific theories of all time: the theory of evolution by natural selection.

FIGURE 1

The Voyage of the *Beagle*

Charles Darwin sailed on the *Beagle* to the Galápagos Islands. He saw many unusual organisms on the islands, such as giant tortoises and the blue-footed booby.
Interpreting Maps *After leaving South America, where did the Beagle go?*

Replica of the *Beagle* ▶

Darwin's Observations

As you can see in Figure 1, the *Beagle* made many stops along the coast of South America. From there, the ship traveled to the Galápagos Islands. Darwin observed living things as he traveled. He thought about relationships among those organisms. 🔑 **Darwin's important observations included the diversity of organisms, the remains of ancient organisms, and the characteristics of organisms on the Galápagos Islands.**

Diversity Darwin was amazed by the tremendous diversity of living things that he saw. In Brazil, he saw insects that looked like flowers and ants that marched across the forest floor like huge armies. In Argentina, he saw sloths, animals that moved very slowly and spent much of their time hanging in trees.

Today scientists know that organisms are even more diverse than Darwin could ever have imagined. Scientists have identified more than 1.7 million species of organisms on Earth. A **species** is a group of similar organisms that can mate with each other and produce fertile offspring.

Fossils Darwin saw the fossil bones of animals that had died long ago. A **fossil** is the preserved remains or traces of an organism that lived in the past. Darwin was puzzled by some of the fossils he observed. For example, he saw fossil bones that resembled the bones of living sloths. The fossil bones were much larger than those of the sloths that were alive in Darwin's time. He wondered what had happened to the giant creatures from the past.

✓ **Reading Checkpoint** **What is a fossil?**

Video Field Trip
Discovery Channel School
Changes Over Time

▲ **Giant tortoise**

▲ **Blue-footed booby**

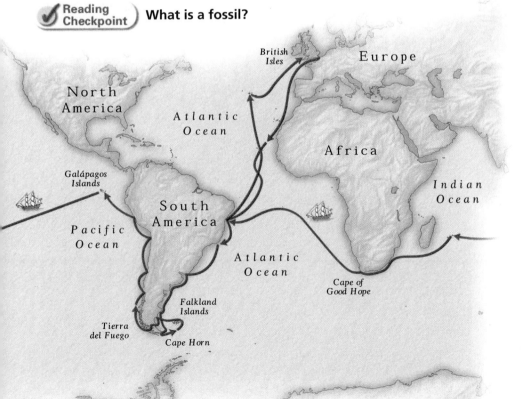

Europe
British Isles
North America
Atlantic Ocean
Africa
Galápagos Islands
South America
Indian Ocean
Pacific Ocean
Atlantic Ocean
Cape of Good Hope
Falkland Islands
Tierra del Fuego
Cape Horn

Galápagos Organisms

In 1835, the *Beagle* reached the Galápagos Islands. Darwin observed many unusual life forms on these small islands, such as giant tortoises, or land turtles. Some of these tortoises could look him in the eye! After returning to England, Darwin thought about the organisms he had seen. He compared Galápagos organisms to organisms that lived elsewhere. He also compared organisms on different islands in the Galápagos group. He was surprised by some of the similarities and differences he saw.

Comparisons to South American Organisms Darwin found many similarities between Galápagos organisms and those in South America. Many of the birds on the islands, including hawks, mockingbirds, and finches, resembled those on the mainland. Many of the plants were similar to plants Darwin had collected on the mainland.

However, there were important differences between the organisms on the islands and those on the mainland. The iguanas on the Galápagos Islands had large claws that allowed them to grip slippery rocks, where they fed on seaweed. The iguanas on the mainland had smaller claws. Smaller claws allowed the mainland iguanas to climb trees, where they ate leaves. You can see these differences in Figure 2.

From his observations, Darwin hypothesized that a small number of different plant and animal species had come to the Galápagos Islands from the mainland. They might have been blown out to sea during a storm or set adrift on a fallen log. Once the plants and animals reached the islands, they reproduced. Eventually, their offspring became different from their mainland relatives.

FIGURE 2
Comparing Iguanas
Iguanas on mainland South America (above) have smaller claws than iguanas on the Galápagos Islands. **Comparing and Contrasting** *In what other ways are the iguanas different?*

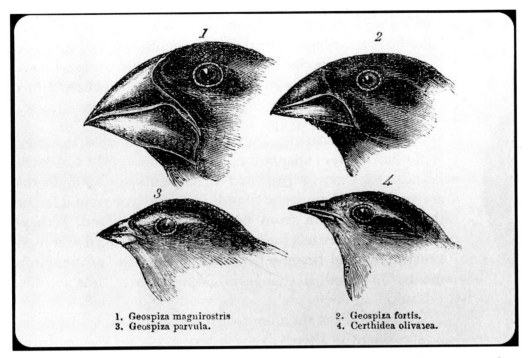

FIGURE 3
Galápagos Finches
Darwin made these drawings of four species of Galápagos finches. The structure of each bird's beak is an adaptation related to the type of food the bird eats. **Comparing and Contrasting** *Identify some specific differences in these finches' beaks.*

1. Geospiza magnirostris
3. Geospiza parvula.
2. Geospiza fortis.
4. Certhidea oliva3ea.

Comparisons Among the Islands As he traveled from one Galápagos island to the next, Darwin also noticed many differences among organisms. For example, the tortoises on one island had dome-shaped shells. Those on another island had saddle-shaped shells. A government official in the islands told Darwin that he could tell which island a tortoise came from just by looking at its shell.

Adaptations Like the tortoises, the finches on the Galápagos were noticeably different from one island to the next. The most obvious differences were the varied sizes and shapes of the birds' beaks, as shown in Figure 3. An examination of the different finches showed that each species was well suited to the life it led. Finches that ate insects had narrow, needle-like beaks. Finches that ate seeds had strong, wide beaks.

Beak shape is an example of an **adaptation,** a trait that helps an organism survive and reproduce in its environment. The finches' beak structures help in obtaining food. Other adaptations help organisms avoid being eaten. For example, some plants, such as milkweed, are poisonous or have a bad taste. A variety of adaptations aid in reproduction. The bright colors of some flowers attract insects. When an insect lands on a flower, the insect may pick up pollen grains, which produce sperm. The insect then may carry the pollen grains to another flower, enabling fertilization to take place.

 **Reading Checkpoint** How did the beaks of Galápagos finches differ from one island to another?

Evolution

After he returned to England, Darwin continued to think about the diversity of species he had seen during his voyage. Darwin spent the next 20 years consulting with other scientists, gathering more information, and thinking through his ideas.

Darwin's Reasoning Darwin especially wanted to understand the different adaptations of organisms on the Galápagos Islands. **Darwin reasoned that plants or animals that arrived on the Galápagos Islands faced environmental factors that were different from those on the mainland. Perhaps, Darwin hypothesized, the species gradually changed over many generations and became better adapted to the new environments.** The gradual change in a species over time is called **evolution.**

Darwin's ideas are often referred to as the theory of evolution. A **scientific theory** is a well-tested concept that explains a wide range of observations. From the evidence he collected, Darwin concluded that organisms on the Galápagos Islands had changed over time. However, Darwin did not know how the changes had happened.

Selective Breeding Darwin studied other examples of changes in living things to help him understand how evolution might occur. One example that Darwin studied was the offspring of animals produced by selective breeding. English farmers in Darwin's time used selective breeding to produce sheep with fine wool. Pigeon breeders had produced pigeons with two or three times the usual number of tail feathers. The pigeon breeders did this by repeatedly allowing only those pigeons with many tail feathers to mate. Darwin thought that a process similar to selective breeding might happen in nature. But he wondered what process selected certain traits.

Reading Checkpoint **What is a scientific theory?**

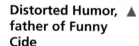

Seattle Slew, ▲
grandfather of Funny Cide

Distorted Humor, ▲
father of Funny Cide

Funny Cide ▶

FIGURE 4
Selective Breeding
Race horses are selectively bred to obtain the trait of speed. Funny Cide's father, Distorted Humor, and great-grandfather, Seattle Slew, were known for their speed.

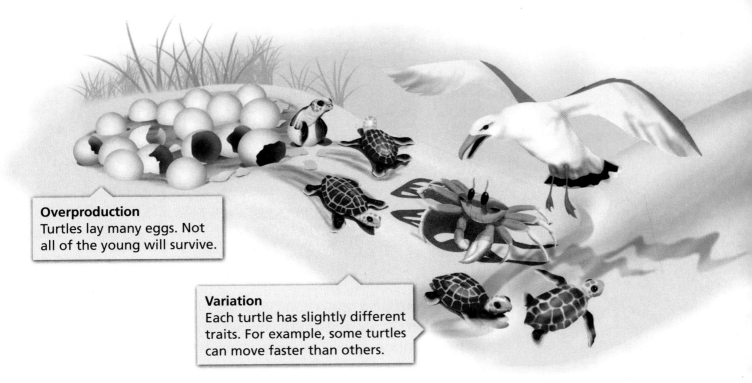

Overproduction
Turtles lay many eggs. Not all of the young will survive.

Variation
Each turtle has slightly different traits. For example, some turtles can move faster than others.

Natural Selection

In 1859, Darwin published a book called *On the Origin of Species by Natural Selection.* In it, Darwin proposed that evolution occurs in nature through a mechanism he called natural selection. In **natural selection,** individuals that are better adapted to their environment are more likely to survive and reproduce than other members of the same species. Darwin identified factors that affect the process of natural selection: overproduction, variations, and competition. Figure 5 and Figure 6 show how natural selection might happen in a group of turtles.

Overproduction Darwin read *Essay on the Principle of Population* by an Englishman named Thomas Robert Malthus. Malthus argued that humans and other organisms tend to produce a lot of offspring. Malthus pointed out that sometimes the food supply is not large enough to feed all these offspring. Darwin knew that, in addition to food, living things needed other resources, such as water and living space. He also knew that overproduction occurs in many species. Many female insects, for example, lay thousands of eggs. If all newly hatched insects survived, they would soon crowd out all other plants and animals. Darwin knew that this doesn't happen. Why not?

Variations As you learned in genetics, members of a species differ from one another in many of their traits. A difference between individuals of the same species is called a genetic **variation.** For example, certain insects may be able to eat foods that other insects of their species avoid. This characteristic gives the insects an advantage over most insects in their species.

FIGURE 5
Overproduction and Variation
Like actual sea turtles, the turtles in this illustration produce many more offspring than will survive. Some turtles are better adapted than others to survive in their environment.
Relating Cause and Effect *What adaptations might help young sea turtles survive?*

Lab zone Skills **Activity**

Making Models
Scatter 15 black buttons and 15 white buttons on a sheet of white paper. Have a partner time you to see how many buttons you can pick up in 10 seconds. Pick up the buttons one at a time. Did you collect more buttons of one color than the other? Why? How can a variation such as color affect the process of natural selection?

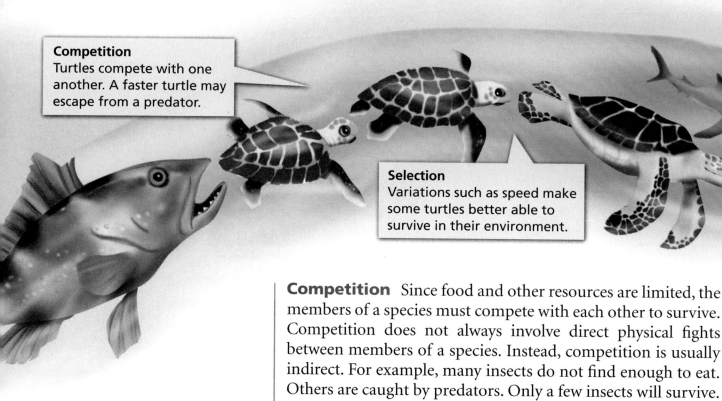

Competition
Turtles compete with one another. A faster turtle may escape from a predator.

Selection
Variations such as speed make some turtles better able to survive in their environment.

FIGURE 6
Competition and Selection
Variations among turtles make some of them better able to survive. Turtles that survive to become adults will be able to reproduce.
Applying Concepts What are some variations that sea turtles might exhibit?

Competition Since food and other resources are limited, the members of a species must compete with each other to survive. Competition does not always involve direct physical fights between members of a species. Instead, competition is usually indirect. For example, many insects do not find enough to eat. Others are caught by predators. Only a few insects will survive.

Selection Darwin observed that some variations make individuals better adapted to their environment. Those individuals are more likely to survive and reproduce. Their offspring may inherit the helpful characteristic. The offspring, in turn, will be more likely to survive and reproduce, and thus pass on the characteristic to their offspring. After many generations, more members of the species will have the helpful characteristic.

In effect, the environment has "selected" organisms with helpful traits to become parents of the next generation. **Darwin proposed that, over a long time, natural selection can lead to change. Helpful variations may gradually accumulate in a species, while unfavorable ones may disappear.**

Environmental Factors Factors in the environment can affect an organism's ability to survive. Environmental factors can therefore lead to selection. For example, monkey flowers are a type of plant. Most monkey flowers cannot grow in soil that has a high concentration of copper. However, because of genetic variation, some varieties of monkey flower now grow near copper mines, in spite of the copper in the soil.

Here is how natural selection might have resulted in monkey flowers that can grow in copper-contaminated soil. When the soil around a mine first became contaminated, a small number of monkey-flower plants may have been able to survive in the high level of copper. These plants grew and reproduced. After many generations, most of the seeds that sprouted in the soil produced monkey flowers that could withstand the copper.

Survival and Reproduction
Only a few turtles survive long enough to reproduce. The offspring may inherit the favorable traits of the parents.

Genes and Natural Selection Like environmental factors, genetic variation contributes to evolution. Without variations, all members of a species would have the same traits. Natural selection would not occur because all individuals would have an equal chance of surviving and reproducing.

Darwin could not explain what caused variations or how they were passed on. As scientists later learned, variations can result from mutation and the shuffling of alleles during meiosis. Genes are passed from parents to their offspring. Because of this, only traits that are inherited, or controlled by genes, can be acted upon by natural selection.

Section 1 Assessment

S 7.3.a, 7.3.b, E-LA: Writing 7.2.1, Reading 7.1.0

Vocabulary Skill Identify Multiple Meanings
What does *competition* mean to a scientist studying evolution? What is another meaning of *competition*?

Reviewing Key Concepts

1. a. **Listing** List three general kinds of observations that Darwin made during his voyage.
   b. **Comparing and Contrasting** Contrast Galápagos iguanas to South American iguanas.
   c. **Applying Concepts** What is an adaptation? Explain how the claws of the Galápagos and South American iguanas are adaptations.
2. a. **Reviewing** How did Darwin explain why Galápagos species had different adaptations than similar South American species?
   b. **Developing Hypotheses** How does selective breeding support Darwin's hypothesis?

3. a. **Defining** What is variation? What is natural selection?
   b. **Relating Cause and Effect** How do genetic variation and environmental factors work together to cause natural selection?
   c. **Applying Concepts** How do monkey flowers near mines show that natural selection causes evolution?

Writing in Science

Interview You are a nineteenth-century reporter interviewing Charles Darwin about his theory of evolution. Write three questions you would ask him. Then write answers that Darwin might have given.

Lab zone Skills Lab

Nature at Work  S 7.3.a, 7.3.b, 7.7.c, 7.7.e

Problem

How do species change over time?

Skills Focus

predicting, making models

Materials

- scissors
- marking pen
- construction paper, 2 colors

Procedure

1. Work on this lab with two other students. One student should choose construction paper of one color and make the team's 50 "mouse" cards, as described in Table 1. The second student should choose a different color construction paper and make the team's 25 "event" cards, as described in Table 2. The third student should copy the data table and record all the data.

PART 1 A White Sand Environment

2. Mix up the mouse cards.

3. Begin by using the cards to model what might happen to a group of mice in an environment of white sand dunes. Choose two mouse cards. Allele pairs *WW* and *Ww* produce a white mouse. Allele pair *ww* produces a brown mouse. Record the color of the mouse with a tally mark in the data table.

4. Choose an event card. An "S" card means the mouse survives. A "D" or a "P" card means the mouse dies. A "C" card means the mouse dies if its color contrasts with the white sand dunes. (Only brown mice will die when a "C" card is drawn.) Record each death with a tally mark in the data table.

5. If the mouse lives, put the two mouse cards in a "live mice" pile. If the mouse dies, put the cards in a "dead mice" pile. Put the event card at the bottom of its pack.

6. Repeat Steps 3 through 5 with the remaining mouse cards to study the first generation of mice. Record your results.

7. Leave the dead mice cards untouched. Mix up the cards from the live mice pile. Mix up the events cards.

8. Repeat Steps 3 through 7 for the second generation. Then repeat Steps 3 through 6 for the third generation.

PART 2 A Forest Floor Environment

9. How would the data differ if the mice in this model lived on a dark brown forest floor? Record your prediction in your notebook.

10. Make a new copy of the data table. Then use the cards to test your prediction. Remember that a "C" card now means that any mouse with white fur will die.

Data Table				
Type of Environment:				
Generation	Population		Deaths	
	White Mice	Brown Mice	White Mice	Brown Mice
1				
2				
3				

Table 1: Mouse Cards		
Number	Label	Meaning
25	*W*	Dominant allele for white fur
25	*w*	Recessive allele for brown fur

Table 2: Event Cards		
Number	Label	Meaning
5	S	Mouse survives.
1	D	Disease kills mouse.
1	P	Predator kills mice of all colors.
18	C	Predator kills mice that contrast with the environment.

Analyze and Conclude

1. **Calculating** In Part 1, how many white mice were there in each generation? How many brown mice? In each generation, which color mouse had the higher death rate? (*Hint:* To calculate the death rate for white mice, divide the number of white mice that died by the total number of white mice, then multiply by 100%.)

2. **Predicting** If the events in Part 1 occurred in nature, how would the group of mice change over time?

3. **Observing** How did the results in Part 2 differ from those in Part 1?

4. **Making Models** How would it affect your model if you increased the number of "C" cards? What would happen if you decreased the number of "C" cards?

5. **Communicating** Imagine that you are trying to explain the point of this lab to Charles Darwin. Write an explanation that you could give to him. To prepare to write, answer the following questions: What are some ways in which this investigation models natural selection? What are some ways in which natural selection differs from this model?

Design an Experiment

Choose a different species with a trait that interests you. Make a set of cards similar to these cards to investigate how natural selection might bring about the evolution of that species. *Obtain your teacher's permission before carrying out your investigation.*

- What evidence supports the theory of evolution?
- How do fossils form?
- What do scientists learn from fossils?

Key Terms

- comparative anatomy
- homologous structures
- mold
- cast
- petrified fossil
- trace fossil
- paleontologist
- gradualism
- punctuated equilibria

Lab zone Standards **Warm-Up**

What Can You Learn From Fossils?

1. Look at the fossil in the photograph. Describe the fossil's characteristics in as much detail as you can.

2. From your description in Step 1, try to figure out how the organism lived. How did it move? Where did it live?

Think It Over
Inferring What type of present-day organism do you think is related to the fossil? Why?

Does natural selection occur today? Evidence indicates that the answer is yes. Consider, for example, what happens when chemicals called pesticides are used to kill harmful insects such as the cockroaches below. When a pesticide is first used in a building, it kills almost all the insects. But a few insects have traits that protect them from the pesticide. These insects survive.

The surviving insects reproduce. Some of their offspring inherit the pesticide protection. The surviving offspring, in turn, reproduce. Every time the pesticide is used, the only insects that survive are those that are not harmed by the pesticide. After many years, most of the cockroaches in the building are resistant to the pesticide. The development of pesticide resistance is one type of evidence that supports the theory of evolution.

Forms of Evidence

Since Darwin's time, scientists have found a great deal of evidence that supports the theory of evolution. **Similar body structures, patterns of early development, molecular structure, and fossils all provide evidence that organisms have changed over time.**

FIGURE 7
Pesticide Resistance
Many insects, including cockroaches such as these, are no longer killed by some pesticides. Increased pesticide resistance is evidence that natural selection is happening.

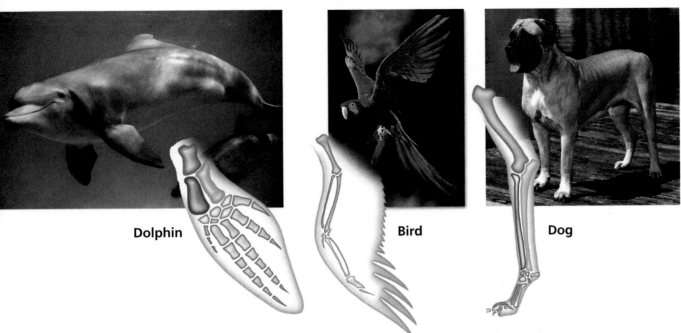

Dolphin   Bird   Dog

Similarities in Body Structure The comparison of the structures of different organisms is called **comparative anatomy.** An organism's anatomy is its body structure. Fishes, amphibians, reptiles, birds, and mammals all have a similar anatomy—an internal skeleton with a backbone. This is why scientists classify all five groups as vertebrates. All these groups probably inherited a similar structure from an early vertebrate ancestor that they shared.

Figure 8 shows that the bones of the front limbs of dolphins, birds, and dogs are arranged in a similar way. These similarities provide evidence that these three organisms all evolved from a common ancestor. Similar structures that related species have inherited from a common ancestor are known as **homologous structures** (hoh MAHL uh gus).

Similarities in Early Development Scientists make inferences about evolutionary relationships by comparing how different species develop before birth. During early development, all vertebrates have a tail and rows of tiny slits in their throats. These similarities suggest that vertebrate species share a common ancestor.

Similarities in DNA and Proteins The structure of organisms' DNA and protein molecules also provides evidence of evolution. If two species have similar DNA and proteins, they probably evolved from the same ancestor.

 **Reading Checkpoint** What are homologous structures?

FIGURE 8
Homologous Structures
The structure of the bones in a dolphin's flipper, a bird's wing, and a dog's leg is similar. Homologous bones are shown in the same color. **Interpreting Diagrams** *How are all three orange bones similar?*

Lab zone Skills **Activity**

Drawing Conclusions
Look at the drawing below of the bones in a crocodile's leg. Compare this drawing to Figure 8. Do you think that crocodiles share a common ancestor with birds, dolphins, and dogs? Support your answer with evidence.

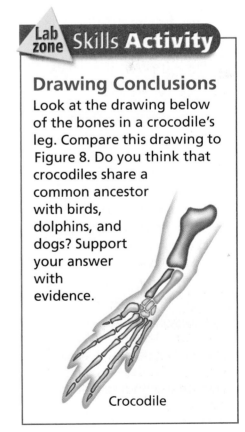

Crocodile

FIGURE 9
Fossil Formation

Most fossils, such as the fossil crocodile shown here, form in sedimentary rock. **Relating Cause and Effect** *In the process of fossil formation, what materials replace the crocodile's remains?*

An ancient crocodile dies and sinks to the bottom of a river.

Layers of sediments cover the crocodile's body.

Lab zone Try This **Activity**

Preservation in Ice

1. Place fresh fruit, such as apple slices, strawberries, and blueberries, in an open plastic container.
2. Completely cover the fruit with water. Put the container in a freezer.
3. Place the same type and amount of fresh fruit in another open container. Leave it somewhere where no one will disturb it.
4. After three days, observe the contents of both containers.

Inferring Use your observations to explain why fossils preserved in ice can include soft, fleshy body parts.

How Do Fossils Form?

Fossil evidence supports the theory of evolution. The formation of any fossil is a rare event. Usually only the hard parts of the organism, such as the bones or shells of animals, form fossils. **Most fossils form when organisms that die become buried in sediments.** Sediments are particles of soil and rock. When a river flows into a lake or ocean, the sediments that the river carries settle to the bottom. Layers of sediments may cover the dead organisms. Over millions of years, the layers may harden to become sedimentary rock.

Molds and Casts The most common fossils are molds and casts. Both copy the shape of ancient organisms. A **mold** is a hollow area in sediment in the shape of an organism or part of an organism. A mold forms when the hard part of the organism, such as a shell, is buried in sediment.

Later, water carrying dissolved minerals and sediment may seep into the empty space of a mold. If the water deposits the minerals and sediments there, the result is a cast. A **cast** is a solid copy of the shape of an organism. A cast is the opposite of its mold. Both the mold and cast preserve details of the animal's structure.

Petrified Fossils A fossil may form when the remains of an organism become petrified. **Petrified fossils** are fossils in which minerals replace all or part of an organism. Fossil tree trunks are an example of petrified wood. These fossils formed after sediment covered the wood. Then water rich in dissolved minerals soaked into spaces in the plant's cells. Over time, the minerals came out of solution and hardened. Some of the original wood remains in petrified wood, but minerals have hardened and preserved the wood.

Over millions of years, the sediments harden to become rock. The crocodile is preserved as a fossil.

The rock erodes. The fossil is exposed on the surface of a rock.

Go Online
active art

For: Fossil Formation activity
Visit: PHSchool.com
Web Code: cep-3053

Trace Fossils Most types of fossils preserve the shapes of ancient animals and plants. In contrast, **trace fossils** provide evidence of the activities of ancient organisms. A fossilized footprint is one example of a trace fossil. The mud or sand that the animal stepped in was buried by layers of sediment. Slowly the sediment became solid rock, preserving the footprint for millions of years.

From fossil footprints, scientists can find answers to questions about an animal's size and behavior. Did the animal walk on two or four legs? Did it live alone or as part of a group?

Other types of trace fossils also provide clues about ancient organisms. A trail or burrow can give clues about the size and shape of an organism, where it lived, and how it obtained food.

Preserved Remains Some processes preserve the remains of organisms with little or no change. For example, some remains are preserved when organisms become trapped in tar. Tar is sticky oil that seeps from Earth's surface. Many fossils preserved in tar have been found at the Rancho La Brea tar pits in Los Angeles, California. Thousands of years ago, animals came to drink the water that covered these pits. Somehow, they became stuck in the tar and then died. The tar soaked into their bones, preserving the bones from decay.

Ancient organisms also have been preserved in amber. Amber is the hardened resin, or sap, of evergreen trees. First, an insect is trapped on sticky resin. After the insect dies, more resin covers it, sealing it from air and protecting its body from decay.

Freezing can also preserve remains. The frozen remains of woolly mammoths, huge ancient relatives of elephants, have been found in very cold regions of Siberia and Alaska. Freezing has preserved even the mammoths' hair and skin.

Reading Checkpoint What are three ways in which the remains of an organism can be preserved with little change?

Fossil Clues to Past Environments

Fossils of many different kinds of organisms were formed in this ancient lakeshore environment.

Inferring *How do you think the fossil of the bat was preserved?*

Learning From Fossils

Paleontologists (pay lee un TAHL uh jists) are scientists who study fossils. Paleontologists collect fossils from all over the world. ⬥ **The fossil record provides evidence about the history of life and past environments on Earth. In addition, scientists use fossils to study the rate at which evolution has occurred.**

History of Life The oldest rock layers contain the oldest fossils. The oldest fossils are simple organisms, such as bacteria. Much younger rocks contain the fossils of more recent—and more complex—organisms, such as plants and birds. In other words, the fossil record shows that life on Earth has evolved, or changed over time. Life began with one-celled organisms. After a long time, plants and animals appeared.

Icaronycteris (bat)

Cattails

Crocodilian

Bat

Sunfish

Gar

Gar fossil

Herring

Sequoia

Frigate birds

Sycamore leaves

Sycamores

Uintatherium

Hyracotherium

Coryphodon

Phenacodus

Palms

Past Environments Paleontologists use fossils to build up a picture of Earth's past environments. The fossils found in an area tell whether the area was a desert, a forest, or a freshwater swamp. Suppose, for example, a fossil looks a lot like a clam. Modern clams live in water. Therefore, the fossil animal probably lived in water, too.

Fossils can show how an environment has changed. For example, coal has been found in Antarctica. But coal only forms from the remains of plants that grow in warm regions. Ice and snow now cover Antarctica. The presence of coal shows that the climate of Antarctica was once much warmer than today.

Scientists can use fossils to learn about changes in Earth's surface. For example, the fossils in Figure 10 are about 50 million years old. They were found in a region of dry plains and plateaus in Wyoming. From these fossils, scientists have inferred that back then the region had many shallow lakes and swamps. Lush forests flourished in a warm, subtropical climate.

Gradualism Scientists also study fossils to try to determine the rate at which evolution occurs. Scientists are not sure how rapidly species change. One hypothesis, called **gradualism,** proposes that evolution occurs slowly but steadily. According to this hypothesis, tiny changes in a species gradually add up to major changes over very long periods of time. This is how Darwin thought evolution occurred.

If gradualism is correct, the fossil record should include intermediate forms between a fossil organism and its descendants. However, there are often long periods in which fossils show little or no change. Then, quite suddenly, fossils appear that are very different. One possible explanation for the lack of intermediate forms is that the fossil record is incomplete. Scientists may eventually find more fossils to fill the gaps.

Punctuated Equilibria The hypothesis of **punctuated equilibria** accounts for the gaps in the fossil record. According to this hypothesis, species evolve quickly during relatively short periods. These periods of rapid change are separated by long periods of little or no change. Today most scientists think that evolution can occur gradually at some times and more rapidly at others.

Reading Checkpoint What hypothesis proposes that evolution occurs slowly but steadily?

Section 2 Assessment

S 7.3.c, 7.4.e,
E-LA: Reading 7.2.0

Target Reading Skill Identify Supporting Evidence Refer to your graphic organizer about evidence for evolution as you answer the questions below.

Reviewing Key Concepts

1. a. Listing List four types of evidence that support evolution.
  b. Applying Concepts What is comparative anatomy and how do scientists use it to study evolution?
  c. Interpreting Diagrams Compare the dolphin, bird, and dog forelimb bones in Figure 8. List one specific way in which the bone structures are similar.

2. a. Reviewing What are sediments? How are they involved in the formation of fossils?
  b. Classifying Identify five types of fossils.
  c. Comparing and Contrasting Which of the major types of fossils does not form in sediments? Describe how this type can form.

3. a. Defining What is a paleontologist?
  b. Reviewing What can paleontologists learn from fossils?
  c. Inferring A paleontologist finds a fossil fish in rocks located in what is now a dry area. What was the environment of that area probably like when the fish was alive?

Lab zone At-Home **Activity**

Modeling Fossil Formation With an adult family member, spread some mud in a shallow pan. Use your fingertips to make "footprints" across the mud. Let the mud dry and harden. Explain how this is similar to fossil formation.

S 7.3.a Students know that both genetic variation and environmental factors are causes of evolution and diversity of organisms.

S 7.3.e Students know that extinction of a species occurs when the environment changes and the adaptive characteristics of a species are insufficient for its survival.

- What factors have contributed to the diversity of species?
- How do new species form?
- How do scientists infer evolutionary relationships among species?
- What causes the extinction of species?

Key Terms
- habitat
- extinct

Standards **Warm-Up**

Which Is the Closer Relative?

1. The pictures show a dog, a coyote, and a wolf. Compare and contrast the pictures carefully.
2. On the basis of your comparison, decide which animal—a coyote or a wolf—is more closely related to a dog.

Think It Over

Classifying Besides anatomical characteristics, what characteristics might scientists use to determine how closely organisms are related?

Dog

Wolf

Coyote

You are hiking in the Mariposa Grove in Yosemite National Park. All around you are giant sequoias, those ancient evergreens that tower over the landscape. Sequoia needles cover the ground, and in some places you see the sequoia's huge cones.

You glimpse a bright spot of red on the forest floor and walk over to examine it. What in the world is it? It looks like a living thing, but you aren't sure what it is. Could it be a fungus? Is it a plant? Whatever it is, it is both strange and beautiful.

You have seen a flower of the snow plant, which grows in the Sierra Nevada mountains. Unlike most plants, the snow plant gets energy from dead and decaying material rather than through photosynthesis. The snow plant is just one of many interesting species of organisms that live in Yosemite.

◄ **Flower of the snow plant**

A Variety of Species

Millions of species exist on Earth, from tiny bacteria to huge sequoias. What factors account for this diversity of species? 🔑 **Over time, different environments and genetic variation have produced, through natural selection, the variety of organisms that exist today.**

Different Environments Think of the many different kinds of environments on Earth, from the deep sea to the tops of mountains. Organisms live in each of those environments. Over millions of years, natural selection has produced different species, each with adaptations enabling it to live in a specific habitat. An organism's **habitat** is the specific environment that provides the things the organism needs to live, grow, and reproduce.

Genetic Diversity Organisms within the same species do not all have identical traits. Think of how humans, for example, are different from one another. Therefore, organisms in a species have different alleles for the genes that govern traits. Some genetic differences, or variations, may result from mutations in DNA. Others may be caused by the rearrangement of genes during meiosis. All the genetic variations in a species make up the total "gene pool" of that species.

Many species have much variety in their gene pools. These species can often adapt to changes in the environment. That is because some individuals will have traits that let them survive in the new conditions.

In some species, however, most of the organisms are genetically similar. Those species may have difficulty surviving environmental change. For example, a fungus once wiped out much of the corn crop in the United States. The corn plants were all very much like one another, and few plants had any resistance to the fungus. Today, many endangered species, such as cheetahs, have little genetic variation. This lack of genetic variation may make them more likely to be destroyed by environmental change.

FIGURE 11
Lack of Diversity
The worldwide population of cheetahs lacks genetic diversity.
Relating Cause and Effect *Why might this lack of genetic variation endanger the cheetah population?*

Kaibab
squirrel ▼

Abert's
squirrel ▼

FIGURE 12
Kaibab and Abert's Squirrels
These two kinds of squirrels have been isolated from one another for a long time. Eventually, this isolation may result in two different species.

UTAH

COLORADO

Colorado River

Lake Mead

Lake Powell

Grand Canyon

NEW MEXICO

ARIZONA

Key
Range of Kaibab squirrel

Range of Abert's squirrel

How Do New Species Form?

Darwin's theory on evolution by natural selection explains how variations can lead to changes in a species. But how does an entirely new species evolve? 🔑 **A new species can form when a group of individuals remains isolated from the rest of its species long enough to evolve different traits.**

Geographic Isolation Scientists now hypothesize that geographic isolation is one of the main ways new species form. Isolation, or complete separation, happens when some members of a species become cut off from the rest of the species.

Sometimes a group is separated from the rest of its species by a river, volcano, or mountain range. Even an ocean wave can separate a few individuals from the rest of their species. The wave can sweep some members of a species out to sea and later wash them up on an island. This may have happened to species on the Galápagos Islands. Once a group becomes isolated, members of the isolated group can no longer mate with the rest of the species.

An Example of Isolation Abert's squirrel and the Kaibab squirrel both live in forests in the Southwest. Look at the map in Figure 12. You can see that the populations of the two kinds of squirrel are separated by the Grand Canyon. The Kaibab and Abert's squirrels belong to the same species, but they have slightly different characteristics. For example, the Kaibab squirrel has a black belly, while Abert's squirrel has a white belly. One day Abert's squirrel and the Kaibab squirrel may become so different from each other that they will be separate species.

 **Reading Checkpoint** How can some members of a species become separated from the main group?

Inferring Species Relationships

Some species are closely related to one another. Other species are distantly related. How do scientists determine relationships between species? Not too long ago, fossils, embryos, and body structures were the only tools that scientists had to determine how species were related. Today, scientists can also compare the DNA and protein sequences of different species. **Scientists have combined the evidence from DNA, protein structure, fossils, early development, and body structure to determine the evolutionary relationships among species.**

Similarities in DNA Why do some species have similar body structures and development patterns? Scientists infer that the species inherited many of the same genes from a common ancestor. Recently, scientists have begun to compare the genes of different species to determine how closely related the species are.

Recall that genes are made of DNA. By comparing the sequence of nitrogen bases in the DNA of different species, scientists can infer how closely related the two species are. The more similar the DNA sequences, the more closely related the species are. For example, DNA analysis has shown that elephants and tiny elephant shrews, shown in Figure 13, are closely related.

The DNA bases along a gene specify what type of protein will be produced. Therefore, scientists can also compare the order of amino acids in a protein to see how closely related two species are.

Combining Evidence In most cases, evidence from DNA and protein structure has confirmed hypotheses based on fossils, embryos, and body structure. For example, recent DNA comparisons show that dogs are more similar to wolves than they are to coyotes. Scientists had already reached this conclusion based on similarities in the structure and development of these three species.

FIGURE 13
DNA and Relationships
Because of its appearance, the tiny elephant shrew was thought to be closely related to mice and other rodents. However, DNA comparisons have shown that the elephant shrew is actually more closely related to elephants.

| Raccoons | Lesser Pandas | Giant Pandas | Bears |

Present

10 million years ago

25 million years ago

40 million years ago

Common Ancestor

FIGURE 14
Species Relationships
This diagram shows how scientists now think that raccoons, lesser pandas, giant pandas, and bears are related.
Interpreting Diagrams *Are giant pandas more closely related to lesser pandas or to bears?*

Sometimes, however, scientists have changed their hypotheses about species relationships. For example, lesser pandas were once thought to be closely related to giant pandas. Recently, however, DNA analysis and other methods have shown that giant pandas and lesser pandas are not closely related. Instead, giant pandas are more closely related to bears, while lesser pandas are more closely related to raccoons.

Extinction of Species

Thousands of years ago, artists painted graceful pictures of woolly mammoths on the walls of caves. Woolly mammoths, which looked a bit like present-day elephants, once lived all over the world. However, they are now extinct. A species is **extinct** if no members of that species are still alive.

Extinction and the Environment Most species that were preserved as fossils are now extinct. What makes a species become extinct? ⊙ **Extinction is caused by a change in a species' environment. The members of the species may not have adaptations that allow them to survive and reproduce in the changed environment.**

There are many ways in which an environment can change. A new disease may strike a species. Predators may kill so many prey animals that the prey becomes extinct. For example, humans may have contributed to the extinction of woolly mammoths by hunting and killing too many of them.

Reading Checkpoint What happened to most fossil species?

Climate Change Climate change has been the leading cause of extinction. Climate change can destroy organisms' habitats. Suppose, for example, an area that was once warm and moist becomes cool and dry. Many plants that need warmth and a lot of water may die. Animals that feed on those plants will be affected, too. Animal species may compete fiercely for the few surviving plants. This competition could result in the extinction of the plants and the animals that eat them.

Climate change may have helped cause the extinction of woolly mammoths. Woolly mammoths had traits that helped them live in a cool climate, such as thick coats of hair. When the climate became warmer, however, these traits were no longer helpful.

Adaptation and Survival Environmental change does not always lead to extinction. Some organisms in a species may have traits that help them survive in a changed environment. Horseshoe crabs, for example, first appeared on Earth long before the dinosaurs. These animals, which are related to spiders, have changed little over time, in spite of the fact that Earth's climate has changed several times.

Section 3 Assessment

S 7.3.a, 7.3.e, E-LA: Writing 7.2.5, Reading 7.1.0

Vocabulary Skill Identify Multiple Meanings
In the term *gene pool,* what does *pool* mean? What is a more common meaning of *pool*?

Reviewing Key Concepts

1. a. **Identifying** Identify two factors that account for the diversity of species.
   b. **Explaining** What is genetic variation?
   c. **Relating Cause and Effect** Explain why species with a diverse gene pool are usually less threatened by environmental change than are species whose members all have similar genes.
2. a. **Reviewing** How can isolation lead to the formation of new species?
   b. **Predicting** A species of snake lives in a forest. A new road separates one group of snakes from another. Is it likely that these two groups of snakes will become separate species? Why or why not?

3. a. **Listing** What kinds of evidence indicate how closely species are related?
   b. **Inferring** Of the kinds of evidence you listed above, which are probably the most reliable? Explain your answer.
4. a. **Reviewing** What causes extinction?
   b. **Relating Cause and Effect** What two factors may have caused the extinction of woolly mammoths?
   c. **Making Generalizations** Explain how natural selection is at work when a species becomes extinct.

Writing in Science

Museum Interpretation Suppose Figure 14 were part of a museum exhibit. Write an explanation of the diagram for museum visitors. Describe the relationships shown in the diagram.

Telltale Molecules  S 7.3.a, 7.7.b

Problem
What information can protein structure reveal about evolutionary relationships among organisms?

Skills Focus
interpreting data, drawing conclusions

Procedure
1. Examine the table below. It shows the sequence of amino acids in one region of a protein, cytochrome c, for six different animals.
2. Predict which of the five other animals is most closely related to the horse. Which animal do you think is most distantly related?
3. Compare the amino acid sequence of the horse to that of the donkey. How many amino acids differ between the two species? Record that number in your notebook.
4. Compare the amino acid sequences of each of the other animals to that of the horse. Record the number of differences in your notebook.

Analyze and Conclude
1. **Interpreting Data** Which animal's amino acid sequence was most similar to that of the horse? What similarities and difference(s) did you observe?
2. **Drawing Conclusions** Based on these data, which species is most closely related to the horse? Which is most distantly related?
3. **Interpreting Data** For the entire protein, the horse's amino acid sequence differs from the other animals' as follows: donkey, 1 difference; rabbit, 6; snake, 22; turtle, 11; and whale, 5. How do the relationships indicated by the entire protein compare with those for the region you examined?
4. **Communicating** Write a paragraph explaining why data about amino acid sequences can provide information about evolutionary relationships among organisms.

More to Explore
Besides amino acid sequences, what characteristics make horses different from donkeys? Do library and World Wide Web research to find out. Then write a report communicating what you have learned.

Section of Cytochrome c Protein in Animals														
Animal	Amino Acid Position													
	39	40	41	42	43	44	45	46	47	48	49	50	51	52	53
Horse	A	B	C	D	E	F	G	H	I	J	K	L	M	N	O
Donkey	A	B	C	D	E	F	G	H	Z	J	K	L	M	N	O
Rabbit	A	B	C	D	E	Y	G	H	Z	J	K	L	M	N	O
Snake	A	B	C	D	E	Y	G	H	Z	J	K	W	M	N	O
Turtle	A	B	C	D	E	V	G	H	Z	J	K	U	M	N	O
Whale	A	B	C	D	E	Y	G	H	Z	J	K	L	M	N	O

Classifying Organisms

S 7.3.d Students know how to construct a simple branching diagram to classify living groups of organisms by shared derived characteristics and how to expand the diagram to include fossil organisms.

🔑 Why do biologists organize living things into groups?

🔑 What do the levels of classification indicate about the relationship between organisms?

🔑 What characteristics are used to classify organisms into domains and kingdoms?

Key Terms
- classification
- taxonomy
- binomial nomenclature
- genus
- prokaryote
- eukaryote

Lab zone **Standards Warm-Up**

Can You Organize a Junk Drawer?

1. Your teacher will give you some items that you might find in the junk drawer of a desk. Your job is to organize the items.
2. Examine the objects and decide on three groups into which you can sort them.
3. Place each object into one of the groups, based on how the item's features match the characteristics of the group.
4. Compare your grouping system with those of your classmates.

Think It Over
Classifying Which of your classmates' grouping systems seemed most useful? Why?

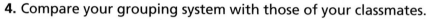

Suppose you had only ten minutes to run into a supermarket to get what you needed—milk and tomatoes. Could you do it? In most supermarkets this would be an easy task. You'd probably find out where the dairy and produce sections are, and head straight to those areas. Now imagine if you had to shop for these same items in a market where things were randomly placed throughout the store. Where would you begin? You'd have to search through a lot of things before you found what you needed. You could be there for a long time!

FIGURE 16
Classifying Vegetables
Vegetables in the produce section of a supermarket are neatly organized.

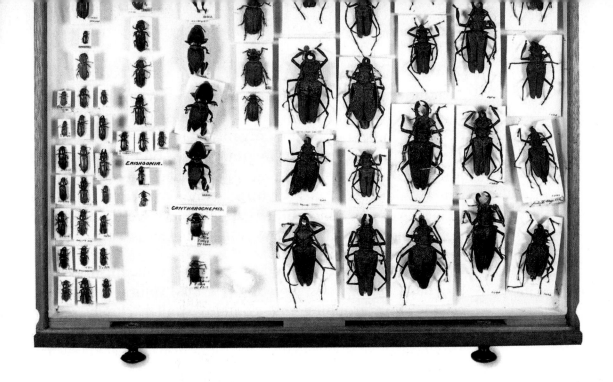

Why Do Scientists Classify?

Just as shopping can be a problem in a disorganized store, finding information about a specific organism can also be a problem. Recall that scientists have identified more than 1.7 million species. Imagine how difficult it would be to find information about one particular organism if you had no idea even where to begin. It would be a lot easier if similar organisms were placed into groups.

Biologists group organisms based on similarities, just as grocers group milk with dairy products and tomatoes with produce. **Classification** is the process of grouping things based on their similarities. Biologists classify fossil organisms as well as those that are alive today.

👄 **Biologists use classification to organize living things into groups so that the organisms are easier to study.** The scientific study of how living things are classified is called **taxonomy** (tak SAHN uh mee). Taxonomy and evolution are closely related. Scientists infer that organisms in the same group, such as the beetles in Figure 17, descended from a common ancestor. Taxonomy is part of the larger field called systematics. In addition to classifying organisms, systematics tries to figure out their evolutionary relationships.

Taxonomists sometimes change the way they classify organisms. New evidence, such as the organism's DNA, might show that the organism belongs in a different group. Also, taxonomists may look at old evidence in a new way.

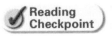 **Reading Checkpoint** What is the scientific study of how living things are classified called?

FIGURE **17**
Classifying Beetles
These beetles belong to a large insect collection in a natural history museum. They have been classified according to characteristics they share.
Observing *What characteristics may have been used to group these beetles?*

The Naming System of Linnaeus

In addition to grouping organisms, taxonomy involves naming them. In the 1750s, the Swedish naturalist Carolus Linnaeus devised a system of naming organisms that is still used today. Linnaeus placed organisms in groups based on their observable features. Based on his observations, Linnaeus gave each organism a unique, two-part scientific name. This naming system Linnaeus used is called **binomial nomenclature** (by NOH mee ul NOH men klay chur). The word *binomial* means "two names."

Genus and Species The first word in an organism's scientific name is its genus. A **genus** (JEE nus) (plural *genera*) is a classification grouping that contains similar, closely related organisms. For example, pumas, marbled cats, and house cats are all classified in the genus *Felis*. Organisms that are classified in the genus *Felis* share characteristics such as sharp, retractable claws and behaviors such as hunting other animals.

The second word in a scientific name often describes a distinctive feature of an organism, such as where it lives or its appearance. Together, the two words indicate a unique species. Recall that species is a group of similar organisms that can mate with each other and produce offspring that can also mate and reproduce.

Reading Checkpoint What kind of name did Linnaeus give each organism?

FIGURE 18
Binomial Nomenclature
These three species of cats belong to the same genus. Their scientific names, written in Latin, share the same first word, *Felis*. The second word of their names describes a feature of the animal. **Classifying** *What characteristics do these species share?*

Felis concolor (Puma)
Concolor means "the same color." Notice that this animal's coat is mostly the same color.

Felis domesticus (House cat) *Domesticus* means "of the house."

Felis marmorata (Marbled cat) Notice the marbled pattern of this animal's coat. *Marmorata* means "marble."

Using Binomial Nomenclature Notice in Figure 19 that a complete scientific name is written in italics. Only the first letter of the first word is capitalized. Notice also that scientific names contain Latin words. Linnaeus used Latin because it was the language that scientists used during that time.

Binomial nomenclature makes it easy for scientists to communicate because everyone uses the same name for the same organism. Using different names can get confusing. For instance, people call the animal in Figure 19 a woodchuck, groundhog, or whistlepig. Fortunately, it has only one scientific name—*Marmota monax.*

Levels of Classification

The classification system that scientists use today is based on the contributions of Linnaeus. But today's classification system uses a series of many levels to classify organisms.

To help you understand the levels in classification, imagine a room filled with everybody from your state. First, all of the people from your town raise their hands. Then, those from your neighborhood raise their hands. Then, those from your street raise their hands. Finally, those from your house raise their hands. Each time, fewer people raise their hands. But you'd be in all of the groups. The most general group you belong to is the state. The most specific group is the house. The more levels you share with others, the more you have in common with them. Of course, organisms are not grouped by where they live, but rather by their shared characteristics.

The Major Levels of Classification Most biologists today classify organisms into eight levels. First, an organism is placed in a broad group, which in turn is divided into more specific groups. **The more classification levels that two organisms share, the more characteristics they have in common.**

Here are the eight classification levels that biologists commonly use.
- A domain is the highest level of organization.
- Within a domain, there are kingdoms.
Within kingdoms, there are phyla (FY luh) (singular *phylum*).
- Within phyla are classes.
- Within classes are orders.
- Within orders are families.
- Each family contains one or more genera.
- Each genus contains one or more species.

FIGURE **19**
Marmota monax
Although there are many common names for this animal, it has only one scientific name, *Marmota monax.*

Go Online
*SCi*LINKS
For: Links on kingdoms
Visit: www.SciLinks.org
Web Code: scn-0113

Classifying an Owl Look at Figure 20 to see how the great horned owl is classified. The top row shows a wide variety of organisms that share the owl's domain. Notice that as you move down the levels, there are fewer kinds of organisms in each group. The organisms in each new group have more in common, however. For example, the class Aves includes all birds. The order Strigiformes includes only owls.

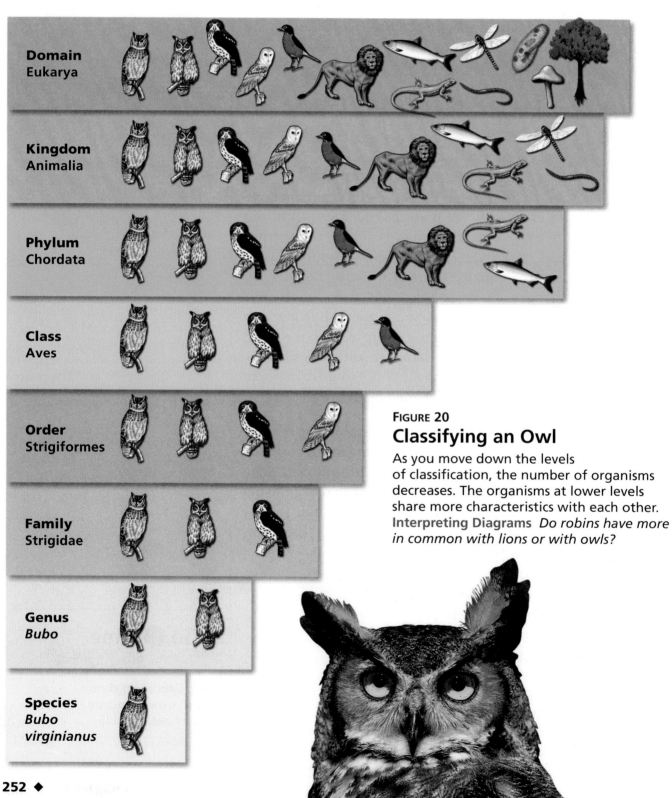

Domain Eukarya

Kingdom Animalia

Phylum Chordata

Class Aves

Order Strigiformes

Family Strigidae

Genus *Bubo*

Species *Bubo virginianus*

FIGURE 20
Classifying an Owl
As you move down the levels of classification, the number of organisms decreases. The organisms at lower levels share more characteristics with each other. **Interpreting Diagrams** *Do robins have more in common with lions or with owls?*

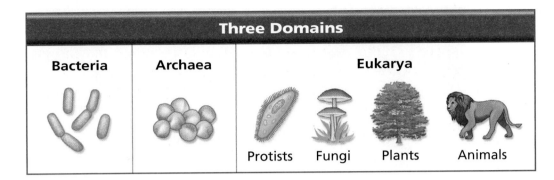

Three Domains

Bacteria	Archaea	Eukarya			
		Protists	Fungi	Plants	Animals

Domains and Kingdoms

Today, a three-domain system of classification is commonly used. Shown in Figure 21, the three domains are Bacteria, Archaea, and Eukarya. Within the domains are kingdoms. 🔑 **Organisms are placed into domains and kingdoms based on their cell type, their ability to make food, and the number of cells in their bodies.**

Bacteria Although you may not know it, members of the domain Bacteria are all around you. You can find them in the yogurt you eat, on every surface you touch, and inside your body, both when you are healthy and sick. Some bacteria are autotrophs, while others are heterotrophs.

Members of the domain Bacteria are prokaryotes (proh KA ree ohtz). **Prokaryotes** are organisms whose cells lack a nucleus. Remember that a nucleus is a dense area in a cell that contains nucleic acids—the chemical instructions that direct the cell's activities. In prokaryotes, nucleic acids are not contained within a nucleus.

Archaea Deep in the Pacific Ocean, hot gases and molten rock spew out from a vent in the ocean floor. Surprisingly, a group of tiny organisms thrives there. They are members of the domain Archaea (ahr KEE uh), whose name comes from the Greek word for "ancient." Archaea can be found in some of the most extreme environments on Earth, including hot springs, very salty water, swamps, and the intestines of cows! Scientists think that the harsh conditions in which archaea live are similar to those of ancient Earth.

Like bacteria, archaea are unicellular prokaryotes. And like bacteria, some archaea are autotrophs while others are heterotrophs. Archaea are classified in their own domain, however, because their structure and chemical makeup differ from that of bacteria.

 **Reading Checkpoint** **What is a nucleus?**

FIGURE 21
Three Domains
In the three-domain system of classification, all known organisms belong to one of three domains—Bacteria, Archaea, or Eukarya.

Lab zone **Skills Activity**

Classifying
Test your classifying skills using Figure 20. Look carefully at the organisms pictured together at the kingdom level. Make a list of the characteristics that the organisms share. Then make two more lists of shared characteristics—one for the organisms at the class level and the other for those at the genus level. How does the number of shared characteristics on your lists change at each level?

FIGURE 22
Domain Eukarya

The four kingdoms in domain Eukarya are protists, fungi, plants, and animals.

Making Generalizations *What characteristic do all Eukarya share?*

Plants

Animal

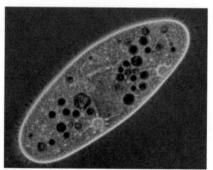
Protist

Fungi

Eukarya What do seaweeds, mushrooms, tomatoes, and dogs have in common? They are all members of the domain Eukarya. Organisms in this domain are **eukaryotes** (yoo KA ree ohtz)—organisms with cells that contain nuclei. 🔑 **Scientists classify eukaryotes into one of four kingdoms: protists, fungi, plants, and animals.**

Other than having cells with nuclei, the members of the four eukaryote kingdoms are very different from one another. A protist (PROH tist) is any eukaryote that cannot be classified as a plant, an animal, or a fungus. Most protists are unicellular.

Mushrooms, molds, and mildew are all fungi (FUN jy). All fungi are heterotrophs, and most are multicellular. In contrast, all plants are multicellular autotrophs. All animals, such as a dog and a flea on the dog's ear, are multicellular eukaryotes. In addition, all animals are heterotrophs.

Section 4 Assessment

S 7.3.d, E-LA: Reading 7.1.0

Vocabulary Skill **Identify Multiple Meanings** Contrast the common meaning of *kingdom* with the meaning of *kingdom* in the classification of living things.

🔑 **Reviewing Key Concepts**

1. **a. Reviewing** Why do biologists classify?
   b. Inferring A jaguarundi is classified in the same genus as a house cat. What characteristics do you think a jaguarundi might have?
2. **a. Listing** List in order the levels of classification, beginning with domain.
   b. Applying Concepts Woodchucks are classified in the same family as squirrels, but in a different family than mice. Do woodchucks have more characteristics in common with squirrels or mice? Explain.

3. **a. Identifying** What are the three domains into which organisms are classified?
   b. Classifying Which two domains include only organisms that are prokaryotes?
   c. Comparing and Contrasting How do the members of the two domains of prokaryotes differ?

Lab zone **At-Home Activity**

Kitchen Classification With a family member, go on a "classification hunt" in the kitchen. Look in your refrigerator, cabinets, and drawers to discover what classification systems your family uses to organize items.

CALIFORNIA
Standards Focus

S 7.3.d Students know how to construct a simple branching diagram to classify living groups of organisms by shared derived characteristics and how to expand the diagram to include fossil organisms.

How does a branching tree diagram show evolutionary relationships?

Key Terms
• branching tree diagram
• shared derived characteristic

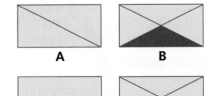

Lab zone Standards Warm-Up

Which Is First?
1. Note the characteristics of figures A, B, C, and D.
2. Which figure is most similar to Figure B?

Think It Over
Inferring Suppose these shapes are fossils of extinct organisms. Which organism do you think might be the ancestor of all the others? Explain your reasoning.

Two groups of organisms with similar characteristics may be descended from a common ancestor. The more similar the two groups are, the more recent the common ancestor probably is. To understand this, think of human families. Brothers and sisters usually look more like one another than they look like their cousins. Cousins share one set of grandparents. But brothers and sisters share a more recent ancestor—their parents.

A **branching tree diagram** shows probable evolutionary relationships among organisms. It also shows the order in which specific characteristics may have evolved. Branching tree diagrams begin at the base with the common ancestor of all the organisms in the diagram. Figure 23, for example, begins with the ancestor of all animals.

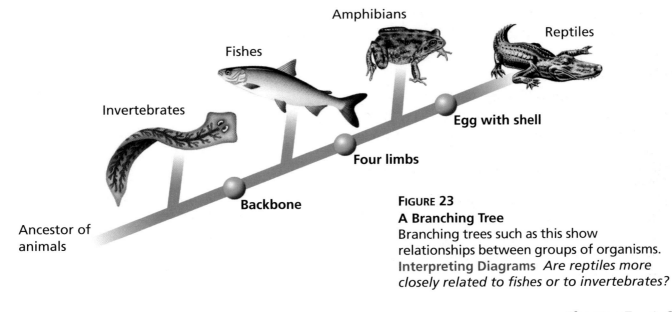

FIGURE 23
A Branching Tree
Branching trees such as this show relationships between groups of organisms.
Interpreting Diagrams *Are reptiles more closely related to fishes or to invertebrates?*

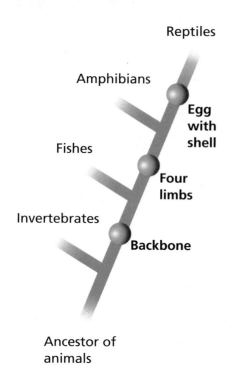

FIGURE 24
Groups of Animals
This branching tree shows relationships between groups of animals.

(Diagram labels: Reptiles, Amphibians, Fishes, Invertebrates, Egg with shell, Four limbs, Backbone, Ancestor of animals)

Shared Derived Characteristics

🔑 A branching tree diagram shows evolutionary relationships by grouping organisms according to shared derived characteristics. A **shared derived characteristic** is usually a homologous structure, such as a backbone, that is shared by all organisms in a group. Notice that, above each fork in Figure 24, a label indicates a shared derived characteristic, such as a backbone or four limbs. On a branching tree, all the organisms above the label have the trait. In Figure 24, for example, all organisms above the Backbone label have a backbone.

Evolutionary Groups A branching tree has groups within groups. In Figure 24, the largest subgroup is the group with backbones. Of the animals shown in the diagram, the backbone group includes fishes, amphibians, and reptiles. Within that group is a smaller group—animals with four limbs. Fishes are not in this group, but amphibians and reptiles are. The smallest group consists only of animals that produce eggs with shells—reptiles. Species within any group are more closely related to one another than to species not in the group.

Order of Characteristics Characteristics that appear lower on a branching tree probably developed before characteristics higher on the tree. Figure 24 shows that, during evolutionary history, animals with backbones appeared earlier than animals with both a backbone and four limbs.

 **Reading Checkpoint** **What is a branching tree diagram?**

Math: Statistics, Data Analysis, and Probability 7.1.1

Math ▸ Analyzing Data

Data for a Branching Tree Diagram
The data in the table show shared derived characteristics of different types of plants.

1. **Interpreting Data** Do mosses have any of the characteristics indicated at the top of the table?

2. **Interpreting Data** Which plant has the greatest number of the characteristics?

3. **Drawing Conclusions** Use the information in the table to draw a branching tree. (*Hint:* Mosses go at the base of the tree.)

4. **Inferring** A fossil plant shows evidence of flowers. Where in the diagram would the plant go?

Characteristics of Plants			
Plant	**True Roots**	**Seeds**	**Flowers**
Moss	No	No	No
Fern	Yes	No	No
Spruce tree	Yes	Yes	No
Apple tree	Yes	Yes	Yes

FIGURE 25
Fossil Fish
The fossil bones of this fish show that it has a backbone but no legs.

Constructing a Branching Tree

Suppose you have a list of organisms and their characteristics. You want to use this information to draw a branching tree. At the base of the tree, write "Common Ancestor." Just above the common ancestor, put the group of organisms with none of the characteristics. On the next higher fork, put the group with one of the shared derived characteristics. On the branch above that, put the organism with two of the characteristics. Continue this process until you get to the organism or group with the greatest number of shared derived characteristics. That group goes at the top of the tree. In Figure 24, that group is reptiles.

Branching tree diagrams can sometimes show fossils as well as living organisms. For example, look at the fossil in Figure 25. The fossil has a backbone, but does it have four limbs? No. So you would put the fossil on the branch with fishes. In fact, the fossil in the photograph is an extinct fish.

Section 5 Assessment

S 7.3.d, E-LA: Writing 7.2.0, Reading 7.1.0

Vocabulary Skill Identify Multiple Meanings In the term *branching tree*, what does *tree* mean? What is a common meaning of *tree*?

Reviewing Key Concepts

1. **a. Reviewing** How does a branching tree diagram divide organisms into groups?
   b. Interpreting Diagrams Choose one animal group in Figure 23. Identify the characteristics shared by group members.
   c. Classifying A fossil animal has four legs. What additional information would you need to put it on a branch in Figure 23?

Writing in Science

Conversation Suppose that Carolus Linnaeus were alive today and saw Figure 23. Write an imaginary conversation in which he asks you questions about the diagram and you answer him.

Chapter 7 Study Guide

The BIG Idea

Genetic variation and environmental factors have together resulted in evolution of species.

1 Darwin's Theory

Key Concepts S 7.3.a, 7.3.b

- Darwin's important observations included the diversity of organisms, the remains of ancient organisms, and the characteristics of organisms on the Galápagos Islands.

- Darwin reasoned that plants or animals that arrived on the Galápagos Islands faced environmental factors that were different from those on the mainland. Perhaps, Darwin hypothesized, the species gradually changed over many generations and became better adapted to the new environments.

- Darwin proposed that, over a long period, natural selection can lead to change. Helpful variations may accumulate in a species, while unfavorable ones may disappear.

Key Terms

species	scientific theory
fossil	natural selection
adaptation	variation
evolution	

2 Evidence of Evolution

Key Concepts S 7.3.c, 7.4.e

- Similar body structures, patterns of early development, molecular structure, and fossils all provide evidence of evolution.

- Most fossils form when organisms that die become buried in sediments.

- The fossil record provides evidence about the history of life and past environments on Earth.

Key Terms

comparative anatomy
homologous structures
mold
cast
petrified fossil
trace fossil
paleontologist
gradualism
punctuated equilibria

3 Evolution of Species

Key Concepts S 7.3.a, 7.3.e

- Over time, different environments and genetic variation have produced, through natural selection, the variety of organisms that exist today.

- A new species can form when a group of individuals remains isolated from the rest of its species long enough to evolve different traits.

- Extinction is caused by a change in a species' environment.

- DNA, protein structure, fossils, early development, and body structure are used to determine species relationships.

Key Terms

habitat	extinct

4 Classifying Organisms

Key Concepts S 7.3.d

- Biologists use classification to organize living things into groups so that the organisms are easier to study.

- The more classification levels that two organisms share, the more characteristics they have in common.

- Organisms are placed into domains and kingdoms based on cell type, ability to make food, and the number of cells in their bodies.

Key Terms

classification	genus
taxonomy	prokaryote
binomial nomenclature	eukaryote

5 Branching Trees

Key Concepts S 7.3.d

- A branching tree diagram shows evolutionary relationships by grouping organisms according to shared derived characteristics.

Key Terms

branching tree diagram
shared derived characteristic

⊙ Target Reading Skill

Identify Supporting Evidence In Section 3, you learned how scientists infer how closely species are related. To review this information, copy the partly completed graphic organizer at the right. Fill in the kinds of evidence that are missing.

Evidence

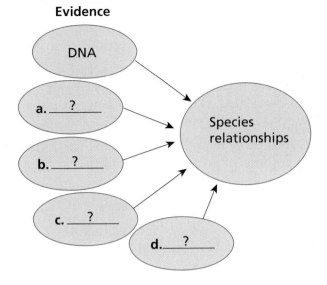

Reviewing Key Terms

Choose the letter of the best answer.

1. Changes in a species over long periods of time are called
   a. scientific theories.
   b. evolution.
   c. homologous structures.
   d. developmental stages.

2. A trait that helps an organism survive and reproduce is called a(n)
   a. variation.
   b. adaptation.
   c. species.
   d. selection.

3. Similar structures that related species have inherited from a common ancestor are called
   a. adaptations.
   b. punctuated equilibria.
   c. ancestral structures.
   d. homologous structures.

4. The specific environment that provides an organism's needs is called the organism's
   a. genus.
   b. taxonomy.
   c. habitat.
   d. natural selection.

5. An organism whose cells lack nuclei is called a(n)
   a. protist
   b. fungus
   c. eukaryote
   d. prokaryote

Complete the following sentences so that your answers clearly explain the key terms.

6. Darwin's theory of evolution is an example of a **scientific theory**, which is a(n) _____ .

7. **Comparative anatomy** is the comparison of _____ .

8. A species is **extinct** only if _____ .

9. **Classification** brings order to the study of organisms because it is the process of _____ .

10. A **branching tree diagram** shows evolutionary relationships by _____ .

Writing in Science

Notebook Entry Imagine that you are a biologist exploring the Galápagos Islands. Write a notebook entry on one of the unusual species you have found on the islands. Include a description of how it is adapted to its environment.

Video Assessment
Discovery Channel School
Changes Over Time

Review and Assessment

Checking Concepts

11. What role does the overproduction of organisms play in natural selection?

12. On the basis of similar body structures, scientists hypothesize that two species are closely related. What other evidence would support their hypothesis?

13. Contrast the hypothesis of gradualism to the hypothesis of punctuated equilibria.

14. Explain how geographic isolation can result in the formation of a new species.

15. What is meant by *extinct*? Explain how environmental factors might cause extinction.

16. What are the advantages of identifying an organism by its scientific name?

17. What is a shared derived characteristic?

Thinking Critically

18. **Relating Cause and Effect** Why did Darwin's visit to the Galápagos Islands have such an important influence on his development of the theory of evolution?

19. **Applying Concepts** Some insects look just like sticks. How could this be an advantage to the insects? How could this trait have evolved through natural selection?

20. **Predicting** Which of the organisms shown below is least likely to become a fossil? Explain.

21. **Making Judgments** What type of evidence is the best indicator of how closely two species are related? Explain your anwer.

22. **Comparing and Contrasting** How are selective breeding and natural selection similar? How are they different?

Applying Skills

Use the diagram below to answer Questions 23–25.

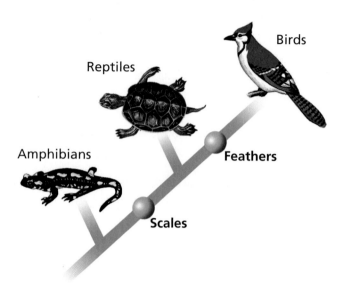

Common ancestor

23. **Applying Concepts** In the branching tree diagram above, what are the shared derived characteristics?

24. **Interpreting Diagrams** Which organisms in the diagram have scales? How do you know?

25. **Interpreting Diagrams** On the basis of the diagram, which group probably appeared first, birds or reptiles?

▲Lab zone Standards Investigation

Performance Assessment Complete your poster, booklet, or whatever way you choose to present your findings to the class. Be prepared to explain why you chose the fossil species that you did. Also indicate where you found information about that fossil.

Choose the letter of the best answer.

1. The process by which individuals that are better adapted to their environment are more likely to survive and reproduce than other members of the same species is called
   A natural selection.
   B evolution.
   C competition.
   D overproduction.   **S 7.3.b**

2. Which of the following is the best example of an adaptation that helps an organism survive in its environment?
   A green coloring in a lizard living on gray rocks
   B a thick coat of fur on an animal that lives in the desert
   C extensive root system in a desert plant
   D thin, delicate leaves on a plant in a cold climate   **S 7.3.a**

3. Which of the following is the weakest evidence supporting a close evolutionary relationship between two animals?
   A The bones of a bird's wings are similar to the bones of a dog's legs.
   B Human embryos look like turtle embryos in their early development.
   C Lesser pandas look like bears.
   D The amino acid sequence in mouse hemoglobin is similar to the amino acid sequence in chimpanzee hemoglobin.   **S 7.3.c**

4. Most members of species of cat depend mainly on mice for food. For several summers in a row, a disease kills off most of the mice in an area. Over time, what is the most likely effect on the cat species?
   A All of the cats will die of starvation.
   B Those cats that can eat foods other than mice will survive and reproduce.
   C The cat species will lose its genetic diversity.
   D There will be no long-term effect on the cat species.   **S 7.3.a**

Use the table below and your knowledge of science to answer Questions 5–7.

Some Types of Trees			
Common Name of Tree	Kingdom	Family	Species
Bird cherry	Plants	Rosaceae	*Prunus avium*
Flowering cherry	Plants	Rosaceae	*Prunus serrula*
Smooth-leaved elm	Plants	Ulmaceae	*Ulmus minor*
Whitebeam	Plants	Rosaceae	*Sorbus aria*

5. Which of the following organisms is most different from the other three?
   A *Prunus avium*
   B *Prunus serrula*
   C *Ulmus minor*
   D *Sorbus aria*   **S 7.3.d**

6. Which of the following pairs of organisms should share the most characteristics?
   A *Prunus serrula* and *Prunus avium*
   B *Ulmus minor* and *Prunus avium*
   C *Sorbus aria* and *Prunus serrula*
   D *Prunus serrula* and *Ulmus minor*   **S 7.3.d**

7. Scientists have discovered fossils of ancient whalelike animals that had legs instead of flippers. This evidence most likely indicates that the ancestors of present-day whales
   A lived in the ocean.
   B lived on land.
   C evolved gradually rather than during short periods of rapid change.
   D never became extinct.   **S 7.4.e**

Apply the
BIG Idea

8. Predict how an extreme change in climate might affect natural selection in a species with little genetic variation.   **S 7.3.e**

Chapter 8

Earth's History

A paleontologist examines a fossilized dinosaur skeleton in the Denver Museum of Nature and Science.

Focus on the
BIG Idea

S 7.4.d

How does evidence from rocks help scientists understand Earth's history?

Check What You Know

While hiking, you find a rock containing a small fossil. The fossil looks like the shell of a present-day clam. When this fossilized organism was alive, what kind of environment existed in the area where you are hiking? Explain your answer.

Fossil brachiopod ▲

Build Science Vocabulary

The images shown here represent some of the key terms in this chapter. You can use this vocabulary skill to help you understand the meaning of some key terms in this chapter.

Use Clues to Determine Meaning

In this textbook, important new words, or key terms, first appear in dark type with a yellow highlight. The meanings, or definitions, of these words usually follow the new terms. In addition to the definitions themselves, there are often other clues that help you understand the meanings. The example below introduces the key term *relative age*.

> What *relative age* means

> A similar example

The **relative age** of a rock is its <u>age compared to the ages of other rocks.</u> You have probably used the idea of relative age when <u>comparing your age with someone else's age, such as the age of an older brother or younger sister.</u> The relative age of a rock <u>does not give the exact number in years since the rock was formed.</u>

> What the term does not mean

Apply It!

1. In your own words, explain what *relative age* means.
2. What familiar example is relative age compared to?

index fossil

igneous rock

mass extinction

plates

mammal

Chapter 8 Vocabulary

Interactive Textbook

Build Science Vocabulary
Online
Visit: PHSchool.com
Web Code: cvj-2080

How to Read Science

Reading Skill

Create Outlines

In an outline, you show the relationship between main ideas and supporting ideas. An outline is usually set up like the example shown below. Roman numerals show the main topics. Capital letters and regular numerals show the subtopics. Use the chapter's headings, subheadings, key concepts, and key terms to help you decide what to include in your outline. Look at the sample outline for part of Section 1.

Use text headings as main topics.

Include key terms and their definitions.

Express key concepts in your own words.

I. Hutton's Big Idea
   A. Geology
      1. Structure of Earth
      2. Forces that shape Earth
   B. Erosion—breakdown of rock
   C. Uniformitarianism—geological processes
      of today also happened in past
II. Types of Rocks

Apply It!

1. What is the first main topic in the outline above?
2. What are the three subtopics under this main topic?
3. Compare the definition of uniformitarianism in the outline to the definition in Section 1. How are they similar? How are they different?

Complete the outline above for Section 1 in this chapter. Create an outline for Section 5 in this chapter.

266 ◆

Standards **Investigation**

A Journey Through Geologic Time

S 7.4.g

This chapter will take you on a journey through geologic time. You will learn how fossils reveal the history of life on Earth. To guide you on your journey, you and your classmates will make a timeline showing the many periods of geologic time.

Your Goal

To become an expert on one geologic time period and assist in constructing a timeline

To complete this investigation, you must

- research a geologic time period of your choice
- create a travel brochure that shows what life was like in this time period
- illustrate your time period for the timeline
- follow the safety guidelines in Appendix A

Plan It!

Begin by selecting a time period you would like to investigate. Check with your teacher to be sure that all the time periods will be covered by members of your class. Then, collect information on your time period's animals, plants, and environment. Use this information to write a travel brochure about your time period. Create illustrations that depict your time period and place them on the timeline. Use the travel brochure to present your geologic time period to your classmates.

1

The Rock Cycle

CALIFORNIA
Standards Focus

S 7.4.a Students know Earth processes today are similar to those that occurred in the past and slow geologic processes have large cumulative effects over long periods of time.

S 7.4.c Students know that the rock cycle includes the formation of new sediment and rocks and that rocks are often found in layers, with the oldest generally on the bottom.

 What is uniformitarianism?

 What is the rock cycle?

Key Terms
- geology
- erosion
- uniformitarianism
- igneous rock
- sedimentary rock
- metamorphic rock
- rock cycle
- magma
- lava

Lab zone Standards **Warm-Up**

How Does Pressure Affect Particles of Rock?

1. Place a sheet of paper over a slice of soft bread.
2. Put a stack of several heavy books on top of the paper. After 10 minutes, remove the books. Observe what happened to the bread.
3. Slice the bread so you can observe its cross section.
4. Carefully slice a piece of fresh bread and compare its cross section to that of the pressed bread.

Think It Over

Observing How did the bread change after you removed the books? Describe the texture of the bread. How does the bread feel? What can you predict about how pressure affects rocks?

Visitors to Badlands National Park in South Dakota see some of the strangest scenery on Earth. The park contains jagged peaks, steep cliffs, and deep canyons sculpted in colorful rock that is layered like a birthday cake. The layers of this cake are red, orange, pink, yellow, or tan. These rocks formed over millions of years as particles of mud, sand, and volcanic ash were deposited in thick layers. The mud and sand slowly changed to sedimentary rock. Then, uplift of the land exposed the rocks to the forces that wear away Earth's surface.

Badlands National Park ▲

Hutton's Big Idea

Geology is the study of the structure of planet Earth and the forces that make and shape Earth. The modern science of geology began in the late 1700s. James Hutton, a Scottish doctor and farmer, studied the rocks and landscape around him. He observed the structure of mountains and valleys. Hutton watched streams cutting through the land in the process of erosion. **Erosion** occurs when running water, ice, or wind break down rocks and carry the pieces away. After studying geologic processes in his own time, Hutton concluded that those same processes had occurred long ago.

Fossil sand ripples

Modern sand ripples

Hutton's idea is called the principle of **uniformitarianism** (yoo nuh for muh TEHR ee un iz um). ○ **The principle of uniformitarianism states that the geologic processes that operate today also operated in the past.** Ancient rocks can be understood by observing present-day geologic processes.

Hutton observed that most geologic processes happen very slowly. He inferred that these processes must have been at work for a very long time to produce such enormous features as mountains and deep valleys. Hutton concluded that Earth must be much older than was commonly thought in his time.

 **Reading Checkpoint** Who first proposed the principle of uniformitarianism?

Types of Rocks

○ **Geologists classify rocks into three main groups—igneous, sedimentary, and metamorphic.** **Igneous rocks** form when molten material from beneath Earth's surface cools and hardens. Igneous rock may form on or below Earth's surface.

Sedimentary rock is made of sediments that have been deposited and then pressed together to form solid rock. Most sediments are tiny pieces of rocks and minerals. Sediments may also include the remains of plants or animals, such as leaves or shells. Most fossils are found in sedimentary rocks. Through fossils, geology provides evidence that supports the theory of evolution.

Metamorphic rock forms when an existing rock is changed by heat, pressure, or chemical reactions. Most metamorphic rock forms under pressure deep underground.

FIGURE 1
Sand Ripples
Ancient, fossilized sand ripples, are similar to sand ripples that form today.
Applying Concepts *What do the fossilized ripples tell you about conditions when the rocks formed?*

Volcanic activity can produce igneous rock.

Erosion and deposition may produce layers of sedimentary rock.

Heat and pressure can cause rocks to bend.

FIGURE 2
Processes That Change Rocks
Processes such as volcanic activity and erosion can change rock from one kind to another. **Relating Cause and Effect** *What factors cause sediments to become sedimentary rock?*

The Rock Cycle

The **rock cycle** is a series of processes on and beneath Earth's surface that slowly change rocks from one kind to another. ☛ **Forces inside Earth and at the surface produce a rock cycle that builds, changes, and destroys rocks.** The rock cycle is a very slow process, taking place over millions of years. Figure 3 shows the rock cycle. Notice that it can follow many pathways.

Volcanic Activity One possible pathway through the rock cycle begins with **magma**—molten material beneath Earth's surface. As the magma is forced toward the surface, it may form a volcanic mountain. Some of the magma hardens underground, forming igneous rock, such as basalt or granite. Some of the magma flows onto the surface as **lava**.

Erosion Over time, erosion wears away the mountain, exposing the igneous rock core. Rain and snow fall on the rock. Oxygen and other chemicals in the air react with minerals in the rock. These conditions break the rock into tiny particles. Water, ice, and wind then carry the particles away.

Deposition Streams carry the particles of rock to the ocean. There they are deposited as sediment. Over millions of years, layers of sediment pile up on the ocean floor. The weight of the layers presses the sediments together. Chemicals in the water cement the particles together. Sedimentary rock such as sandstone is formed.

Heat and Pressure As more and more sediments pile up on the sandstone, the sandstone becomes deeply buried. Pressure increases. The rock becomes hot. Heat and pressure change the rock's texture from gritty to smooth. After millions of years, the sandstone is changed into a metamorphic rock such as quartzite.

Melting The formation of metamorphic rock does not end the rock cycle. Forces inside Earth can push all three types of rock many kilometers beneath the surface. There, intense heat and pressure melt the rock. This molten material can then form new igneous rock. And so the cycle continues.

FIGURE 3

The Rock Cycle
Igneous, sedimentary, and metamorphic rock change continuously through the rock cycle.

Go Online active art

For: Rock Cycle activity
Visit: PHSchool.com
Web Code: cfp-1056

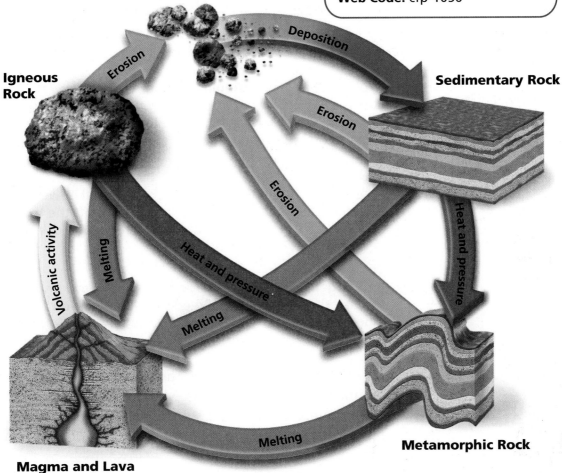

Sediment

Igneous Rock

Erosion

Deposition

Sedimentary Rock

Erosion

Erosion

Volcanic activity

Melting

Heat and pressure

Heat and pressure

Melting

Melting

Magma and Lava

Metamorphic Rock

Section 1 Assessment

S 7.4.a, 7.4.c, E-LA: Writing 7.2.1, Reading 7.2.0

Target Reading Skill Create Outlines
Complete your outline of this section. Use your outline to help answer the questions below.

Reviewing Key Concepts

1. a. **Defining** What is uniformitarianism?
   b. **Explaining** How does uniformitarianism help geologists understand Earth's history?
   c. **Applying Concepts** Do you think that earthquakes happened millions of years ago? Explain your answer.
2. a. **Identifying** What are the three types of rock?
   b. **Explaining** What is the rock cycle?

c. **Making Generalizations** How does the rock cycle relate to the principle of uniformitarianism?

Writing in Science

Rock Legend Pick one type of rock and write a possible "biography" of the rock as it moves through the rock cycle. Your story should state the type of rock, how the rock formed, and how it might change.

The Relative Age of Rocks

CALIFORNIA
Standards Focus

S 7.4.c Students know that the rock cycle includes the formation of new sediment and rocks and that rocks are often found in layers, with the oldest generally on the bottom.

- What is the law of superposition?
- How do geologists determine the relative age of rocks?
- How are index fossils useful to geologists?

Key Terms

- relative age
- absolute age
- law of superposition
- extrusion
- intrusion
- fault
- unconformity
- inclusion
- index fossil

Lab zone Standards Warm-Up

Which Layer Is the Oldest?

1. Make a stack of different-colored layers of clay. Each layer should be about the size and thickness of a pancake. If these flat layers are sediments, which layer of sediment was deposited first? (*Hint:* This is the oldest layer.)

2. Now form the stack into a dome by pressing it over a small rounded object, such as a small bowl. With a cheese-slicer or plastic knife, carefully cut off the top of the dome. Look at the layers that you have exposed. Which layer is the oldest?

Think It Over
Inferring If you press the stack into a small bowl and trim away the clay that sticks above the edge, where will you find the oldest layer?

As sedimentary rock forms, the remains of organisms in the sediment may become fossils. Millions of years later, if you split open the rock, you might see the petrified bones of an extinct reptile or insect.

Your first question about a new fossil might be, "What is it?" Your next question would probably be, "How old is it?" Geologists have two ways to express the age of a rock and any fossil it contains. The **relative age** of a rock is its age compared to the ages of other rocks. You have probably used the idea of relative age when comparing your age with someone else's age. For example, if you say that you are older than your brother but younger than your sister, you are describing your relative age.

The relative age of a rock does not provide its absolute age. The **absolute age** of a rock is the number of years since the rock formed. It may be impossible to know a rock's absolute age exactly. But sometimes geologists can determine a rock's absolute age to within a certain number of years.

◄ The age of each family member could be given as relative age or absolute age.

The Position of Rock Layers

Have you ever seen rock layers of different colors on a cliff beside a road? What are these layers, and how did they form? The sediment that forms sedimentary rocks is deposited in flat layers one on top of the other. Over time, the sediment hardens and changes into sedimentary rock. These rock layers provide a record of Earth's geologic history.

It can be difficult to determine the absolute age of a rock. So geologists use a method to find a rock's relative age. Geologists use the **law of superposition** to determine the relative ages of sedimentary rock layers. **According to the law of superposition, in horizontal sedimentary rock layers the oldest layer is at the bottom. Each higher layer is younger than the layers below it.** Relative dating only establishes the order in which rocks were formed. Scientists cannot use the law of superposition to determine the absolute age of rocks.

The walls of the Grand Canyon in Arizona illustrate the law of superposition. You can see some of the rock layers found in the Grand Canyon in Figure 4. The deeper down you go in the Grand Canyon, the older the rocks.

 **Reading Checkpoint** **Why do sedimentary rocks have layers?**

Video Field Trip
Discovery Channel School
A Trip Through Geologic Time

FIGURE 4
The Grand Canyon
More than a dozen rock layers make up the walls of the Grand Canyon. You can see five layers clearly in the photograph.
Applying Concepts *In which labeled layers would you find the oldest fossils? Explain.*

Younger rock layers

Kaibab Limestone
250 million years old

Toroweap Limestone
255 million years old

Coconino Sandstone
260 million years old

Hermit Shale
265 million years old

Supai Sandstone
285 million years old

Older rock layers

Fault

Igneous intrusion

FIGURE 5
Faults and Intrusions
Faults and intrusions give clues to the relative ages of
rocks. Rock layers are broken and shifted along a fault
(left). An intrusion cuts through rock layers (right).

Determining Relative Age

There are other clues besides the position of rock layers to the
relative ages of rocks. 🔑 **To determine relative age, geologists
also study extrusions and intrusions of igneous rock, faults,
gaps in the geologic record, and inclusions.**

Clues From Igneous Rock Igneous rock forms when
magma or lava hardens. Magma is molten material beneath
Earth's surface. Magma that flows onto the surface is called lava.

Lava that hardens on the surface is called an **extrusion.**
An extrusion is always younger than the rocks below it.

Beneath the surface, magma may push into bodies of rock.
There, the magma cools and hardens into a mass of igneous
rock called an **intrusion.** An intrusion is always younger
than the rock layers around and beneath it. Figure 5 shows an
intrusion. Geologists study where intrusions and extrusions
formed in relation to other rock layers. This helps geologists
understand the relative ages of the different types of rock.

Clues From Faults More clues come from the study of faults.
A **fault** is a break in Earth's crust. Forces inside Earth cause
movement of the rock on opposite sides of a fault.

A fault is always younger than the rock it cuts through. To
determine the relative age of a fault, geologists find the relative
age of the youngest layer cut by the fault.

Movements along faults can make it harder for geologists
to determine the relative ages of rock layers. You can see in
Figure 5 how the rock layers no longer line up because of
movement along the fault.

Lab zone Try This **Activity**

Sampling a Sandwich
Your teacher will give you a
sandwich that represents
rock layers in Earth's crust.

1. Use a round, hollow,
   uncooked noodle as a
   coring tool. Push the
   noodle through the layers
   of the sandwich.
2. Pull the noodle out of the
   sandwich. Break the
   noodle gently to remove
   your core sample.
3. Draw a picture of what
   you see in each layer of
   the core.

Making Models Which layer
of your sandwich is the
"oldest"? The "youngest"?
Why do you think scientists
study core samples?

Cross-Cutting Relationships When geologists use extrusions, intrusions, or faults to date rocks, they apply the principle of cross-cutting relationships. That principle states: When something cuts across a body of rock, that "something" is younger than the rock it cuts across.

To understand this principle, think of a sandwich made from a roll and a slice of cheese. The roll must be made before the cheese can be put inside. The roll is like a body of rock, and the cheese is like an intrusion. Look again at the igneous intrusion in the photo on the right in Figure 5. The igneous intrusion is something like a sandwich filling.

Gaps in the Geologic Record The geologic record of sedimentary rock layers is not always complete. Deposition slowly builds layer upon layer of sedimentary rock. But some of these layers may erode away, exposing an older rock surface. Then deposition begins again, building new rock layers.

The surface where new rock layers meet a much older rock surface beneath them is called an **unconformity**. An unconformity is a gap in the geologic record. An unconformity shows where some rock layers have been lost because of erosion. Figure 6 shows how an unconformity forms.

✓ **Reading Checkpoint** What is an unconformity?

Inclusions Inclusions can help date rocks when an unconformity is present. An **inclusion** is a piece of rock that is contained in another rock. Unlike an intrusion, which starts out as liquid magma, an inclusion starts as a solid rock piece that breaks off from an existing rock. Then, after a long time, the broken-off piece of rock becomes part of a second rock.

The rock containing an inclusion is younger than the rock from which the inclusion came. Look at the bottom frame of Figure 6. Notice the inclusions in the bright pink layer. They broke off from the eroded surface of the unconformity. The rock pieces later became part of sediments that were deposited on the eroded surface. These sediments, including the broken rock pieces, hardened into sedimentary rock.

Inclusions

FIGURE 6
Unconformity
An unconformity occurs where erosion wears away layers of sedimentary rock. Other rock layers then form on top.
Sequencing *What two processes must take place before an unconformity can occur?*

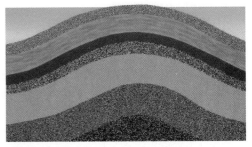

❶ Sedimentary rocks form in horizontal layers.

❷ Folding tilts the rock layers.

❸ The surface is eroded.

Unconformity

❹ New sediment is deposited, forming rock layers above the unconformity. Notice the inclusions in the new rock.

FIGURE 7
Looking for Fossils
These scientists are removing fossils from rock layers.
Applying Concepts *How can fossils help geologists match rock layers?*

Using Fossils to Date Rocks

To date rock layers, geologists first give a relative age to a layer of rock at one location. Then they can give the same age to matching layers of rock at other locations.

Certain fossils, called index fossils, help geologists match rock layers. To be useful as an **index fossil,** a fossil must be widely distributed and represent a type of organism that existed only briefly. A fossil is considered widely distributed if it occurs in many different areas. Geologists look for index fossils in layers of rock. **Index fossils are useful because they tell the relative ages of the rock layers in which they occur.**

Geologists use particular types of organisms as index fossils—for example, certain types of ammonites. Ammonites (AM uh nyts) were a group of hard-shelled animals. Ammonites evolved in shallow seas more than 500 million years ago and became extinct about 65 million years ago.

Ammonite fossils make good index fossils for two reasons. First, they are widely distributed. Second, many different types of ammonites evolved and then became extinct after a few million years. Geologists can identify the different types of ammonites through differences in the structure of their shells. Based on these differences, geologists can identify the rock layers in which a particular type of ammonite fossil occurs.

You can use index fossils to match rock layers. Look at Figure 8, which shows rock layers from four different locations. Notice that two of the fossils are each found in only one of these rock layers. These are the index fossils.

 **Reading Checkpoint** What characteristics must a fossil have to be useful as an index fossil?

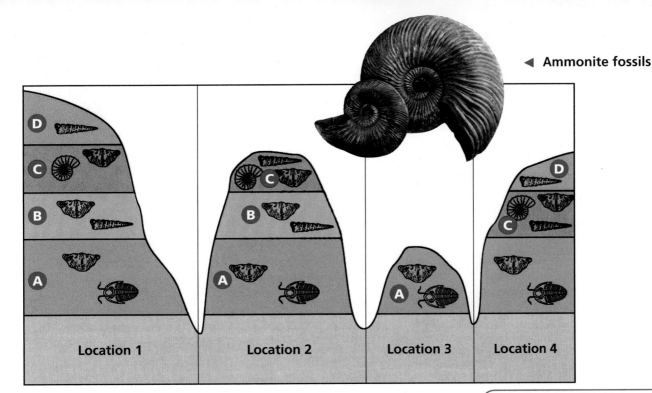

◄ **Ammonite fossils**

Location 1 **Location 2** **Location 3** **Location 4**

FIGURE 8
Using Index Fossils
Scientists use index fossils to match up rock layers at locations that may be far apart. The ammonites in layer C are index fossils. **Interpreting Diagrams** *Can you find another index fossil in the diagram? (Hint: Look for a fossil that occurs in only one layer, but in several different locations.)*

Go Online
active art

For: Index Fossils activities
Visit: PHSchool.com
Web Code: cfp-2042

Section 2 Assessment

S 7.4.c, E-LA: Reading 7.1.3

Vocabulary Skill Use Clues to Determine Meaning Reread the definition of *extrusion*. Identify two phrases that help you understand the meaning of *extrusion*.

Reviewing Key Concepts

1. **a. Defining** In your own words, define the terms *relative age* and *absolute age*.
   b. Explaining What is the law of superposition?
   c. Inferring A geologist finds a cliff where the edges of several different rock layers can be seen. Which layer is the oldest? Explain.
2. **a. Reviewing** Besides the law of superposition, what are three types of clues to the relative age of rock layers?
   b. Comparing and Contrasting Compare and contrast extrusions and intrusions.
   c. Sequencing An intrusion crosses an extrusion. Which layer is the older? Explain.

3. **a. Defining** What is an index fossil?
   b. Applying Concepts The fossil record shows that horseshoe crabs have existed with very little change for about 200 million years. Would horseshoe crabs be useful as an index fossil? Explain why or why not.

Lab zone At-Home **Activity**

Drawer to the Past Collect ten items out of a drawer full of odds and ends such as keys, coins, receipts, photographs, and souvenirs. Have your family members put them in order from oldest to newest. What clues will you use to determine their relative ages? Do you know the absolute age of any of the items?

Finding Clues to Rock Layers

S 7.4.c, 7.7.c

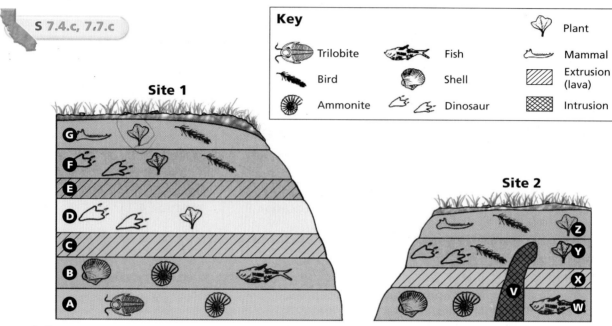

Key

Trilobite   Fish   Plant

Bird   Shell   Mammal

Ammonite   Dinosaur   Extrusion (lava)

Intrusion

Site 1

Site 2

Problem

How can you use fossils and geologic features to interpret the relative ages of rock layers?

Skills Focus

interpreting data, drawing conclusions

Procedure

1. Study the rock layers at Sites 1 and 2. Write down the similarities and differences between the layers at the two sites.
2. List the kinds of fossils that are found in each rock layer of Sites 1 and 2.

Analyze and Conclude

Site 1

1. **Interpreting Data** What "fossil clues" in layers A and B indicate the kind of environment that existed when these rock layers were formed? How did the environment change in layer D?
2. **Drawing Conclusions** Which layer is the oldest? How do you know?
3. **Drawing Conclusions** Which of the layers formed most recently? How do you know?

4. **Inferring** Why are there no fossils in layers C and E?
5. **Observing** What kind of fossils are found in layer F?

Site 2

6. **Inferring** Which layer at Site 1 might have formed at the same time as layer W at Site 2?
7. **Interpreting Data** What clues show an unconformity or gap in the horizontal rock layers? Which rock layers are missing? What might have happened to these rock layers?
8. **Drawing Conclusions** Which is older, intrusion V or layer Y? How do you know?
9. **Communicating** Write a journal entry describing how the environment at Site 2 changed over time. Starting with the earliest layer, describe the types of organisms, their environment, and how the environment changed.

More to Explore

Draw a sketch similar to Site 2 and include a fault that cuts across the intrusion. Have a partner then identify the relative age of the fault, the intrusion, and the layers cut by the fault.

Radioactive Dating

S 7.4.d Students know that evidence from geologic layers and radioactive dating indicates Earth is approximately 4.6 billion years old and that life on this planet has existed for more than 3 billion years.

- What happens during radioactive decay?
- What can be learned from radioactive dating?
- What is the probable age of Earth?

Key Terms
- atom
- element
- radioactive decay
- half-life

Lab zone Standards Warm-Up

How Long Till It's Gone?

1. Make a small cube—about 5 cm × 5 cm × 5 cm —from modeling clay.
2. Carefully use a knife to cut the clay in half. Put one half of the clay aside.
3. Cut the clay in half two more times. Each time you cut the clay, put one half of it aside.

Think It Over

Predicting How big will the remaining piece of clay be if you repeat the process several more times?

In Australia, scientists have found sedimentary rocks that contain some of the world's oldest fossils. These are fossils of stromatolites (stroh MAT uh lyts). Stromatolites are the remains of reefs built by organisms similar to present-day bacteria. Sediment eventually covered these reefs. As the sediment changed to rock, so did the reefs. Using absolute dating, scientists have determined that some stromatolites are more than 3 billion years old. To understand absolute dating, you need to learn more about the chemistry of rocks.

FIGURE 9
Stromatolites
Scientists think that ancient stromatolites were formed by organisms similar to blue-green bacteria (above). Modern stromatolites (right) still form reefs along the western coast of Australia.

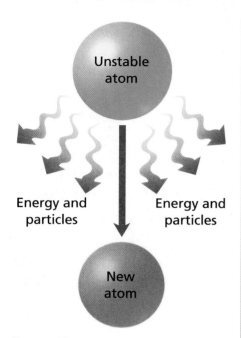

FIGURE 10
Radioactive Decay
In the process of radioactive decay, a "parent" atom releases energy and particles as it changes to a new kind of atom, a "daughter" atom.

Radioactive Decay

Rocks are a form of matter. All the matter you see, including rocks, is made of tiny particles called **atoms.** When all the atoms in a particular type of matter are the same, the matter is an **element.** Carbon, oxygen, iron, lead, and potassium are just some of the more than 110 currently known elements.

Most elements are stable. They do not change under normal conditions. But some elements exist in forms that are unstable. Over time, these elements break down, or decay, by releasing particles and energy in a process called **radioactive decay.** These unstable elements are said to be radioactive. ◑ **During the process of radioactive decay, the atoms of one element break down to form atoms of another element.**

Radioactive elements occur naturally in igneous rocks. Scientists use the rate at which these elements decay to calculate the rock's age. You calculate your age based on a specific day—your birthday. What's the "birthday" of a rock? For an igneous rock, that "birthday" is when it first hardens to become rock. As a radioactive element within the igneous rock decays, it changes into another element. So the composition of the rock changes slowly over time. The amount of the radioactive element goes down. But the amount of the new element goes up.

The rate of decay of each radioactive element is constant—it never changes. Scientists can measure it experimentally. This rate of decay is the element's half-life. The **half-life** of a radioactive element is the time it takes for half of the radioactive atoms to decay. You can see in Figure 11 how a radioactive element decays over time.

 **Reading Checkpoint** **What is the meaning of the term "half-life"?**

FIGURE 11
The half-life of a radioactive element is the amount of time it takes for half of the radioactive atoms to decay. The half-life of potassium-40 is 1.3 billion years.
Calculating After three half-lives, how much of the radioactive element remains?

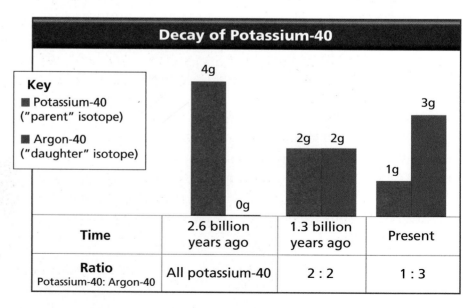

Decay of Potassium-40

Key
■ Potassium-40 ("parent" isotope)
■ Argon-40 ("daughter" isotope)

Time	2.6 billion years ago	1.3 billion years ago	Present
Ratio Potassium-40 : Argon-40	All potassium-40	2 : 2	1 : 3

Elements Used in Radioactive Dating		
Radioactive Element	Half-life (years)	Dating Range (years)
Carbon-14	5,730	500–50,000
Potassium-40	1.3 billion	50,000–4.6 billion
Rubidium-87	48.8 billion	10 million–4.6 billion
Thorium-232	14 billion	10 million–4.6 billion
Uranium-235	713 million	10 million–4.6 billion
Uranium-238	4.5 billion	10 million–4.6 billion

FIGURE 12
The half-lives of different radioactive elements vary greatly.

Determining Absolute Ages

Radioactive dating is used to determine the absolute ages of rocks. In radioactive dating, scientists first measure the amount of a radioactive element (the "parent" element) in a mineral in a rock. Then they measure the amount of the stable element into which the radioactive element decays (the "daughter" element). By calculating the ratio of the radioactive element to the stable element, scientists can determine the age of the rock.

Potassium–Argon Dating Scientists often date rocks using potassium-40. This form of potassium decays to stable argon-40 and has a half-life of 1.3 billion years. Potassium-40 is useful in dating the most ancient rocks because of its long half-life.

Carbon-14 Dating A radioactive form of carbon is carbon-14. All plants and animals contain carbon, including some carbon-14. As plants and animals grow, carbon atoms are added to their tissues. After an organism dies, no more carbon is added. But the carbon-14 in the organism's body decays. It changes to stable nitrogen-14. To determine the age of a sample, scientists measure the amount of carbon-14 that is left in the organism's remains. From this amount, they can determine its absolute age. Carbon-14 has been used to date fossils such as frozen mammoths, as well as pieces of wood and bone.

Carbon-14 is very useful in dating materials from plants and animals that lived up to about 50,000 years ago. Carbon-14 has a half-life of only 5,730 years. For this reason, it can't be used to date very ancient fossils or rocks. The amount of carbon-14 left would be too small to measure accurately.

Math Skills

Percentage What percentage of a radioactive element will be left after 3 half-lives? First, multiply $\frac{1}{2}$ three times to determine what fraction of the element will remain.

$$\frac{1}{2} \times \frac{1}{2} \times \frac{1}{2} = \frac{1}{8}$$

You can convert this fraction to a percentage by setting up a proportion:

$$\frac{1}{8} = \frac{d\%}{100\%}$$

To find the value of d, begin by cross multiplying, as for any proportion:

$1 \times 100 = 8 \times d$

$d = \frac{100}{8}$

$d = 12.5\%$

Practice Problems What percentage of a radioactive element will remain after 5 half-lives?

How Old Is Earth?

Scientists haven't found it easy to figure out the age of planet Earth. Earth is always changing, through erosion and other processes. Most of the matter that made up early Earth has been destroyed or changed. Radioactive dating shows that the oldest rocks ever found on Earth are about 4.0 billion years old. But scientists hypothesize that Earth formed even earlier than that.

Scientists have used moon rocks and meteorites to estimate the age of Earth. Meteorites are chunks of rocks from space that have hit Earth's surface. According to one hypothesis, Earth, meteorites, and the moon are about the same age. When Earth was very young, a large object from space collided with it. This collision threw a large amount of material from both bodies into orbit around Earth. Some of this material combined to form the moon.

In the 1970s, astronauts who visited the moon brought several moon rocks back to Earth. Scientists have used radioactive dating to determine the age of those moon rocks. **Radioactive dating shows that the oldest moon rocks are about 4.6 billion years old. Scientists infer that Earth is only a little older than those moon rocks—roughly 4.6 billion years old.** The oldest fossils of living things appear in geologic layers that are 3.5 billion years old.

FIGURE 13
Rocks from the Moon
By determining the age of moon rocks, scientists have inferred that Earth is about 4.6 billion years old.

For: More on radioactive dating
Visit: PHSchool.com
Web Code: cfd-2043

Section 3 Assessment

S 7.4.d, E-LA: Reading 7.1.3

Vocabulary Skill Use Clues to Determine Meaning Reread the definition of *radioactive decay*, and the text near the definition. In your own words, explain what *radioactive decay* means.

Reviewing Key Concepts

1. a. **Defining** In your own words, define the term *radioactive element*.
   b. **Describing** How does the composition of a rock containing a radioactive element change over time?
   c. **Applying Concepts** How is a radioactive element's rate of decay like the ticking of a clock? Explain.

2. a. **Identifying** What method do geologists use to determine the absolute age of a rock?
   b. **Explaining** Why is it difficult to determine the absolute age of a sedimentary rock?

   c. **Problem Solving** A geologist finds a fossil in a layer of sedimentary rock that lies in between two igneous extrusions. How could the geologist determine the age of the fossil?

3. a. **Reviewing** How old are the oldest rocks found on the moon?
   b. **Explaining** What do scientists estimate Earth's age to be?
   c. **Summarizing** How were scientists able to infer Earth's age?

Math Practice

4. **Percentage** What percentage of a radioactive element will remain after 7 half-lives?

Movement of Earth's Plates

S 7.4.f Students know how movements of Earth's continental and oceanic plates through time, with associated changes in climate and geographic connections, have affected the past and present distribution of organisms.

- How does the theory of plate tectonics explain the movement of Earth's landmasses?

- How has the movement of Earth's plates affected organisms?

Key Terms
- plate
- theory of plate tectonics
- continental drift

Lab zone Standards **Warm-Up**

Where Were the Fossils Found?

1. *Mesosaurus* is an animal that became extinct over 200 million years ago. Make labels by writing *Mesosaurus* on two small stick-on notes.
2. Fossils of *Mesosaurus* have been found in Africa and South America. On a globe of the world, place one *Mesosaurus* label on South America. Put the second label on Africa.
3. Observe the distances that separate these labels.

Think It Over

Inferring Would you expect fossils of the same extinct organism to be found on two different continents? Why or why not?

Have you ever noticed that Earth's landmasses resemble pieces of a giant jigsaw puzzle? It's true. The east coast of South America, for example, would fit nicely into the west coast of Africa. The Arabian Peninsula would fit fairly well with the northeastern coast of Africa. Since the 1600s, people have wondered why Earth's landmasses look as if they would fit together. After all, land can't move. Or can it?

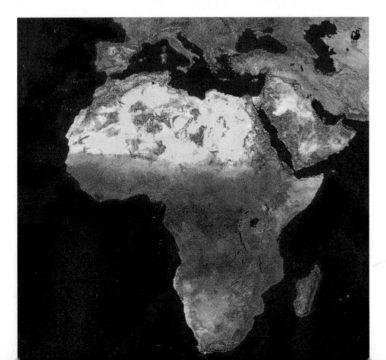

FIGURE 14
Landmasses Fit Together
The Arabian peninsula, which looks something like a foot, fits between the continents of Africa and Asia almost like a puzzle piece.

225 Million Years Ago

180–200 Million Years Ago

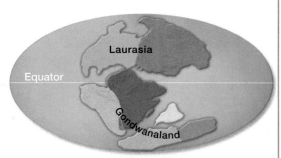

135 Million Years Ago

Earth Today

For: Continental Drift activity
Visit: PHSchool.com
Web Code: cfp-1015

FIGURE 15
Continental Drift
The movement of the continents is one factor affecting the distribution of organisms. **Interpreting Maps** *How has Australia's location changed?*

Earth's Plates

Earth's outer layer consists of pieces that fit together like a jigsaw puzzle. This outer layer is made of more than a dozen major pieces called **plates.** Plate boundaries do not always lie along the edges of continents. The eastern boundary of the North American plate, for example, lies under the Atlantic Ocean.

Scientists use the concept of plates to explain how landmasses have changed over time. The **theory of plate tectonics** states that Earth's plates move slowly in various directions. The plates move, on average, about 5 centimeters per year. Some plates slowly pull away from each other, some plates push toward each other, and some plates slide past each other.

🔑 **According to the theory of plate tectonics, Earth's landmasses have changed position over time because they are part of plates that are slowly moving.** About 260 million years ago, all the continents were joined together in a supercontinent called Pangaea. Then, about 225 million years ago, the different continents began to drift apart. The very slow movement of continents is called **continental drift**.

 **Reading Checkpoint** What is continental drift?

Distribution of Organisms

The movement of Earth's plates has affected the evolution of living things. 🔑 **As Earth's plates moved, landmasses changed their locations. These changes affected where different kinds of organisms, past and present, are located.**

Climate As the plates move, the continents may move north and south. As the continents move, their climate may change. As the climate changes, so do the kinds of organisms that live on the continent. For example, millions of years ago, the North American plate was much closer to the equator than it is now. North America's climate was warm and tropical then. Huge ferns grew in forests. Plants such as those ancient ferns could not grow in North America today, because the climate is too cool.

FIGURE 16
Marsupials in Australia
Because of continental drift,
Australia became isolated.
Today, most mammals in
Australia, including this koala,
are marsupials.

Separation of Organisms As plates pulled apart, organisms on different plates became separated from one another. Fossils of *Brachiosaurus*, a dinosaur, have been found in Europe, Africa, and North America. The locations of these fossils suggest that those continents were once joined.

Continental drift has also affected organisms that are alive today. When populations of organisms become widely separated, their genetic makeup may change in different ways. Therefore, the separated populations often evolve differently. Organisms in Australia have been isolated from all other organisms on Earth for millions of years. Unusual organisms have evolved in Australia. For example, most mammals in Australia are marsupials. Unlike other mammals, female marsupials have pouches in which their young develop after birth. In contrast, few marsupials exist on other continents.

Section 4 Assessment

S 7.4.f, E-LA: Writing 7.2.0, Reading 7.1.3

Vocabulary Skill Use Clues to Determine Meaning How does Figure 15 help you understand the meaning of *continental drift*?

Reviewing Key Concepts

1. a. **Identifying** Name the theory that explains the movement of pieces of Earth's surface.
   b. **Explaining** Explain why the continent of North America is not where it was 225 million years ago.
   c. **Predicting** In 250 million years, would you expect North America to be where it is now? Explain your answer.

2. a. **Reviewing** What is continental drift?
   b. **Describing** Describe how continental drift has affected mammals in Australia.
   c. **Predicting** Suppose that, millions of years from now, Australia moves so that it connects to South America. Would Australia still have the same kinds of mammals? Explain your answer.

Writing in Science

Description Look at Figure 15. Then draw your own labeled diagram to show how India moved between 135 million years ago and today. Write a caption that explains how India moved.

5 The Geologic Time Scale

CALIFORNIA
Standards Focus

S 7.4.b Students know the history of life on Earth has been disrupted by major catastrophic events, such as major volcanic eruptions or the impacts of asteroids.

S 7.4.g Students know how to explain significant developments and extinctions of plant and animal life on the geologic time scale.

- Why is the geologic time scale used to show Earth's history?
- What were early Precambrian organisms like?
- What were the major events of the Paleozoic, Mesozoic, and Cenozoic Eras?

Key Terms
- geologic time scale
- era
- period
- invertebrate
- vertebrate
- amphibian
- reptile
- mass extinction
- mammal

Lab zone Standards Warm-Up

Your Time Scale
1. Make a list of about 10 to 15 important events that you remember in your life.
2. On a sheet of paper, draw a timeline to represent your life. Use a scale of 3.0 cm to 1 year.
3. Write each event in the correct year along the timeline.
4. Now divide the timeline into parts that describe major periods in your life, such as preschool years, elementary school years, and middle school years.

Think It Over
Making Models Along which part of your timeline are most of the events located? Which period of your life does this part of the timeline represent? Why do you think this is so?

Imagine squeezing Earth's 4.6-billion-year history into a 24-hour day. Earth forms at midnight. About seven hours later, the earliest one-celled organisms appear. Over the next 14 hours, simple, soft-bodied organisms such as jellyfish and worms develop. A little after 9:00 P.M.—21 hours later—larger, more complex organisms evolve in the oceans. Reptiles and insects first appear about an hour after that. Dinosaurs arrive just before 11:00 P.M., but are extinct by 11:30 P.M. Modern humans don't appear until less than a second before midnight!

The Geologic Time Scale

Months, years, or even centuries aren't very helpful for thinking about Earth's long history. **Because the time span of Earth's past is so great, geologists use the geologic time scale to show Earth's history.** The **geologic time scale** is a record of the life forms and geologic events in Earth's history.

You can see in Figure 17 that the geologic time scale begins with Precambrian Time (pree KAM bree un). Precambrian Time covers about 88 percent of Earth's history. After Precambrian Time, the basic units of the geologic time scale are eras and periods. **Eras** are the three long units between Precambrian Time and the present. Eras are subdivided into **periods**.

FIGURE 17
The Geologic Time Scale

The eras and periods of the geologic time scale are used to date the events in Earth's long history.
Interpreting Diagrams *How long ago did the Paleozoic Era end?*

Cenozoic Era
The Cenozoic (sen uh ZOH ik) began about 66 million years ago and continues to the present. The word part *ceno-* means "recent," and *-zoic* means "life." Mammals became common during this time.

Mesozoic Era
People often call the Mesozoic (mez uh ZOH ik) the Age of Dinosaurs. The Mesozoic began about 245 million years ago and lasted about 180 million years. The word part *meso-* means "middle."

Paleozoic Era
The Paleozoic (pay lee uh ZOH ik) began about 544 million years ago and lasted for 300 million years. The word part *paleo-* means "ancient or early."

Geologic Time Scale			
Era	**Period**	**Millions of Years Ago**	**Duration (millions of years)**
Cenozoic	Quaternary	1.6	1.6 to present
Cenozoic	Tertiary	66.4	65
Mesozoic	Cretaceous	144	78
Mesozoic	Jurassic	208	64
Mesozoic	Triassic	245	37
Paleozoic	Permian	286	41
Paleozoic	Carboniferous	360	74
Paleozoic	Devonian	408	48
Paleozoic	Silurian	438	30
Paleozoic	Ordovician	505	67
Paleozoic	Cambrian	544	39
Precambrian			544 million years ago– 4.6 billion years ago

FIGURE 18
Early Earth
This artist's illustration shows Earth
shortly after the moon formed.
Notice the rocky objects from space
striking Earth, and the molten rock
flowing over the surface.

Early Earth

Precambrian Time begins when the Earth formed, about 4.6 billion years ago. Scientists hypothesize that early Earth was very hot. Over time, however, the outer layers cooled and became solid. Less than 500 million years after Earth's formation, rock on the surface formed continents.

At this time, the atmosphere, which is the blanket of gases surrounding Earth, was made up mostly of the gases nitrogen, carbon dioxide, and water vapor. There was little oxygen.

Scientists cannot pinpoint when or where life began. **But scientists have found fossils of single-celled organisms in rocks that formed about 3.5 billion years ago. These earliest life forms were probably similar to present-day bacteria.** Unlike most organisms today, these single-celled organisms did not need oxygen. Scientists hypothesize that all other forms of life on Earth arose from these simple organisms.

About 2.5 billion years ago, many organisms began using energy from the sun to make their own food. This process is called photosynthesis. Among these early photosynthetic organisms were cyanobacteria. These bacteria, which were once called blue-green algae, have been extremely successful. They are still alive today, and they have changed very little.

One product of photosynthesis is oxygen. Organisms released oxygen into the atmosphere. The amount of oxygen in the air slowly increased. Processes in the atmosphere changed some of this oxygen into a form called ozone. The ozone layer blocked out some of the ultraviolet rays of the sun. Shielded from the ultraviolet rays, organisms could live on land.

Go Online
SCiLINKS_™ NSTA

For: Links on Precambrian Earth
Visit: www.SciLinks.org
Web Code: scn-0745

The Paleozoic Era

You have traveled in a time machine to the beginning of the Paleozoic Era. The time machine is now moving forward, toward the present. You are about to see a period of rapid change.

The Cambrian Explosion In the Cambrian Period, life took a big leap forward. 🔑 **At the beginning of the Paleozoic Era, many different kinds of organisms evolved.** Paleontologists call this event the Cambrian Explosion because so many new life forms appeared within a relatively short time (approximately 30 million years). For the first time, many organisms had hard parts, including shells and outer skeletons. Many animals, such as sponges, jellyfish, and worms, were invertebrates. **Invertebrates** are animals without backbones.

Scientists infer that at this time, all animals lived in the sea. Fossils provide evidence of a watery environment. That is because many Cambrian fossils are similar to modern sea animals. For example, brachiopods were small animals with two shells. Brachiopods looked like modern clams. Therefore, like clams, brachiopods probably lived in water.

Vertebrates Arise During the Ordovician (awr duh VISH ee un) and Silurian (sih LOOR ee un) periods, invertebrates shared the seas with a new type of organism. 🔑 **Jawless fishes evolved. Jawless fishes were the first vertebrates.** A **vertebrate** is an animal that has a backbone. These early fishes had sucker-like mouths.

FIGURE 19
The Cambrian Explosion
During the early Cambrian period, Earth's oceans were home to many strange organisms unlike any animals that are alive today.

FIGURE 20
Devonian Armored Fish
Paleontologists have found fossils of huge armored fish, like this *Dunkleosteus,* that lived during the Devonian Period.

Life Reaches Land Until the Silurian Period, only one-celled organisms lived on the land. But during the Silurian Period, plants became abundant. These first, simple plants grew low to the ground in damp areas. By the Devonian Period (dih VOH nee un), plants that could grow in drier areas had evolved. Among these plants were the earliest ferns. The first insects also appeared during the Silurian Period.

Both invertebrates and vertebrates lived in the Devonian seas. Even though the invertebrates were more numerous, the Devonian Period is often called the Age of Fishes. Every main group of fishes was present in the oceans at this time. Most fishes now had jaws, bony skeletons, and scales on their bodies. Some fishes, like the one in Figure 20, were huge. Sharks appeared in the late Devonian Period.

During the Devonian Period, vertebrates began to invade the land. The first vertebrates to crawl onto land were lungfish with strong, muscular fins. The first amphibians evolved from these lungfish. An **amphibian** (am FIB ee un) is an animal that lives part of its life on land and part of its life in water.

FIGURE 21
The Coal Forest
Forests of the Carboniferous Period later formed coal deposits. **Predicting** *What types of fossils would you expect to find from the Carboniferous Period?*

The Carboniferous Period Throughout the rest of the Paleozoic, life expanded over Earth's continents. Other vertebrates evolved from the amphibians. For example, small reptiles developed during the Carboniferous Period. **Reptiles** have scaly skin and lay eggs with tough, leathery shells. Some types of reptiles became very large during the later Paleozoic.

Math ➤ Analyzing Data

Mass Extinctions

The graph shows how the number of families of animals in Earth's oceans has changed.

1. **Reading Graphs** What variable is shown on the *x*-axis? On the *y*-axis of the graph?

2. **Interpreting Data** How long ago did the most recent mass extinction occur?

3. **Interpreting Data** Which mass extinction produced the greatest drop in the number of families of ocean animals?

4. **Relating Cause and Effect** In general, how did the number of families change between mass extinctions?

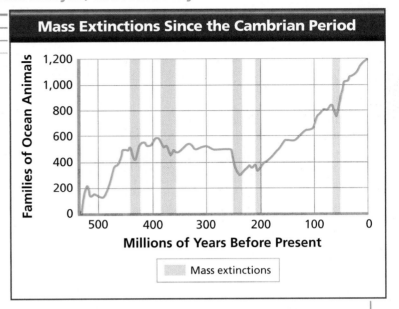

Mass Extinctions Since the Cambrian Period

y-axis: Families of Ocean Animals (0, 200, 400, 600, 800, 1,000, 1,200)
x-axis: Millions of Years Before Present (500, 400, 300, 200, 100, 0)

☐ Mass extinctions

During the Carboniferous Period, winged insects evolved into many forms, including huge dragonflies. Giant ferns and cone-bearing plants formed vast swampy forests called "coal forests." The remains of these plants formed thick deposits of sediment that changed into coal over millions of years.

Mass Extinction Ends the Paleozoic At the end of the Paleozoic Era, many kinds of organisms died out. This was a **mass extinction,** in which many types of living things became extinct at the same time. ⚷ **The mass extinction, known as the Permian extinction, affected both plants and animals on land and in the seas.** Scientists do not know what catastrophic event caused the mass extinction, but many kinds of organisms suddenly became extinct. As much as 90 percent of marine species may have died out.

The Supercontinent Pangaea Scientists hypothesize that climate change resulting from continental drift may have caused the mass extinction at the end of the Paleozoic. ⚷ **During the Permian Period, about 260 million years ago, Earth's continents moved together to form a great landmass, or supercontinent, called Pangaea** (pan JEE uh). The formation of Pangaea caused deserts to expand in the tropics. At the same time, sheets of ice covered land closer to the South Pole. Many organisms could not survive the new climate. After Pangaea formed, it broke apart again.

 **Reading Checkpoint** What was Pangaea?

Go **O**nline
active art

For: Continental Drift activity
Visit: PHSchool.com
Web Code: cfp-1015

FIGURE 22
The Geologic Time Scale
Sequencing Events *Which organisms appear first—amphibians or fishes?*

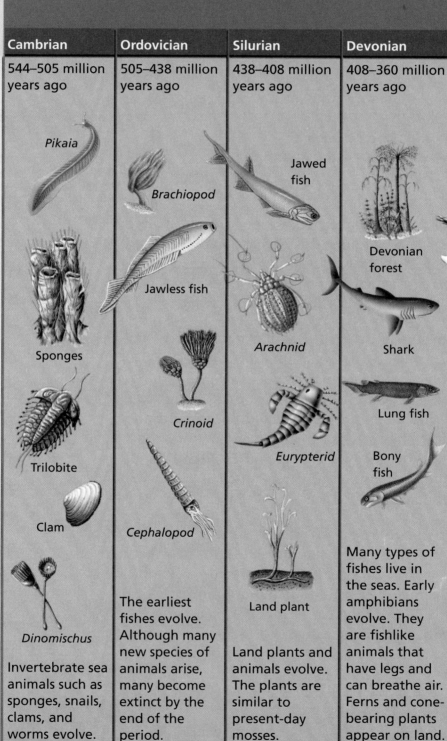

Precambrian Time
4.6 billion–544 million years ago

Early bacteria

Early algae

Jellyfish-like animal

Sea pen

Precambrian Time begins with the formation of Earth. The first living things — bacteria — appeared in seas 3.5 billion years ago. Algae and fungi evolved 1 billion years ago. Animals first appeared 600 million years ago.

Paleozoic Era
544–245 million years ago

Cambrian
544–505 million years ago

Pikaia

Sponges

Trilobite

Clam

Dinomischus

Invertebrate sea animals such as sponges, snails, clams, and worms evolve.

Ordovician
505–438 million years ago

Brachiopod

Jawless fish

Crinoid

Cephalopod

The earliest fishes evolve. Although many new species of animals arise, many become extinct by the end of the period.

Silurian
438–408 million years ago

Jawed fish

Arachnid

Eurypterid

Land plant

Land plants and animals evolve. The plants are similar to present-day mosses.

Devonian
408–360 million years ago

Devonian forest

Shark

Lung fish

Bony fish

Many types of fishes live in the seas. Early amphibians evolve. They are fishlike animals that have legs and can breathe air. Ferns and cone-bearing plants appear on land.

Carboniferous
360–286 million years ago

Cockroach

Dragonfly

Coal forest

Amphibian

Tropical forests become widespread. Many different insects and amphibians evolve. The earliest reptiles appear.

Mesozoic Era
245–66 million years ago

Cenozoic Era
66 million years ago to the present

Permian	Triassic	Jurassic	Cretaceous	Tertiary	Quaternary
286–245 million years ago	245–208 million years ago	208–144 million years ago	144–66 million years ago	66–1.8 million years ago	1.8 million years ago to the present

Triceratops

Saber-toothed cat

Conifer

Cycad

Morganucodon

Magnolia

Uintatherium

Early mammal

Diplodocus

Dimetrodon

Megatherium

Plesiadapis

Tyrannosaurus rex

Coelophysis

Hyracotherium

Dicynodon

Archaeopteryx

Creodont

Homo sapiens

Seed plants, insects, and reptiles become common. Reptile-like mammals appear. At the end of the period, most sea animals and amphibians become extinct.

The first dinosaurs evolve. First turtles and crocodiles appear. Mammals first appear. Cone-bearing trees and palmlike trees dominate forests.

Large dinosaurs roam the world. The first birds appear. Mammals become more common and varied.

The first flowering plants appear. At the end of the period, a mass extinction causes the disappearance of many organisms, including the dinosaurs.

New groups of animals, including the first monkeys and apes, appear. Flowering plants become the most common kinds of plants. First grasses appear.

Mammals, flowering plants, and insects dominate land. Humans appear. Later in the period, many large mammals, including mammoths, become extinct.

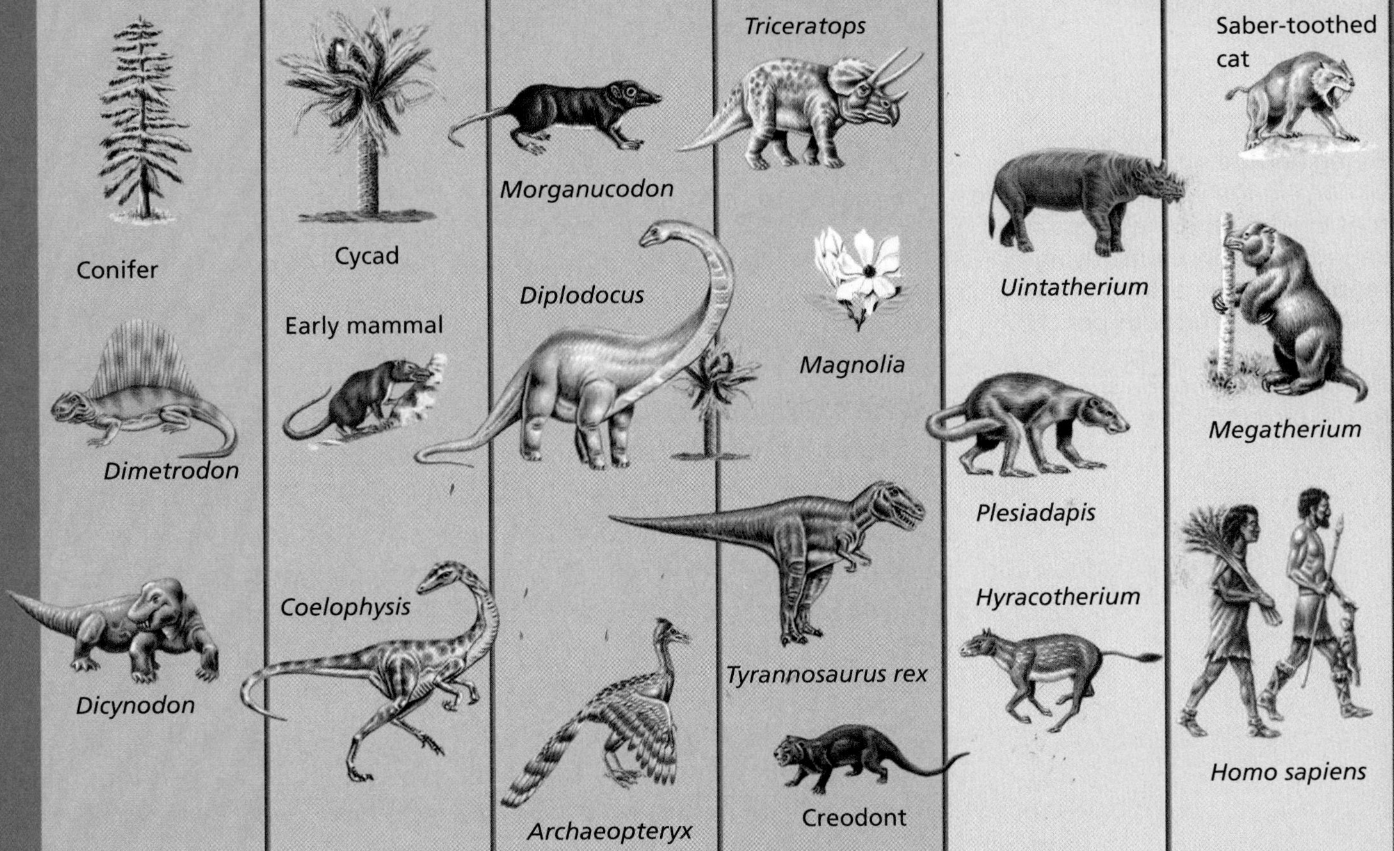

FIGURE 23
Flying Reptile
Dimorphodon was a flying reptile that lived during the Jurassic Period. Like dinosaurs, flying reptiles became extinct at the end of the Cretaceous period.
Comparing and Contrasting
How is Dimorphodon *similar to the bird in Figure 24?*

The Mesozoic Era

Millions of years flash by as your time machine travels. Watch out—there's a dinosaur! You're observing an era that you've read about in books and seen in movies.

The Triassic Period Some living things survived the Permian mass extinction. These organisms became the main forms of life early in the Triassic Period (try AS ik). Plants and animals that survived included fish, insects, reptiles, and cone-bearing plants called conifers. **Reptiles were so successful during the Mesozoic Era that this time is sometimes called the Age of Reptiles.** About 225 million years ago, the first dinosaurs appeared. Mammals also first appeared during the Triassic Period. A **mammal** is a warm-blooded vertebrate that feeds its young milk. Mammals probably evolved from warm-blooded reptiles. The mammals of the Triassic Period were very small.

The Jurassic Period During the Jurassic Period (joo RAS ik), dinosaurs became the dominant animals on land. Scientists have identified several hundred different kinds of dinosaurs. Some were plant eaters, while others were meat eaters. Dinosaurs "ruled" Earth for about 150 million years.

One of the first birds, called *Archaeopteryx*, appeared during the Jurassic Period. The name *Archaeopteryx* means "ancient winged thing." Many paleontologists now think that birds evolved from dinosaurs.

 **Reading Checkpoint** What is a mammal?

FIGURE 24
Early Bird
The artist of the illustration (left) has given *Archaeopteryx* colorful feathers. From a fossil (right), paleontologists can tell that *Archaeopteryx* was about 30 centimeters long, had feathers and teeth, and also had claws on its wings.

The Cretaceous Period Reptiles, including dinosaurs, were still the dominant vertebrates throughout the Cretaceous Period (krih TAY shus). Flying reptiles and birds competed for places in the sky. The hollow bones and feathers of birds made them better adapted to their environment than the flying reptiles, which became extinct during the Cretaceous Period. The Cretaceous Period also brought new forms of life. Flowering plants like the ones you see today evolved. Unlike the conifers, flowering plants produce seeds that are inside a fruit. The fruit helps the seeds disperse.

Another Mass Extinction Catastrophic, or destructive, events have changed the history of life on Earth. Catastrophic happenings can include volcanoes erupting or objects from space hitting Earth. ⬡ **At the close of the Cretaceous Period, about 65 million years ago, another mass extinction occurred. Some scientists hypothesize that this mass extinction, known as the Cretaceous-Tertiary (K-T) extinction, occurred when an object from space struck Earth.** This object may have been an asteroid. Asteroids are rocky masses that orbit the sun between Mars and Jupiter.

When the asteroid hit Earth, the impact threw huge amounts of dust and water vapor into the atmosphere. Many organisms on land and in the oceans died immediately. Dust and heavy clouds blocked sunlight around the world for years. Without sunlight, organisms' habitats changed. Plants died, and plant-eating animals starved. This mass extinction wiped out over half of all plant and animal groups. No dinosaurs survived.

Not all scientists agree that an asteroid impact alone caused the mass extinction. Some scientists think that climate changes caused by increased volcanic activity were partly responsible.

FIGURE 25
The End of the Dinosaurs
Many scientists hypothesize that during the Cretaceous an asteroid hit Earth near the present-day Yucatán Peninsula, in southeastern Mexico.

The Cenozoic Era

Your voyage through time continues on through the Cenozoic Era—often called the Age of Mammals. During the Mesozoic Era, mammals had a hard time competing with dinosaurs for food and places to live. **The extinction of dinosaurs created an opportunity for mammals. During the Cenozoic Era, mammals evolved to live in many different environments—on land, in water, and even in the air.**

The Tertiary Period During the Tertiary Period, Earth's climates were generally warm. In the oceans, marine mammals such as whales evolved. On land, flowering plants, insects, and mammals flourished. When grasses evolved, they provided food for grazing mammals. These were the ancestors of today's cattle, deer, sheep, and other grass-eating mammals. Some mammals and birds became very large.

The Quaternary Period The mammals that had evolved during the Tertiary Period eventually faced a changing environment. **Earth's climate cooled, causing a series of ice ages during the Quaternary Period.** Thick continental glaciers advanced and retreated over parts of Europe and North America. Then, about 20,000 years ago, Earth's climate began to warm. Over thousands of years, the continental glaciers melted, except in Greenland and Antarctica.

FIGURE 26
Ice-Age Environment
Large mammals roamed the ice-free parts of North America during the Ice Ages of the Quaternary Period.

In the oceans, algae, coral, mollusks, fish, and mammals thrived. Insects and birds shared the skies. On land, flowering plants and mammals such as bats, cats, dogs, cattle, and humans—just to name a few—became common.

The fossil record suggests that modern humans, or *Homo sapiens,* may have evolved as early as 100,000 years ago. By about 12,000 to 15,000 years ago, humans had migrated around the world to every continent except Antarctica.

Your time machine has now arrived back in the present. You and all organisms on Earth are living in the Quaternary Period of the Cenozoic Era. Is this the end of evolution and the changing of Earth's surface? No, these processes will continue as long as Earth exists. But you'll have to take your time machine into the future to see just what happens!

FIGURE 27
Ice Age Art
An early ancestor of modern humans painted these beautiful images of animals in a cave in France more than 15,000 years ago.

 **Reading Checkpoint** **How did Earth's climate change during the Quaternary Period?**

Section 5 Assessment

S 7.4.b, 7.4.g, E-LA: Writing 7.2.1, Reading 7.2.0

Target Reading Skill Create Outlines Use your outline of this section to help answer the questions below.

Reviewing Key Concepts

1. **a. Defining** What is the geologic time scale?
   b. Inferring What information did geologists use to develop the geologic time scale?
2. **a. Reviewing** When did the earliest organisms appear on Earth?
   b. Relating Cause and Effect How did early photosynthetic organisms change Earth's atmosphere?
3. **a. Listing** List the periods of the Paleozoic.
   b. Describing How did organisms change during the first period of the Paleozoic?
   c. Relating Cause and Effect What event do scientists think may have caused the mass extinction at the end of the Paleozoic?
4. **a. Reviewing** Which group of animals was dominant during the Mesozoic Era?
   b. Inferring How was their small size helpful to the mammals of the Mesozoic?

   c. Developing Hypotheses Many scientists think that the asteroid impact at the end of the Cretaceous prevented plant growth for many years. Although many dinosaurs were plant eaters, some were meat eaters. Develop a hypothesis to explain why all dinosaurs became extinct.
5. **a. Identifying** What term do scientists apply to the Cenozoic Era?
   b. Inferring What conditions allowed so many different kinds of mammals to evolve during the Cenozoic Era?

Writing in Science

Description Suppose that you are going on a tour of Earth during one era of geologic time. Write a paragraph describing the organisms and environments that you see on the tour. Your tour should include at least one stop in each geologic period of the era.

Skills Lab

As Time Goes By

S 7.4.g, 7.7.d

Problem

How can you make a scale model of geologic time?

Skills

measuring, calculating, making models

Materials

- worksheet with 2,000 asterisks
- one ream of paper

Procedure

PART 1 Table A

1. Copy Table A into your lab notebook. Figure how long ago these historic events happened and write the answers on your chart.

2. Obtain a worksheet with 2,000 asterisks printed on it. Each asterisk represents one year. The first asterisk at the top represents one year ago.

3. Starting from this asterisk, circle the asterisk that represents how many years ago each event in Table A occurred.

4. Label each circled asterisk to indicate the event.

5. Obtain a ream of copy paper. There are 500 sheets in a ream. If each sheet had 2,000 asterisks on it, there would be a total of 1 million asterisks. Therefore, each ream would represent 1 million years.

Table A: Historic Events		
Event	Date	Number of Years Ago
You are born.		
One of your parents is born.		
First space shuttle sent into space.	1981	
Neil Armstrong first walks on the moon.	1969	
World War I ends.	1918	
Civil War ends.	1865	
Declaration of Independence is signed.	1776	
Columbus crosses Atlantic Ocean.	1492	
Leif Ericson visits North America.	1000	

Table B: Geologic Events			
Event	Number of Years Ago	Reams or Sheets of Paper	Thickness of Paper
Last ice age ends.	10,000		
Whales evolve.	50 million		
Pangaea begins to break up.	225 million		
First vertebrates develop.	530 million		
Multicellular organisms (algae) develop.	1 billion		
Single-celled organisms develop.	3.5 billion		
Oldest known rocks form.	4.0 billion		
Earth forms.	4.6 billion		

PART 2 Table B

6. Copy Table B into your lab notebook. Determine how much paper in reams or sheets would be needed to represent the events in geologic time found in Table B. (*Hint:* Recall that each ream represents 1 million years.)

7. Measure the thickness of a ream of paper. Use this thickness to calculate how thick a stack of paper would need to be to represent how long ago each geologic event occurred. (*Hint:* Use a calculator to multiply the thickness of the ream of paper by the number of reams.) Enter your results in Table B.

Analyze and Conclude

1. **Measuring** Measure the height of your classroom. How many reams of paper would you need to reach the ceiling? How many years would the height of the ceiling represent? Which geologic events listed in Table B would fall on a ream of paper inside your classroom?

2. **Calculating** At this scale, how many classrooms would have to be stacked on top of each other to represent the age of Earth? The time when vertebrates appeared?

3. **Calculating** How many times higher would the thickness of the stack be for the age of Earth than for the breakup of Pangaea?

4. **Making Models** On your model, how could you distinguish one era or period from another? How could you show when particular organisms evolved and when they became extinct?

5. **Communicating** Is the scale of your model practical? What would be the advantages and disadvantages of a model that fit geologic time on a timeline 1 meter long?

More to Explore

This model represents geologic time as a straight line. Can you think of other ways of representing geologic time graphically? Using colored pencils, draw your own version of the geologic time scale so that it fits on a single sheet of typing paper. (*Hint:* You could represent geologic time as a wheel, a ribbon, or a spiral.)

 **The BIG Idea** Evidence from rocks shows that life has existed for billions of years and how Earth has changed over time.

① The Rock Cycle

Key Concepts S 7.4.a, 7.4.c

- The principle of uniformitarianism states that the geologic processes that operate today also operated in the past.
- Rocks are classified into three groups—igneous, sedimentary, and metamorphic.
- Internal and surface forces produce a rock cycle that builds, destroys, and changes rocks.

Key Terms
- geology • erosion • uniformitarianism
- igneous rock • sedimentary rock
- metamorphic rock • rock cycle
- magma • lava

② The Relative Age of Rocks

Key Concepts S 7.4.c

- According to the law of superposition, in horizontal sedimentary rock layers, each higher layer is younger than the layers below it.
- To determine relative age, geologists also study extrusions, intrusions, faults, gaps in the geologic record, and inclusions.
- Index fossils indicate the relative ages of the rock layers in which they occur.

Key Terms
- relative age • absolute age
- law of superposition • extrusion • intrusion
- fault • unconformity • inclusion • index fossil

③ Radioactive Dating

Key Concepts S 7.4.d

- During radioactive decay, the atoms of one element break down to form atoms of another.
- Radioactive dating is used to determine the absolute age of rocks.
- Radioactive dating indicates that Earth is roughly 4.6 billion years old.

Key Terms
- atom • element • radioactive decay • half-life

④ Movement of Earth's Plates

Key Concepts S 7.4.f

- According to the theory of plate tectonics, Earth's landmasses have changed position over time because they are part of plates that are slowly moving.
- As Earth's plates moved, landmasses changed their locations. These changes have affected where different kinds of organisms, past and present, are located.

Key Terms
- plate • theory of plate tectonics
- continental drift

⑤ The Geologic Time Scale

Key Concepts S 7.4.b, 7.4.g

- Scientists have found fossils of single-celled organisms in rocks that formed about 3.5 billion years ago. These earliest life forms were probably similar to present-day bacteria.
- Geologists use the geologic time scale to show the time span of Earth's history.
- At the beginning of the Paleozoic Era, many different kinds of organisms evolved.
- At the close of the Mesozoic Era, about 65 million years ago, a mass extinction occurred. Scientists hypothesize that this mass extinction occurred when an object from space struck Earth.
- During the Cenozoic Era, mammals evolved to live in many environments.

Key Terms
- geologic time scale • era • period
- invertebrate • vertebrate • amphibian
- reptile • mass extinction • mammal

Review and Assessment

⟳ Target Reading Skill

Outlining To help you review Section 4, copy the incomplete outline at the right. Complete the outline by adding subtopics and details. Be sure to include key concepts and key terms.

> I. Earth's Plates
>
> II. Plate Movement and Organisms
>   A. Climate
>
>   B. Separation of Organisms

Reviewing Key Terms

Choose the letter of the best answer.

1. The type of rock that forms when an existing rock is changed by pressure or other factors is
   a. radioactive rock.
   b. sedimentary rock.
   c. metamorphic rock.
   d. igneous rock.

2. A gap in the geologic record formed when sedimentary rocks cover an eroded surface is called a(n)
   a. intrusion.
   b. unconformity.
   c. fault.
   d. extrusion.

3. The time it takes for half of a radioactive element's atoms to decay is a(n)
   a. era.
   b. half-life.
   c. relative age.
   d. absolute age.

4. Earth's outer layer consists of pieces called
   a. extrusions.
   b. eras.
   c. plates.
   d. faults.

5. The geologic time scale is subdivided into
   a. relative ages.
   b. absolute ages.
   c. unconformities.
   d. eras and periods.

Complete the following sentences so that your answers clearly explain the key terms.

6. The principle of **uniformitarianism** states that _____.

7. Unlike absolute age, the **relative age** of a rock indicates only _____.

8. **Radioactive decay** is the process in which _____.

9. The **theory of plate tectonics** states that _____.

10. A **mass extinction** is a catastrophic event because _____.

Writing in Science

Field Guide Write a field guide for visitors to the Grand Canyon. In your guide, explain how geologists have learned about Earth's past by studying the canyon walls and the fossils they contain.

Video Assessment
Discovery Channel School
A Trip Through Geologic Time

Review and Assessment

Checking Concepts

11. How does igneous rock form?

12. Describe a process that could cause an unconformity.

13. How would a scientist determine the absolute age of a fossil?

14. Use the theory of plate tectonics to explain why fossils of *Brachiosaurus* have been found on several different continents.

15. What was Earth's early atmosphere like?

16. How did Earth's environments change from the Tertiary Period to the Quaternary Period? Explain.

Thinking Critically

17. Applying Concepts Trilobites are index fossils. Paleontologists find a trilobite fossil in a rock layer at the top of a hill in South America. Then they find the same kind of fossil in a rock layer at the bottom of a cliff in Africa. What could the paleontologists conclude about the two rock layers?

18. Problem Solving Which of the elements in the table below would be better to use in dating a fossil from Precambrian time? Explain.

Radioactive Elements	
Element	**Half-life (years)**
Carbon-14	5,730
Uranium-235	713 million

19. Relating Cause and Effect When Pangaea formed, the climate on Earth became drier. How was this climate change more favorable to reptiles than amphibians?

20. Making Judgments If you see a movie in which early humans fight giant dinosaurs, how would you judge the scientific accuracy of that movie? Give reasons for your judgment.

Math Practice

21. Percentage What percentage of a radioactive element will remain after 9 half-lives?

Applying Skills

Use the diagram of rock layers below to answer Questions 22–25.

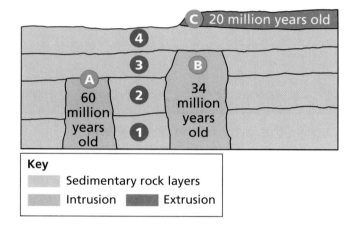

22. Inferring According to the Law of Superposition, which is the oldest layer of sedimentary rock? Which is the youngest? How do you know?

23. Measuring What method did a scientist use to determine the age of the intrusion and extrusion?

24. Interpreting Data What is the relative age of layer 3? (*Hint:* With what absolute ages can you compare it?)

25. Interpreting Data What is the relative age of layer 4?

Lab zone Standards Investigation

Performance Assessment You have completed your illustrations for the timeline and travel brochure. Now you are ready to present the story of the geologic time period you researched. Be sure to include the awesome sights people will see when they travel to this time period. Don't forget to warn them of any dangers that await them. In your journal, reflect on what you have learned about Earth's history.

Choose the letter of the best answer.

1. Which of the following best shows that slow geologic processes can have a major impact on Earth?
   A extrusions
   B continental drift
   C unconformities
   D index fossils   **S 7.4.a**

Use the diagram below and your knowledge of science to answer Question 2.

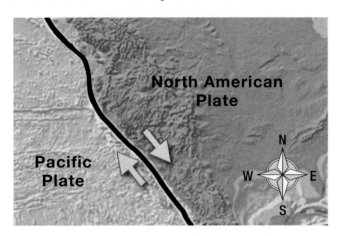

2. The diagram shows part of the boundary between the Pacific plate and the North American plate. The arrows show the plates' direction of movement. In 100 years, how is the North American plate likely to have moved along this boundary?
   A far to the northwest of the Pacific plate
   B slightly to the northwest of the Pacific plate
   C far to the southeast of the Pacific plate
   D slightly to the southeast of the Pacific plate
                                        S 7.4.f

3. A geologist finds identical index fossils in a rock layer in the Grand Canyon in Arizona and in a rock layer in northern Utah, more than 675 kilometers away. What inference can she make about the ages of the two rock layers?
   A The rock layer in the Grand Canyon is older.
   B The rock layer in Utah is older.
   C The two rock layers are about the same age.
   D no inferences   **S 7.4.c**

Use the diagram below and your knowledge of science to answer Question 4.

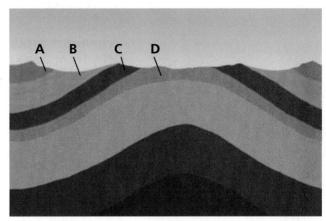

4. According to the law of superposition, the youngest layer of rock in this diagram is
   A Layer A.
   B Layer B.
   C Layer C.
   D Layer D.   **S 7.4.c**

5. What should you use so that the geologic time scale covering Earth's 4.6-billion-year history can be drawn as a straight line on a poster board one meter high?
   A 1 cm = 1 million years
   B 1 cm = 10,000 years
   C 1 cm = 100,000 years
   D 1 cm = 50,000,000 years   **S 7.4.g**

6. Dinosaurs most likely became extinct because
   A disease killed most of the dinosaurs.
   B large mammals preyed on them and reduced dinosaur populations.
   C the dinosaurs couldn't obtain enough water to survive.
   D an asteroid hit Earth, causing severe climate change.   **S 7.4.b**

Apply the
BIG Idea

7. Describe two methods geologists use to determine the age of a rock. In your answer, be sure to mention igneous rock, sedimentary rock, the law of superposition, index fossils, radioactive decay, and half-life.   **S 7.4.d**

Genetics and Evolution
Unit 2 Review

Chapter 5
Genetics: The Science of Heredity

🔑 The **BIG Idea**

Organisms produced by sexual reproduction inherit half their DNA from each parent. The new combination of DNA determines an organism's traits.

🔑 What controls the inheritance of traits in organisms?
🔑 What is probability, and how does it help explain the results of genetic crosses?
🔑 What role do chromosomes play in inheritance?
🔑 What forms the genetic code?

Chapter 6
Modern Genetics

🔑 The **BIG Idea**

A person's traits depend on which alleles are inherited from each parent, how those alleles work together, and environmental factors.

🔑 What are some patterns of inheritance in humans?
🔑 How do geneticists trace the inheritance of traits?
🔑 What are three ways of producing organisms with desired traits?

Chapter 7
Changes Over Time

🔑 The **BIG Idea**

Genetic variation and environmental factors have together resulted in the evolution of species.

🔑 How does natural selection lead to evolution?
🔑 What evidence supports the theory of evolution?
🔑 What factors have contributed to the diversity of species?
🔑 How does a branching tree diagram show evolutionary relationships?

Chapter 8
Earth's History

🔑 The **BIG Idea**

Evidence from rocks shows that life has existed for billions of years and how Earth has changed over time.

🔑 How do geologists determine the relative age of rocks?
🔑 How does the theory of plate tectonics explain the movement of Earth's landmasses?
🔑 What were the major events of the Paleozoic, Mesozoic, and Cenozoic Eras?

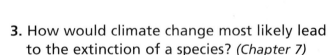

Connecting the BIG Ideas

In northern Alaska and Siberia, part of the ground remains frozen all year round. This frozen layer is called permafrost. Scientists have drilled into the permafrost and found the remains of plants and animals, including woolly mammoths, giant bison, and other large animals that became extinct around 10,000 years ago. Scientists have been able to take DNA samples from these remains and compare the results to other living and extinct organisms. Evidence from this DNA may help scientists determine how changes in climate and the environment may have led to the extinction of these large mammals.

Scientists can use carbon–14 dating to determine when some organisms lived in the past. These data help scientists learn whether or not the organisms lived in a region at the same time.

1. What is the function of DNA? *(Chapter 5)*
   a. carrying genetic information from parents to offspring
   b. converting genetic instructions into proteins
   c. controlling the process of meiosis
   d. producing chains of amino acids

2. What technique allows scientists to see if two individuals are related? *(Chapter 6)*
   a. genetic engineering
   b. selective breeding
   c. DNA fingerprinting
   d. Punnett squares

3. How would climate change most likely lead to the extinction of a species? *(Chapter 7)*
   a. Colder temperatures cause all organisms in an area to freeze.
   b. The species cannot adapt to the new climate.
   c. Predators kill more prey in order to survive in the changed climate.
   d. The species becomes geographically isolated due to the climate change.

4. What process makes carbon-14 useful for dating objects? *(Chapter 8)*
   a. sedimentation   b. superposition
   c. radioactive decay   d. plate tectonics

5. **Summary** Summarize how scientists determine the genetic and evolutionary relationships between individuals and between species. What types of evidence do they use to support their conclusions?

Egyptian Art
More than 3,000 years ago, an artist drew three dogs chasing a hyena.

Dogs— Loyal Companions

What's your image of a dog?

- A powerful Great Dane?
- A tiny, lively Chihuahua?
- A protective German shepherd guide dog?
- A friendly, lovable mutt?

Most dogs are descendants of the gray wolf, which was originally found throughout Europe, Asia, and North America. Dogs were the first animals to be domesticated, or tamed. As far back as 9,000 years ago, farmers who raised sheep, cattle, and goats tamed dogs to herd and guard the livestock.

After taming dogs, people began to breed them for traits that people valued. Early herding dogs helped shepherds. Speedy hunting dogs learned to chase deer and other game. Strong, sturdy working dogs pulled sleds and even rescued people. Small, quick terriers hunted animals, such as rats. "Toy" dogs were companions to people of wealth and leisure. More recently, sporting dogs were trained to flush out and retrieve birds. Still others were bred to be guard dogs. But perhaps the real reasons people bred dogs were for loyalty and companionship.

Girl with dalmatian

From Wolf to Purebred

About 10,000 years ago, some wolves may have been attracted to human settlements. They may have found it easier to feed on food scraps than to hunt for themselves. Gradually the wolves came to depend on people for food. The wolves, in turn, kept the campsites clean and safe. They ate the garbage and barked to warn of approaching strangers. These wolves were the ancestors of the dogs you know today.

Over time, dogs became more and more a part of human society. People began to breed dogs for the traits needed for tasks such as herding sheep and hunting. Large, aggressive dogs, for example, were bred to be herding dogs, while fast dogs with a keen sense of smell were bred to be hunting dogs. Today, there are hundreds of breeds. They range from the tiny Chihuahua to the massive Saint Bernard, one of which can weigh as much as 50 Chihuahuas.

Today, people breed dogs mostly for their appearance and personality. Physical features such as long ears or a narrow snout are valued in particular breeds of dogs. To create "pure" breeds of dogs, breeders use a method known as inbreeding. Inbreeding involves mating dogs that are genetically very similar. Inbreeding is the surest way to produce dogs with a uniform physical appearance.

One undesirable result of inbreeding is an increase in genetic disorders. Experts estimate that 25 percent of all purebred dogs have a genetic disorder. Dalmatians, for example, often inherit deafness. German shepherds may develop severe hip problems. Mixed-breed dogs, in contrast, are less likely to inherit genetic disorders.

Fur Color in Retrievers
In Labrador retrievers, the allele for dark-colored fur is dominant over the allele for yellow fur.

Science Activity

Most traits that dogs are bred for are controlled by more than one gene. A few traits, however, show simpler inheritance patterns. For example, in Labrador retrievers, a single gene with one dominant and one recessive allele determines whether the dog's fur will be dark or yellow. The allele for dark fur (D) is dominant over the allele for yellow fur (d).

- Construct a Punnett square for a cross between two Labrador retrievers that are both heterozygous for dark fur (Dd).

- Suppose there were eight puppies in the litter. Predict how many would have dark fur and how many would have yellow fur.

- Construct a second Punnett square for a cross between a Labrador retriever with yellow fur (dd) and one with dark fur (Dd). In a litter with six puppies, predict how many would have dark fur and how many would have yellow fur.

Dogs and People

Over thousands of years, people have developed many different breeds of dogs. Each of the dogs shown on the map was bred for a purpose— hunting, herding, guarding, pulling sleds—as well as companionship. Every breed has its own story.

Border Collie
Great Britain, after A.D. 1100
This breed was developed in the counties near the border between England and Scotland for herding sheep. The border collie's ancestors were crossbreeds of local sheepdogs and dogs brought to Scotland by the Vikings.

R u s s i a

Dachshund
Germany, A.D. 1600s
These dogs were bred to catch badgers or rats. Their short legs and long body can fit into a badger's burrow. In fact, in German the word *Dachshund* means "badger dog."

EUROPE

Golden Retriever
Great Britain, A.D. 1870s
Lord Tweedmouth developed this breed to help hunters retrieve waterfowl and other small animals.

Basset Hound
France, A.D. 1500s
Second only to the blood-hound at following a scent, the basset hound has short legs and a compact body that help it run through underbrush.

AFRICA

Greyhound
Egypt, 3000 B.C.
These speedy, slender hounds were bred for chasing prey. Today, greyhounds are famous as racers.

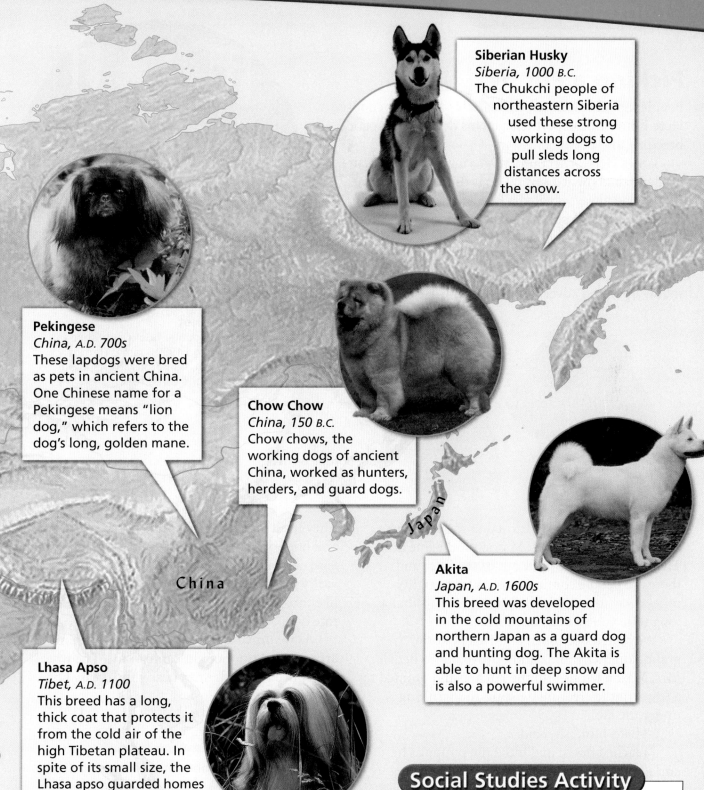

Siberian Husky
Siberia, 1000 B.C.
The Chukchi people of northeastern Siberia used these strong working dogs to pull sleds long distances across the snow.

Pekingese
China, A.D. *700s*
These lapdogs were bred as pets in ancient China. One Chinese name for a Pekingese means "lion dog," which refers to the dog's long, golden mane.

Chow Chow
China, 150 B.C.
Chow chows, the working dogs of ancient China, worked as hunters, herders, and guard dogs.

China

Japan

Akita
Japan, A.D. *1600s*
This breed was developed in the cold mountains of northern Japan as a guard dog and hunting dog. The Akita is able to hunt in deep snow and is also a powerful swimmer.

Lhasa Apso
Tibet, A.D. *1100*
This breed has a long, thick coat that protects it from the cold air of the high Tibetan plateau. In spite of its small size, the Lhasa apso guarded homes and temples.

Social Studies Activity

Draw a timeline that shows the approximate date of origin of different breeds of domestic dogs from 7000 B.C. to the present. Use the information on the map to fill out your timeline. Include information about where each breed was developed.

Picking a Puppy

People look for different traits in the dogs they choose. Here is how one expert selected his dog based on good breeding and personality.

James Herriot, a country veterinarian in Yorkshire, England, had owned several dogs during his lifetime. But he had always wanted a Border terrier. These small, sturdy dogs are descendants of working terrier breeds that lived on the border of England and Scotland. For centuries they were used to hunt foxes, rats, and other small animals. In this story, Herriot and his wife, Helen, follow up on an advertisement for Border terrier puppies.

James Herriot
In several popular books published in the 1970s and 1980s, James Herriot wrote warm, humorous stories about the animals he cared for.

◀ **Border terriers**

She [Helen, his wife] turned to me and spoke agitatedly, "I've got Mrs. Mason on the line now. There's only one pup left out of the litter and there are people coming from as far as eighty miles away to see it. We'll have to hurry. What a long time you've been out there!"

We bolted our lunch and Helen, Rosie, granddaughter Emma and I drove out to Bedale. Mrs. Mason led us into the kitchen and pointed to a tiny brindle creature twisting and writhing under the table.

"That's him," she said.

I reached down and lifted the puppy as he curled his little body round, apparently trying to touch his tail with his nose. But that tail wagged furiously and the pink tongue was busy at my hand. I knew he was ours before my quick examination for hernia and overshot jaw.

The deal was quickly struck and we went outside to inspect the puppy's relations. His mother and grandmother were out there.

They lived in little barrels which served as kennels and both of them darted out and stood up at our legs, tails lashing, mouths panting in delight. I felt vastly reassured. With happy, healthy ancestors like those I knew we had every chance of a first rate dog.

As we drove home with the puppy in Emma's arms, the warm thought came to me. The wheel had indeed turned. After nearly fifty years I had my Border terrier.

Language Arts Activity

James Herriot describes this scene using dialog and first-person narrative. The narrative describes Herriot's feelings about a memorable event—finally finding the dog he had wanted for so long. Write a first-person narrative describing a memorable event in your life. You might choose a childhood memory or a personal achievement at school. What emotions did you feel? How did you make your decision? If possible, use dialog in your writing.

Popular Breeds

The popularity of different breeds of dogs changes over time. For example, the line graph shows how the number of poodles registered with the American Kennel Club changed between 1970 and 2000.

Standard poodle and puppy ▶

Math Activity

Use the table below to create your own line graph for Labrador retrievers and cocker spaniels. Which breed was more popular in 1980, Labrador retrievers or cocker spaniels?

How has the number of Labrador retrievers changed from 1970 to 2000? How has the number of cocker spaniels changed over the same time?

Dog Populations				
Breed	**1970**	**1980**	**1990**	**2000**
Poodle	265,879	92,250	71,757	45,868
Labrador Retriever	25,667	52,398	95,768	172,841
Cocker Spaniel	21,811	76,113	105,642	29,393

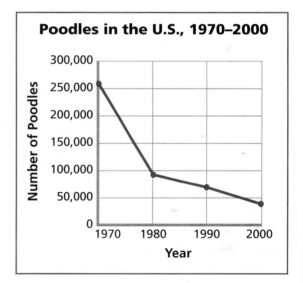

Poodles in the U.S., 1970–2000

Tie It Together

Best-of-Breed Show

In many places, proud dog owners of all ages bring their animals to compete in dog shows.

Organize your own dog show.

With a partner, choose one specific breed of dog. Pick a breed shown on the map on the previous page, or use library resources to research another breed.

- Find out what the breed looks like, the time and place where it originated, and what traits it was first bred for.

- List your breed's characteristics, height, weight, and coloring.

- Research the breed's personality and behavior.

- Find out your breed's strengths. Learn what weaknesses may develop as a result of inbreeding.

- Make a poster for your breed. Include a drawing or photo and the information that you researched.

- With your class, organize the dog displays into categories of breeds, such as hunting dogs, herding dogs, and toy dogs.

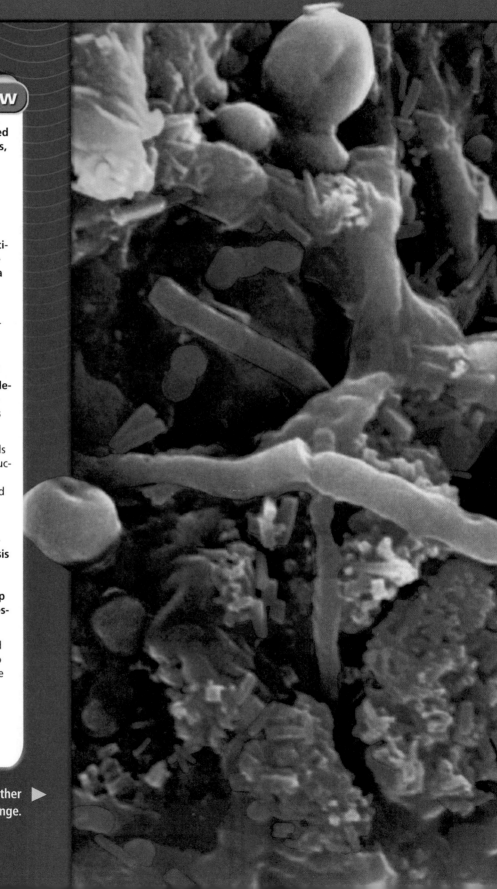

CALIFORNIA Standards Preview

S 7.1 All living organisms are composed of cells, from just one to many trillions, whose details usually are visible only through a microscope.

  a. *Students know* cells function similarly in all living organisms.

S 7.2 A typical cell of any organism contains genetic instructions that specify its traits. Those traits may be modified by environmental influences. As a basis for understanding this concept:

  a. *Students know* the differences between the life cycles and reproduction methods of sexual and asexual organisms.

S 7.5 The anatomy and physiology of plants and animals illustrate the complementary nature of structure and function. As a basis for understanding this concept:

  a. *Students know* plants and animals have levels of organization for structure and function, including cells, tissues, organs, organ systems, and the whole organism.

S 7.7 Scientific progress is made by asking meaningful questions and conducting careful investigations. As a basis for understanding this concept and addressing the content in the other three strands, students should develop their own questions and perform investigations. Students will:

  d. Construct scale models, maps, and appropriately labeled diagrams to communicate scientific knowledge (e.g. motion of Earth's plates and cell structure).

▶ Bacteria (blue and purple rods) and other microorganisms lurk in a kitchen sponge.

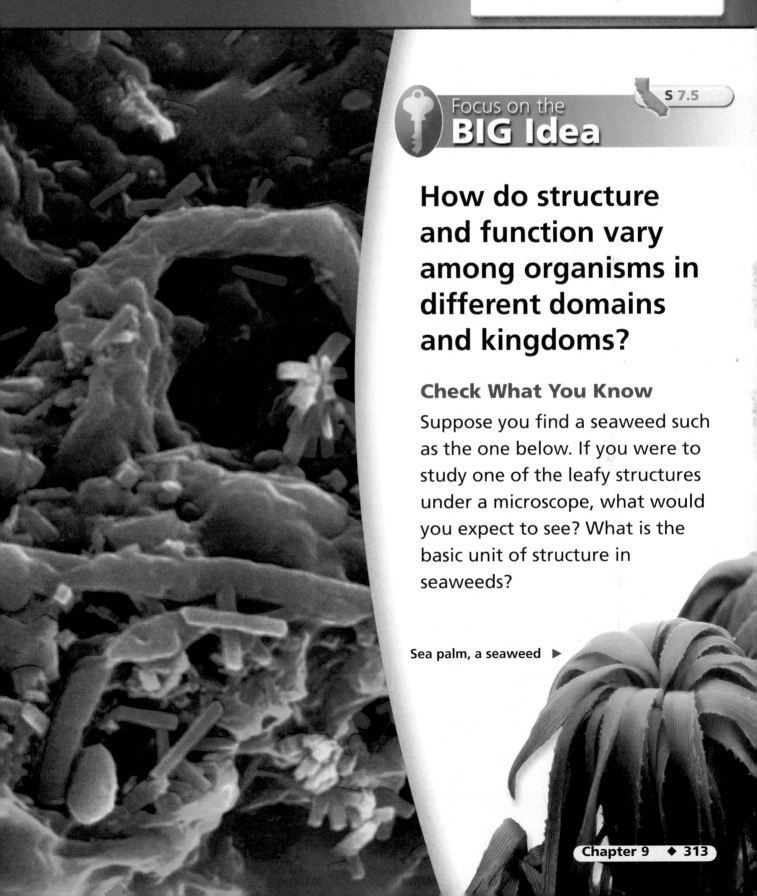

Focus on the
BIG Idea

S 7.5

How do structure and function vary among organisms in different domains and kingdoms?

Check What You Know

Suppose you find a seaweed such as the one below. If you were to study one of the leafy structures under a microscope, what would you expect to see? What is the basic unit of structure in seaweeds?

Sea palm, a seaweed ▶

The images shown here represent some of the key terms in this chapter. You can use this vocabulary skill to help you understand the meaning of some key terms in this chapter.

Prefixes

When you talk about word parts, a root is the part of the word that carries the basic meaning. A prefix is a word part placed in front of the root to change the meaning of the root or to form a new word. Look at the examples in the table below.

Prefix	Meaning of Prefix	Example and Meaning of Example
bi-	two, twice	**bicolor** Having two colors
con-, com-	with, together	**compare** To look at together to note similarities and differences
de-	down, from, reverse the action of	**defrost** To remove ice or frost

Apply It!

Answer the following questions. After reading the chapter, check to see whether your answers are accurate or need to be changed.

1. The word *fission* means "division into parts." When a one-celled organism reproduces by binary fission, how many new organisms are produced?

2. Some bacteria are decomposers. The root *-compose* means "to put together." What do decomposers do to dead organisms?

3. The root *-jugate* means "to join." What might *conjugation* mean?

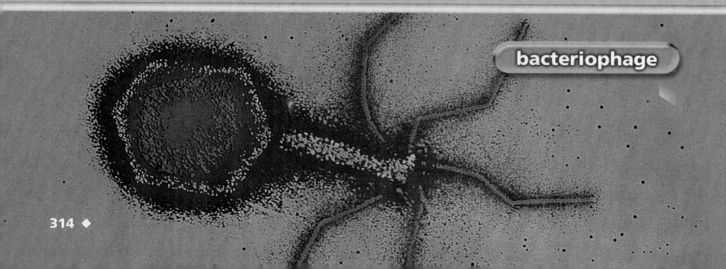

bacteriophage

conjugation

fungi

protists

Chapter 9 Vocabulary

Interactive Textbook

Build Science Vocabulary
Online
Visit: PHSchool.com
Web Code: cvj-3090

How to Read Science

Compare and Contrast

Science texts often make comparisons. When you compare and contrast, you examine similarities and differences between two things. You can compare and contrast by using a Venn diagram.

Follow these steps to set up a Venn diagram in your notebook.

- Draw two overlapping circles. Label each circle with one of the two items being compared. In the example below, oranges and lemons are being compared.
- In the area where the circles overlap, write the characteristics that the items share.
- Think of how the items are different. Write these differences in the parts of the circles that do not overlap.

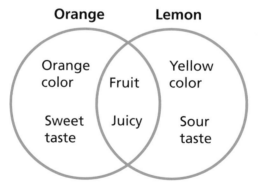

Apply It!

Review the Venn diagram above. Then answer the questions.

1. In the Venn diagram above, what are the similarities between lemons and oranges?

2. What are the differences written in the Venn diagram?

When you read Section 1, draw a Venn diagram comparing viruses and organisms.

S 7.2.a

A Mushroom Life Cycle

The fungi you're most familiar with are probably mushrooms. In some ways, mushrooms resemble plants, often growing near plants or even on them like small umbrellas. But mushrooms are very different from plants in some important ways. In this investigation, you'll learn about these differences.

Your Goal

To determine the conditions needed for mushrooms to grow and reproduce

To complete this investigation, you must

- choose one variable and design a way to test how it affects mushroom growth
- make daily observations and record them in a data table
- prepare a poster that describes the results of your experiment
- follow the safety guidelines in Appendix A

Plan It!

List possible hypotheses about the way variables such as light or moisture could affect the growth and reproduction of mushrooms. Choose one variable and write out a plan for testing that variable. After your teacher approves your plan, start growing your mushrooms!

Viruses

CALIFORNIA
Standards Focus

S 7.2.a *Students know* the differences between the life cycles and reproduction methods of sexual and asexual organisms.

S 7.5 The anatomy and physiology of plants and animals illustrate the complementary nature of structure and function.

- How are viruses like organisms?
- What is the structure of a virus?
- How do viruses multiply?
- How can you treat a viral disease?

Key Terms
- virus
- host
- parasite
- bacteriophage
- vaccine

Lab zone Standards **Warm-Up**

Which Lock Does the Key Fit?

1. Your teacher will give you a key.
2. Study the key closely. Think about what shape the keyhole on its lock must have. On a piece of paper, draw the shape of the keyhole.
3. The lock for your key is contained in the group of locks your teacher will provide. Try to match your key to its lock without inserting the key into the keyhole.

Think It Over
Inferring How might a unique "lock" on its surface help a cell protect itself from invading organisms?

It is a dark and quiet night. An enemy spy slips silently across the border. Invisible to the guards, the spy creeps cautiously along the edge of the road, heading toward the command center. Undetected, the spy sneaks by the center's security system and reaches the door. Breaking into the control room, the spy takes command of the central computer. The enemy is in control.

What Is a Virus?

Although this spy story may read like a movie script, it describes events similar to those that can occur in your body. The spy acts very much like a virus invading an organism.

Characteristics of Viruses A **virus** is a tiny, nonliving particle that invades and then multiplies inside a living cell. Viruses are not cells. They do not have the characteristics of organisms. **The only way in which viruses are like organisms is that they can multiply.** Although viruses can multiply, their reproduction is different than the reproduction of organisms. Viruses can only multiply when they are inside a living cell.

No organisms are safe from viruses. The organism that a virus multiplies inside is called a host. A **host** is a living thing that provides a source of energy for a virus or an organism. Viruses act like **parasites** (PA ruh syts), organisms that live on or in a host and cause it harm. Almost all viruses destroy their host cells.

The Structure of Viruses Viruses are smaller than cells and vary in size and shape. Some viruses are round. Others are shaped like rods, bricks, threads, or bullets. There are even viruses that have complex, robot-like shapes, such as the bacteriophage in Figure 1. A **bacteriophage** (bak TEER ee oh fayj) is a virus that infects bacteria. In fact, its name means "bacteria eater."

Although viruses may look different from one another, they all have a similar structure. ⌬ **All viruses have two basic parts: a protein coat that protects the virus and an inner core made of genetic material.** A virus's genetic material contains the instructions for making new viruses. Some viruses are also surrounded by an additional outer membrane, or envelope.

The proteins on the surface of a virus play an important role during the invasion of a host cell. Each virus contains unique surface proteins. The shape of the surface proteins allows the virus to attach to certain cells in the host. Like keys, a virus's proteins fit only into certain "locks," or proteins, on the surface of a host's cells. Figure 2 shows how the lock-and-key action works.

Because the lock-and-key action of a virus is specific, a certain virus can attach only to one or a few types of cells. For example, most cold viruses infect cells only in the nose and throat of humans. These cells are the ones with proteins on their surface that complement or "fit" those on the virus.

Reading Checkpoint What information does a virus's genetic material contain?

FIGURE 1
Bacteriophage
This robot-like virus infects bacteria.

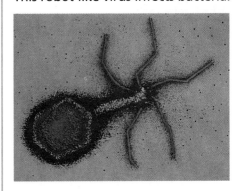

FIGURE 2
Virus Structure and Infection

All viruses consist of genetic material surrounded by a protein coat. Some viruses, like the ones shown here, are surrounded by an outer membrane envelope. A virus can attach to a cell only if the virus' surface proteins can fit those on the cell.

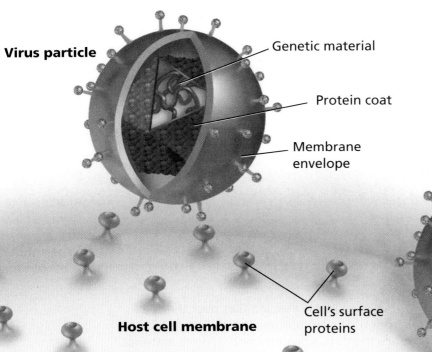

Virus particle

Genetic material

Protein coat

Membrane envelope

Host cell membrane

Cell's surface proteins

Virus's outer membrane proteins

How Viruses Multiply

After a virus attaches to a cell, it enters the cell. **Once inside a cell, a virus's genetic material takes over many of the cell's functions. It instructs the cell to produce the virus's proteins and genetic material. These proteins and genetic material then assemble into new viruses.** Some viruses take over cell functions immediately. Other viruses wait for a while.

Active Viruses After entering a cell, an active virus immediately goes into action. The virus's genetic material takes over cell functions, and the cell quickly begins to produce the virus's proteins and genetic material. Then these parts assemble into new viruses. Like a photocopy machine left in the "on" position, the invaded cell makes copy after copy of new viruses. When it is full of new viruses, the host cell bursts open, releasing hundreds of new viruses as it dies.

FIGURE 3
Active and Hidden Viruses

Active viruses enter host cells and immediately begin to multiply, leading to the quick death of the invaded cells. Hidden viruses "hide" for a while inside host cells before becoming active.

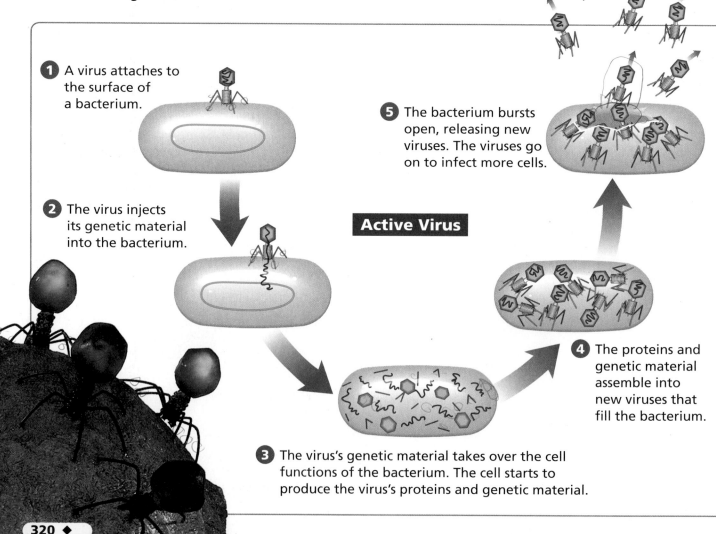

1 A virus attaches to the surface of a bacterium.

2 The virus injects its genetic material into the bacterium.

Active Virus

3 The virus's genetic material takes over the cell functions of the bacterium. The cell starts to produce the virus's proteins and genetic material.

4 The proteins and genetic material assemble into new viruses that fill the bacterium.

5 The bacterium bursts open, releasing new viruses. The viruses go on to infect more cells.

Hidden Viruses Other viruses do not immediately become active. Instead, they "hide" for a while. After a hidden virus enters a host cell, its genetic material becomes part of the cell's genetic material. The virus does not appear to affect the cell's functions and may stay in this inactive state for years. Each time the host cell divides, the virus's genetic material is copied along with the host's genetic material. Then, under certain conditions, the virus's genetic material suddenly becomes active. It takes over the cell's functions in much the same way that active viruses do. Soon, the cell is full of new viruses and bursts open.

The virus that causes cold sores is an example of a hidden virus. It can remain inactive for months or years inside nerve cells in the face. While hidden, the virus causes no symptoms. When it becomes active, the virus causes a swollen, painful sore to form near the mouth. Strong sunlight and stress are two factors that scientists believe may activate a cold sore virus. After an active period, the virus once again "hides" in the nerve cells until it becomes active again.

Reading Checkpoint — Where in a host cell does a hidden virus "hide" while it is inactive?

Go Online
active art

For: Active and Hidden Viruses activity
Visit: PHSchool.com
Web Code: cep-1021

1 A virus attaches to the surface of a bacterium.

Hidden Virus

2 The virus injects its genetic material into the bacterium.

3 The virus's genetic material becomes part of the genetic material of the bacterium.

4 After some time, the virus's genetic material removes itself and becomes active.

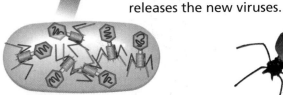

5 The cell begins to produce the virus's proteins and genetic material, which assemble into new viruses.

6 The new viruses crowd the bacterium. Finally, the cell bursts open and releases the new viruses.

Viruses and Disease

If you've ever had a cold or been sick with the flu, you know that viruses can cause disease. Some diseases, such as colds, are mild—people are sick for a short time but soon recover. Other diseases, such as acquired immunodeficiency syndrome, or AIDS, have much more serious consequences on the body.

Viruses also cause diseases in organisms other than humans. For example, apple trees infected by the apple mosaic virus may produce less fruit. House pets, such as dogs and cats, can get deadly viral diseases, such as rabies and distemper.

The Spread of Viral Diseases Viral diseases can be spread in various ways. For example, some viral diseases can be spread through contact with a contaminated object, while others are spread through the bite of an infected animal. Some viruses, such as cold and flu viruses, can travel in tiny drops of moisture that an infected person sneezes or coughs into the air. Other viruses can spread only through contact with body fluids, such as blood.

Treating Viral Diseases There are currently no cures for viral diseases. However, many over-the-counter medicines can help relieve symptoms of a viral infection. While they can make you feel better, these medicines can also delay your recovery if you resume your normal routine while you are still sick. The best treatment for viral infections is often bed rest. **Resting, drinking plenty of fluids, and eating well-balanced meals may be all you can do while you recover from a viral disease.**

FIGURE 4
Viral Diseases
Although there is currently no cure for viral diseases, there are ways to treat the symptoms and prevent their transmission.
Relating Cause and Effect *Why does the flu often pass quickly from one family member to another?*

INFLUENZA (Flu)

Symptoms:	High fever; sore throat; headache; cough
How It Spreads:	Contact with contaminated objects; inhaling droplets
Treatment:	Bed rest; fluids
Prevention:	Vaccine (mainly for the high-risk ill, elderly, and young)

CHICKENPOX

Symptoms:	Fever; red, itchy rash
How It Spreads:	Contact with the rash; inhaling droplets
Treatment:	Antiviral drug (for adults)
Prevention:	Vaccine

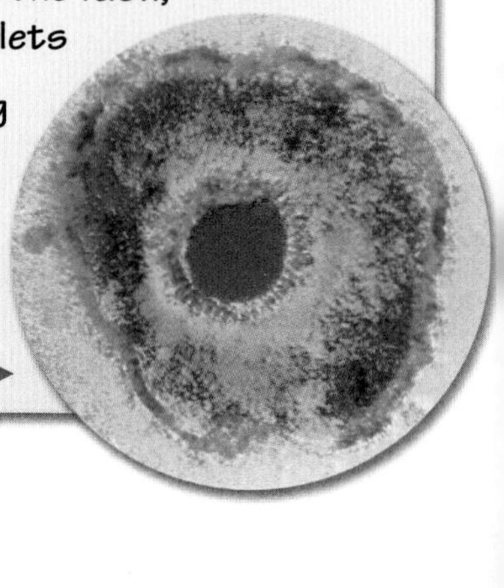

Chickenpox virus ▶

Preventing Viral Diseases Of course, you'd probably rather not get sick in the first place. An important tool that helps prevent the spread of many viral diseases is vaccines. A **vaccine** is a substance introduced into the body to stimulate the production of chemicals that destroy specific disease-causing viruses and organisms. A viral vaccine may be made from weakened or altered viruses. Because they have been weakened or altered, the viruses in the vaccine do not cause disease. Instead, they trigger the body's natural defenses. In effect, the vaccine puts the body "on alert." If that disease-causing virus ever invades the body, it is destroyed before it can cause disease. You may have been vaccinated against diseases such as polio, measles, and chickenpox.

Another important way to protect against viral diseases is to keep your body healthy. You need to eat nutritious food, as well as get enough sleep, fluids, and exercise. You can also protect yourself by washing your hands often and by not sharing eating or drinking utensils.

Unfortunately, despite your best efforts, you'll probably get viral infections, such as colds, from time to time. When you do get ill, get plenty of rest, and follow your doctor's recommendations. Also, it's very important to try not to infect others.

FIGURE 5
Vaccines
Veterinarians can give pets vaccine injections that protect the animals against many viral diseases.

 **Reading Checkpoint** Why don't vaccines cause disease themselves?

Section **1** **Assessment**

S 7.2.a, 7.5 E-LA: Writing 7.2.4, Reading 7.2.0

Target Reading Skill Compare and Contrast Complete the Venn diagram compairing viruses and organisms. Use the diagram to help answer Question 1 below.

Reviewing Key Concepts

1. a. **Defining** What is a virus?
   b. **Comparing and Contrasting** How are viruses similar to organisms?
   c. **Inferring** Scientists hypothesize that viruses could not have existed on Earth before organisms appeared. Use what you know about viruses to support this hypothesis.
2. a. **Identifying** What basic structure do all viruses share?
   b. **Relating Cause and Effect** What role do the proteins in a virus's outer coat play in the invasion of a host cell?

3. a. **Reviewing** How does an active virus multiply?
   b. **Sequencing** List the additional steps that occur when a hidden virus multiplies.
   c. **Classifying** Do you think that the cold virus is an active virus or a hidden virus? Explain.
4. a. **Reviewing** What is often the best treatment for viral diseases?
   b. **Explaining** How are vaccines important in preventing viral diseases?

Writing in Science

Public Service Announcement Write a public service announcement for a radio show that teaches young children how to stay healthy during cold and flu season.

Lab zone Skills Lab

How Many Viruses Fit on a Pin? S 7.5.a, 7.7.d

Problem

How can a model help you understand how small viruses are?

Skills Focus

calculating, making models

Materials

- straight pin • long strips of paper • pencil
- meter stick • scissors • tape
- calculator (optional)

Procedure

1. Examine the head of a straight pin. Write a prediction about the number of viruses that could fit on the pinhead. **CAUTION:** *Avoid pushing the pin against anyone's skin.*

2. Assume that the pinhead has a diameter of about 1 mm. If the pinhead were enlarged 10,000 times, then its diameter would measure 10 m. Create a model of the pinhead by cutting and taping together narrow strips of paper to make a strip that is 10 m long. The strip of paper represents the diameter of the enlarged pinhead.

3. Lay the 10-m strip of paper on the floor of your classroom or in the hall. Imagine creating a large circle that had the strip as its diameter. The circle would be the pinhead at the enlarged size. Calculate the area of the enlarged pinhead using this formula:

$$\text{Area} = \pi \times \text{Radius}^2$$

Remember that you can find the radius by dividing the diameter by 2.

4. A virus particle may measure 200 nm on each side (1 nm equals a billionth of a meter). If the virus were enlarged 10,000 times, each side would measure 0.002 m. Cut out a square 0.002 m by 0.002 m to serve as a model for a virus. (*Hint*: 0.002 m = 2 mm.)

5. Next, find the area in meters of one virus particle at the enlarged size. Remember that the area of a square equals side × side.

6. Now divide the area of the pinhead that you calculated in Step 3 by the area of one virus particle to find out how many viruses could fit on the pinhead.

7. Exchange your work with a partner, and check each other's calculations.

Analyze and Conclude

1. **Calculating** Approximately how many viruses can fit on the head of a pin?

2. **Predicting** How does your calculation compare with the prediction you made? If the two numbers are very different, explain why your prediction may have been inaccurate.

3. **Making Models** What did you learn about the size of viruses by magnifying both the viruses and pinhead to 10,000 times their actual size?

4. **Communicating** In a paragraph, explain why scientists sometimes make and use enlarged models of very small things such as viruses.

More to Explore

Think of another everyday object that you could use to model some other facts about viruses, such as their shapes or how they infect cells. Describe your model and explain why the object would be a good choice.

These papilloma viruses, which cause warts, are about 50 nm in diameter. ▼

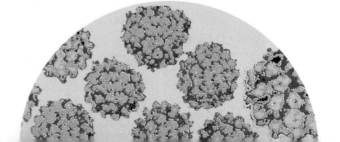

2 Bacteria

CALIFORNIA
Standards Focus

S 7.1 All living organisms are composed of cells, from just one to many trillions, whose details usually are visible only through a microscope.

S 7.2.a *Students know* the differences between the life cycles and reproduction methods of sexual and asexual organisms.

- How do the cells of bacteria differ from those of eukaryotes?
- What do bacteria need to survive?
- Under what conditions do bacteria thrive and reproduce?
- What positive roles do bacteria play in people's lives?

Key Terms
- bacteria
- flagellum
- binary fission
- asexual reproduction
- sexual reproduction
- conjugation
- endospore
- pasteurization
- decomposer

Lab zone Standards **Warm-Up**

How Quickly Can Bacteria Multiply?

1. Your teacher will give you some beans and paper cups. Number the cups 1 through 8. Each bean will represent a bacterial cell.

2. Put one bean into cup 1 to represent the first generation of bacteria. Approximately every 20 minutes, a bacterial cell reproduces by dividing into two cells. Put two beans into cup 2 to represent the second generation of bacteria.

3. Calculate how many bacterial cells there would be in the third generation if each cell in cup 2 divided into two cells. Place the correct number of beans in cup 3.

4. Repeat Step 3 five more times. All the cups should now contain beans. How many cells are in the eighth generation? How much time has elapsed since the first generation?

Think It Over

Inferring Based on this activity, explain why the number of bacteria can increase rapidly in a short period of time.

They thrive in your container of yogurt. They lurk in your kitchen sponge. They coat your skin and swarm inside your nose. You cannot escape them because they live almost everywhere—under rocks, in the ocean, and all over your body. In fact, there are more of these organisms in your mouth than there are people on Earth! You don't notice them because they are very small. These organisms are bacteria.

The Bacterial Cell

Although there are billions of bacteria on Earth, they were not discovered until the late 1600s. A Dutch merchant named Anton van Leeuwenhoek (LAY vun hook) found them by accident. Leeuwenhoek made microscopes as a hobby. One day, while using one of his microscopes to look at scrapings from his teeth, he saw some tiny, wormlike organisms in the sample. However, Leeuwenhoek's microscopes were not powerful enough to see any details inside these organisms.

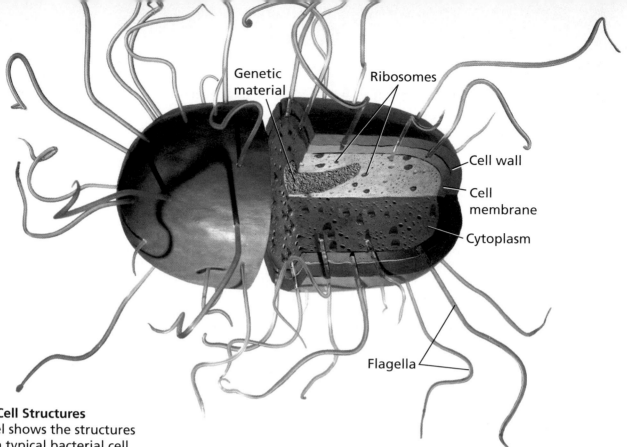

Genetic material

Ribosomes

Cell wall

Cell membrane

Cytoplasm

Flagella

FIGURE 6
Bacterial Cell Structures
This model shows the structures found in a typical bacterial cell.
Relating Diagrams and Photos
What structures does the Salmonella *bacterium in the photograph use to move?*

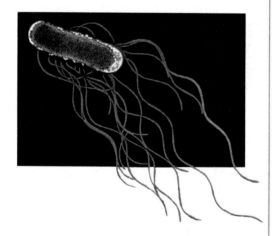

Cell Structures What Leeuwenhoek saw were single-celled organisms called **bacteria** (singular *bacterium*). ◉ **Bacteria are prokaryotes. The genetic material in their cells is not contained in a nucleus.** A bacterial cell lacks a nucleus and also lacks many other structures, such as mitochondria and Golgi bodies, that are found in the cells of eukaryotes.

Most bacterial cells, like plant cells, are surrounded by a rigid cell wall. Just inside the cell wall is the cell membrane. Located in the cytoplasm are ribosomes and the genetic material, which looks like a tangled string. If you could untangle the genetic material, you would see that it forms a circular shape.

A bacterial cell may also have a **flagellum** (fluh JEL um) (plural *flagella*), a long, whiplike structure that helps a cell to move. A flagellum moves the cell by spinning in place like a propeller. A bacterial cell can have many flagella, one, or none. Most bacteria that do not have flagella cannot move on their own. Instead, they are carried from place to place by the air, water currents, objects, or other methods.

Cell Sizes and Shapes Bacteria vary greatly in size. The largest known bacterium is about as big as the period at the end of this sentence. An average bacterium, however, is much smaller. For example, strep throat bacteria are about 0.5 to 1 micrometer in diameter. Most bacterial cells have one of three basic shapes: spherical, rodlike, or spiral. The chemical makeup of the cell wall determines the shape of a bacterial cell.

Obtaining Food and Energy

Like other organisms, there are significant differences among bacteria that live in different environments. For example, *Thermus thermophilus* bacteria live in extremely hot geysers. They contain enzymes that help them function at high temperatures.

However, no matter how different, all bacteria need certain things to survive. 🔑 **Bacteria must have a source of food and a way of breaking down the food to release its energy.**

Obtaining Food Some bacteria are autotrophs and make their own food. Autotrophic bacteria make food in one of two ways. Some capture and use the sun's energy as plants do. Others, such as bacteria that live deep in mud, do not use the sun's energy. Instead, these bacteria use the energy from chemical substances in their environment to make their food.

Some bacteria are heterotrophs and cannot make their own food. Instead, these bacteria consume other organisms or the food that other organisms make. Heterotrophic bacteria consume a variety of foods—from milk and meat, which you might also eat, to the decaying leaves on a forest floor.

Respiration Like all organisms, bacteria need a constant supply of energy. This energy comes from breaking down food in the process of respiration. Like many other organisms, most bacteria need oxygen to break down their food. But a few kinds of bacteria, such as *Escherichia coli* living in your intestines, do not need oxygen for respiration. Some kinds of bacteria will even die if exposed to oxygen.

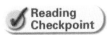 **Reading Checkpoint** What do most bacteria need in order to break down their food?

FIGURE 7
Obtaining Food
Bacteria obtain food in several ways.

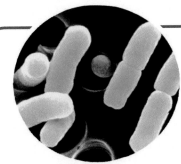

▲ These heterotrophic bacteria, found in yogurt, break down the sugars in milk for food.

▲ The autotrophic bacteria that cause the green, cloudy scum in some ponds use the sun's energy to make food.

▲ These autotrophic bacteria, found in hot springs, use chemical energy from their environment to make food.

Go Online
PHSchool.com

For: More on bacteria
Visit: PHSchool.com
Web Code: ced-1022

Reproduction

When bacteria have enough food, the right temperature, and other suitable conditions, they thrive and reproduce frequently. Under these ideal conditions, some bacteria can reproduce as often as once every 20 minutes. So it's a good thing that growing conditions for bacteria are rarely ideal!

Asexual Reproduction Bacteria reproduce by a process called **binary fission,** in which one cell divides to form two identical cells. Binary fission is a form of asexual reproduction. **Asexual reproduction** is a reproductive process that involves only one parent and produces offspring that are identical to the parent. During binary fission, a cell first duplicates its genetic material and then divides into two separate cells. Each new cell gets its own complete copy of the parent cell's genetic material as well as some of the parent's ribosomes and cytoplasm.

Sexual Reproduction Some bacteria may at times undergo a form of sexual reproduction. In **sexual reproduction,** two parents combine their genetic material to produce a new organism, which differs from both parents. During a process called **conjugation** (kahn juh GAY shun), one bacterium transfers some genetic material to another bacterium through a threadlike bridge. After the transfer, the cells separate.

Conjugation results in bacteria with new combinations of genetic material. Then, when these bacteria divide by binary fission, the new combinations of genetic material pass to the offspring. Conjugation does not increase the number of bacteria. However, it does result in bacteria that are genetically different.

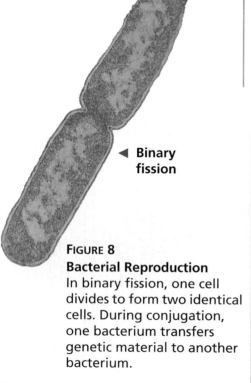

◄ **Binary fission**

FIGURE 8
Bacterial Reproduction
In binary fission, one cell divides to form two identical cells. During conjugation, one bacterium transfers genetic material to another bacterium.

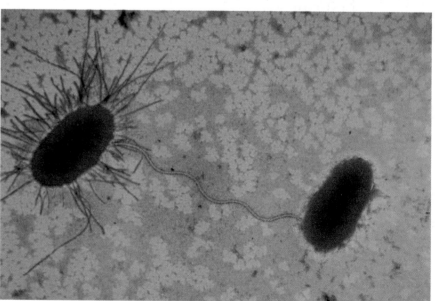

Conjugation ▶

Math
Analyzing Data

Bacterial Reproduction by Binary Fission

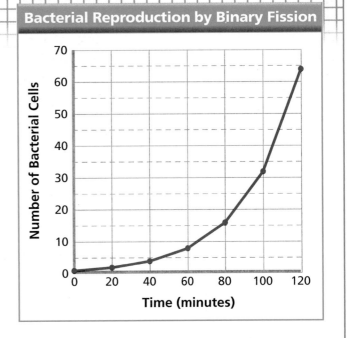

Population Explosion

Suppose a bacterium reproduces by binary fission every 20 minutes. The new cells survive and reproduce at the same rate. This graph shows how the bacterial population would grow from a single bacterium.

1. **Reading Graphs** What variable is being plotted on the horizontal axis? What is being plotted on the vertical axis?

2. **Interpreting Data** According to the graph, how many cells are there after 20 minutes? After 1 hour? After 2 hours?

3. **Drawing Conclusions** Describe the pattern you see in the way the bacterial population increases over 2 hours.

Endospore Formation Sometimes, conditions in the environment become unfavorable for the growth of bacteria. For example, food sources can disappear, water can dry up, or the temperature can fall or rise dramatically. Some bacteria can survive harsh conditions by forming endospores like those in Figure 9. An **endospore** is a small, rounded, thick-walled, resting cell that forms inside a bacterial cell. It contains the cell's genetic material and some of its cytoplasm.

Because endospores can resist freezing, heating, and drying, they can survive for many years. For example, the bacteria that cause botulism, *Clostridium botulinum*, produce heat-resistant endospores that can survive in improperly canned foods. Endospores are also light—a breeze can carry them to new places. If an endospore lands where conditions are suitable, it opens up. Then the bacterium can begin to grow and multiply.

 Under what conditions do endospores form?

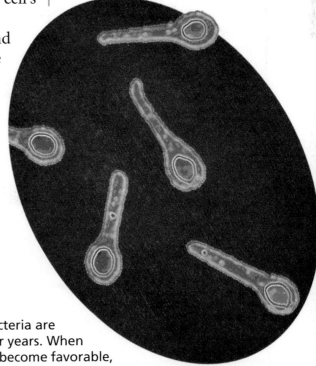

FIGURE 9
Endospores
The red circles within these bacteria are endospores that can survive for years. When conditions in the environment become favorable, the bacteria can begin to grow and multiply.

The Role of Bacteria in Nature

When you hear the word *bacteria*, you may think about getting sick. After all, strep throat, many ear infections, and other diseases are caused by bacteria. However, most bacteria are either harmless or helpful to people. In fact, in many ways, people depend on bacteria. **Bacteria are involved in oxygen and food production, environmental recycling and cleanup, and in health maintenance and medicine production.**

Oxygen Production Would it surprise you to learn that the air you breathe depends in part on bacteria? As autotrophic bacteria use the sun's energy to produce food, they also release oxygen into the air. Billions of years ago, there was little oxygen in Earth's atmosphere. Scientists think that autotrophic bacteria were responsible for first adding oxygen to Earth's atmosphere. Today, the distant offspring of those bacteria help keep oxygen levels in the air stable.

Science and History

Bacteria and Foods of the World

Ancient cultures lacked refrigeration and other modern methods of preventing food spoilage. People in these cultures developed ways of using bacteria to preserve foods. You may enjoy some of these foods today.

2300 B.C. Cheese
Ancient Egyptians made cheese from milk. Cheese-making begins when bacteria feed on the sugars in milk. The milk separates into solid curds and liquid whey. The curds are processed into cheeses, which keep longer than milk.

1000 B.C. Pickled Vegetables
The Chinese salted vegetables and packed them in containers. Naturally occurring bacteria fed on the vegetables and produced a sour taste. The salt pulled water out of the vegetables and left them crisp. These vegetables were part of the food rations given to workers who built the Great Wall of China.

500 B.C. Dried Meat
People who lived in the regions around the Mediterranean Sea chopped meat, seasoned it with salt and spices, rolled it, and hung it to dry. Bacteria in the drying meat gave unique flavors to the food. The rolled meat would keep for weeks in cool places.

2500 B.C.	1500 B.C.	500 B.C.

Food Production Do you like cheese, sauerkraut, or pickles? The activities of helpful bacteria produce all of these foods and more. For example, bacteria that grow in apple cider change the cider to vinegar. Bacteria that grow in milk produce dairy products such as buttermilk, yogurt, sour cream, and cheeses.

However, some bacteria cause food to spoil when they break down the food's chemicals. Spoiled food ususally smells or tastes foul and can make you very sick. Refrigerating and heating foods are two ways to slow down food spoilage. Another method, called pasteurization, is most often used to treat beverages such as milk and juice. During **pasteurization** (pas chur ih ZAY shun), the food is heated to a temperature that is high enough to kill most harmful bacteria without changing the taste of the food. As you might have guessed, this process was named after Louis Pasteur, its inventor.

Writing in Science

Research and Write Use the Internet to find out more about one of these ancient food-production methods and the culture that developed it. Write a report about the importance of the food to the culture.

A.D. 1500
Chocolate Beverage
People in the West Indies mixed beans from the cocoa plant with bacteria and other microorganisms and then dried and roasted them. The roasted beans were then brewed to produce a beverage with a chocolate flavor. The drink was served cold with honey, spices, and vanilla.

A.D. 500
Soy Sauce
People in China crushed soybeans into mixtures of wheat, salt, bacteria, and other microorganisms. The microorganisms fed on the proteins in the wheat and soybeans. The salt pulled water out of the mixture. The protein-rich soy paste that remained was used to flavor foods. The soy sauce you may use today is made in a similar manner.

A.D. 1850
Sourdough Bread
Gold prospectors in California ate sourdough bread. The *Lactobacillus sanfrancisco* bacteria gave the bread its sour taste. Each day before baking, cooks would set aside some dough that contained the bacteria to use in the next day's bread.

A.D. 500	A.D. 1500	A.D. 2500

FIGURE 10
Environmental Recycling
Decomposing bacteria are at work recycling the chemicals in these leaves. **Predicting** *What might a forest be like if there were no decomposing bacteria in the soil?*

Environmental Recycling If you recycle glass or plastic, then you have something in common with some heterotrophic bacteria. These bacteria, which live in the soil, are **decomposers**—organisms that break down large chemicals in dead organisms into small chemicals.

Decomposers are "nature's recyclers." They return basic chemicals to the environment for other living things to reuse. For example, the leaves of many trees die in autumn and drop to the ground. Decomposing bacteria spend the next months breaking down the chemicals in the dead leaves. The broken-down chemicals mix with the soil and can then be absorbed by the roots of nearby plants.

Another type of recycling bacteria, called nitrogen-fixing bacteria, help plants survive. Nitrogen-fixing bacteria live in the soil and in swellings on the roots of certain plants, such as peanut, pea, and soybean. These helpful bacteria convert nitrogen gas from the air into nitrogen products that plants need to grow. On their own, plants cannot use nitrogen present in the air. Therefore, nitrogen-fixing bacteria are vital to the plants' survival.

Environmental Cleanup Some bacteria help to clean up Earth's land and water. Can you imagine having a bowl of oil for dinner instead of soup? Well, some bacteria prefer the oil. They convert the poisonous chemicals in oil into harmless substances. Scientists have put these bacteria to work cleaning up oil spills in oceans and gasoline leaks in the soil under gas stations.

 **Reading Checkpoint** **What role do bacterial decomposers play in the environment?**

FIGURE 11
Environmental Cleanup
Scientists use bacteria such as these *Ochrobactrum anthropi* to help clean up oil spills.

Health and Medicine Did you know that many of the bacteria living in your body actually keep you healthy? In your digestive system, for example, your intestines teem with bacteria. Some help you digest your food. Some make vitamins that your body needs. Others compete for space with disease-causing organisms, preventing the harmful bacteria from attaching to your intestines and making you sick.

Scientists have put some bacteria to work making medicines and other substances. The first medicine-producing bacteria were made in the 1970s. By manipulating the bacteria's genetic material, scientists engineered bacteria to produce human insulin. Although healthy people can make their own insulin, those with some types of diabetes cannot. Many people with diabetes need to take insulin daily. Thanks to bacteria's fast rate of reproduction, large numbers of insulin-making bacteria can be grown in huge vats. The human insulin they produce is then purified and made into medicine.

FIGURE 12
Bacteria and Digestion
Bacteria living naturally in your intestines help you digest food.

Section 2 Assessment

S 7.2.a, 7.1,
E-LA: Reading 7.1.0

Vocabulary Skill **Prefixes** The prefix *a-* means "without." Use the meaning of the prefix to contrast asexual reproduction and sexual reproduction.

Reviewing Key Concepts

1. a. Reviewing Where is the genetic material located in a bacterial cell?
   b. Describing What is the role of flagella in a bacterial cell?
2. a. Listing What are the three ways in which bacteria obtain food?
   b. Describing How do bacteria obtain energy to carry out their functions?
   c. Inferring You have just discovered a new bacterium that lives inside sealed cans of food. How do you think these bacteria obtain food and energy?
3. a. Defining What is binary fission?
   b. Explaining Under what conditions do bacteria thrive and reproduce frequently by binary fission?

   c. Inferring Why might bacteria that undergo conjugation be better able to survive when conditions become less than ideal?
4. a. Listing A friend states that all bacteria are harmful to people. List three reasons why this statement is inaccurate.
   b. Applying Concepts In what ways might bacteria contribute to the success of a garden in which pea plants are growing?

Lab zone **At-Home Activity**

Edible Bacteria With a family member, look around your kitchen for foods that are made using bacteria. Read the food labels to see if bacteria are used in the food's production. Discuss with your family member the helpful roles that bacteria play in people's lives.

Protists

CALIFORNIA
Standards Focus

S 7.5.a *Students know* plants and animals have levels of organization for structure and function, including cells, tissues, organs, organ systems, and the whole organism.

🔑 What are the characteristics of animal-like, plantlike, and funguslike protists?

🔑 How do algae vary in organization, structure, and function?

Key Terms
- protist
- protozoan
- pseudopod
- contractile vacuole
- cilia
- symbiosis
- mutualism
- algae
- spore

Lab zone **Standards Warm-Up**

What Lives in a Drop of Pond Water?

1. Use a plastic dropper to place a drop of pond water on a microscope slide.
2. Put the slide under your microscope's low-power lens. Focus on the objects you see.
3. Find at least three different objects that you think might be organisms. Observe them for a few minutes.
4. Draw the three organisms in your notebook. Below each sketch, describe the movements or behaviors of the organism. Wash your hands thoroughly when you have finished.

Think It Over

Observing What characteristics did you observe that made you think that each organism was alive?

Look at the objects in Figure 13. What do they look like to you? Jewels? Beads? Stained glass ornaments? You might be surprised to learn that these beautiful, delicate structures are the walls of unicellular organisms called diatoms. Diatoms live in both fresh water and salt water and are an important food source for many marine organisms. They have been called the "jewels of the sea."

FIGURE 13
Diatoms
These glasslike organisms are classified as protists.

FIGURE 14 **Protists**
Protists include animal-like, plantlike, and funguslike organisms.
Comparing and Contrasting *In what ways do protists differ from one another?*

▲ These shells are the remains of unicellular, animal-like protists called foraminifera.

What Is a Protist?

Diatoms are only one of the vast varieties of protists. **Protists** are eukaryotes that cannot be classified as animals, plants, or fungi. The word that best describes protists is *diversity*. For example, most protists are unicellular, but some are multicellular. Some are heterotrophs, some are autotrophs, and others are both. Some protists cannot move, while others can. In fact, protists are so diverse some scientists think that protists belong in separate kingdoms. Biologists continue to study the DNA sequences and evolutionary histories of the various groups of protists.

Despite their diversity, protists do share some characteristics. In addition to being eukaryotes, all protists live in moist surroundings. Most protists reproduce asexually—the cells simply grow and divide. However, some types of protists can reproduce sexually as well. One useful way of grouping protists is to divide them into three categories, based on characteristics they share with organisms in other kingdoms: animal-like protists, plantlike protists, and funguslike protists.

▲ This red alga is a multicellular, plantlike protist found on ocean floors.

Animal-Like Protists

What image pops into your head when you think of an animal? A tiger chasing its prey? A snake slithering onto a rock? Most people immediately associate animals with movement. In fact, movement is often involved with an important function of animals—obtaining food. All animals are heterotrophs that must obtain food by eating other organisms.

Like animals, animal-like protists are heterotrophs, and most are able to move from place to place to obtain food. But unlike animals, animal-like protists, or **protozoans** (proh tuh ZOH unz), are unicellular. Protozoans can be classified into four groups, based on the way they move and live.

▲ The yellow slime mold oozing off the leaf is a funguslike protist.

Figure 15
Amoeba
Amoebas are sarcodines that live in either water or soil. They feed on bacteria and smaller protists.

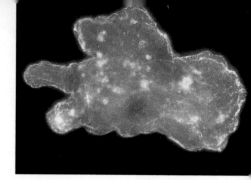

Food Vacuole
When the ends of two pseudopods fuse around food, they form a food vacuole. Food is broken down inside the food vacuole in the cytoplasm.

Pseudopod
An amoeba uses pseudopods to move and feed. Pseudopods form when cytoplasm flows toward one location and the rest of the amoeba follows.

Nucleus
The nucleus controls the cell's functions and is involved in reproduction. Amoebas usually reproduce by binary fission.

Cytoplasm

Contractile Vacuole
The contractile vacuole collects excess water from the cytoplasm and expels it from the cell.

Cell Membrane
Because the cell membrane is very thin and flexible, an amoeba's shape changes constantly.

Go Online
active art

For: Amoeba and Paramecium activity
Visit: PHSchool.com
Web Code: cep-1031

Protozoans With Pseudopods The amoeba in Figure 15 belongs to the group of protozoans called sarcodines. Sarcodines move and feed by forming **pseudopods** (SOO duh pahdz)—temporary bulges of the cell. The word *pseudopod* means "false foot." Pseudopods form when cytoplasm flows toward one location and the rest of the organism follows. Pseudopods enable sarcodines to move. For example, amoebas use pseudopods to move away from bright light. Sarcodines also use pseudopods to trap food. The organism extends a pseudopod on each side of the food particle. The two pseudopods then join together, trapping the particle inside.

Protozoans that live in fresh water, such as amoebas, have a problem. Small particles, like those of water, pass easily through the cell membrane into the cytoplasm. If excess water were to build up inside the cell, the amoeba would burst. Fortunately, amoebas have a **contractile vacuole** (kun TRAK til VAK yoo ohl), a structure that collects the extra water and then expels it from the cell.

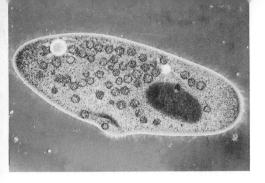

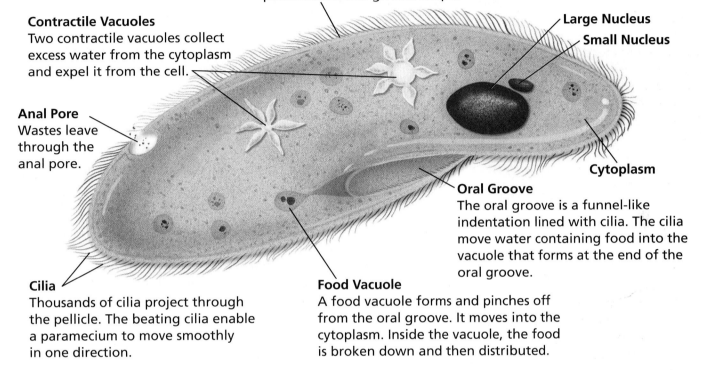

FIGURE 16
Paramecium
Paramecia are ciliates that live mostly in fresh water. Like amoebas, paramecia feed on bacteria and smaller protists.

Pellicle
A stiff but flexible covering, called the pellicle, surrounds a paramecium and gives it shape.

Contractile Vacuoles
Two contractile vacuoles collect excess water from the cytoplasm and expel it from the cell.

Anal Pore
Wastes leave through the anal pore.

Cilia
Thousands of cilia project through the pellicle. The beating cilia enable a paramecium to move smoothly in one direction.

Large Nucleus

Small Nucleus

Cytoplasm

Oral Groove
The oral groove is a funnel-like indentation lined with cilia. The cilia move water containing food into the vacuole that forms at the end of the oral groove.

Food Vacuole
A food vacuole forms and pinches off from the oral groove. It moves into the cytoplasm. Inside the vacuole, the food is broken down and then distributed.

Protozoans With Cilia The second group of animal-like protists are the ciliates. Ciliates have structures called **cilia** (SIL ee uh), which are hairlike projections from cells that move with a wavelike motion. Ciliates use their cilia to move and obtain food. Cilia act something like tiny oars to move a ciliate. Their movement sweeps food into the organism.

The cells of ciliates, like the paramecium in Figure 16, are complex. Notice that the paramecium has two contractile vacuoles that expel water from the cell. It also has more than one nucleus. The large nucleus controls the everyday tasks of the cell. The small nucleus functions in reproduction.

Paramecia usually reproduce asexually by binary fission. Sometimes, however, paramecia reproduce by conjugation. This occurs when two paramecia join together and exchange some of their genetic material.

 **Reading Checkpoint** What are cilia?

FIGURE 17
Giardia
When people drink from freshwater streams and lakes, they can get hiker's disease. *Giardia intestinalis* (inset) is the protozoan responsible for this disease.
Inferring *Why is it important for hikers to filter stream water?*

Protozoans With Flagella The third group of protozoans are flagellates (FLAJ uh lits), protists that use long, whiplike flagella to move. A flagellate may have one or more flagella.

Some of these protozoans live inside the bodies of other organisms. For example, one type of flagellate lives in the intestines of termites. There, they digest the wood that the termites eat, producing sugars for themselves and for the termites. In turn, the termites protect the protozoans. The interaction between these two species is an example of **symbiosis** (sim bee OH sis)—a close relationship in which at least one of the species benefits. When both partners benefit from living together, the relationship is a type of symbiosis called **mutualism.**

Sometimes, however, a protozoan harms its host. For example, *Giardia* is a parasite in humans. Wild animals, such as beavers, deposit *Giardia* in freshwater streams, rivers, and lakes. When a person drinks water containing *Giardia*, these protozoans attach to the person's intestine, where they feed and reproduce. The person develops a serious intestinal condition commonly called hiker's disease.

Protozoans That Are Parasites The fourth type of protozoans are characterized more by the way they live than by the way they move. They are all parasites that feed on the cells and body fluids of their hosts. These protozoans move in a variety of ways. Some have flagella, and some depend on hosts for transport. One even produces a layer of slime that allows it to slide from place to place!

Many of these parasites have more than one host. For example, *Plasmodium* is a protozoan that causes malaria, a disease of the blood. Two hosts are involved in *Plasmodium's* life cycle—humans and a species of mosquitoes found in tropical areas. The disease spreads when a healthy mosquito bites a person with malaria. The mosquito then becomes infected with *Plasmodium*. When the mosquito next bites a healthy person, the mosquito passes the *Plasmodium* to that person. Symptoms of malaria include high fevers that alternate with severe chills.

 **Reading Checkpoint** **What is symbiosis?**

FIGURE 18
Malaria Mosquito
Anopheles mosquitoes can carry the parasitic protozoan *Plasmodium*, which causes malaria in people.

Plantlike Protists

Plantlike protists, which are commonly called **algae** (AL jee), are extremely diverse. Like plants, algae are autotrophs. Most are able to use the sun's energy to make their own food. They can perform photosynthesis.

Algae play a significant role in many environments. For example, algae that live near the surface of ponds, lakes, and oceans are an important food source for other organisms in the water. In addition, much of the oxygen in Earth's atmosphere is made by these algae.

🔑 **Algae vary greatly in cell organization, structure, and function. Some algae are unicellular. Other algae are multicellular with differentiated tissues and organs. Still others are groups of unicellular organisms that live together in colonies.** Algal colonies can contain from a few cells up to thousands of cells. In a colony, most cells carry out all functions. But, some cells may become specialized to perform certain functions, such as reproduction.

Algae exist in a wide variety of colors because they contain many types of pigments. You may recall that pigments are chemicals that produce color. Depending on their pigments, algae can be green, yellow, red, brown, orange, or even black.

Diatoms Diatoms are unicellular protists with beautiful glasslike cell walls. Some float near the surface of lakes or oceans. Others attach to objects such as rocks in shallow water. Diatoms are a food source for heterotrophs in the water. Many diatoms can move by oozing chemicals out of slits in their cell walls. They then glide in the slime.

When diatoms die, their cell walls collect on the bottoms of oceans and lakes. Over time, they form layers of a coarse substance called diatomaceous (dy uh tuh MAY shus) earth. Diatomaceous earth makes a good polishing agent and is used in household scouring products. It is even used as an insecticide—the diatoms' sharp cell walls puncture the bodies of insects.

Dinoflagellates Dinoflagellates (dy noh FLAJ uh lits) are unicellular algae surrounded by stiff plates that look like a suit of armor. Because they have different amounts of green, orange, and other pigments, dinoflagellates exist in a variety of colors.

All dinoflagellates have two flagella held in grooves between their plates. When the flagella beat, the dinoflagellates twirl like toy tops as they move through the water. Many glow in the dark. They light up the ocean's surface when disturbed by a passing boat or swimmer.

Lab zone Try This **Activity**

Watching Protists

In this activity you will watch the interaction between paramecium, an animal-like protist, and *Chlorella*, a plantlike protist.

1. 🔧 Use a plastic dropper to place 1 drop of paramecium culture on a microscope slide. Add some cotton fibers to slow down the paramecia.
2. Use the microscope's low-power objective to find some paramecia.
3. Add 1 drop of *Chlorella* to the paramecium culture on your slide.
4. Switch to high power and locate a paramecium. Observe what happens. Then wash your hands.

Inferring What evidence do you have that paramecia are heterotrophs? That *Chlorella* are autotrophs?

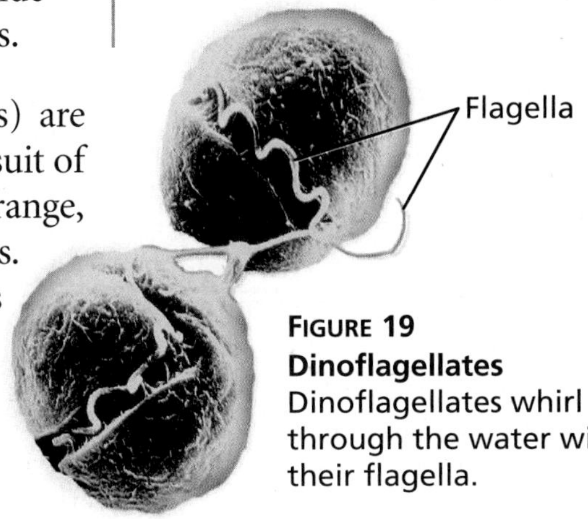

Flagella

FIGURE 19
Dinoflagellates
Dinoflagellates whirl through the water with their flagella.

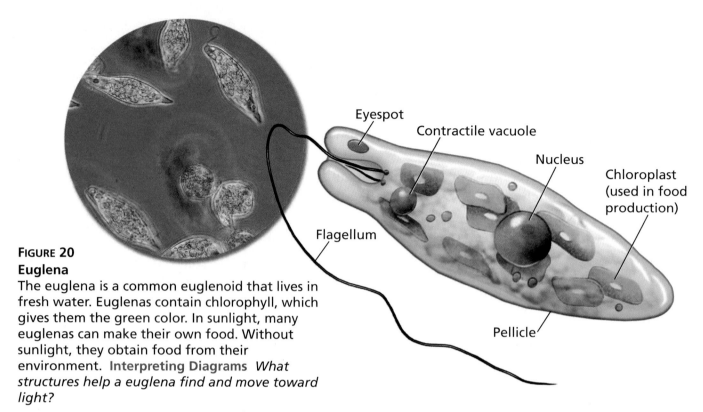

FIGURE 20
Euglena
The euglena is a common euglenoid that lives in fresh water. Euglenas contain chlorophyll, which gives them the green color. In sunlight, many euglenas can make their own food. Without sunlight, they obtain food from their environment. **Interpreting Diagrams** *What structures help a euglena find and move toward light?*

Eyespot
Contractile vacuole
Nucleus
Chloroplast (used in food production)
Flagellum
Pellicle

![Lab zone] **Skills Activity**

Predicting

Predict what will happen when you pour a culture of euglena into a petri dish, and then cover half the dish with aluminum foil. Give a reason for your prediction.

Then carry out the experiment with a culture of euglena in a plastic petri dish. Cover half the dish with aluminum foil. After 10 minutes, uncover the dish. What do you observe? Was your prediction correct? Explain why euglena behave this way.

Euglenoids Euglenoids (yoo GLEE noydz) are green, unicellular algae that are found mostly in fresh water. Unlike other algae, euglenoids have one animal-like characteristic—they can be heterotrophs under certain conditions. When sunlight is available, most euglenoids are autotrophs that produce their own food. However, when sunlight is not available, euglenoids will act like heterotrophs by obtaining food from their environment. Some euglenoids live entirely as heterotrophs.

In Figure 20, you see a euglena, which is a common euglenoid. Notice the long, whiplike flagellum that helps the organism move. Locate the eyespot near the flagellum. Although the eyespot is not really an eye, it contains pigments. These pigments are sensitive to light and help the euglena recognize the direction of a light source. You can imagine how important this response is to an organism that needs light to make food.

Red Algae Almost all red algae are multicellular seaweeds. Divers have found red algae growing more than 260 meters below the ocean's surface. Their red pigments are especially good at absorbing the small amount of light that is able to reach deep ocean waters.

People use red algae in a variety of ways. Carrageenan (ka ruh JEE nun) and agar are substances extracted from red algae. These substances are used in products such as ice cream and hair conditioner. For people in many Asian cultures, red algae are a nutrient-rich food that is eaten fresh, dried, or toasted.

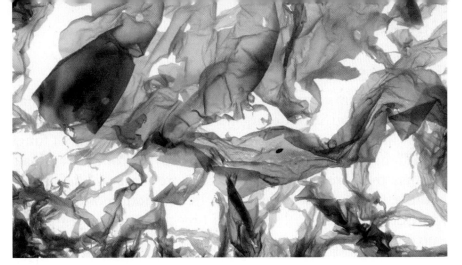

FIGURE 21
Green Algae
Green algae range in size from unicellular organisms to multicellular seaweeds. This multicellular sea lettuce, *Ulva*, lives in oceans.

Green Algae Green algae, which contain green pigments, are quite diverse. Most green algae are unicellular. Some, however, form colonies, and a few are multicellular. Most green algae live in either fresh water or salt water. The few that live on land are found on rocks, in the crevices of tree bark, or in moist soils.

Green algae are actually very closely related to plants that live on land. Green algae and plants contain the same type of chlorophyll and share other important similarities. In fact, some scientists think that green algae belong in the plant kingdom.

Brown Algae Many of the organisms that are commonly called seaweeds are brown algae. In addition to their brown pigment, brown algae also contain green, yellow, and orange pigments.

All brown algae are multicellular. This group has the most complex structure of all the algae. Some brown algae even have differentiated tissues and organs that resemble structures found in plants. Figure 22 shows a typical brown alga. Holdfasts anchor the alga to rocks. Stalks support the blades, which are the leaflike structures of the alga. Many brown algae also have gas-filled sacs called bladders that allow the algae to float upright.

Brown algae flourish in cool, rocky waters. Brown algae called rockweed live along the Atlantic coast of North America. Giant kelps, which can grow as long as 100 meters, live in some Pacific coastal waters. The giant kelps form large underwater "forests" where many organisms, including sea otters and abalone, live.

 **Reading Checkpoint** **What color pigments can brown algae contain?**

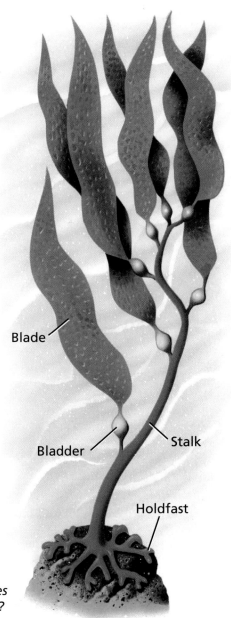

Blade

Bladder

Stalk

Holdfast

FIGURE 22 Brown Algae
Giant kelps are brown algae that have many plantlike organs.
Interpreting Diagrams *What plant structures do the kelp's holdfasts and blades resemble?*

Funguslike Protists

The third group of protists are the funguslike protists. You may recall that fungi include organisms such as mushrooms and yeast. Until you learn more about fungi, you can think of fungi as the "sort of like" organisms. Fungi are "sort of like" animals because they are heterotrophs. They are "sort of like" plants because their cells have cell walls. In addition, most fungi use spores to reproduce. A **spore** is a tiny cell that is able to grow into a new organism.

🔑 **Like fungi, funguslike protists are heterotrophs, have cell walls, and use spores to reproduce.** All funguslike protists are able to move at some point in their lives. The three types of funguslike protists are slime molds, water molds, and downy mildews.

Slime Molds Slime molds are often brilliantly colored. They live on forest floors and other moist, shady places. They ooze along the surfaces of decaying materials, feeding on bacteria and other microorganisms. Some slime molds are so small that you need a microscope to see them. Others may cover an area of several meters!

Slime molds begin their life cycle as tiny, individual amoeba-like cells. The cells use pseudopods to feed and creep around. Later, the cells grow bigger or join together to form a giant, jellylike mass. In some species, the giant mass is multicellular and forms when food is scarce. In others, the giant mass is actually a giant cell with many nuclei.

The mass oozes along as a single unit. When environmental conditions become harsh, spore-producing structures grow out of the mass and release spores. Eventually the spores develop into a new generation of slime molds.

Figure 23
Slime Molds
The chocolate tube slime mold first forms a tapioca-like mass (top). When conditions become harsh, the mass grows spore-producing stalks (right). The stalks, or "chocolate tubes," are covered with millions of brown spores.

Water Molds and Downy Mildews Most water molds and downy mildews live in water or moist places. These organisms often grow as tiny threads that look like fuzz. Figure 24 shows a fish attacked by a water mold and a leaf covered by downy mildew.

Water molds and downy mildews attack many food crops, such as potatoes, corn, and grapes. A water mold impacted history when it destroyed the Irish potato crops in 1845 and 1846. The loss of these crops led to a famine. More than one million people in Ireland died, and many others moved to the United States and other countries.

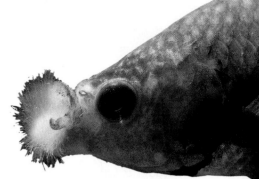
▲ **Water mold on fish**

▼ **Downy mildew on grape leaf**

 **Reading Checkpoint** In what environments are water molds found?

FIGURE 24
Water Molds and Downy Mildews
Many water molds are decomposers of dead aquatic organisms. Others are parasites of fish and other animals. Downy mildews are parasites of many food crops.

Section 3 Assessment

S 7.5.a, E-LA: Reading 7.1.0

Vocabulary Skill **Prefixes** In the word *pseudopod*, the prefix *pseudo-* means "false." What do you think the root *-pod* means?

Reviewing Key Concepts

1. a. **Listing** List the four types of animal-like protists. How does each type move or live?
   b. **Comparing and Contrasting** How are these four types of protists similar to animals? How are they different?
   c. **Classifying** You observe an animal-like protist under the microscope. It has no hairlike or whiplike structures. It moves by forming temporary bulges of cytoplasm. How would you classify this protist?

2. a. **Reviewing** What characteristics do diatoms, dinoflagellates, and other plantlike protists share?
   b. **Making Generalizations** In what ways are plantlike protists different from one another?
   c. **Comparing and Contrasting** Describe the similarities and differences in the organization, structure, and function of euglena and brown algae.

3. a. **Listing** What are the three types of funguslike protists?
   b. **Describing** How are funguslike protists like fungi?

Lab zone At-Home Activity

Algae Scavenger Hunt Look around your house with a family member to find products that contain substances made from algae. Look at both food and nonfood items. Before you begin, tell your family member that substances such as diatomaceous earth, algin, and carrageenan are products that come from algae. Make a list of the products and the algae-based ingredients they contain. Share your list with the class.

Fungi

S 7.1.a *Students know* cells function similarly in all organisms.

S 7.2.a *Students know* the differences between the life cycles and reproduction methods of sexual and asexual organisms.

- What characteristics do fungi share?
- How do fungi reproduce?
- What roles do fungi play in nature?

Key Terms

- fungi
- hyphae
- fruiting body
- budding
- lichen

Lab zone Standards Warm-Up

Do All Molds Look Alike?

1. Your teacher will give you two sealed, clear plastic bags—one containing moldy bread and another containing moldy fruit. **CAUTION:** *Do not open the sealed bags at any time.*
2. In your notebook, describe what you see.
3. Next, use a hand lens to examine each mold. Sketch each mold in your notebook and list its characteristics.
4. Return the sealed bags to your teacher. Wash your hands.

Think It Over

Observing How are the molds similar? How are they different?

A speck of dust lands on a cricket's back. But this is no ordinary dust—it is alive! Tiny glistening threads emerge from the dust and begin to grow into the cricket's moist body. As they grow, the threads release chemicals that slowly dissolve the cricket's tissues. Soon, the cricket's body is little more than a hollow shell filled with a tangle of the threads. Then the threads begin to grow up and out of the dead cricket, producing long stalks with knobs at their tips. When a knob breaks open, it will release thousands of dustlike specks, which the wind can carry to new victims.

What Are Fungi?

The strange cricket-killing organism is a member of the fungi kingdom. Although you may not have heard of a cricket-killing fungus before, you are probably familiar with other kinds of fungi. For example, the molds that grow on stale bread and the mushrooms that sprout in yards are all fungi.

Most **fungi** share several important characteristics. **Fungi are eukaryotes that have cell walls, are heterotrophs that feed by absorbing their food, and use spores to reproduce.** In addition, fungi need moist, warm places in which to grow. They thrive on moist foods, damp tree barks, lawns coated with dew, and even wet bathroom tiles.

A killer fungus has attacked this bush cricket.

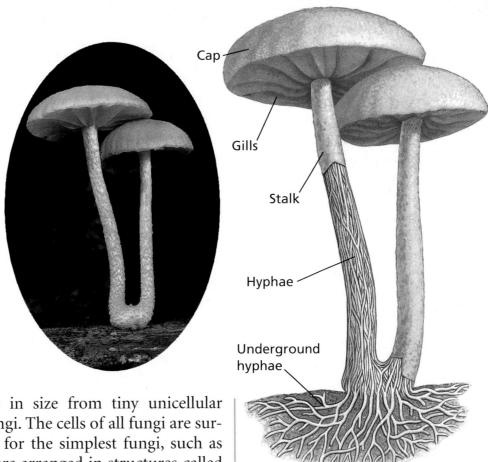

Cap

Gills

Stalk

Hyphae

Underground hyphae

FIGURE 25
Structure of a Mushroom
The hyphae in the stalk and cap of a mushroom are packed tightly to form firm structures. Underground hyphae are arranged loosely.
Inferring What function might underground hyphae perform?

Cell Structure Fungi range in size from tiny unicellular yeasts to large multicellular fungi. The cells of all fungi are surrounded by cell walls. Except for the simplest fungi, such as yeast, the cells of most fungi are arranged in structures called hyphae. **Hyphae** (HY fee) (singular hypha) are the branching, threadlike tubes that make up the bodies of multicellular fungi. The hyphae of some fungi are continuous threads of cytoplasm that contain many nuclei. Substances move quickly and freely through the hyphae.

What a fungus looks like depends on how its hyphae are arranged. In some fungi, the threadlike hyphae are loosely tangled. Fuzzy-looking molds that grow on old foods have loosely tangled hyphae. Other fungi have tightly packed hyphae. The stalks and caps of mushrooms are made of hyphae packed so tightly that they appear solid. Underground, however, a mushroom's hyphae form a loose, threadlike maze in the soil.

Obtaining Food Fungi absorb food through hyphae that grow into a food source. First, the fungus grows hyphae into the food source. Then digestive chemicals ooze from the hyphae into the food. The chemicals break down the food into small substances that can be absorbed by the hyphae. As an analogy, imagine yourself sinking your fingers down into a chocolate cake and dripping digestive chemicals out of your fingertips. Then imagine your fingers absorbing the digested particles of the cake!

 **Reading Checkpoint** What do the bodies of multicellular fungi consist of?

FIGURE 26
Mold Growing on Food Source
The mold *Penicillium* often grows on old fruits such as oranges. Some of its hyphae grow deep into the food source.

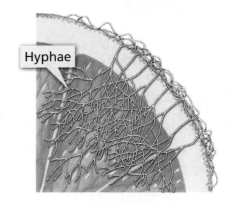

Hyphae

Spreading Spores

In this activity, you will make a model of a fruiting body.

1. Break a cotton ball into five equal pieces. Roll each piece into a tiny ball.
2. Insert the cotton balls into a balloon.
3. Repeat Steps 1 and 2 until the balloon is almost full.
4. Inflate the balloon. Tie a knot in its neck. Tape the knotted end of the balloon to a stick.
5. Stand the stick upright in a mound of modeling clay.
6. ✂ Pop the balloon with a pin. Observe what happens.

Making Models Draw a diagram of the model you made. Label the stalk, the spore case, and the spores. Use your model to explain why fungi are found just about everywhere.

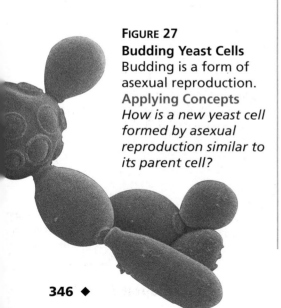

FIGURE 27
Budding Yeast Cells
Budding is a form of asexual reproduction.
Applying Concepts *How is a new yeast cell formed by asexual reproduction similar to its parent cell?*

Reproduction in Fungi

Like it or not, fungi are everywhere. The way they reproduce helps guarantee their survival and spread. ⊙ **Fungi usually reproduce by making spores. The lightweight spores are surrounded by a protective covering and can be carried easily through air or water to new sites.** Fungi produce millions of spores, more than can ever survive. Only a few spores will fall where conditions are right for them to grow.

Fungi produce spores in reproductive structures called **fruiting bodies.** The appearances of fruiting bodies vary among different fungi. For some fungi, such as mushrooms, the part of the fungus that you see is the fruiting body. In other fungi, such as bread molds, the fruiting bodies are tiny, stalk-like hyphae that grow upward from the rest of the hyphae. A knoblike spore case at the tip of each stalk contains the spores. As you can imagine, the structure of the fruiting body is very important to the fungi's success in reproduction.

Asexual Reproduction Most fungi reproduce both asexually and sexually. When there is adequate moisture and food, the fungi make spores asexually. Cells at the tips of their hyphae divide to form spores. The spores grow into fungi that are genetically identical to the parent.

Unicellular yeast cells undergo a form of asexual reproduction called **budding.** In budding, no spores are produced. Instead, a parent cell undergoes mitosis and a small yeast cell grows from the parent cell. This process is somewhat similar to the way a bud forms on a tree branch. The new cell then breaks away and lives on its own.

Sexual Reproduction Most fungi can also reproduce sexually, especially when growing conditions become unfavorable. In sexual reproduction, the hyphae of two fungi grow together and genetic material is exchanged. Eventually, a new reproductive structure grows from the joined hyphae and produces spores. The spores develop into fungi that differ genetically from either parent.

Classification of Fungi Figure 28 shows three major groups of fungi. The groups are named for the appearance of their reproductive structures. Additional groups include water species that produce spores with flagella and those that form tight associations with plant roots.

 **Reading Checkpoint** What is budding?

The Role of Fungi in Nature

Fungi affect humans and other organisms in many different ways. ⊂⊃ **Many fungi provide foods for people. Fungi play important roles as decomposers and recyclers on Earth. Some fungi cause disease while others fight disease. Still other fungi live in symbiosis with other organisms.**

Food and Fungi Yeasts, molds, and mushrooms are important food sources. Bakers add yeast to bread dough to make it rise. Yeast cells use the sugar in the dough for food and produce carbon dioxide gas as they feed. The gas forms bubbles, which cause the dough to rise. You see these bubbles as holes in a slice of bread. Molds are used to make foods such as some cheeses. The blue streaks in blue cheese, for example, are actually growths of *Penicillium roqueforti*. People enjoy eating mushrooms in salads and on pizza. You should never pick or eat wild mushrooms, however, because some mushrooms are extremely poisonous.

Video Field Trip
Discovery Channel School

Protists and Fungi

FIGURE 28
Classification of Fungi

Three major groups of fungi include sac fungi, club fungi, and zygote fungi.

Sac Fungi ▶
Sac fungi produce spores in structures that look like long sacs, such as these. The largest group of fungi, they include yeasts, morels, and truffles.

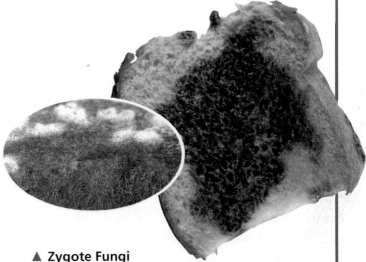

▲ **Club Fungi**
Club fungi produce spores in tiny clublike structures. This group includes mushrooms, rusts, and puffballs, such as these.

▲ **Zygote Fungi**
Zygote fungi produce very resistant spores. This group includes many common fruit and bread molds, like this *Rhizopus*.

Environmental Recycling Like bacteria, many fungi are decomposers. For example, many fungi live in the soil and break down the chemicals in dead plant matter. This process returns important nutrients to the soil. Without fungi and bacteria, Earth would be buried under dead plants and animals!

Disease-Fighting Fungi In 1928, a Scottish biologist named Alexander Fleming was examining petri dishes in which he was growing bacteria. To his surprise, Fleming noticed a spot of a bluish-green mold growing in one dish. Curiously, no bacteria were growing near the mold. Fleming hypothesized that the mold, a fungus named *Penicillium*, produced a substance that killed the bacteria near it.

Fleming's work contributed to the development of the first antibiotic, penicillin. Since the discovery of penicillin, many antibiotics have been isolated from both fungi and bacteria.

Disease-Causing Fungi Many fungi are parasites that cause serious diseases in plants. The sac fungus that causes Dutch elm disease is responsible for killing millions of elm trees in North America and Europe. Corn smut and wheat rust are two club fungi that cause diseases in important food crops. Fungal plant diseases also affect other crops, including rice, cotton, and soybeans, resulting in huge crop losses every year.

Some fungi cause diseases in humans. Athlete's foot fungus causes an itchy irritation in the damp places between toes. Ringworm, another fungal disease, causes an itchy, circular rash on the skin. Because the fungi that cause these diseases produce spores at the site of infection, the diseases can spread easily from person to person. Both diseases can be treated with antifungal medications.

Fungus-Plant Root Associations Some types of fungi help plants grow larger when their hyphae grow into, or on, the plant's roots. The hyphae spread out underground and absorb water and nutrients from the soil for the plant. With more water and nutrients, the plant grows larger than it would have grown without its fungal partner. The plant is not the only partner that benefits. The fungi get to feed on the extra food that the plant makes and stores.

Most plants have fungal partners. Many plants are so dependent on the fungi that they cannot survive without them. For example, orchid seeds cannot develop without their fungal partners.

FIGURE 29
Fungus–Plant Root Associations
An extensive system of fungal hyphae has grown in association with the roots of the pine seedling in the middle.
Classifying *What type of symbiosis do these two organisms exhibit?*

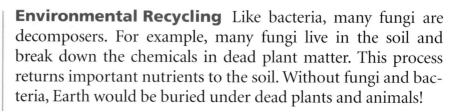

Roots of the pine seedling

Hyphae of fungus

FIGURE 30 Lichens
The British soldier lichen consists of a fungus and an alga. The inset shows how entwined the alga is among the fungus's hyphae.

Alga

Fungus

Lichens A **lichen** (LY kun) consists of a fungus and either algae or autotrophic bacteria that live together in a mutualistic relationship. You have probably seen some familiar lichens—irregular, flat, crusty patches that grow on tree barks or rocks. The fungus benefits from the food produced by the algae or bacteria. The algae or bacteria, in turn, obtain shelter, water, and minerals from the fungus.

Lichens are often called "pioneer" organisms because they are the first organisms to appear on the bare rocks in an area after a volcanic eruption, fire, or rock slide has occurred. Over time, the lichens break down the rock into soil in which other organisms can grow. Lichens are also useful as indicators of air pollution. Many species of lichens are very sensitive to pollutants and die when pollution levels rise. By monitoring the growth of lichens, scientists can assess the air quality in an area.

 **Reading Checkpoint** What two organisms make up a lichen?

Go Online
SciLINKS NSTA

For: Links on fungi
Visit: www.SciLinks.org
Web Code: scn-0133

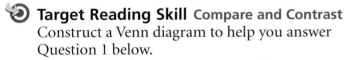

Section 4 Assessment

S 7.2.a, 7.1.a, **E-LA: Writing** 7.2.0, Reading 7.2.0

Target Reading Skill Compare and Contrast Construct a Venn diagram to help you answer Question 1 below.

Reviewing Key Concepts

1. **a. Listing** List three characteristics that a bread mold shares with a mushroom.
   b. Comparing and Contrasting How are the cells of a bread mold arranged? How are the cells of a mushroom arranged?
   c. Summarizing How does the cell structure of a fungus help it obtain food?
2. **a. Reviewing** What role do spores play in the reproduction of fungi?
   b. Sequencing Outline the steps by which fungi produce spores by sexual reproduction.
   c. Inferring Why is it advantageous to a fungus to produce millions of spores?

3. **a. Identifying** Name six roles that fungi play in nature.
   b. Predicting Suppose all the fungi in a forest disappeared. What do you think the forest would be like without fungi?

Writing in Science

Wanted Poster Design a "Wanted" poster for a mold that has been ruining food in your kitchen. Present the mold as a "criminal of the kitchen." Include detailed descriptions of the mold's physical characteristics, what it needs to grow, how it grows, and any other details that will help your family identify this mold. Propose ways to prevent new molds from growing in your kitchen.

What's for Lunch? S 7.1.a

Problem

How does the presence of sugar or salt affect the respiration of yeast?

Skills Focus

measuring, inferring, drawing conclusions

Materials

- 5 small plastic narrow-necked bottles
- 5 round balloons • 5 plastic straws
- dry powdered yeast • sugar • salt
- warm water (40°–45°C) • marking pen
- beaker • graduated cylinder • metric ruler
- string

Procedure

1. Like all other organisms, yeast cells need a source of energy to carry out all their functions. Copy the data table into your notebook. Then read over the entire procedure to see how you will test the respiration activity of the yeast cells in bottles A through E. Write a prediction about what will happen in each bottle.

2. Gently stretch each of the balloons so that they will inflate easily.

3. Using the marking pen, label the bottles A, B, C, D, and E.

4. Use a beaker to fill each bottle with the same amount of warm water. **CAUTION:** *Glass is fragile. Handle the beaker gently to avoid breakage. Do not touch broken glass.*

5. Put 25 mL of salt into bottle B.

6. Put 25 mL of sugar into bottles C and E.

7. Put 50 mL of sugar into bottle D.

8. Put 6 mL of powdered yeast into bottle A, and stir the mixture with a clean straw. Remove the straw and discard it.

9. Immediately place a balloon over the opening of bottle A. Make sure that the balloon opening fits very tightly around the neck of the bottle.

10. Repeat Steps 8 and 9 for bottle B, bottle C, and bottle D.

Data Table						
			Circumference			
Bottle	Prediction	Observations	10 min	20 min	30 min	40 min
A (Yeast alone)						
B (Yeast and 25 mL of salt)						
C (Yeast and 25 mL of sugar)						
D (Yeast and 50 mL of sugar)						
E (No yeast and 25 mL of sugar)						

11. Place a balloon over bottle E without adding yeast to the bottle.

12. Place the five bottles in a warm spot away from drafts. Every ten minutes for 40 minutes, measure the circumference of each balloon by placing a string around the balloon at its widest point. Include your measurements in the data table.

Analyze and Conclude

1. **Measuring** Which balloons changed in size during this lab? How did they change?

2. **Inferring** Explain why the balloon changed size in some bottles and not in others. What caused that change in size?

3. **Interpreting Data** How did the results from bottles C and D compare? Why was it important to include bottle E in this investigation?

4. **Drawing Conclusions** Do yeast use salt or sugar as a food source? How do you know?

5. **Communicating** In a paragraph, summarize what you learned about yeast from this investigation. Be sure to support each of your conclusions with the evidence you gathered.

Design an Experiment

Develop a hypothesis about whether temperature affects the activity of yeast cells. Then design an experiment to test your hypothesis. *Obtain your teacher's permission before carrying out your investigation.*

For: Data sharing
Visit: PHSchool.com
Web Code: ced-1033

Study Guide

 **BIG Idea** Organisms in different domains and kingdoms display varying levels of organization, from single cells to more complex structures.

① Viruses

Key Concepts   S 7.2.a

- The only way in which viruses are like organisms is that they can multiply.

- All viruses have two basic parts: an outer coat that protects the virus and an inner core made of genetic material.

- Once inside a cell, a virus's genetic material takes over many of the cell's functions. The genetic material instructs the cell to produce the virus's proteins and genetic material, which then assemble into new viruses.

- Resting, drinking plenty of fluids, and eating well-balanced meals may be all you can do while you recover from a viral disease.

Key Terms
virus
host
parasite
bacteriophage
vaccine

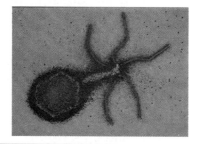

② Bacteria

Key Concepts   S 7.1, 7.2.a

- Bacteria are prokaryotes. The genetic material in their cells is not contained in a nucleus.

- Bacteria must have a source of food and a way of breaking down the food to release its energy.

- When bacteria have plenty of food, the right temperature, and other suitable conditions, they thrive and reproduce frequently.

- Bacteria are involved in oxygen and food production, environmental recycling and cleanup, and in health maintenance and medicine production.

Key Terms

bacteria	conjugation
flagellum	endospore
binary fission	pasteurization
asexual reproduction	decomposer
sexual reproduction	

③ Protists

Key Concepts   S 7.5.a

- Like animals, animal-like protists are heterotrophs, and most are able to move from place to place to obtain food.

- Like plants, algae are autotrophs.

- Like fungi, funguslike protists are heterotrophs, have cell walls, and use spores to reproduce.

Key Terms

protist	symbiosis
protozoan	mutualism
pseudopod	algae
contractile vacuole	spore
cilia	

④ Fungi

Key Concepts   S 7.1.a, 7.2.a

- Fungi are eukaryotes that have cell walls, are heterotrophs that feed by absorbing their food, and use spores to reproduce.

- Fungi usually reproduce by making spores. The lightweight spores are surrounded by a protective covering and can be carried easily through air or water to new sites.

- Many fungi provide foods for people. Fungi play important roles as decomposers and recyclers on Earth. Some fungi cause disease while others fight disease. Still other fungi live in symbiosis with other organisms.

Key Terms
fungi
hyphae
fruiting body
budding
lichen

Review and Assessment

Target Reading Skill

Compare and Contrast To review part of Section 3, copy the Venn diagram, which compares an amoeba to a paramecium. Add at least one additional similarity and one additional difference.

Amoeba   Paramecium

Moves by pseudopods

a. _____?_____

Is a protist

b. _____?_____

Moves by cilia

c. _____?_____

Reviewing Key Terms

Choose the letter of the best answer.

1. Bacteriophages are viruses that attack and destroy
   a. other viruses.
   b. bacteria.
   c. plants.
   d. humans.

2. A tiny, nonliving particle that invades and then multiplies inside a living cell is a
   a. virus.
   b. bacterium.
   c. protist.
   d. fungus.

3. Most bacteria are surrounded by a rigid protective structure called the
   a. cell wall.
   b. cell membrane.
   c. protein coat.
   d. flagellum.

4. Which of the following characteristics describes all protists?
   a. They are unicellular.
   b. They can be seen with the unaided eye.
   c. Their cells have nuclei.
   d. They are unable to move on their own.

5. A lichen is a symbiotic association between
   a. fungi and plant roots.
   b. algae and fungi.
   c. algae and bacteria.
   d. protozoans and algae.

Complete the following sentences so that your answers clearly explain the key terms.

6. Viruses act like **parasites,** which are
   _____ .

7. **Binary fission,** a form of asexual reproduction, does not result in genetically different organisms because _____ .

8. When excess water enters an amoeba, the amoeba does not burst because it has a **contractile vacuole,** a structure that
   _____ .

9. When a protozoan living inside a termite helps the termite digest wood, the relationship is called **mutualism** because
   _____ .

10. Fuzzy-looking molds have loosely tangled **hyphae,** which are the _____ .

Writing in Science

Informational Pamphlet Create a pamphlet to teach young children about fungi. Explain where fungi live, how they feed, and their role in the environment. Include illustrations.

Video Assessment

Discovery Channel School

Protists and Fungi

Review and Assessment

Checking Concepts

11. Explain why a certain virus will attach to only one type or a few types of cells.

12. Describe how a hidden virus multiplies.

13. Describe how bacteria reproduce.

14. How do the bacteria that live in your intestines help you?

15. How does an amoeba obtain food?

16. Compare how animal-like, plantlike, and funguslike protists obtain food.

17. How does sexual reproduction occur in fungi?

Thinking Critically

18. **Comparing and Contrasting** Describe the similarities and differences between active and hidden viruses.

19. **Problem Solving** Bacteria will grow in the laboratory on a gelatin-like substance called agar. Viruses will not grow on agar. If you needed to grow viruses in the laboratory, what kind of substance would you have to use? Explain your reasoning.

20. **Comparing and Contrasting** Identify the organisms below. Describe the method by which each obtains food.

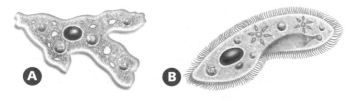

A　　　**B**

21. **Predicting** If all algae suddenly disappeared from Earth's waters, what would happen to living things on Earth? Explain your answer.

22. **Making Judgments** You see an advertisement for a new, powerful fungicide guaranteed to kill most fungi on contact. What should people take into consideration before choosing to buy this fungicide?

Applying Skills

Use the graph to answer Questions 23–26.

When yeast is added to bread dough, the yeast cells produce carbon dioxide, which causes the dough to rise. The graph below shows how temperature affects the amount of carbon dioxide that is produced.

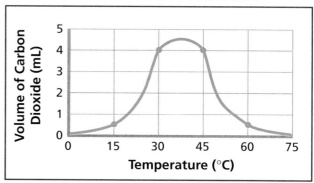

Temperature and Carbon Dioxide Production

23. **Interpreting Data** Based on the graph, at what temperature does yeast produce the most carbon dioxide?

24. **Inferring** Use the graph to explain why yeast is dissolved in warm water, rather than in cold water, when it is used to make bread.

25. **Predicting** Based on the graph, would you expect bread dough to rise if it were placed in a refrigerator (which is kept at about 2° to 5°C)? Explain.

26. **Drawing Conclusions** Explain how temperature affects the amount of carbon dioxide that the yeast cells produce.

Lab zone Standards Investigation

Performance Assessment Create a poster that summarizes your experiment for the class. In your poster, include your hypothesis and describe the conditions that produced the best mushroom growth. Use diagrams and graphs to display your results. Did the investigation raise any new questions about mushrooms for you? If so, how could you answer those questions?

Choose the letter of the best answer.

1. If you know that an organism is a prokaryote, you know that
   A its cell does not contain a nucleus.
   B its cell does not contain ribosomes.
   C the organism is a heteroroph.
   D the organism cannot move on its own.
   S 7.1

2. Which of the following statements about a paramecium is correct?
   A It has two contractile vacuoles that remove excess water from the cytoplasm.
   B It uses cilia to move.
   C It has two nuclei.
   D all of the above
   S 7.5.a

3. Which of the following statements about fungus reproduction is true?
   A Fungi reproduce sexually by budding.
   B Fungi reproduce by making spores.
   C Fungi reproduce asexually when two hyphae join together and exchange genetic material.
   D Fungi do not reproduce sexually.
   S 7.2.a

Use the diagram below and your knowledge of science to answer Question 4.

4. What will most likely happen after the virus in the diagram attaches to the bacterial cell?
   A The virus will inject its proteins into the bacterial cell.
   B The virus will inject its genetic material into the bacterial cell.
   C The bacterial cell will inject its proteins into the virus.
   D The bacterial cell will inject its genetic material into the virus.
   S 7.2.a

5. Which of the following statements about viruses is *not* true?
   A Viruses can multiply only inside a living cell.
   B Viruses have genetic material.
   C Virus particles are smaller than bacterial cells.
   D Viruses are composed of cells.
   S 7.1

Use the diagram below and your knowledge of science to answer Question 6.

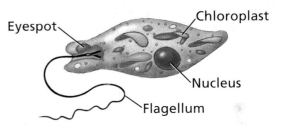

6. Which structure tells you that the euglena shown is an autotroph?
   A eyespot
   B flagellum
   C nucleus
   D chloroplast
   S 7.5.a

7. Paola grew a new culture of bacteria and measured the population's growth over time. The number of bacteria increased sharply over the first few hours but then tapered off. Which of the following statements about these observations is true?
   A The initial conditions for bacterial growth were favorable.
   B The number of bacteria increased as the bacteria reproduced asexually.
   C After a period of time, the bacteria started to run out of food, space, and other resources.
   D all of the above
   S 7.2.a

Apply the
BIG Idea

8. Compare and contrast viruses and bacteria with respect to their sizes, structures, and methods of reproduction.
   S 7.2.a

Structure and Function of Plants

The *Passiflora* plant produces delicate, highly scented flowers. ▶

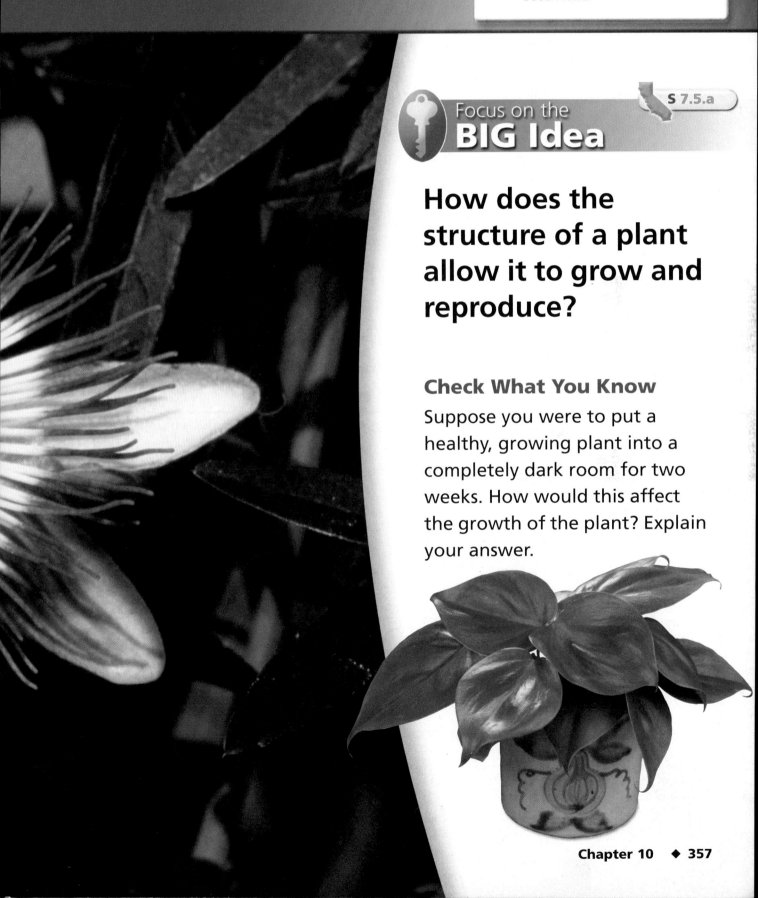

Focus on the
BIG Idea

S 7.5.a

How does the structure of a plant allow it to grow and reproduce?

Check What You Know

Suppose you were to put a healthy, growing plant into a completely dark room for two weeks. How would this affect the growth of the plant? Explain your answer.

Build Science Vocabulary

The images shown here represent some of the key terms in this chapter. You can use this vocabulary skill to help you understand the meaning of some key terms in this chapter.

High-Use Academic Words

High-use academic words are words that are used frequently in classrooms. High-use academic words appear frequently in text-books. Look for the words in the table as you read this chapter.

Word	Definition	Example Sentence
consist (kun SIST) pp. 363, 382	*v.* To be formed or made of	Plant stems <u>consist</u> of several kinds of cells.
diverse (duh VURS) p. 371	*adj.* Different, varied	California has a <u>diverse</u> population, including people from many different countries.
survival (sur VY vul) p. 379	*n.* The act of staying alive or existing	The <u>survival</u> of the accident victim depends on quick medical attention.
transport (trans PAWRT) pp. 365, 381	*v.* To carry from one place to another	Trucks <u>transport</u> products from factories to stores.

Apply It!

Choose the word that best completes the sentence.

1. For their _____, plants need water and sunlight.
2. A plant needs to _____ materials from one part of its body to another.
3. The structure of many plants _____ of leaves, stems, and roots.

frond

Chapter 10
Vocabulary

interactive
Textbook

Build Science Vocabulary
Online
Visit: PHSchool.com
Web Code: cvj-3100

root cap

gymnosperm

germination

flower

How to Read Science

 ## Sequence

Science textbooks often describe sequences—that is, the order in which events happen. A cycle is a sequence that does not have a beginning or end. When the final event is over, the first event begins again. You will learn about complex life cycles of plants in this chapter. Here is a simplified description of one life cycle.

Many plants reproduce by means of seeds. At some point after a seed falls on the ground, the seed sprouts. Slowly, the new plant grows. After a time, flowers appear. Seeds form in flowers. When the seeds are fully developed, they fall onto the ground. Sooner or later, some of these new seeds will sprout.

The partially completed cycle diagram below shows the sequence of events described in the paragraph.

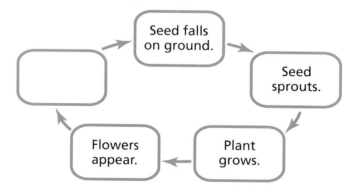

Apply It!

1. In your notebook, complete the diagram shown above.
2. After you read Section 1, draw a cycle diagram of a plant life cycle, including the sporophyte and the gametophyte stages. After reading Section 5, prepare two cycle diagrams—one for gymnosperms and one for angiosperms.

S 7.2.a

Cycle of a Lifetime

How long is a seed plant's life? Redwood trees can live for thousands of years. Tomato plants die after only one season. Can organisms that seem so different have anything in common? In this chapter, you'll find out. Some answers will come from this chapter's investigation. In this project, you'll grow plants from seeds and then care for the plants until they produce seeds.

Your Goal

To care for and observe a plant throughout its life cycle

To complete this investigation, you must

- grow a plant from a seed
- observe and describe key parts of your plant's life cycle, such as seed germination and pollination
- harvest and plant the seeds that your growing plant produces
- follow the safety guidelines in Appendix A

Plan It!

Observe the seeds that your teacher gives you. In a small group, discuss what conditions the seeds might need to grow. What should you look for after you plant the seeds? What changes do you expect your plant to undergo during its life cycle? When you are ready, plant your seeds.

CALIFORNIA
Standards Focus

S 7.5.a Students know plants and animals have levels of organization for structure and function, including cells, tissues, organs, organ systems, and the whole organism.

- What characteristics do all plants share?
- What do plants need to live successfully on land?
- How do nonvascular plants and vascular plants differ?
- What are the different stages of a plant's life cycle?

Key Terms

- cuticle
- vascular tissue
- zygote
- vegetative reproduction
- nonvascular plant
- vascular plant
- sporophyte
- gametophyte

Lab zone ## Standards **Warm-Up**

What Do Leaves Reveal About Plants?

1. Your teacher will give you two leaves from plants that grow in two very different environments: a desert and an area with average rainfall.
2. Carefully observe the color, size, shape, and texture of the leaves. Touch the surfaces of each leaf. Examine each leaf with a hand lens. Record your observations in your notebook.
3. When you have finished, wash your hands thoroughly with soap and water.

Think It Over

Inferring Use your observations of the structure of the leaves to determine which plant lives in the desert. Explain.

There are some very strange plants in the world. There are plants that trap animals, plants that bloom only once every thirty years, and plants with flowers that smell like rotting meat. You don't see these plants every day. But whenever you see moss on a tree trunk, a grassy lawn, or ripe tomatoes in a garden, you see plants. And all plants, both the unfamiliar and the familiar, have a lot in common.

What Is a Plant?

Members of the plant kingdom share several characteristics. **Nearly all plants are autotrophs, organisms that produce their own food. All plants are eukaryotes that contain many cells. In addition, all plant cells are surrounded by cell walls.**

Autotrophs Plants are autotrophs. You can think of a plant as a sun-powered, food-making factory. Sunlight provides the energy for this food-making process, photosynthesis.

Plant Cells Plants are multicellular eukaryotes. Recall that plant cells are enclosed by a cell wall. Many plant cells also contain chloroplasts and a large vacuole for storing water, wastes, food, and other substances.

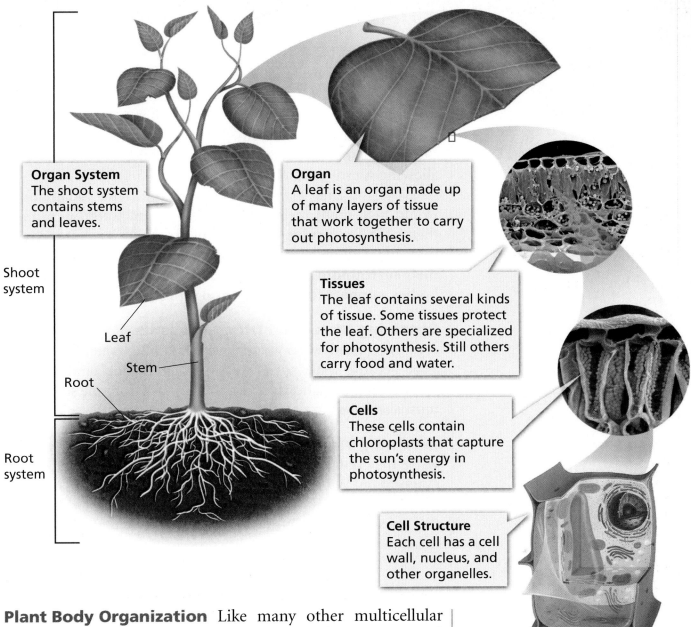

Organ System
The shoot system contains stems and leaves.

Organ
A leaf is an organ made up of many layers of tissue that work together to carry out photosynthesis.

Tissues
The leaf contains several kinds of tissue. Some tissues protect the leaf. Others are specialized for photosynthesis. Still others carry food and water.

Cells
These cells contain chloroplasts that capture the sun's energy in photosynthesis.

Cell Structure
Each cell has a cell wall, nucleus, and other organelles.

Shoot system

Root system

Leaf

Stem

Root

FIGURE 1
Plant Body Structure
The body of a plant is organized into organ systems, organs, tissues, and cells.
Interpreting Diagrams *What functions are the cells of the leaf specialized to do?*

Plant Body Organization Like many other multicellular organisms, plants have levels of organization for structure and function. Figure 1 shows some of the cells, tissues, organs, and organ systems that make up a typical plant.

Take a look at the leaf. Notice that it is made of layers of similar cells. Recall that tissues are groups of similar cells that perform a specific function. The flat layer of cells that cover the outer surfaces of the leaf is one type of tissue. The layers of tightly packed cells with chloroplasts make up another type of tissue. Tissues work together to form organs. Leaves, stems, and roots are organs.

Organs that work together to perform a major function comprise organ systems. A plant has two organ systems—one above ground and one below ground. Above ground is the shoot system, which consists of stems, leaves, and buds. The shoot system produces food for the plant. Below ground is the root system. As you can probably guess, the root system consists of roots, which absorb water and nutrients and anchor the plant in the soil.

FIGURE 2
Retaining Water
Plants have adaptations that help them retain water. The shiny, waterproof cuticle on this leaf slows down evaporation.

Adaptations for Living on Land

Most plants live on land. How is living on land different from living in water? Imagine multicellular algae floating in the ocean. The algae obtain water and other materials directly from the water around them. Their bodies are held up toward the sunlight by the water. The water also aids in reproduction, allowing sperm cells to swim to egg cells.

Now imagine plants living on land. What adaptations would help them meet their needs without water all around them? **To survive on land, plants must have structures that allow them to obtain water and other nutrients from their surroundings, retain water, transport materials in their bodies, support their bodies, and reproduce.**

Obtaining Water and Other Nutrients Recall that all organisms need water to survive. Obtaining water is easy for algae because water surrounds them. To live on land, though, plants need adaptations for obtaining water from the soil. Plants must also have ways of obtaining nutrients from the soil.

Retaining Water Plants must have ways of holding onto the water they obtain. Otherwise, they could easily dry out due to evaporation. When there is more water in plant cells than in the air, the water leaves the plant and enters the air. One adaptation that helps a plant reduce water loss is a waxy, waterproof layer called the **cuticle.** A cuticle covers the leaves of most plants.

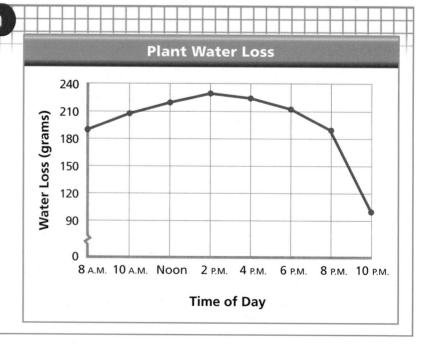

Reviewing Math: Statistics, Data Analysis, and Probability 7.1.2

Math Analyzing Data

Water Loss in Plants

The graph shows how much water a certain plant loses during the hours shown.

1. **Reading Graphs** What variable is plotted along each axis?

2. **Interpreting Data** During what part of the day did the plant lose the most water? The least water?

3. **Drawing Conclusions** What could cause this pattern of water loss?

4. **Predicting** How would you expect the graph to look from 10 P.M. to 8 A.M.? Explain your reasoning.

Plant Water Loss

(graph: Water Loss (grams) vs Time of Day; y-axis 0, 90, 120, 150, 180, 210, 240; x-axis 8 A.M., 10 A.M., Noon, 2 P.M., 4 P.M., 6 P.M., 8 P.M., 10 P.M.)

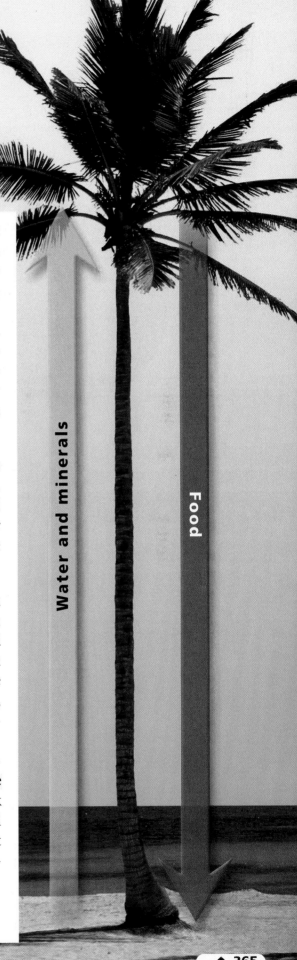

FIGURE 3
Transport and Support
For this tall coconut palm to survive, it must transport water, minerals, and food over long distances. It must also support its body so its leaves are exposed to sunlight.

Water and minerals

Food

Transporting Materials A plant needs to transport water, minerals, food, and other materials from one part of its body to another. In general, water and minerals are taken up by the bottom part of the plant, while food is made in the top part. But all of the plant's cells need water, minerals, and food.

In small plants, materials can simply move from one cell to the next. But larger plants need a more efficient way to transport materials farther, from one part of the plant to another. These plants have transporting tissue called vascular tissue. **Vascular tissue** consists of tubelike structures inside a plant through which water, minerals, and food move.

Support A plant on land must support its own body. It's easier for small, low-growing plants to support themselves. But for larger plants to survive, the leaves must be exposed to as much sunlight as possible. Rigid cell walls and vascular tissue strengthen and support the large bodies of these plants.

Reproduction All plants undergo sexual reproduction that involves fertilization, the joining of a sperm cell with an egg cell. The fertilized egg is called a **zygote.** For algae and some plants, fertilization can only occur if there is water in the environment. This is because the sperm cells of these plants swim through the water to the egg cells. Other plants, however, have adaptations that makes it possible for fertilization to occur in dry environments.

Many plants can also reproduce asexually. Reproduction in plants by asexual methods is called **vegetative reproduction.** For example, pieces of a parent plant may break off and develop into a whole new plant. Many plants will also grow from a cutting, which may be a leaf, stem, or root cut from a plant. Of course, a plant that is produced asexually is genetically identical to the plant from which it came.

Reading Checkpoint Why do plants need adaptations to prevent water loss?

FIGURE 4
Plant Classification

The hundreds of thousands of plants that exist today can be classified as either nonvascular plants or vascular plants. Nonvascular plants are small and live in moist environments. Vascular plants can grow tall and live in diverse habitats. **Classifying** *What are the three groups of vascular plants?*

Nonvascular Plants

Nonvascular Plants

Nonvascular plants do not have true vascular tissue for support or transport. They grow low to the ground.

Mosses grow in damp, shady places.

Liverworts grow on moist soil and rocks.

Classification of Plants

🔑 **Scientists informally group plants into two major groups— nonvascular plants and vascular plants.** Figure 4 shows examples of the major groups of plants living today.

Nonvascular Plants Plants that lack a well-developed system of tubes for transporting water and other materials are known as **nonvascular plants.** Nonvascular plants are low-growing and do not have roots for absorbing water from the ground. Instead, they obtain water and materials directly from their surroundings. The materials then simply pass from one cell to the next. This means that materials do not travel very far or very quickly. This slow method of transport helps explain why most nonvascular plants live in damp, shady places.

Most nonvascular plants have only thin cell walls to provide support. This is one reason why these plants cannot grow more than a few centimeters tall.

Vascular Plants Plants with true vascular tissue are called **vascular plants.** Vascular plants are better suited to life in dry areas than are nonvascular plants. Their well-developed vascular tissue solves the problem of transport, moving materials more quickly and efficiently throughout the plant's body.

Vascular tissue also provides strength, stability, and support to a plant. Thus, vascular plants are able to grow quite tall.

Go Online
SciLINKS NSTA

For: Links on plant classification
Visit: www.SciLinks.org
Web Code: cvn-3101

Vascular Plants

Seedless Vascular Plants

Seedless vascular plants reproduce by making spores.

◄ The staghorn fern produces spores at the tips of its antler-shaped leaves. This fern clings to the bark of trees in tropical areas.

Gymnosperms

Gymnosperms are vascular plants that reproduce by seeds. They do not form flowers or fruits.

◄ Ginkgo trees produce fleshy seeds that resemble fruits but are not. The seeds smell like vomit!

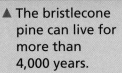
▲ The bristlecone pine can live for more than 4,000 years.

Angiosperms

Angiosperms are vascular plants that flower, and produce seeds that are surrounded by fruit.

The beavertail cactus produces brilliantly colored flowers. ▼

Wheat has been an important food crop for thousands of years. The grains, or fruits, are ground to make flour. ►

Rock containing two plant fossils ▶

FIGURE 5
Ancient and Modern Plants
Fossils of ancient plants help scientists understand the origin of plants. These fossils are of two plants that lived about 300 million years ago. Notice the similarities between the fossils and modern-day ferns (top right) and horsetails (above).

Origin of Plants Which organisms were the ancestors of today's plants? In search of answers, biologists studied fossils. The oldest plant fossils are about 400 million years old. The fossils provide evidence that even that early, plants already had many adaptations for life on land, including vascular tissue.

Better clues to the origin of plants came from comparing the chemicals in modern plants to those in other organisms. In particular, biologists studied the green pigment chlorophyll, which is found in the chloroplasts of plants, algae, and some bacteria. Land plants and green algae contain the same forms of chlorophyll. This evidence led biologists to infer that ancient green algae were the ancestors of today's land plants. Further comparisons of genetic material clearly showed that plants and green algae are very closely related. In fact, some scientists think that green algae should be classified in the plant kingdom.

Complex Life Cycles

🔑 **Plants have complex life cycles that include two stages, the sporophyte stage and the gametophyte stage.** In the **sporophyte** (SPOH ruh fyt) stage, the plant produces spores, tiny cells that can grow into new organisms. A spore develops into the plant's other stage, called the gametophyte. In the **gametophyte** (guh MEE tuh fyt) stage, the plant produces sex cells, or gametes. The gametophyte stage produces two kinds of sex cells: sperm cells and egg cells.

Figure 6 shows a typical plant life cycle. A sperm cell and egg cell join to form a zygote. The zygote then develops into a sporophyte. The sporophyte produces spores, which develop into the gametophyte. Then the gametophyte produces sperm cells and egg cells, and the cycle starts again. The sporophyte of a plant usually looks quite different from the gametophyte.

 **Reading Checkpoint** During which stage does a plant produce spores?

FIGURE 6
Plant Life Cycle
Plants have complex life cycles that consist of two stages—the sporophyte stage and the gametophyte stage.
Interpreting Diagrams *During which stage are sperm and egg cells produced?*

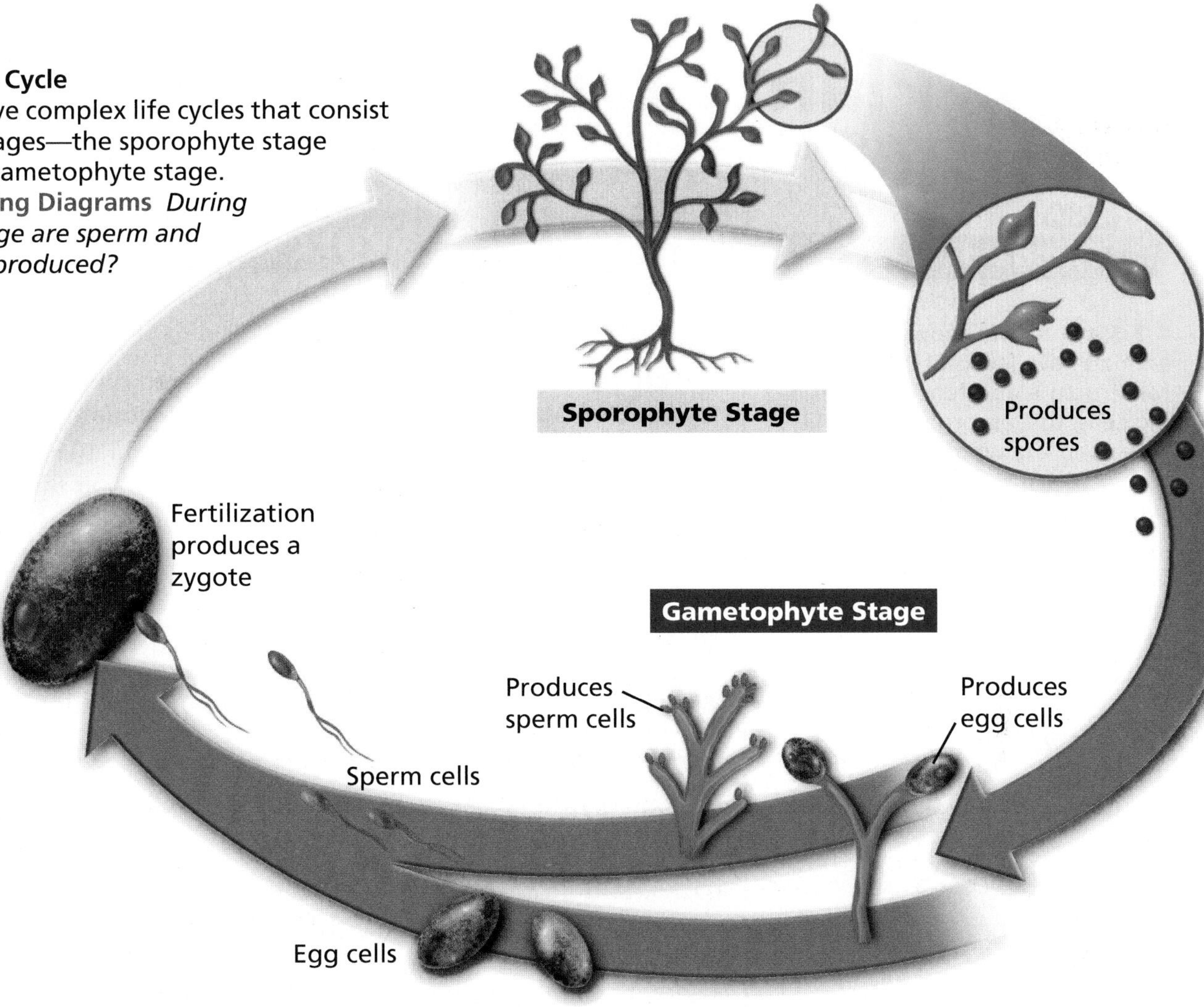

Sporophyte Stage

Produces spores

Fertilization produces a zygote

Gametophyte Stage

Produces sperm cells

Produces egg cells

Sperm cells

Egg cells

Section 1 Assessment

S 7.5.a, E-LA: Reading 7.2.0

Target Reading Skill Sequencing Events
Use your cycle diagram to help answer Question 4.

Reviewing Key Concepts

1. a. **Listing** List three characteristics of plants.
   b. **Comparing and Contrasting** Describe three ways that plant cells differ from the cells of some other eukaryotes.
   c. **Predicting** How might a plant cell be affected if it lacked chloroplasts?

2. a. **Identifying** What are five adaptations that plants need to survive on land?
   b. **Inferring** Why is a cuticle a useful adaptation in plants but not in algae?

3. a. **Reviewing** How do vascular plants differ from nonvascular plants?
   b. **Explaining** Explain why vascular plants are better suited to life in dry areas.

   c. **Classifying** Would you expect a tall desert plant to be a vascular plant? Explain.

4. a. **Describing** What are the two major stages of a plant's life cycle?
   b. **Sequencing** Describe in order the major events in the life cycle of a plant, starting with a zygote.

Lab zone At-Home **Activity**

Classifying Plants Look through old magazines and cut out pictures of plants. Classify each plant as vascular or nonvascular. Create a poster of your classification. Present your poster to your family and explain the differences between nonvascular and vascular plants.

Plants Without Seeds

CALIFORNIA
Standards Focus

S 7.5.a Students know plants and animals have levels of organization for structure and function, including cells, tissues, organs, organ systems, and the whole organism.

- What characteristics do the three groups of nonvascular plants share?

- What characteristics do the three groups of seedless vascular plants share?

Key Terms
- rhizoid
- frond

Go Online
SciLINKS NSTA

For: Links on nonvascular plants
Visit: www.SciLinks.org
Web Code: scn-0143

Lab zone Standards Warm-Up

Will Mosses Absorb Water?

1. Place 20 mL of sand into a plastic graduated cylinder. Place 20 mL of peat moss into a second plastic graduated cylinder.
2. Predict what would happen if you were to pour 10 mL of water slowly into each graduated cylinder and then wait five minutes.
3. To test your prediction, add 10 mL of water slowly to the sand. Then add 10 mL of water to the moss. After five minutes, record your observations.

Think It Over
Predicting How did your prediction compare with your results? What did you learn about moss from this investigation?

As you hike in the forest, you see ferns along the trail. Near a stream, you see mosses everywhere—on the forest floor, on rocks, and along the banks of the stream. Although ferns and mosses look very different, they have something in common. Both reproduce without forming seeds.

Nonvascular Plants

Mosses are a type of seedless plant with no true vascular tissue. **There are three major groups of nonvascular plants: mosses, liverworts, and hornworts. These low-growing plants live in moist areas where they can absorb water and other nutrients directly from their environment.** The watery environment enables sperm cells to swim to egg cells during sexual reproduction.

Mosses With more than 10,000 species, mosses are the most diverse group of nonvascular plants. You have probably seen mosses growing in sidewalk cracks, on tree trunks, and in other damp, shady spots.

Figure 7 shows the structure of a moss plant. The familiar green, fuzzy moss is the gametophyte generation of the plant. Structures that look like tiny leaves grow off a small, stemlike structure. Thin, rootlike structures called **rhizoids** anchor the moss and absorb water and nutrients from the soil. The sporophyte generation grows out of the gametophyte. It consists of a slender stalk with a capsule at the end. The capsule contains spores.

Liverworts There are more than 8,000 species of liverworts. Liverworts are often found growing as a thick crust on moist rocks or soil along the sides of a stream. This group of plants is named for the shape of the plant's leaflike gametophyte, which looks somewhat like a human liver. *Wort* is an old English word for "plant." Liverworts have sporophytes that are too small to see.

Hornworts There are fewer than 100 species of hornworts. Unlike mosses or liverworts, hornworts are seldom found on rocks or tree trunks. Instead, hornworts usually live in moist soil, often mixed in with grass plants. Hornworts are named for the slender, curved structures that grow out of the gametophytes. These horn-shaped structures are the sporophytes.

Reading Checkpoint What does a hornwort sporophyte look like?

FIGURE 7
A Moss Plant
A moss gametophyte has stemlike, leaflike, and rootlike structures.
Interpreting Diagrams *What structures anchor the moss plant?*

Moss plants growing on rock ▶

Capsule

Stalk

Sporophyte

Gametophyte

Stemlike structure

Leaflike structure

Rhizoid

Seedless Vascular Plants

Figure 8 shows what an ancient forest on Earth might have looked like 340 million years ago. Among the plants were huge, tree-sized ferns as well as trees with branches that grew in a series of circles along the trunk. Other trees resembled giant sticks with leaves up to one meter long. When the leaves dropped off, they left diamond-shaped scars. These tall, odd-looking trees were the ancestors of three groups of plants that are alive today—ferns, horsetails, and club mosses. They are seedless plants that have vascular tissue.

Characteristics of Seedless Vascular Plants

Seedless vascular plants share two characteristics. **Ferns, horsetails, and club mosses have true vascular tissue, and they do not produce seeds. Instead of seeds, these plants reproduce by releasing spores.**

Unlike mosses, seedless vascular plants can grow tall because their vascular tissue provides an effective way of transporting materials. The cells making up their vascular tissue have strong cell walls. Therefore, vascular tissue also provides vascular plants with strength and stability.

Like mosses, seedless vascular plants need to grow in moist surroundings. This is because the plants release spores into their surroundings, where they grow into gametophytes. When the gametophytes produce egg cells and sperm cells, there must be enough water available for fertilization.

FIGURE 8
An Ancient Forest
Giant ferns, horsetails, and club mosses dominated ancient forests on Earth.

Spore cases on undersides of fronds.

Frond

Stem

Root

FIGURE 9
A Fern Plant
Fern leaves, or fronds, grow above ground. Most ferns have underground stems in addition to roots. Ferns can reproduce asexually by sending up fronds from the stems. **Relating Diagrams and Photos** *Where are spore cases found on a fern plant?*

Ferns There are more than 12,000 species of ferns alive today. Like other vascular plants, ferns have true stems, roots, and leaves. The stems of most ferns run horizontally underground. Leaves grow upward from the top side of the stems, while roots grow downward from the bottom of the stems. The roots anchor the fern to the ground and absorb water and nutrients from the soil. These substances enter the root's vascular tissue and travel through the tissue into the stems and leaves.

Figure 9 shows a fern's structure. Notice that the fern's leaves, or **fronds,** are divided into many smaller parts that look like small leaves. The upper surface of each frond is coated with a cuticle that helps the plant retain water.

The familiar fern, with its visible fronds, is the sporophyte stage of the plant. On the underside of mature fronds, spores develop in tiny spore cases. Wind and water can carry the spores great distances. If a spore lands in moist, shaded soil, it develops into a gametophyte. Fern gametophytes are tiny plants that grow low to the ground.

 **Reading Checkpoint** How are seedless vascular plants like mosses?

Lab zone Try This **Activity**

Examining a Fern
1. Your teacher will give you a fern plant to observe.
2. Draw a diagram of the plant and label the structures that you see.
3. Use a hand lens to observe the top and lower surfaces of the leaf. Run a finger over both surfaces.
4. With a plastic dropper, add a few drops of water to the top surface of the leaf. Note what happens.

Inferring Use your observations to explain how ferns are adapted to life on land.

Horsetails There are very few species of horsetails on Earth today. As you can see in Figure 10, the stems of horsetails are jointed. Long, coarse, needle-like branches grow in a circle around each joint. Small leaves grow flat against the stem just above each joint. The whorled pattern of growth somewhat resembles the appearance of a horse's tail. The stems contain silica, a gritty substance also found in sand. During colonial times, Americans used the plants to scrub their pots and pans. Another name for horsetails is scouring rushes.

Club Mosses Like ferns, club mosses have true stems, roots, and leaves. They also have a similar life cycle. However, there are only a few hundred species of club mosses alive today.

Do not be confused by the name *club mosses*. Unlike true mosses, club mosses have vascular tissue. The plant, which looks a little like the small branch of a pine tree, is sometimes called ground pine or princess pine. Club mosses usually grow in moist woodlands and near streams.

FIGURE 10
Horsetails and Club Mosses
Horsetails (left) have branches and leaves that grow in a circle around each joint. Club mosses (right) look like tiny pine trees.
Inferring *Which grow taller—true mosses or club mosses?*

 **Reading Checkpoint** **Where do club mosses usually grow?**

Section **2** **Assessment**

S 7.5.a, E-LA: Reading 7.1.0, Writing 7.2.0

Vocabulary Skill High-Use Academic Words
Which are more *diverse*—liverworts or hornworts? Explain your answer.

Reviewing Key Concepts

1. a. **Describing** What two characteristics do mosses, liverworts, and hornworts share?
   b. **Relating Cause and Effect** How are these two characteristics related?
   c. **Comparing and Contrasting** In what ways are mosses, liverworts, and hornworts similar? In what ways do they differ?
2. a. **Listing** What two characteristics do ferns, horsetails, and club mosses share?

   b. **Comparing and Contrasting** In what ways do ferns, horsetails, and club mosses differ from true mosses? In what way are they similar to mosses?
   c. **Inferring** Although ferns have vascular tissue, they still must live in moist environments. Explain why.

Writing in Science

Product Label Create a product label to be attached to pots of fern plants for sale at a garden shop. Describe the structure of ferns and growing instructions. Include other helpful information or diagrams.

What characteristics do seed plants share?

How do seeds become new plants?

Key Terms
- phloem
- xylem
- pollen
- seed
- embryo
- cotyledon
- germination

▲ A salad of seed plants

Lab zone Standards **Warm-Up**

What's the "In-Seed" Story?

1. Your teacher will give you a hand lens and two different seeds that have been soaked in water.
2. Carefully observe the outside of each seed. Draw what you see.
3. Gently remove the covering of each seed. Then carefully separate the structures. Use a hand lens to examine them. Draw what you see.

Think It Over
Posing Questions Write two questions about the structures in each seed. How could you find out the answers?

Have you ever planted seeds in a garden? If so, then you may remember how it seemed to take forever before those first green shoots emerged. Shortly afterwards, you saw one set of leaves, and then others. Then a flower may have appeared. Did you wonder where all those plant parts came from? How did they develop from one small seed? Read on to find out.

What Is a Seed Plant?

The plant growing in your garden was a seed plant. So are most of the other plants around you. In fact, seed plants outnumber seedless plants by more than ten to one. You eat many seed plants—rice, peas, and squash, for example. You wear clothes made from seed plants, such as cotton and flax. You may live in a home built from seed plants— oak, pine, or maple trees. In addition, seed plants produce much of the oxygen you breathe.

 Seed plants share two important characteristics. They have vascular tissue, and they use pollen and seeds to reproduce. In addition, most seed plants have organs that include roots, stems, and leaves. Like seedless plants, seed plants have complex life cycles that include the sporophyte and the gametophyte stages. In seed plants, the plants that you see are the sporophytes. The gametophytes are microscopic.

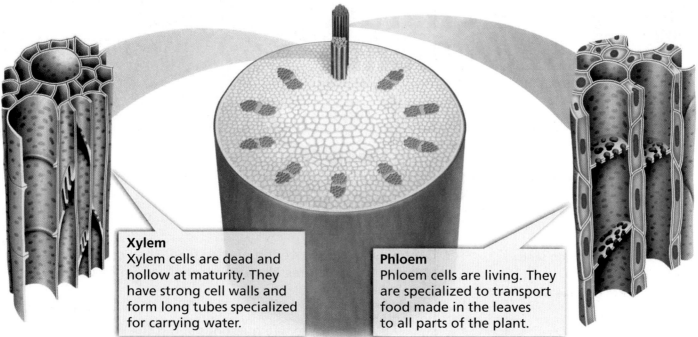

Xylem
Xylem cells are dead and hollow at maturity. They have strong cell walls and form long tubes specialized for carrying water.

Phloem
Phloem cells are living. They are specialized to transport food made in the leaves to all parts of the plant.

FIGURE 11
Phloem and Xylem
The stems of vascular plants contain bundles of phloem and xylem. **Observing** *How is the structure of vascular tissue adapted for transporting materials?*

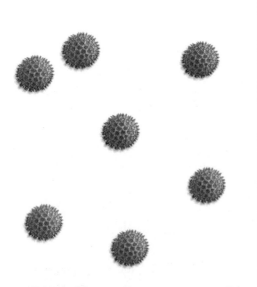

FIGURE 12
Morning Glory Pollen
These greatly magnified grains of pollen contain cells that will develop into sperm.

Vascular Tissue Most seed plants live on land. Recall that land plants face many challenges, including standing upright and supplying all their cells with food and water. Like ferns, seed plants meet these two challenges with vascular tissue. The thick walls of the cells in the vascular tissue help support the plant body. In addition, vascular tissue transports food, water, and nutrients throughout the plant.

There are two types of vascular tissue. Figure 11 shows these two tissues. **Phloem** (FLOH um) is the vascular tissue through which food moves. When food is made in the leaves, it enters the phloem and travels to other parts of the plant. Water and minerals, on the other hand, travel in the vascular tissue called **xylem** (ZY lum). Roots absorb water and minerals from the soil. These materials enter the root's xylem and move upward into the stems and leaves.

Pollen and Seeds Unlike seedless plants, seed plants can live in a wide variety of environments. Recall that seedless plants need water in their surroundings for fertilization to occur. Seed plants do not need water for sperm to swim to the eggs. Instead, seed plants produce **pollen,** tiny structures that contain the cells that will later become sperm cells. Pollen delivers sperm cells near to the eggs.

After sperm cells fertilize the eggs, seeds develop. A **seed** is a structure that contains a young plant inside a protective covering. Seeds protect the young plant from drying out.

How Seeds Become New Plants

All seeds share several important similarities. 🔑 **Inside a seed is a partially developed plant. If a seed lands in an area where conditions are favorable, the plant sprouts out of the seed and begins to grow.**

Seed Structure A seed has three main parts—an embryo, stored food, and a seed coat. The young plant that develops from the zygote, or fertilized egg, is the **embryo** (em BREE oh). The embryo already has the beginnings of roots, stems, and leaves. In the seeds of most plants, the embryo stops growing when it is quite small. When the embryo begins to grow again, it uses the food stored in the seed until it can make its own food by photosynthesis.

The embryo has one or more seed leaves, or **cotyledons** (kaht uh LEED unz). In some seeds, food is stored in the cotyledons. In other seeds, food is stored outside the embryo, in tissue called endosperm. Figure 13 compares the structure of corn, bean, and pine seeds.

The outer covering of a seed is called the seed coat. Some familiar seed coats are the "skins" on lima beans and peanuts. The seed coat acts like plastic wrap, protecting the embryo and its food from drying out. This allows a seed to remain inactive for a long time. In many plants, the seeds are surrounded by a structure called a fruit.

 **Reading Checkpoint** What is a cotyledon?

Go Online

SciLINKS

For: Links on seed plants
Visit: www.SciLinks.org
Web Code: cvn-3103

FIGURE 13
Seed Structure
The structures of three different seeds are shown here. In bean seeds, the cotyledon stores food. In corn and pine seeds, food is stored in endosperm. **Inferring** *How is the stored food used?*

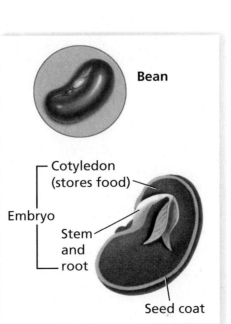

Corn

Cotyledon — Stored food

Embryo — Stem and root — Seed coat

Bean

Cotyledon (stores food)

Embryo — Stem and root — Seed coat

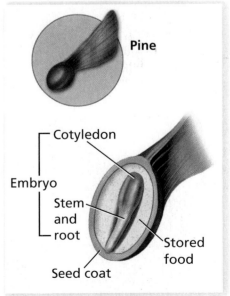

Pine

Cotyledon

Embryo — Stem and root — Seed coat — Stored food

Video Field Trip

Discovery Channel School

Seed Plants

Seed Dispersal After seeds have formed, they are usually scattered, sometimes far from where they were produced. The scattering of seeds is called seed dispersal. Seeds are dispersed in many ways. One method involves other organisms. For example, some animals eat fruits, such as cherries or grapes. The seeds inside the fruits pass through the animal's digestive system and are deposited in new areas. Other seeds are enclosed in barblike structures that hook onto an animal's fur or a person's clothes. The structures then fall off the fur or clothes in a new area.

A second means of dispersal is water. Water can disperse seeds that fall into oceans and rivers. A third dispersal method involves wind. Wind disperses lightweight seeds that often have structures to catch the wind, such as those of dandelions and maple trees. Finally, some plants eject their seeds in a way that might remind you of popping popcorn. The force scatters the seeds in many directions.

FIGURE 14
Seed Dispersal
The seeds of these plants are enclosed in fruits with adaptations that help them disperse.

◀ **Dispersal by wind:** Dandelion fruits with "parachutes"

◀ **Dispersal by water:** Floating coconut palm fruit

▲ **Dispersal by animals:** Barblike fruits

Germination After a seed is dispersed, it may remain inactive for a while before it germinates. **Germination** (jur muh NAY shun) occurs when the embryo begins to grow again and pushes out of the seed. Germination starts when the seed absorbs water from the environment. Then the embryo uses its stored food to grow. As shown in Figure 15, first the embryo's roots grow downward. Then its stem and leaves grow upward. Once you can see a plant's leaves, the plant is called a seedling.

Environmental conditions, such as temperature and moisture, must be just right in order for a seed to germinate. For example, some seeds will germinate only after a cold winter or after being exposed to a fire. If environmental conditions are not suitable for germination, some seeds may remain inactive for years.

A seed that is dispersed far from its parent plant usually has a better chance of survival. When a seed does not have to compete with its parent for light, water, and nutrients, it has a better chance of becoming a seedling.

 **Reading Checkpoint** **What conditions are needed in order for germination to begin?**

FIGURE 15
Germination
The embryo in this peanut seed uses its stored food to germinate. First, the embryo's roots grow downward. Then, its stem and leaves begin to grow upward.

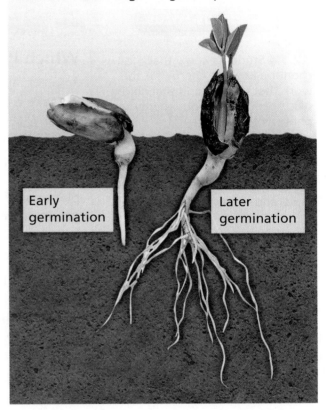

Early germination

Later germination

Section 3 Assessment

S 7.5.a, E-LA: Reading 7.1.0, Writing 7.2.0

Vocabulary Skill High-Use Academic Words
Why is the way in which a seed is dispersed important? Use the word *survival* in your answer.

Reviewing Key Concepts

1. **a. Reviewing** What two characteristics do all seed plants share?
   b. Relating Cause and Effect What characteristics enable seed plants to live in a wide variety of environments? Explain.
2. **a. Listing** Name the three main parts of a seed.
   b. Sequencing What steps must occur for a seed to grow into a new plant? List the steps in sequence.

c. Applying Concepts If a cherry seed were to take root right below its parent tree, what three challenges might the cherry seedling face?

Writing in Science

Product Label Write a "packaging label" for a seed. Include a name and description for each structure of the seed. Be sure to describe the function of each structure in producing a new plant.

Roots, Stems, and Leaves

CALIFORNIA
Standards Focus

S 7.1.d Students know that mitochondria liberate energy for the work that cells do and that chloroplasts capture sunlight energy for photosynthesis.

S 7.5.a Students know plants and animals have levels of organization for structure and function, including cells, tissues, organs, organ systems, and the whole organism.

What are the main functions of roots, stems, and leaves?

Key Terms
- root cap
- cambium
- transpiration

Lab zone Standards **Warm-Up**

Which Plant Part Is It?
1. Carefully observe the items of food your teacher gives you.
2. Make a list of the food items.
3. For each food item, write the name of the plant part—root, stem, or leaf—from which you think it is obtained.

Think It Over
Classifying Classify the items into groups depending on the plant part from which the food is obtained. Compare your groupings with those of your classmates.

Chances are you've eaten carrots, potatoes, and lettuce. But how much do you know about these common seed plants? For example, did you know that when you eat a carrot, you are eating a root? A potato is actually a stem. And lettuce leaves have many adaptations for photosynthesis. The structure of roots, stems, and leaves varies greatly among seed plants. However, they perform similar functions critical to the plants' survival.

FIGURE 16
Root Systems
Some plants have fibrous roots while others have taproots.

Fibrous root system: Onion

Taproot system: Dandelion

Roots

Have you ever tried to pull a dandelion plant out of the soil? It's not easy, is it? That is because most roots are good anchors. Roots have three main functions. ⬤ **Roots anchor a plant in the ground, absorb water and minerals from the soil, and sometimes store food.** The more root area a plant has, the more water and minerals it can absorb.

Types of Roots The two main types of root systems are fibrous root systems and taproot systems. A fibrous root system consists of many similarly sized roots that form a dense, tangled mass. Plants with fibrous roots take much soil with them when you pull them out of the ground. Lawn grass, corn, and onions have fibrous root systems. In contrast, a taproot system has one long, thick main root. Many smaller roots branch off the main root. A plant with a taproot system is hard to pull out of the ground. Carrots, dandelions, and cacti have taproots.

The Structure of a Root Figure 17 shows the structure of a typical root. Notice that the tip of the root is rounded and is covered by a structure called the root cap. The **root cap** protects the root from injury from rocks as the root grows through the soil. Behind the root cap are the unspecialized cells that differentiate into new root cells.

Root hairs grow out of the root's surface. These tiny hairs can enter the spaces between soil particles, where they absorb water and minerals. By increasing the surface area of the root that touches the soil, root hairs help the plant absorb large amounts of water and other substances.

Locate the vascular tissue in the center of the root. The water and nutrients that are absorbed from the soil quickly move into the xylem. From there, these substances are transported upward to the plant's stems and leaves.

Phloem transports food manufactured in the leaves to the root. The root tissues may then use the food for growth or store it for future use by the plant.

 **Reading Checkpoint** What is the function of a root cap?

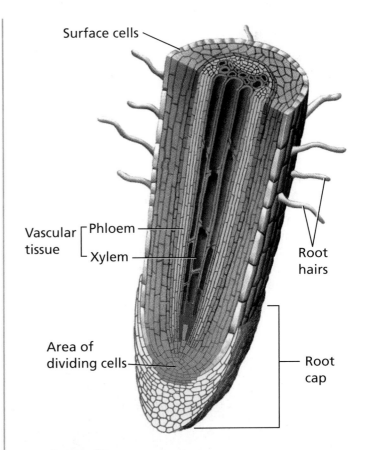

FIGURE 17

Root Structure

A root's structure is adapted for absorbing water and minerals from the soil.
Relating Cause and Effect *How do root hairs help absorb water and minerals?*

FIGURE 18
Structure of a Stem
Leafs are attached at nodes along the stem. Buds are also at the nodes. Buds can develop into new branches, leaves, or flowers.

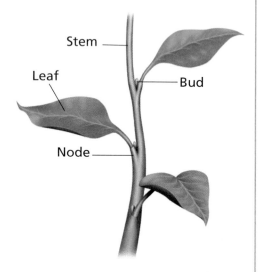

Stem

Leaf

Bud

Node

Stems

A plant stem has several main functions. ⬤ **The stem produces branches, leaves, and flowers. It carries substances between the plant's roots and leaves. The stem also provides support for the plant and holds up the leaves so they are exposed to the sun.** In addition, some stems store food. For example, a potato is a stem that is adapted to store food.

The Structure of a Stem Stems consist of vascular tissue as well as many other supporting cells. Bundles of xylem and phloem run all the way up from the roots to the leaves. Depending on the type of plant, the bundles of vascular tissue can be scattered randomly throughout the stem, or arranged in rings within the stem.

In most plants, a stem has regions called nodes where leaves are attached. Buds are found at the nodes. Buds contain tissue that can differentiate into new branches, leaves, or flowers. Figure 19 shows the structure of a typical stem. Stems can either be herbaceous (hur BAY shus) or woody.

Herbaceous Stems You are probably familiar with many plants that have herbaceous stems. Daisies, geraniums, and parsley have herbaceous stems. Herbaceous stems contain no wood and are often soft. Figure 19 shows the inner structure of a herbaceous stem with one type of vascular tissue arrangement.

FIGURE 19

A Herbaceous Stem

Herbaceous stems, like those on these coneflowers, are often soft. The inset shows the inner structure of one type of herbaceous stem. The bundles of vascular tissue in this stem are arranged in a ring.

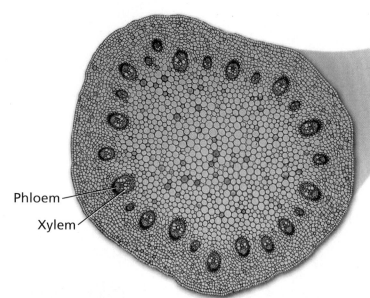

Phloem

Xylem

Woody Stems As you can see in Figure 20, a woody stem contains several layers of tissue. The outermost layer is bark. Bark includes an outer protective layer and an inner layer of living phloem, which transports food through the stem. Next is a layer of cells called the **cambium** (KAM bee um), which divide to produce new phloem and xylem. It is xylem that makes up most of what you call "wood." Sapwood is active xylem that transports water and minerals through the stem. The older, darker, heartwood is inactive but provides support.

Notice the pattern of circles that looks something like a target in woody stems. These circles are called annual rings because they represent a tree's yearly growth. Annual rings are made of xylem. Xylem cells that form in the spring are large and have thin walls because they grow rapidly. They produce a wide, light brown ring. Xylem cells that form in the summer grow slowly and, therefore, are small and have thick walls. They produce a thin, dark ring. One pair of light and dark rings represents one year's growth. You can estimate a tree's age by counting its annual rings.

The width of a tree's annual rings can also provide important clues about past weather conditions, such as rainfall. In rainy years, more xylem is produced, so the tree's annual rings are wide. In dry years, rings are narrow.

 **Reading Checkpoint** What function does the bark of a woody stem perform?

FIGURE 20
A Woody Stem

A typical woody stem is made up of many layers. The layers of xylem form annual rings that can reveal the age of the tree and the growing conditions it has experienced.
Interpreting Diagrams *Where is the cambium located?*

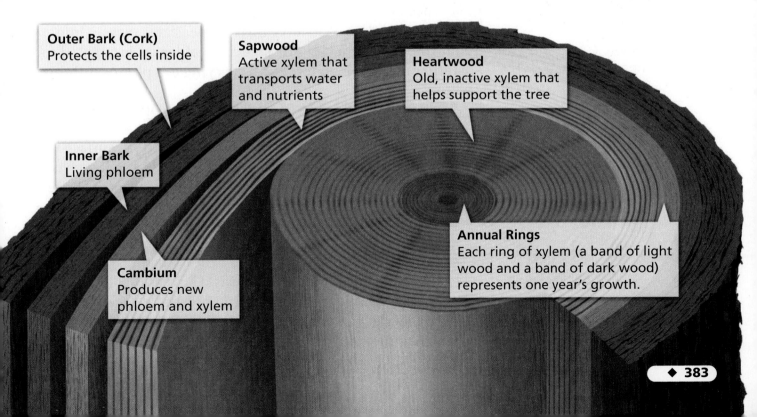

Outer Bark (Cork)
Protects the cells inside

Sapwood
Active xylem that transports water and nutrients

Heartwood
Old, inactive xylem that helps support the tree

Inner Bark
Living phloem

Cambium
Produces new phloem and xylem

Annual Rings
Each ring of xylem (a band of light wood and a band of dark wood) represents one year's growth.

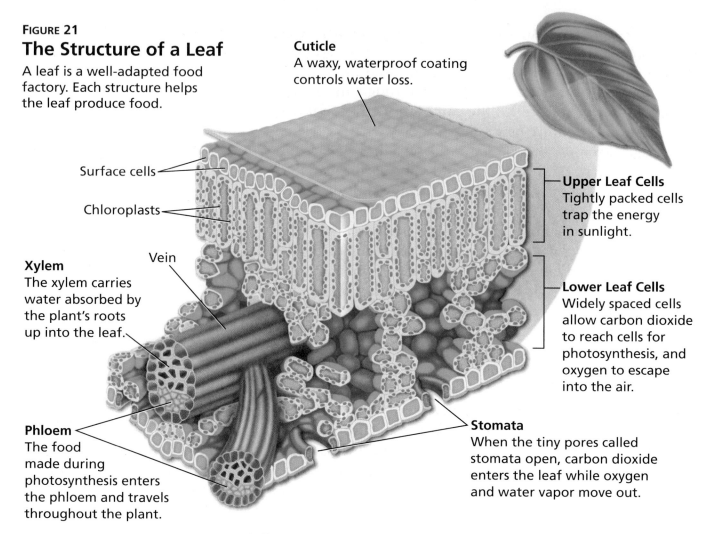

FIGURE 21

The Structure of a Leaf

A leaf is a well-adapted food factory. Each structure helps the leaf produce food.

Cuticle
A waxy, waterproof coating controls water loss.

Surface cells

Chloroplasts

Upper Leaf Cells
Tightly packed cells trap the energy in sunlight.

Xylem
The xylem carries water absorbed by the plant's roots up into the leaf.

Vein

Lower Leaf Cells
Widely spaced cells allow carbon dioxide to reach cells for photosynthesis, and oxygen to escape into the air.

Phloem
The food made during photosynthesis enters the phloem and travels throughout the plant.

Stomata
When the tiny pores called stomata open, carbon dioxide enters the leaf while oxygen and water vapor move out.

Leaves

Leaves vary greatly in size and shape. Pine trees, for example, have needle-shaped leaves. Birch trees have flat rounded leaves with jagged edges. Whatever their shape, leaves play an important role in a plant. 🔄 **The structure of leaves is adapted for capturing the sun's energy and carrying out photosynthesis.**

The Structure of a Leaf If you were to cut through a leaf and look at the edge under a microscope, you would see the structures in Figure 21. The leaf's top and bottom surface layers protect the cells inside. Between the layers of cells are veins that contain xylem and phloem. The surface layers of the leaf have stomata, the pores that open and close to control when gases enter and leave the leaf.

The Leaf and Photosynthesis The structure of a leaf is ideal for carrying out photosynthesis. The cells that contain the most chloroplasts are located near the leaf's upper surface, where they get the most light. Chlorophyll in the chloroplasts traps the sun's energy.

Carbon dioxide enters the leaf through open stomata. Water, which is absorbed by the plant's roots, travels up the stem to the leaf through the xylem. Recall that during photosynthesis, sugar and oxygen are produced from the carbon dioxide and water. Oxygen passes out of the leaf through the open stomata. The sugar enters the phloem and then travels throughout the plant. The many chemical reactions of photosynthesis can be summarized by this equation:

$$\text{carbon dioxide} + \text{water} \xrightarrow{\text{light energy}} \text{sugar} + \text{oxygen}$$

Controlling Water Loss Because such a large area of a leaf is exposed to the air, water can quickly evaporate, or be lost, from a leaf into the air. The process by which water evaporates from leaves is called **transpiration** (tran spuh RAY shun).

A plant can lose a lot of water through transpiration. A corn plant, for example, can lose almost 4 liters of water on a hot summer day. Without a way to slow down the process of transpiration, a plant would shrivel up and die.

Fortunately, plants have ways to slow down transpiration. One way that plants retain water is by closing the stomata. The stomata often close when leaves start to dry out. Figure 22 shows open and closed stomata.

FIGURE 22
Stomata
Stomata open (top) and close (bottom) to control when gases enter and exit the leaf.
Relating Cause and Effect *What gases enter and exit when the stomata open?*

 **Reading Checkpoint** **How does water get into a leaf?**

Section 4 Assessment

S 7.1.d, 7.5.a E-LA: Reading 7.1.0

Vocabulary Skill High-Use Academic Words
How does food get from a plant's leaves to its roots? Use the word *transport* in your answer.

Reviewing Key Concepts

1. a. **Listing** Name three main functions of roots.
   b. **Explaining** How do root hairs aid in the function of roots?
   c. **Inferring** Weeds have taken over your garden. While removing the weeds, you notice that the roots grow very deep. How do you think the weeds' roots contribute to their success in your garden?
2. a. **Identifying** What roles do stems play?
   b. **Sequencing** List in order the layers of tissue within a woody stem, moving from the center of the stem to the outermost layer.

3. a. **Reviewing** What food-making process are leaves adapted to carry out?
   b. **Relating Cause and Effect** How are stomata adapted to carry out this process?
   c. **Predicting** Water lilies live in fresh water, with leaves that float on the water's surface. Where would you expect to find the stomata on the leaves of water lilies?

Lab zone **At-Home Activity**

Plant Walk With a family member, go on a plant walk in your neighborhood. Look for different kinds of seed plants. Describe the adaptations in their roots, stems, and leaves that enable the plants to survive.

Lab zone ▸ Design Your Own Lab

Eye on Photosynthesis

S 7.1.d, 7.7.c

Problem

What raw materials and conditions are involved in photosynthesis?

Skills Focus

observing, controlling variables, designing experiments

Materials

- *Elodea* plants
- water (boiled, then cooled)
- wide-mouthed container
- sodium bicarbonate solution
- 2 test tubes
- wax pencil
- lamp (optional)

Procedure

PART 1   Observing Photosynthesis

1. Use a wax pencil to label two test tubes *1* and *2*. Fill test tube 1 with sodium bicarbonate solution. Sodium bicarbonate provides a source of carbon dioxide for photosynthesis.

2. Fill the wide-mouthed container about three-fourths full of sodium bicarbonate solution.

3. Hold your thumb over the mouth of test tube 1. Turn the test tube over, and lower it to the bottom of the container. Do not let in any air. If necessary, repeat this step so that test tube 1 contains no air pockets. **CAUTION:** *Glass test tubes are fragile. Handle the test tubes carefully. Do not touch broken glass.*

4. Fill test tube 2 with sodium bicarbonate solution. Place an *Elodea* plant in the tube with the cut stem at the bottom. Put your thumb over the mouth of the test tube, and lower it into the container without letting in any air. Wash your hands.

5. Place the container with the two test tubes in bright light. After a few minutes, examine both test tubes for bubbles.

6. If bubbles form in test tube 2, observe the *Elodea* stem to see if it is producing the bubbles. The bubbles are oxygen bubbles. The production of oxygen signals that photosynthesis is taking place.

7. Leave the setup in bright light for 30 minutes. Observe what happens to any bubbles that form. Record your observations.

PART 2   Is Carbon Dioxide Needed for Photosynthesis?

8. Your teacher will provide a supply of water that has been boiled and then cooled. Boiling removes gases that are dissolved in the water, including carbon dioxide.

9. Based on what you learned in Part 1, design an experiment to show whether or not carbon dioxide is needed for photosynthesis. Obtain your teacher's approval before carrying out your experiment. Record all your observations.

PART 3 What Other Conditions Are Needed for Photosynthesis?

10. Make a list of other conditions that may affect photosynthesis. For example, think about factors such as light, the size of the plant, and the number of leaves.

11. Choose one factor from your list. Then design an experiment to show how the factor affects photosynthesis. Obtain your teacher's approval before carrying out your experiment. Record all your observations.

Analyze and Conclude

1. **Observing** What process produced the bubbles you observed in Part 1? In what cell organelle did this process occur?

2. **Controlling Variables** In Part 1, what was the purpose of test tube 1?

3. **Designing Experiments** For the experiments you carried out in Parts 2 and 3, identify the manipulated variable and the responding variable. Explain whether or not your experiments were controlled experiments.

4. **Drawing Conclusions** Based on your results in Part 2, is carbon dioxide necessary for photosynthesis?

5. **Posing Questions** What question about photosynthesis did you explore in Part 3? What did you learn?

6. **Communicating** In a paragraph, summarize what you learned about photosynthesis from this investigation. Support your conclusions with data you collected during your experiments.

More to Explore

A small animal in a closed container will die, even if it has enough water and food. A small animal in a closed container with a plant, water, and food might live. Use what you have learned from this experiment to explain these facts.

Reproduction in Seed Plants

CALIFORNIA
Standards Focus

S 7.2.a Students know the differences between the life cycles and reproduction methods of sexual and asexual organisms.

S 7.5.f Students know the structures and processes by which flowering plants generate pollen, ovules, seeds, and fruit.

- What are the characteristics of gymnosperms and how do they reproduce?
- What are the characteristics of angiosperms?
- How do angiosperms reproduce?
- What are the two types of angiosperms?

Key Terms

- gymnosperm • cone • ovule
- pollination • angiosperm
- flower • sepal • petal
- stamen • pistil • ovary
- fruit • monocot • dicot

Go Online

SciLINKS **NSTA**

For: Links on gymnosperms
Visit: www.SciLinks.org
Web Code: scn-0152

Lab zone Standards **Warm-Up**

What Is a Fruit?

1. Your teacher will give you three different fruits that have been cut in half.
2. Use a hand lens to carefully observe the outside of each fruit. For each fruit, record its color, shape, size, and other external features. Record your observations in your notebook.
3. Carefully observe the structures inside the fruit. Record your observations.

Think It Over
Forming Operational Definitions Based on your observations, how would you define the term *fruit?*

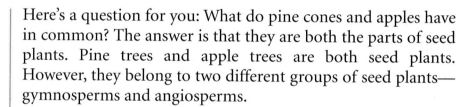

Here's a question for you: What do pine cones and apples have in common? The answer is that they are both the parts of seed plants. Pine trees and apple trees are both seed plants. However, they belong to two different groups of seed plants—gymnosperms and angiosperms.

Gymnosperms

Pine trees belong to the group of seed plants known as gymnosperms. A **gymnosperm** (JIM nuh spurm) is a seed plant that produces naked seeds. The seeds of gymnosperms are referred to as "naked" because they are not enclosed by a protective fruit.

All gymnosperms produce naked seeds. In addition, many gymnosperms have needle-like or scalelike leaves, and deep-growing root systems. Gymnosperms are the oldest type of seed plant. According to fossil evidence, gymnosperms first appeared on Earth about 360 million years ago. Fossils also indicate that there were many more species of gymnosperms on Earth in the past than there are today. Four groups of gymnosperms exist today.

FIGURE 23

Types of Gymnosperms

Gymnosperms are the oldest seed plants. Cycads, conifers, ginkgoes, and gnetophytes are the only groups that exist today.

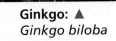

Ginkgo: ▲
Ginkgo biloba

Gnetophyte: ▲
Welwitschia

Cycad: ▲
Sago palm

Cycads About 175 million years ago, the majority of plants were cycads. Today, cycads (SY kadz) grow mainly in tropical and subtropical areas. Cycads look like palm trees with cones. A cycad cone can grow as large as a football.

Conifers Conifers (KAHN uh furz), or cone-bearing plants, are the largest and most diverse group of gymnosperms today. Most conifers, such as pines, sequoias, and junipers, are evergreens—plants that keep their leaves, or needles, year-round. When needles drop off, they are replaced by new ones.

Ginkgoes Ginkgoes (GING kohz) also grew hundreds of millions of years ago. But today, only one species of ginkgo, *Ginkgo biloba*, exists. It probably survived only because the Chinese and Japanese cared for it in their gardens. Today, ginkgo trees are planted along city streets because they can tolerate air pollution.

Gnetophytes Gnetophytes (NEE tuh fyts) live in hot deserts and in tropical rain forests. Some gnetophytes are trees, some are shrubs, and others are vines. The *Welwitschia* shown in Figure 23 grows in the deserts of West Africa and can live for more than 1,000 years.

Conifer: ▶
Giant
sequoia

Reading Checkpoint What are the four types of gymnosperms?

Gymnosperm Life Cycle

Most gymnosperms have reproductive structures called **cones.** Cones are covered with scales. Most gymnosperms produce two types of cones: male cones and female cones. Usually, a single plant produces both male and female cones. In some types of gymnosperms, however, individual trees produce either male cones or female cones. A few types of gymnosperms produce no cones at all.

In Figure 24, you can see the male and female cones of a Ponderosa pine. Male cones produce tiny grains of pollen—the male gametophyte. Pollen contains the cells that will later become sperm cells. Each scale on a male cone produces thousands of pollen grains.

The female gametophyte develops in structures called ovules. An **ovule** (OH vyool) is a structure that contains an ovum, or egg cell. Female cones contain at least one ovule at the base of each scale. After fertilization occurs, the ovule develops into a seed.

You can follow the process of gymnosperm reproduction in Figure 24. **First, pollen falls from a male cone onto a female cone. In time, a sperm cell and an egg cell join together in an ovule on the female cone.** After fertilization occurs, the seed develops on the scale of the female cone.

Pollination The transfer of pollen from a male reproductive structure to a female reproductive structure is called **pollination.** In gymnosperms, wind often carries the pollen from the male cones to the female cones. The pollen collects in a sticky substance produced by each ovule.

Fertilization Once pollination has occurred, the ovule closes and seals in the pollen. The scales also close, and a sperm cell fertilizes an egg cell inside each ovule. The fertilized egg then develops into the embryo part of the seed.

Seed Development Female cones remain on the tree while the seeds mature. As the seeds develop, the female cone increases in size. It can take up to two years for the seeds of some gymnosperms to mature. Male cones, however, usually fall off the tree after they have shed their pollen.

Seed Dispersal When the seeds are mature, the scales open. The wind shakes the seeds out of the cone and carries them away. Only a few seeds will land in suitable places and grow into new plants.

 **Reading Checkpoint** What structure produces pollen?

FIGURE 24
The Life Cycle of a Gymnosperm

Ponderosa pines have a typical life cycle for a gymnosperm. Follow the steps of pollination, fertilization, seed development, and dispersal in the pine tree.
Interpreting Diagrams *Where do the pine seeds develop?*

1 A pine tree produces male and female cones.

2 A A male cone produces pollen grains, which contain cells that will mature into sperm cells.

Scale on male cone

Egg cells   Ovule

Scale on female cone

2 B Each scale on a female cone has two ovules at its base.

3 In time, two egg cells form inside each ovule.

4 The wind scatters pollen grains. Some become trapped in a sticky substance produced by the ovule.

5 The ovule closes, and a pollen grain produces a tube that grows into the ovule. A sperm cell moves through the tube and fertilizes the egg cell.

6 The ovule develops into a seed. The fertilized egg becomes the seed's embryo. Other parts of the ovule develop into the seed coat and the seed's stored food.

7 Wind disperses the pine seeds. A seed grows into a seedling and then into a tree.

FIGURE 25 Rafflesia
Rafflesia plants grow in the jungles of Southeast Asia. The giant flowers measure about 1 meter across and weigh about 7 kilograms!
Classifying *What kind of seeds do Rafflesia plants produce—uncovered seeds or seeds enclosed in fruits?*

Angiosperms

You probably associate the word *flower* with a sweet-smelling plant growing in a garden. You certainly wouldn't think of something that smells like rotting meat. But that's exactly what the corpse flower, or rafflesia, smells like.

Rafflesia belongs to the group of seed plants known as angiosperms. An **angiosperm** (AN jee uh spurm) is a flowering plant. ◔ **All angiosperms share two important traits. First, they produce flowers. Second, in contrast to gymnosperms, which produce uncovered seeds, angiosperms produce seeds that are enclosed in fruits.**

Angiosperms live almost everywhere on Earth. They grow in frozen areas in the Arctic, tropical jungles, barren deserts, and at the ocean's edge.

 **Reading Checkpoint**) **Where do angiosperms live?**

The Structure of Flowers

◔ **Flowers come in all sorts of shapes, sizes, and colors. But, despite their differences, all flowers have the same function—reproduction.** A **flower** is the reproductive structure of an angiosperm. Figure 26 shows the parts of a typical flower. As you read about the parts, keep in mind that some flowers lack one or more of the parts. For example, some flowers have male structures, but no female reproductive structures. Other flowers lack petals.

Sepals and Petals When a flower is still a bud, it is enclosed by leaflike structures called **sepals** (SEE pulz). Sepals protect the developing flower and are often green in color. When the sepals fold back, they reveal the flower's colorful, leaflike **petals.** The petals are generally the most colorful parts of a flower. The shape, size, and number of petals vary greatly from flower to flower.

Stamens Within the petals are the flower's male and female reproductive structures. The **stamens** (STAY munz) are the male reproductive structures. Locate the stamens inside the flower in Figure 26. The thin stalk of the stamen is called the filament. Pollen is produced in the anther, at the top of the filament. The filament connects the anther to the base of the flower, which is called the receptacle.

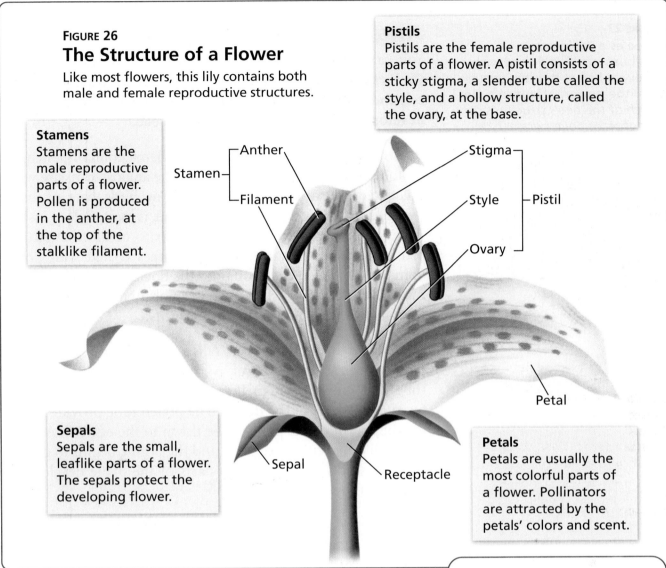

FIGURE 26

The Structure of a Flower

Like most flowers, this lily contains both male and female reproductive structures.

Stamens
Stamens are the male reproductive parts of a flower. Pollen is produced in the anther, at the top of the stalklike filament.

Pistils
Pistils are the female reproductive parts of a flower. A pistil consists of a sticky stigma, a slender tube called the style, and a hollow structure, called the ovary, at the base.

Stamen — Anther
— Filament

Stigma
Style — Pistil
Ovary

Petal

Sepals
Sepals are the small, leaflike parts of a flower. The sepals protect the developing flower.

Sepal

Receptacle

Petals
Petals are usually the most colorful parts of a flower. Pollinators are attracted by the petals' colors and scent.

Go Online
active art

For: The Structure of a Flower activity
Visit: PHSchool.com
Web Code: cep-1053

Pistils The female parts, or **pistils** (PIS tulz), are found in the center of most flowers. Some flowers have two or more pistils; others have only one. The sticky tip of the pistil is called the stigma. A slender tube, called a style, connects the stigma to a hollow structure at the base of the flower. This hollow structure is the **ovary,** which protects the seeds as they develop. An ovary contains one or more ovules.

Pollinators The colors and shapes of most petals and the scents produced by most flowers attract insects and other animals. These organisms carry pollen from one flower to another. Pollinators include birds, bats, and insects such as bees and flies. The rafflesia flower you read about at the beginning of the section is pollinated by flies. The flies are attracted by the strong, rotting-meat smell.

 **Reading Checkpoint** **What are the male and female parts of a flower?**

FIGURE 27
A Bee as a Pollinator
This bee is getting dusted with yellow pollen as it drinks nectar from the flower. **Observing** *On which of the bee's structures can you observe pollen grains?*

Angiosperm Life Cycle

You can follow the life cycle of an angiosperm in Figure 29. **First, pollen falls on a flower's stigma. In time, the sperm cell and egg cell join together in the flower's ovule. The zygote develops into the embryo part of the seed.**

Pollination A flower is pollinated when a grain of pollen falls on the stigma. Like gymnosperms, some angiosperms are wind-pollinated. But most angiosperms rely on birds, bats, or insects for pollination. Nectar, a sugar-rich food, is located deep inside a flower. When an animal enters a flower to obtain the nectar, it brushes against the anthers and becomes coated with pollen. Some of the pollen can drop onto the flower's stigma as the animal leaves the flower. The pollen can also be brushed onto the stigma of the next flower the animal visits.

Fertilization If the pollen falls on the stigma of a similar plant, fertilization can occur. A pollen grain produces a pollen tube that grows through the style into the ovule, within the ovary at the base of the flower. The pollen tube provides a path for the sperm of the pollen tube down to the egg cell. A sperm cell then joins with an egg cell, and the zygote begins to develop into the seed's embryo. Other parts of the ovule develop into the rest of the seed.

Fruit Development and Seed Dispersal As the seed develops after fertilization, the ovary changes into a **fruit**—a ripened ovary and other structures that enclose one or more seeds. Apples and cherries are fruits. So are many foods you usually call vegetables, such as tomatoes and squash. Fruits are the means by which angiosperm seeds are dispersed. Animals that eat fruits help to disperse their seeds.

 **What flower part develops into a fruit?**

FIGURE 28
Fruits
The seeds of angiosperms are enclosed in fruits, which protect and help disperse the seeds.

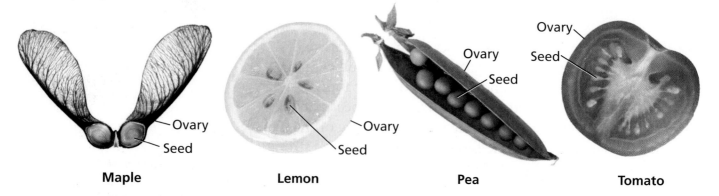

Maple Lemon Pea Tomato

FIGURE 29
The Life Cycle of an Angiosperm
All angiosperms have a similar life cycle. Follow the steps of pollination, fertilization, seed development, and dispersal in this apple tree.
Interpreting Diagrams *What plant part does the ovule develop into?*

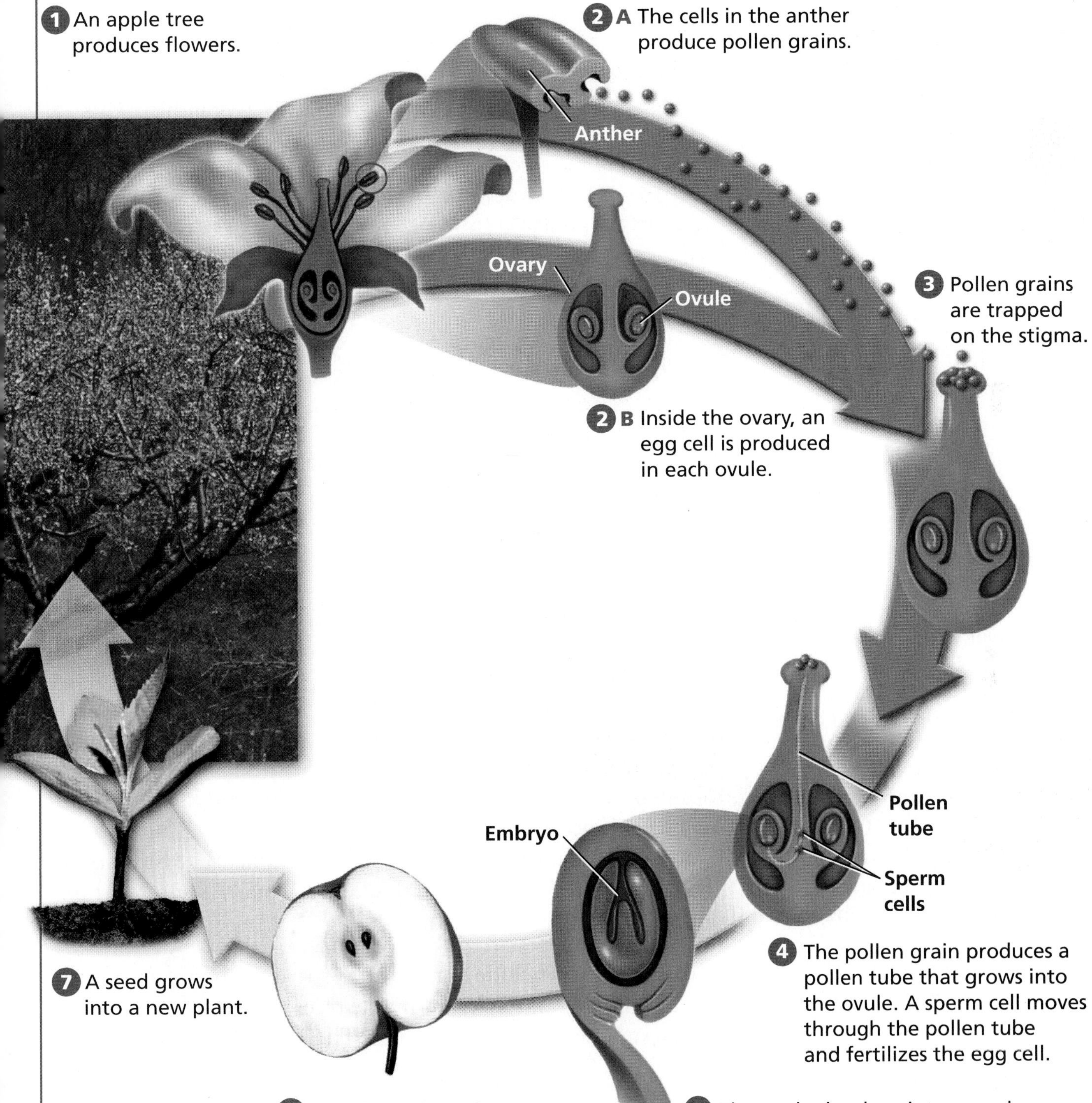

1 An apple tree produces flowers.

2 A The cells in the anther produce pollen grains.

Anther

Ovary

Ovule

2 B Inside the ovary, an egg cell is produced in each ovule.

3 Pollen grains are trapped on the stigma.

Pollen tube

Sperm cells

Embryo

4 The pollen grain produces a pollen tube that grows into the ovule. A sperm cell moves through the pollen tube and fertilizes the egg cell.

5 The ovule develops into a seed. The fertilized egg becomes the seed's embryo. Other parts of the ovule develop into the seed coat and the seed's stored food.

6 The ovary and other structures develop into a fruit that encloses the seeds. The fruit helps in seed dispersal.

7 A seed grows into a new plant.

FIGURE 30
Monocots and Dicots
Monocots and dicots differ in the number of cotyledons, the pattern of veins and vascular tissue, and the number of petals.
Interpreting Tables
How do monocot and dicot leaves differ?

Plant Part	Monocots		Dicots	
Seed	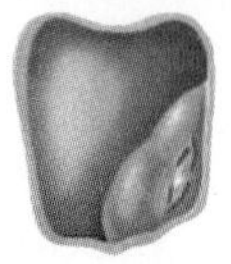	One cotyledon	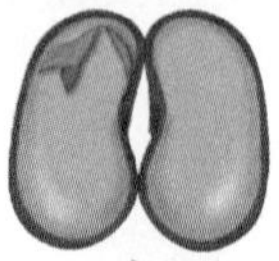	Two cotyledons
Leaf		Parallel veins		Branching veins
Stem		Bundles of vascular tissue scattered throughout stem		Bundles of vascular tissue arranged in a ring
Flower		Flower parts in threes		Flower parts in fours or fives

Comparing Monocots and Dicots

Math Skills

Multiples

Is a flower with 6 petals a monocot? To answer this question, you need to determine if 6 is a multiple of 3. A number is a multiple of 3 if there is a nonzero whole number that, when multiplied by 3, gives you that number.

In this case, 6 is a multiple of 3 because you can multiply 2 (a nonzero whole number) by 3 to get 6.

$$2 \times 3 = 6$$

Therefore, a flower with 6 petals is a monocot. Other multiples of 3 include 9 and 12.

Practice Problem Which of these numbers are multiples of 4?

6, 10, 12, 16

Types of Angiosperms

⚷ **Angiosperms are divided into two major groups: monocots and dicots.** "Cot" is short for *cotyledon*. Recall that in some seeds, the cotyledon, or seed leaf, provides food for the embryo. *Mono* means "one" and *di* means "two." **Monocots** are angiosperms that have only one seed leaf. **Dicots,** on the other hand, produce seeds with two seed leaves. In Figure 30, you can compare the characteristics of monocots and dicots.

Monocots Grasses, including corn, wheat, and rice, and plants such as lilies and tulips are monocots. The flowers of a monocot usually have either three petals or a multiple of three petals. Monocots usually have long, slender leaves with veins that run parallel to one another like train rails. The bundles of vascular tissue in monocot stems are usually scattered randomly throughout the stem.

Dicots Dicots include plants such as roses and violets, as well as dandelions. Both oak and maple trees are dicots, as are food plants such as beans and apples. The flowers of dicots often have either four or five petals or multiples of these numbers. The leaves are usually wide, with veins that branch many times. Dicot stems usually have bundles of vascular tissue arranged in a ring.

 **Reading Checkpoint** How do the petals of monocots and dicots differ in number?

396 ◆

Seed Plants in Everyday Life

Products from seed plants are all around you. Gymnosperms, especially conifers, provide useful products such as paper and the lumber used to build homes. Conifers are also used to produce turpentine, the rayon fibers in clothes, and the rosin used by baseball pitchers, gymnasts, and musicians.

Angiosperms are an important source of food, clothing, and medicine for other organisms. Plant-eating animals eat various parts of flowering plants, including stems, leaves, buds, and flowers. People eat vegetables, fruits, and cereals, all of which are angiosperms. People also make clothing and many other products from angiosperms. For example, cotton fibers come from cotton plants. The sap of rubber trees is used to make rubber for tires and other products. The wood of maple, cherry, and oak trees is often used to make furniture.

FIGURE 31
Cotton Bolls
Angiosperms, such as cotton plants, provide many important products. Cotton seeds, which develop in fruits called bolls, are covered with fibers that are manufactured into cotton fabric.

 **Reading Checkpoint** What are two products made from gymnosperms?

Section 5 Assessment

S 7.2.a, 7.5.f
E-LA: Reading 7.2.0

Target Reading Skill Sequencing Events Use your sequence diagram to help answer Question 1.

Reviewing Key Concepts

1. a. **Listing** What characteristics do all gymnosperms share? What other characteristics do many gymnosperms have?
   b. **Describing** What is a cone? What role do cones play in gymnosperm reproduction?
   c. **Sequencing** Briefly describe the steps in the reproduction of a gymnosperm.
2. a. **Reviewing** What two characteristics do all angiosperms share?
   b. **Identifying** What is the function of an angiosperm's flowers?
3. a. **Reviewing** On what part of a flower must pollen land for pollination to occur?
   b. **Sequencing** Briefly describe the steps in the reproduction of an angiosperm, from pollination to seed dispersal.

4. a. **Listing** Name the two major groups of angiosperms.
   b. **Comparing and Contrasting** How do the seeds, leaves, stems, and flowers of these two groups differ?
   c. **Classifying** A plant's leaves have parallel veins, and each of its flowers has six petals. To which group does it belong? Explain.

Math Practice

5. **Multiples** Which of the following numbers are multiples of 3? Which of the numbers are multiples of 4?

   5, 6, 8, 10, 12, 15

6. **Multiples** Suppose you found a flower with 12 petals. Would you know from the number of petals whether the flower is a monocot or a dicot? Explain.

A Close Look at Flowers

S 7.5.f, 7.7.a

Problem

What is the function of a flower, and what roles do its different parts play?

Skills Focus

observing, inferring, measuring

Materials

- paper towels
- plastic dropper
- hand lens
- microscope
- slide
- large flower
- coverslip
- scalpel
- tape
- water
- metric ruler
- lens paper

Procedure

PART 1   The Outer Parts of the Flower

1. Tape four paper towel sheets on your work area. Obtain a flower from your teacher. While handling the flower gently, observe its shape and color. Use the ruler to measure it. Notice whether the petals have any spots or other markings. Does the flower have a scent? Record your observations with sketches and descriptions.

2. Observe the sepals. How many are there? How do they relate to the rest of the flower? (*Hint:* The sepals are often green, but not always.) Record your observations.

3. Use a scalpel to carefully cut off the sepals without damaging the structures beneath them. **CAUTION:** *Scalpels are sharp. Cut in a direction away from yourself and others.*

4. Observe the petals. How many are there? Are all the petals the same, or are they different? Record your observations.

PART 2   The Male Part of the Flower

5. Carefully pull off the petals to examine the male part of the flower. Try not to damage the structures beneath the petals.

6. Observe the stamens. How many are there? How are they shaped? How tall are they? Record your observations.

7. Use a scalpel to carefully cut the stamens away from the rest of the flower without damaging the structures beneath them. Lay the stamens on the paper towel.

8. Obtain a clean slide and coverslip. Hold a stamen over the slide, and gently tap some pollen grains from the anther onto the slide. Add a drop of water to the pollen. Then place the coverslip over the water and pollen.

9. Observe the pollen under both the low-power objective and the high-power objective of a microscope. Draw and label a pollen grain.

PART 3 The Female Part of the Flower

10. Use a scalpel to cut the pistil away from the rest of the flower. Measure the height of the pistil. Examine its shape. Observe the top of the pistil. Determine if that surface will stick to and lift a tiny piece of lens paper. Record your observations.

11. Lay the pistil on the paper towel. Holding it firmly at its base, use a scalpel to cut the pistil in half at its widest point, as shown in the diagram below. **CAUTION:** *Cut away from your fingers.* How many compartments do you see? How many ovules do you see? Record your observations.

Analyze and Conclude

1. **Observing** Based on your observations, describe how the sepals, petals, stamens, and pistils of a flower are arranged.

2. **Inferring** How are the sepals, petals, stamens, and pistil involved in the function of this flower?

3. **Measuring** Based on your measurements of the heights of the pistil and stamens, how do you think the flower you examined is pollinated? Use additional observations to support your answer.

4. **Classifying** Did you find any patterns in the number of sepals, petals, stamens, or other structures in your flower? If so, describe that pattern. Is your flower a monocot or a dicot?

5. **Communicating** Write a paragraph explaining all you can learn about a plant by examining one of its flowers. Use your observations in this lab to support your conclusions.

More to Explore

Some kinds of flowers do not have all the parts found in the flower in this lab. Obtain a different flower. Find out which parts that flower has, and which parts, if any, are missing. *Obtain your teacher's permission before carrying out your investigation.*

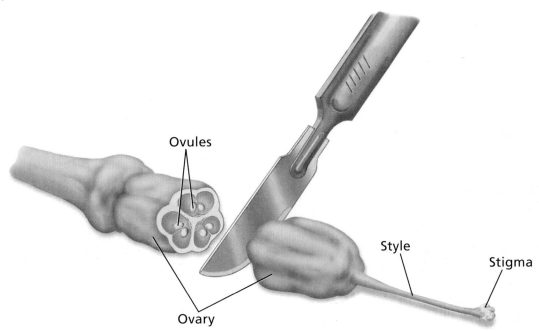

Ovules

Ovary

Style

Stigma

 The **BIG Idea** The structure of plants enables them to obtain water and nutrients, make food, grow, develop, and reproduce.

① The Plant Kingdom

Key Concepts
S 7.5.a

- Nearly all plants are autotrophs. All plants are multicellular eukaryotes with cell walls.
- Land plants must have ways to obtain water and other nutrients from their surroundings, retain water, transport materials in their bodies, support their bodies, and reproduce.
- Scientists informally group plants as nonvascular plants and vascular plants.
- Plants have complex life cycles that include the sporophyte stage and the gametophyte stage.

Key Terms
cuticle
vascular tissue
zygote
nonvascular plant
vascular plant
sporophyte
gametophyte

② Plants Without Seeds

Key Concepts
S 7.5.a

- Mosses, liverworts, and hornworts are low-growing plants that live in moist areas where they can absorb water and other nutrients.
- Ferns, horsetails, and club mosses have true vascular tissue and do not produce seeds. They reproduce by releasing spores.

Key Terms
rhizoid
frond

③ Characteristics of Seed Plants

Key Concepts
S 7.5.a

- Seed plants have vascular tissue and use pollen and seeds to reproduce.
- If a seed lands in an area where conditions are favorable, it can begin to develop into a plant.

Key Terms
phloem
xylem
pollen
seed
embryo
cotyledon
germination

④ Roots, Stems, and Leaves

Key Concepts
S 7.1.d, 7.5.a

- Roots anchor a plant, absorb water and minerals, and sometimes store food.
- The stem carries substances between the plant's roots and leaves. The stem also provides support for the plant and holds up the leaves so they are exposed to the sun.
- A leaf's structure is adapted for capturing the sun's energy and carrying out photosynthesis.

Key Terms
root cap
cambium
transpiration

⑤ Reproduction in Seed Plants

Key Concepts
S 7.2.a, 7.5.f

- All gymnosperms produce naked seeds. In addition, many gymnosperms have needle-like or scalelike leaves, and deep-growing roots.
- During gymnosperm reproduction, pollen falls from a male cone onto a female cone. In time, sperm and egg cells join in an ovule on the female cone.
- All angiosperms produce flowers and fruits.
- All flowers function in reproduction. During angiosperm reproduction, pollen falls on a flower's stigma. In time, sperm and egg cells join in the flower's ovule.
- Angiosperms are divided into two major groups: monocots and dicots.

Key Terms
gymnosperm
cone
ovule
pollination
angiosperm
flower
sepal
petal
stamen
pistil
ovary
fruit
monocot
dicot

Review and Assessment

Target Reading Skill

To review part of Section 5, copy the sequence diagram at right, which shows the main events in the life cycle of angiosperms.

Angiosperm Life Cycle

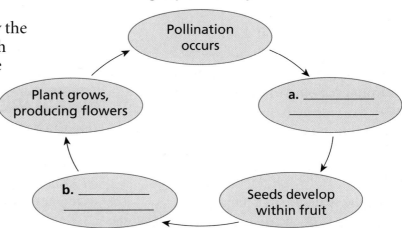

Reviewing Key Terms

Choose the letter of the best answer.

1. The waxy, waterproof layer that covers leaves is called the
   a. zygote.
   b. cuticle.
   c. frond.
   d. cambium.

2. You see a fuzzy, green moss growing at the base of a tree. To which generation does this familiar leaf-like structure belong?
   a. frond
   b. rhizoid
   c. gametophyte
   d. sporophyte

3. The leaves of ferns are called
   a. rhizoids.
   b. sporophytes.
   c. fronds.
   d. cuticles.

4. The process by which a seed sprouts is called
   a. pollination.
   b. fertilization.
   c. dispersal.
   d. germination.

5. Which of the following is the male part of a flower?
   a. pistil   b. ovule
   c. stamen   d. petal

Complete the following sentences so that your answers clearly explain the key terms.

6. Water from the soil can reach the highest branches of a tall tree because the tree has **vascular tissue,** which is _____ .

7. The rootlike **rhizoids** of a moss plant are structures that serve to _____ .

8. On a hot day, a plant can dry out due to **transpiration,** the process by which _____ .

9. After fertilization, an ovule develops into a **seed,** which is _____ .

10. For fertilization to occur, pollen must reach the **pistil,** which is _____ .

Writing in Science

Firsthand Account Write a story from the viewpoint of a seedling. Describe how you were dispersed as a seed and how you grew into a seedling.

Video Assessment

Discovery Channel School
Seed Plants

Review and Assessment

Checking Concepts

11. What are three plant organs?

12. Name one adaptation that distinguishes plants from algae.

13. In what ways do mosses and club mosses differ from each other? In what ways are they similar?

14. Describe four different ways that seeds can be dispersed.

15. Explain the role that stomata play in leaves.

16. Describe the structure of a female cone.

17. What role does a fruit play in an angiosperm's life cycle?

Thinking Critically

18. Comparing and Contrasting How does the sporophyte generation of a plant differ from the gametophyte generation?

19. Applying Concepts A friend tells you that he has seen moss plants that are about 2 meters tall. Is your friend correct? Explain.

20. Relating Cause and Effect When a strip of bark is removed all the way around the trunk of a tree, the tree dies. Explain why.

21. Predicting Pesticides are designed to kill harmful insects. Sometimes, however, pesticides kill helpful insects as well. What effect could this have on angiosperms?

22. Classifying Which of the plants below is a monocot? Which is a dicot? Explain your conclusions.

A

B

Math Practice

23. Multiples Use what you know about multiples to determine which flower is a monocot and which is a dicot: a flower with nine petals; a flower with eight petals. Explain.

Applying Skills

Use the data in the graph below to answer Questions 24–26.

A scientist measured transpiration in an ash tree over an 18-hour period. She also measured how much water the tree's roots took up in the same period.

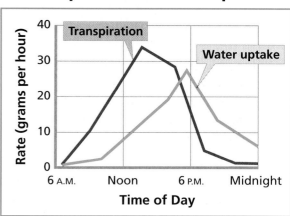

Transpiration and Water Uptake

24. Interpreting Data At what time is the rate of transpiration highest? At what time is the rate of water uptake highest?

25. Inferring Why do you think the transpiration rate increases and decreases as it does during the 18-hour period?

26. Drawing Conclusions Based on the graph, what is one conclusion you can reach about the pattern of water loss and gain in the ash tree?

⟨Lab zone⟩ Standards Investigation

Performance Assessment Design a poster that shows the results of your investigation. You may wish to use a cycle diagram to show the main events in the plant's life. What new information did you learn about seed plants by doing this investigation?

Choose the letter of the best answer.

1. Based on the diagram below, which of the following statements about a plant's life cycle is true?

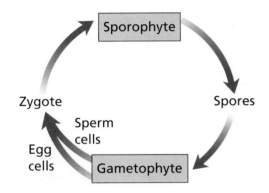

A Plants spend part of their lives producing spores.

B Plants spend part of their lives producing sperm and egg cells.

C A zygote develops into the spore-producing stage of the plant.

D all of the above   **S 7.2.a**

2. You examine plant cells under a microscope and notice many green round bodies within the cells. The green structures are most likely involved in

A directing the cell's functions.

B photosynthesis.

C storing food and water.

D making proteins.   **S 7.1.d**

3. Which statement below best explains why mosses and liverworts cannot grow tall?

A They have no rootlike structures.

B Taller plants in their surroundings release chemicals that slow down their growth.

C They cannot take in enough oxygen from their surroundings.

D They do not have true vascular tissue.   **S 7.5.a**

4. The diagram below shows the parts of a flower. In which flower part is pollen produced?

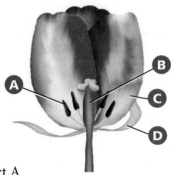

A part A

B part B

C part C

D part D   **S 7.5.f**

5. Which would a student expect to find when examining a dicot?

A one cotyledon

B flower parts in multiples of threes

C stems with bundles of vascular tissue arranged in a ring

D leaves with parallel veins   **S 7.5.a**

6. Which of the following statements is true about gymnosperms and angiosperms?

A Both gymnosperms and angiosperms produce flowers.

B Gymnosperms produce flowers, while angiosperms produce cones.

C Most gymnosperms have broad leaves, while angiosperms do not.

D Angiosperm seeds are enclosed within fruits, while gymnosperm seeds are not.   **S 7.2.a**

Apply the
BIG Idea

7. Describe three adaptations that plants have for living on land. Explain why each adaptation is important for a plant to survive on land.   **S 7.5.a**

Structure and Function of Invertebrates

S 7.2 A typical cell of any organism contains genetic instructions that specify its traits. Those traits may be modified by environmental influences. As a basis for understanding this concept:

a. Students know the differences between the life cycles and reproduction methods of sexual and asexual organisms.

S 7.3 Biological evolution accounts for the diversity of species developed through gradual processes over many generations. As a basis for understanding this concept:

d. Students know how to construct a simple branching diagram to classify living groups of organisms by shared derived characteristics and how to expand the diagram to include fossil organisms.

S 7.5 The anatomy and physiology of plants and animals illustrate the complementary nature of structure and function. As a basis for understanding this concept:

a. Students know plants and animals have levels of organization for structure and function, including cells, tissues, organs, organ systems, and the whole organism.

b. Students know organ systems function because of the contributions of individual organs, tissues, and cells. The failure of any part can affect the entire system.

This Asian weevil uses its front ▶ legs to court females.

Focus on the
BIG Idea

S 7.5.a

What major functions do animals' bodies perform?

Check What You Know

On a walk through the park, you stop to look closely at the leaves of a plant. You see an insect laying eggs. The eggs are the result of sexual reproduction. The cells in each insect egg contain many genes. Where do these genes come from? Explain your answer.

Build Science Vocabulary

The images shown here represent some of the key terms in this chapter. You can use this vocabulary skill to help you understand the meaning of some key terms in this chapter.

Vocabulary Skill

Use Clues to Determine Meaning

In this textbook, important new words, or key terms, first appear in dark type with a yellow highlight. The dark type and yellow highlight are clues that the meanings, or definitions, of these words are given in the text. Sometimes the meaning is in the same sentence as the key term. Other times, you need to look at several sentences to understand the key term's meaning completely. Look at the example below.

> What a polyp is → The animals called cnidarians have two different body plans. One form looks something like a vase. The vase-shaped body plan is called a **polyp.** A polyp's mouth opens at the top and its tentacles spread out from around the mouth. ← Additional information about a polyp

Apply It!

1. In your own words, what is the meaning of *polyp*?
2. What sentence contains the definition of *polyp*?
3. What other clues help you understand the meaning of *polyp*?

echinoderms

gastropod

arthropod

bilateral symmetry

cnidarians

Build Science Vocabulary
Online
Visit: PHSchool.com
Web Code: cvj-3110

How to Read Science

Take Notes

When you take notes, you write the important ideas from the textbook in shortened form. See the sample notes below, which are notes on the beginning of Section 1 in this chapter.

- Use a red or blue heading as the title of your notes.
- In the left column, write questions about the text that follows the heading. The questions should ask for important information.
- Write the answers in the right column.
- Write a summary statement that expresses the main idea of the information under the heading.

Questions	Notes: Structure of Animals
What *do anatomy* and *physiology* mean?	Anatomy—organism's structure Physiology—function in organisms
How are animal cells organized?	Into tissues, organs, organ systems
What are tissues, organs, and organ systems?	Tissues—similar cells doing similar functions Organ—group of tissues doing complex function Organ system—group of structures that perform broadest function
	<u>Summary Statement:</u> In most animals, cells are organized into tissues, organs, and organ systems.

Apply It!

In your notebook, complete the notes for Section 1. Then take notes on Section 2.

S 7.2.a

Going Through Changes

Most of the animals you will read about in this chapter change form during their development. In this investigation, you will observe firsthand how mealworms change as they develop.

Your Goal

To observe mealworm development and how different conditions affect that development

To complete this investigation, you must

- compare mealworm development under two different conditions
- record your mealworm observations daily for several weeks
- describe the process of development that you observe
- draw conclusions about the effects of those conditions on development
- follow the safety guidelines in Appendix A

Plan It!

Find two containers, such as clean margarine tubs with lids, in which to keep the mealworms. Get some mealworm food, such as cornflakes, and a plastic spoon to transfer the food and count the mealworms. Choose two conditions, such as two different temperatures or food sources, and plan how to test the two conditions. Once you begin, record your daily observations in a data table, and sketch each stage of development.

What Is an Animal?

CALIFORNIA
Standards Focus

S 7.5.a Students know plants and animals have levels of organization for structure and function, including cells, tissues, organs, organ systems, and the whole organism.

- How are animal bodies typically organized?
- What are four major functions of animals?
- What is symmetry?
- How are animals classified?

Key Terms
- anatomy
- physiology
- bilateral symmetry
- radial symmetry
- vertebrate
- invertebrate
- phylum

Lab zone Standards **Warm-Up**

Is It an Animal?

1.  Carefully examine each of the organisms that your teacher gives you.
2. Decide which ones are animals. For each organism, write down the reasons for your decision. Wash your hands after handling each of the organisms.

Think It Over
Forming Operational Definitions
Use your notes about each organism to write a definition of "animal."

Your parents may have told you not to eat with your fingers, but they probably never worried that you'd eat with your feet! But animals called barnacles do just that.

A barnacle begins life as a many-legged speck that swims in the ocean. After a while, it settles its head down on a hard surface. Then it builds a hard cone around its body. To feed, the barnacle flicks its feathery feet in and out of the cone, as shown below. The feet trap tiny organisms that float in the water.

A barnacle may look like a rock, but it is actually an animal. Animals are many-celled organisms that typically obtain food by eating other organisms.

A barnacle feeding (inset) ▲ and many barnacles at rest (right)

Structure of Animals

An organism's structure is called its **anatomy.** In animals, as in all living things, the basic unit of anatomy is the cell. The cell is also the basic unit that carries out life processes, or functions. **Physiology** is the study of functions in organisms. 🔑 **The cells of most animals are organized into higher levels of structure, including tissues, organs, and organ systems.** A group of similar cells that perform a specific function is called a tissue. One type of tissue is bone tissue, a hard tissue that gives bones their strength.

Tissues may combine to form an organ, which is a group of several different tissues. For example, a frog's thigh bone is composed of bone tissue, nerve tissue, and blood. An organ performs a more complex function than each tissue could perform alone.

Groups of structures that perform the broadest functions of an animal are called organ systems. One example is the skeletal system of a frog shown in Figure 1. The skeletal system and the body's other organ systems together make up a whole organism. In this case, the organism is a frog.

Whole Organism
The skeletal system works with other organ systems to carry out all of the frog's life functions.

 Reading Checkpoint) **What is an organ?**

FIGURE 1
Levels of Organization
A frogs skeletal system has different levels of organization. **Interpreting Diagrams** *List the five levels of organization in order from smallest to largest.*

Organ System
Together, all of the bones form the skeletal system.

Organ
A group of different kinds of tissues make up an organ such as the thigh bone.

Tissue
Many bone cells make up bone tissue.

Cells
Cells are the basic unit of animal structure.

FIGURE 2
Obtaining Food
This tarantula uses its fangs
to kill a grasshopper.

For: Links on the animal kingdom
Visit: www.SciLinks.org
Web Code: scn-0211

FIGURE 3
Keeping Cool
This dog is keeping cool by getting
wet and panting.

Functions of Animals

All animals carry out the same basic physiological processes. **Some major functions of animals are obtaining food and oxygen, keeping internal conditions stable, moving, and reproducing.** Adaptations are structures or behaviors that allow animals to perform these functions.

In animals, anatomy is closely related to physiology. In other words, the structures of cells, tissues, organs, and organ systems are closely related to their functions. Think of the frog's skeletal system. Bones have a strong, tough structure. This structure functions to support the frog's body.

Obtaining Food and Oxygen An animal obtains food by eating other organisms. Animals may feed on plants, other animals, or a combination of plants and animals. They have adaptations that allow them to eat particular foods. For example, the tarantula in Figure 2 has fangs. Fangs are structures it uses to pierce other animals and suck up their juices.

Food provides animals with raw materials for growth and with energy for their bodies' activities, such as breathing and moving. Most animals take food into a cavity inside their bodies. Inside this cavity the food is digested, or broken down into substances that the animal's body can absorb and use.

To release energy from food, the body's cells need oxygen. Some animals, like birds, get oxygen from air. Others, like fish, get oxygen from water.

Keeping Conditions Stable Animals must maintain a stable environment within their bodies. If this balance is lost, the animal cannot survive for long. For example, cells that get too hot start to die. Therefore, animals in hot environments have adaptations to keep their bodies cool. During hot days, earthworms stay in moist soil, lizards crawl to shady places, and dogs pant.

Movement All animals move in some way at some point in their lives. Most animals move freely from place to place throughout their lives—for example, by swimming, walking, or hopping. Other animals, such as oysters and barnacles, move from place to place only during the earliest stage of their lives. After they find a good place to attach, these animals stay in one place.

Many animals have muscles and bones, which are structures that enable them to move. When muscles contract, or shorten, an animal's body moves. Many animals have internal skeletons. In these animals, muscles are attached to bones by structures called tendons. When the muscles contract, they pull on the bones. This pulling makes the bones move.

Reproduction Like all organisms, animals must reproduce. Most animals reproduce sexually. Sexual reproduction is the process by which a new organism develops from the joining of two sex cells—a male sperm cell and a female egg cell. The joining of an egg cell and a sperm cell is called fertilization. Sperm and egg cells carry information about the characteristics of the parents that produced them, such as size and color. New individuals resulting from sexual reproduction have a combination of characteristics from both parents.

Some animals can reproduce asexually as well as sexually. Asexual reproduction is the process by which a single organism produces a new organism identical to itself. For example, animals called sea anemones sometimes split down the middle, producing two identical organisms.

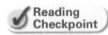 **Reading Checkpoint** What is asexual reproduction?

Lab zone Try This **Activity**

Get Moving

Design an animal with a new and different way of moving. Your design should help your animal obtain food or get out of danger.

1. Make and label a drawing that shows how the animal would move.
2. Using clay, aluminum cans, construction paper, pipe cleaners, and whatever other materials are available, create a three-dimensional model of your animal.
3. Compare your animal to those of other classmates. What are some similarities? What are some differences?

Making Models What features of your design help your animal obtain food or escape danger?

FIGURE 4
Owl Family
Baby owls are produced by sexual reproduction. **Classifying** *Which kind of reproduction involves fertilization?*

Bilateral Symmetry

Radial Symmetry

No Symmetry

FIGURE 5
Types of Symmetry
Most animals have either bilateral or radial symmetry. Most sponges, however, have no symmetry.

Symmetry

The functions an animal carries out are closely related to its body structure. One part of body structure is the presence or absence of symmetry. **Symmetry is a balanced arrangement of body parts that is characteristic of many animals.**

Animals have different types of symmetry. An animal has **bilateral symmetry** if there is just one line that divides it into halves that are mirror images. Fishes, such as the one in Figure 5, have bilateral symmetry. In contrast, an animal with **radial symmetry,** such as a sea star, has many lines of symmetry that divide it into two identical halves. A few animals, such as sponges, have no symmetry.

Animals With Radial Symmetry The external body parts of animals with radial symmetry are equally spaced around a central point, like spokes on a wheel. Animals with radial symmetry, such as sea urchins and jellyfishes, do not have distinct front or back ends. All animals with radial symmetry live in the water. Most of them do not move very fast.

Animals With Bilateral Symmetry In general, animals with bilateral symmetry, such as insects and frogs, are larger and more complex than those with radial symmetry. They have a front end that typically goes first as the animal moves along. These animals move more quickly and efficiently than most animals with radial symmetry. In addition, most animals with bilateral symmetry have sense organs in their front ends that pick up information about what is in front of them. A fish, for example, has eyes on its head.

 **Reading Checkpoint** **Where are the sense organs of an animal with bilateral symmetry typically found?**

Classification of Animals

Biologists have identified more than 1.5 million species, or distinct types, of animals. Classifying animals helps biologists make sense of this diversity. In Figure 6, you can see some of the largest groups of animals. The pattern of the diagram in Figure 6 shows how some of the major groups of animals may be related. For example, by looking at their positions on the tree, you can see that segmented worms are probably more closely related to arthropods than to sponges.

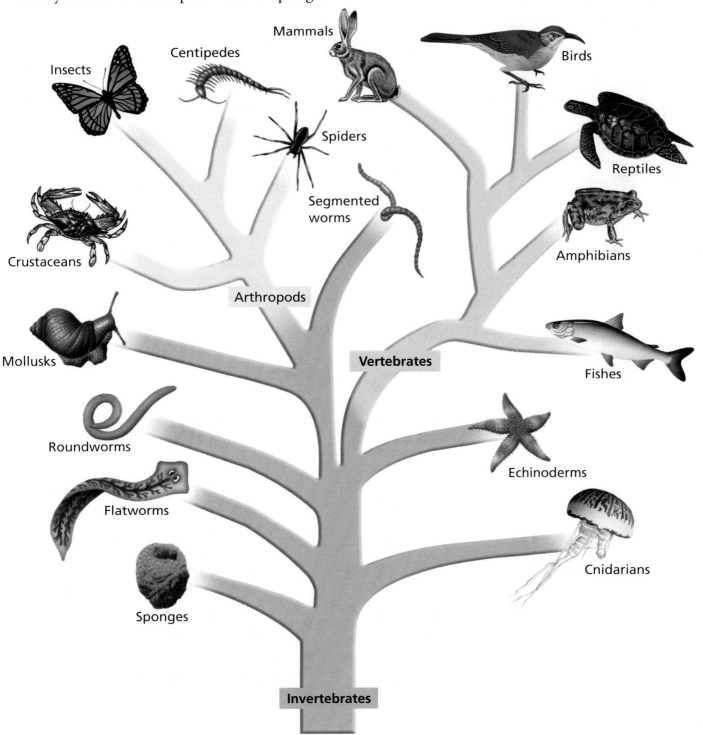

Insects

Centipedes

Mammals

Birds

Spiders

Reptiles

Crustaceans

Segmented worms

Amphibians

Arthropods

Mollusks

Vertebrates

Fishes

Roundworms

Echinoderms

Flatworms

Cnidarians

Sponges

Invertebrates

FIGURE 7
Discovering New Species
This biologist is surveying the leaves of rain forest plants, looking for new insect species.

Animals are classified according to how they are related to other animals. These relationships are determined by an animal's body structure, the way the animal develops, and its DNA. DNA is a chemical in cells that controls an organism's inherited characteristics. All **vertebrates,** or animals with a backbone, are classified in only one phylum. All the other animal phyla contain **invertebrates,** or animals without backbones. Of all the types of animals, about 97 percent are invertebrates!

Biologists such as the one in Figure 7 continue to find new animal species. New species are classified based on the kinds of evidence identified above. Biologists have classified animals into about 35 major groups, each of which is called a **phylum** (FY lum) (plural *phyla*).

Biologists think animal life has evolved, or changed over time. Biologists do not know the exact way in which animal evolution took place. Instead, they can only make inferences on the basis of the best evidence available. Biologists hypothesize that all animals arose from single-celled ancestors.

Section 1 Assessment

S 7.5.a, E-LA: Writing 7.2.0, Reading 7.2.0

Target Reading Skill Take Notes Use the notes you wrote about this section to help answer the questions below.

Reviewing Key Concepts

1. a. **Defining** What is the basic unit of structure and function in an animal?
   b. **Sequencing** Arrange in order from simplest to most complex structure: tissue, organ system, whole organism, cell, organ.
2. a. **Reviewing** What are five major functions of animals?
   b. **Identifying** Identify the two ways in which animals reproduce.
   c. **Relating Cause and Effect** Which type of reproduction produces offspring with a combination of characteristics of two parents? How does it produce the combination?

3. a. **Defining** What is symmetry?
   b. **Comparing and Contrasting** How are radial and bilateral symmetry different?
   c. **Applying Concepts** An animal runs rapidly forward to catch its prey. Which type of symmetry does the animal probably have? Explain.
4. a. **Defining** What is a vertebrate?
   b. **Classifying** How do biologists classify animals?
   c. **Interpreting Diagrams** According to Figure 6, are reptiles more closely related to mammals or to fishes? Explain your answer.

Writing in Science

Functional Description Write a few paragraphs about how a pet you have observed performs the basic functions of an animal.

Sponges and Cnidarians

CALIFORNIA
Standards Focus

S 7.2.a Students know the differences between the life cycles and reproduction methods of sexual and asexual organisms.

S 7.5.a Students know plants and animals have levels of organization for structure and function, including cells, tissues, organs, organ systems, and the whole organism.

- What are the main characteristics of sponges?
- What are the main characteristics of cnidarians?

Key Terms
- larva
- cnidarian
- polyp
- medusa

Lab zone **Standards Warm-Up**

How Do Natural and Synthetic Sponges Compare?

1. Examine a natural sponge, and then use a hand lens or a microscope to take a closer look. Look carefully at the holes in the sponge. Draw what you see through the lens.
2. ✂ Cut out a small piece of sponge and examine it with a hand lens. Draw what you see.
3. Repeat Steps 1 and 2 with a synthetic kitchen sponge.

Think It Over

Observing What are three ways a natural and a synthetic sponge are similar? What are three ways they are different?

Eagerly but carefully, you and the others in your group put on scuba gear as you prepare to dive into the ocean. Over the side of the boat you go. As you descend through the water, you see many kinds of fishes. When you get to the bottom, you notice other organisms, too. Some are as strange as creatures from a science fiction movie. A few of these unusual organisms may be invertebrate animals called sponges.

Sponges don't look or act like most animals you know. In fact, they are so different that for a long time, people thought that sponges were plants. Like plants, adult sponges stay in one place. But unlike most plants, sponges take food into their bodies.

◀ **Diver investigating a barrel sponge**

Sponges

Sponges live all over the world—mostly in oceans, but also in freshwater rivers and lakes. Adult sponges are attached to hard surfaces underwater. Water currents carry food and oxygen to them and take away their waste products. Water currents also play a role in their reproduction and help transport their young to new places to live.

Body Structure  **Sponges are invertebrates that usually have no body symmetry and never have tissues or organs.** Although sponges do not have tissues, they have cells that are specialized for different functions. For example, collar cells move water through a sponge and trap food.

Reproduction Sponges reproduce sexually, but they do not have separate sexes. A sponge produces both sperm cells and egg cells. Sperm cells are released into the water. They enter another sponge and fertilize its eggs. After fertilization, a larva develops. A **larva** (plural *larvae*) is an immature form of an animal that looks very different from an adult. Sponges also reproduce asexually.

✓ **Reading Checkpoint** What is the function of collar cells?

For: Structure of a Sponge activity
Visit: PHSchool.com
Web Code: cep-2013

FIGURE 8
Structure of a Sponge
Structures surrounding the central cavity of a sponge are adapted for different functions. **Interpreting Diagrams** *Which kind of cell in the sponge digests and distributes food?*

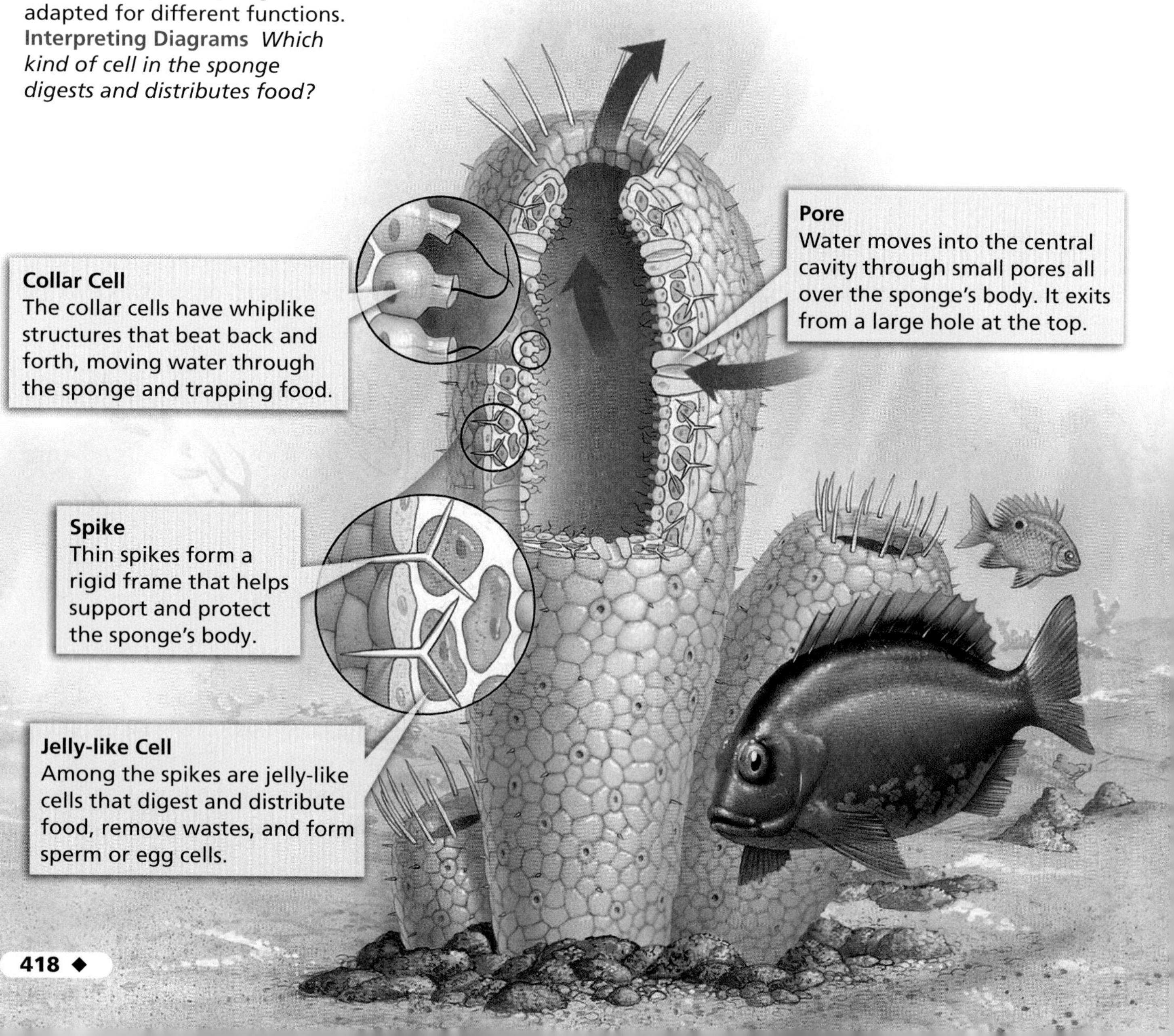

Collar Cell
The collar cells have whiplike structures that beat back and forth, moving water through the sponge and trapping food.

Spike
Thin spikes form a rigid frame that helps support and protect the sponge's body.

Jelly-like Cell
Among the spikes are jelly-like cells that digest and distribute food, remove wastes, and form sperm or egg cells.

Pore
Water moves into the central cavity through small pores all over the sponge's body. It exits from a large hole at the top.

Cnidarians

Some other animals you might notice on an underwater dive are jellyfishes, sea anemones, and the tiny corals that build coral reefs. These animals are **cnidarians** (ny DEHR ee unz), invertebrates that have stinging cells and take food into a central body cavity. 👄 **Cnidarians use stinging cells to capture food and defend themselves.**

Body Structure Cnidarians have two different body plans. One form looks something like a vase and the other form looks like an upside-down bowl. Both body plans have radial symmetry, a central hollow cavity, and tentacles with stinging cells.

The vase-shaped body plan is called a **polyp** (PAHL ip). The sea anemone you see in Figure 9 is a polyp. A polyp's mouth opens at the top and its tentacles spread out from around the mouth. Most polyps are adapted for a life attached to an underwater surface.

The bowl-shaped body plan is called a **medusa** (muh DOO suh). The jellyfish you see in Figure 9 is a medusa. A medusa, unlike a polyp, is adapted for a swimming life. Medusas have mouths that open downward and tentacles that trail down. Some cnidarians go through both a polyp stage and a medusa stage during their lives. Others are either polyps or medusas for their entire lives.

Lab zone Try This **Activity**

Hydra Doing?

1. 🐭 Put a drop of water containing hydras in a small unbreakable bowl or petri dish. Allow it to sit for about 15 minutes.

2. Use a hand lens to examine the hydras as they swim. Then gently touch the tentacles of a hydra with the end of a toothpick. Watch what happens.

3. Return the hydras to your teacher. Wash your hands.

Classifying Is a hydra a polyp or a medusa? Describe its method of movement.

FIGURE 9
Cnidarian Body Plans

Cnidarians have two basic body forms, the vase-shaped polyp and the bowl-shaped medusa. **Comparing and Contrasting** *Contrast the location of the mouth in the polyp and the medusa.*

Jellyfish ▶

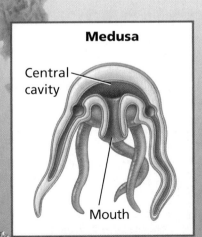

▼ **Sea anemone**

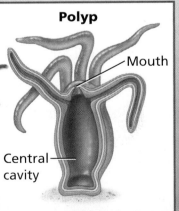

Polyp

Mouth

Central cavity

Medusa

Central cavity

Mouth

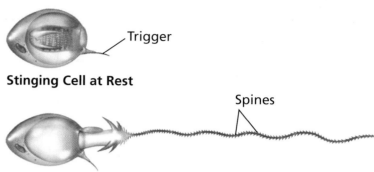

Stinging Cell at Rest

Trigger

Spines

Stinging Cell After Firing

FIGURE 10
Cnidarian Attack!
A stinging cell fires when its trigger brushes against prey, such as a fish.
Applying Concepts *What is the function of stinging cells?*

Obtaining Food Cnidarians use stinging cells to catch the animals they eat, which are called prey. You can see a stinging cell in Figure 10. The cell contains a threadlike structure, which has many sharp spines. When the stinging cell touches prey, this threadlike structure explodes out of the cell and into the prey. Some stinging cells also release venom into the prey. When the prey becomes helpless, the cnidarian uses its tentacles to pull the prey into its mouth. From there, the prey passes into a hollow central body cavity, where it is digested. Undigested food is expelled through the mouth.

Movement Unlike adult sponges, many cnidarians can move to escape danger and to obtain food. Some cnidarians have muscle-like tissues that allow them to move in different ways. Jellyfishes swim through the water, and hydras turn slow somersaults. A cnidarian's movements are directed by nerve cells that are spread out like a basketball net.

Reproduction Cnidarians reproduce both asexually and sexually. For polyps such as hydras, corals, and sea anemones, budding is the most common form of asexual reproduction. In budding, small new animals grow from the side of an adult animal. Asexual reproduction allows the numbers of polyps to increase rapidly in a short time.

Sexual reproduction in cnidarians occurs in a variety of ways. Some species of cnidarians have both sexes within one individual. In others, the sexes are separate individuals. Many cnidarians have life cycles, or a sequence of different stages of development. In Figure 11, you can see the life cycle of a moon jelly, which involves both asexual and sexual reproduction.

 **Reading Checkpoint** What is an example of asexual reproduction seen in polyps?

FIGURE 11
Life Cycle of a Jellyfish
The life cycle of a moon jelly has both a polyp and a medusa stage, and both asexual and sexual reproduction.

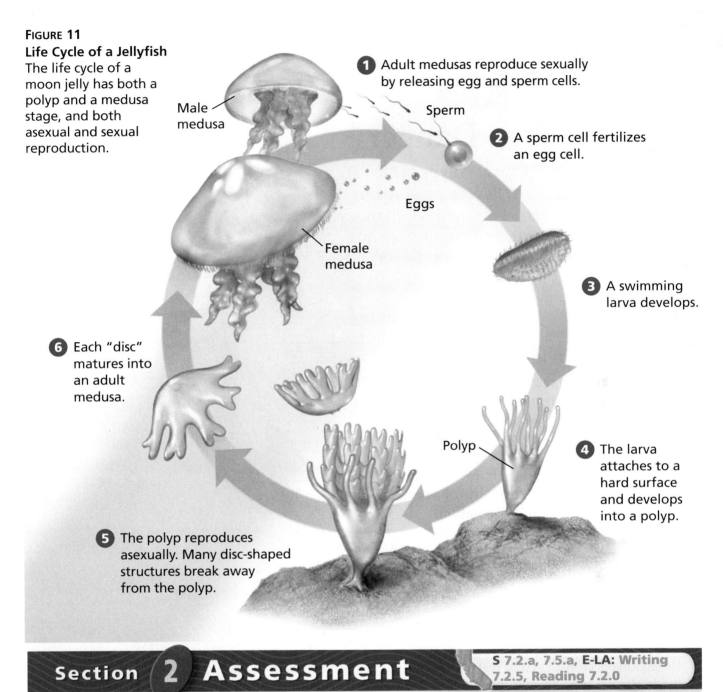

Male medusa

Female medusa

1 Adult medusas reproduce sexually by releasing egg and sperm cells.

Sperm

Eggs

2 A sperm cell fertilizes an egg cell.

3 A swimming larva develops.

4 The larva attaches to a hard surface and develops into a polyp.

Polyp

5 The polyp reproduces asexually. Many disc-shaped structures break away from the polyp.

6 Each "disc" matures into an adult medusa.

Section 2 Assessment

S 7.2.a, 7.5.a, E-LA: Writing 7.2.5, Reading 7.2.0

Target Reading Skill Take Notes Use the notes you wrote about this section to help answer the questions below.

Reviewing Key Concepts

1. a. **Describing** What are the characteristics of a sponge?
   b. **Explaining** How does a sponge reproduce sexually?
2. a. **Identifying** What is one type of cell that all cnidarians have?
   b. **Sequencing** What steps are involved in how a cnidarian obtains food?
   c. **Inferring** How might a cnidarian protect itself?

Writing in Science

Summary Write a summary, in your own words, of the life cycle of a moon jelly. Include brief descriptions of the polyp and medusa body plans.

S 7.3.e

Coral Reefs in Danger

Coral reefs are built by coral polyps, which are tiny, delicate cnidarians. Recreational divers can damage coral reefs. This damage changes the corals' environment, and corals may not have adaptations that enable them to survive the damage.

Diving supports local businesses

The Issues

What's the Harm in Diving?

More than 1.5 million recreational divers live in the United States. With so many divers it is hard to guarantee that no harm will occur to coral reefs. Divers can cause significant damage by standing on or even touching these fragile reefs. Harm to the reefs is even more likely to occur when divers collect coral for their own enjoyment or to sell for profit. You can see brightly colored coral from the sea in jewelry and in decorations.

Should Reefs Be Further Protected?

The United States government has passed laws making it illegal, under most circumstances, to remove coral from the sea. Because a few divers break these laws, some people want to ban diving altogether. However, many divers say it's unfair to ban diving just because of a few lawbreakers.

Many divers consider coral reefs the most exciting and beautiful places in the ocean to explore. As divers and other people visit and learn more about these delicate coral reefs, they increase others' awareness of them. Public awareness may be the best way to ensure that these rich environments are protected.

More Than a Diving Issue

Coral reefs are major tourist attractions that bring money and jobs to people in local communities. If diving were banned, local businesses would suffer significantly. Also, although divers can harm coral reefs, other human activities that result in ocean pollution, oil spills, and illegal fishing can also cause harm. In addition, natural events, such as tropical storms, changes in sea level, and changes in sea temperature, can also damage the fragile reefs.

Reefs house and protect many species of sea animals, including sponges, shrimp, sea turtles, and fishes.

What Would You Do?

1. Identify the Problem
In your own words, explain the controversy surrounding diving near coral reefs.

2. Analyze the Options
List the arguments on each side of the issue. Note the pros and cons. How well would each position protect the reefs? Who might be harmed or inconvenienced?

3. Find a Solution
Write a newspaper editorial stating your position on whether diving should be allowed near coral reefs. State your position and reasons clearly.

Go Online
PHSchool.com

For: More on coral reefs
Visit: PHSchool.com
Web Code: ceh-2010

Worms and Mollusks

S 7.2.a Students know the differences between the life cycles and reproduction methods of sexual and asexual organisms.

S 7.5.a Students know plants and animals have levels of organization for structure and function, including cells, tissues, organs, organ systems, and the whole organism.

- What are the main characteristics of worms?
- What are the main characteristics of each phylum of worms?
- What are the main characteristics of mollusks?
- What are the main groups of mollusks?

Key Terms

- brain
- parasite
- host
- anus
- closed circulatory system
- mollusk
- open circulatory system
- gill
- gastropod
- radula
- bivalve
- cephalopod

What Does a Flatworm Look Like?

1. Your teacher will give you a planarian, a kind of flatworm. Pick the worm up with the tip of a small paintbrush. Place it carefully in a container. Use a dropper to cover the planarian with spring water.

2. Observe the planarian with a hand lens for a few minutes. Describe how the planarian moves. Draw a picture of the planarian.

3. Return the planarian to your teacher, and wash your hands.

Think It Over

Observing How does a planarian differ from a sponge?

Worms in the soil and snails in an aquarium don't seem to have much in common. But worms and snails are both invertebrates with soft bodies. In fact, some mollusks even look like worms.

Characteristics of Worms

You might think that all worms are small, slimy, and wriggly. But many worms do not fit that description. Some worms are almost three meters long and are as thick as your arm. **All worms are invertebrates that have long, narrow bodies without legs.** Biologists classify worms into three major phyla—flatworms, roundworms, and segmented worms. Flatworms belong to the phylum Platyhelminthes (plat ee HEL minth eez). Roundworms belong to the phylum Nematoda. Segmented worms belong to the phylum Annelida.

FIGURE 12
Giant Earthworm
A giant Gippsland earthworm can grow to be more than 1 meter long. It is one of approximately 1,000 earthworm species found in Australia.

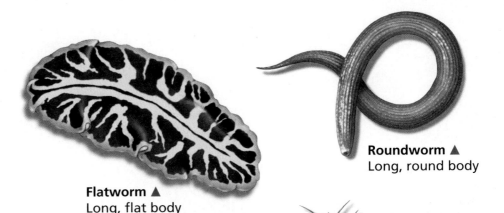

FIGURE 13
Three Phyla of Worms
The three major phyla of worms are flatworms, roundworms, and segmented worms.
Observing *How are the body shapes of these three types of worms similar?*

Flatworm ▲
Long, flat body

Roundworm ▲
Long, round body

Segmented Worm ▲
Long, round body made up of linked segments

Body Structure Unlike sponges or cnidarians, worms have bilateral symmetry. Therefore, they have head and tail ends. In addition, they all have tissues, organs, and body systems.

Nervous System Worms are the simplest organisms with a **brain,** which is a knot of nerve tissue located in the head end. The brain controls most of the animal's body functions. Sense organs pick up information from the environment. The brain interprets that information and directs the animal's response. For example, suppose an earthworm on the surface of the ground senses the vibrations of a footstep. The worm will respond by returning to its underground burrow. A worm can detect objects, food, mates, and predators quickly. It can respond quickly, too.

Reproduction Both sexual and asexual reproduction are found in the worm phyla. Some worms, such as the flatworm *Planaria,* reproduce asexually by dividing into two separate organisms. The two new organisms are genetically identical.

Most worm species can reproduce sexually. In many species, there are separate males and females, as in humans. In other species, each animal has both male and female sex organs. An animal with both male and female sex organs is called a hermaphrodite (hur MAF ruh dyt). Usually, two individual hermaphrodites mate and exchange sperm. It is rare for a hermaphrodite to fertilize its own eggs. When self-fertilization happens, it is still a form of sexual reproduction, even though there is only one parent.

 **What type of symmetry do worms have?**

FIGURE 14
Planarian
Planarians are free-living flatworms that live in ponds, streams, and oceans.
Comparing and Contrasting
How does a free-living organism differ from a parasite?

Flatworms

As you'd expect from their name, flatworms are flat. They include such organisms as tapeworms, planarians, and flukes. Although tapeworms can grow to be 10 to 12 meters long, some other flatworms are almost too small to be seen. **Flatworms are flat and as soft as jelly.**

Many flatworms are parasites. A **parasite** is an organism that lives inside or on another organism. The parasite takes its food from its **host,** the organism in or on which it lives. Parasites may rob their hosts of food and make them weak. They may injure the host's tissues or organs, but they rarely kill their host. All tapeworms and flukes are parasites.

In contrast, some flatworms are free-living. A free-living organism does not live in or on other organisms. Free-living flatworms may glide over the rocks in ponds, slide over damp soil, or swim slowly through the ocean like ruffled, brightly patterned leaves.

Planarians Planarians are free-living flatworms. Planarians are scavengers—they feed on dead or decaying material. But they are also predators. A predator is an animal that captures another animal for food. Planarians will attack any animal smaller than they are. A planarian feeds like a vacuum cleaner. The planarian glides onto its food and inserts a feeding tube into it. Digestive juices flow out of the planarian and into the food. These juices begin to break down the food while it is still outside the worm's body. Then the planarian sucks up the partly digested bits. Digestion is completed within a cavity inside the planarian. Undigested food exits through the feeding tube.

Go Online
PHSchool.com

For: More on worms
Visit: PHSchool.com
Web Code: ced-2014

If you look at the head of the planarian shown in Figure 14, you can see two dots. These dots are called eyespots. The eyespots can detect light but cannot see a detailed image as human eyes can. A planarian's head also has cells that pick up odors. Planarians rely mainly on smell, not light, to locate food.

Tapeworms Tapeworms are one kind of parasitic flatworm. The structure of a tapeworm's body is adapted to the function of absorbing food from the host's digestive system. Some kinds of tapeworms can live in human hosts. Many tapeworms live in more than one host during their lifetime. Figure 15 shows the life cycle of the dog tapeworm. This tapeworm has two different hosts—a dog and a rabbit.

 **Reading Checkpoint** How does a scavenger obtain food?

FIGURE 15
Life Cycle of a Dog Tapeworm
The tapeworm is a parasite that lives in more than one host during its life cycle.

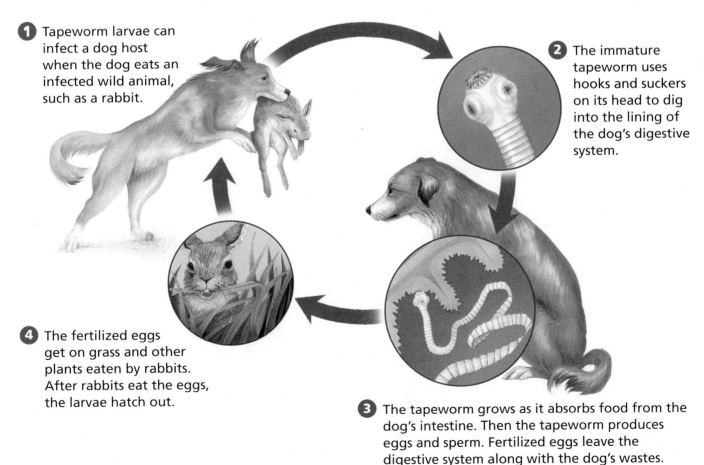

1. Tapeworm larvae can infect a dog host when the dog eats an infected wild animal, such as a rabbit.

2. The immature tapeworm uses hooks and suckers on its head to dig into the lining of the dog's digestive system.

4. The fertilized eggs get on grass and other plants eaten by rabbits. After rabbits eat the eggs, the larvae hatch out.

3. The tapeworm grows as it absorbs food from the dog's intestine. Then the tapeworm produces eggs and sperm. Fertilized eggs leave the digestive system along with the dog's wastes.

FIGURE 16
A Roundworm
The transparent body of this roundworm has been stained for better viewing under a microscope.

Roundworms

The next time you walk along a beach, consider that about a million roundworms live in each square meter of damp sand. Roundworms can live in nearly any moist environment—including forest soils, Antarctic sands, and pools of super-hot water. Most roundworms are tiny and difficult to see, but they may be the most abundant animals on Earth. Some species are free-living and some are parasites.

Unlike flatworms, roundworms have cylindrical bodies. They look like tiny strands of cooked spaghetti that are pointed at each end.  **Unlike cnidarians or flatworms, roundworms have a digestive system that is like a tube, open at both ends.** Food travels in one direction through the roundworm's digestive system. Food enters at the animal's mouth, and wastes exit through an opening, called the **anus,** at the far end of the tube.

The structure of a one-way digestive system is efficient. It is something like an assembly line, with a different part of the digestive function happening at each place along the line. Digestion happens in orderly stages. First, food is broken down by digestive juices. Then the digested food is absorbed into the animal's body. Finally, wastes are eliminated. This type of digestive system enables the animal's body to absorb a large amount of the needed substances in foods.

Reading Checkpoint   What are the openings at opposite ends of a roundworm's digestive tube called?

Math: Algebra and Functions 7.1.5

Math ▶ Analyzing Data

Roundworm Numbers

Biologists counted all the roundworms living in a plot of soil. Then they calculated the percentages that live in different centimeter depths of soil. Their results are graphed to the right.

1. **Reading Graphs** Where in the soil was the largest percentage of roundworms found?

2. **Calculating** What is the total percentage of roundworms found in the first 3-cm depth of soil?

3. **Drawing Conclusions** What is the relationship between the depth of the soil and the abundance of roundworms in the soil?

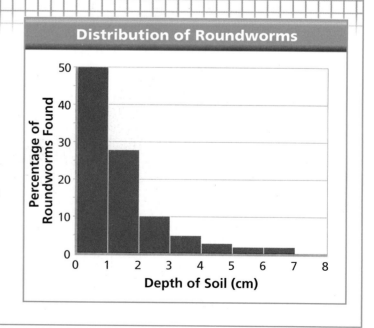

Segmented Worms

If you have ever dug in a garden, you have probably seen earthworms wriggling through the moist soil. Earthworms are segmented worms. So are leeches and some sea-floor worms.

Body Structure When you look at an earthworm, you see a body made up of a series of rings separated by grooves, something like a vacuum cleaner hose. ⬬ **Earthworms and other segmented worms have bodies made up of many linked sections called segments.** On the outside, the segments look nearly identical, as you can see in Figure 17. On the inside, some organs are repeated in most segments. For example, each segment has tubes that remove wastes. Other organs, however, such as the earthworm's reproductive organs, are found only in certain segments.

Segmented worms have well-developed organ systems. For example, segmented worms have a nervous system that includes a brain and a nerve cord that runs the length of the worm's body. Like roundworms, segmented worms have a one-way digestive system with two openings.

Circulatory System Segmented worms have a closed circulatory system. In a **closed circulatory system,** blood moves only within a connected network of tubes called blood vessels. In contrast, some animals, such as snails and lobsters, have an open circulatory system in which blood leaves the blood vessels and sloshes around inside the body. In both open and closed circulatory systems, blood carries out the physiological process of bringing oxygen and food to cells. But a closed circulatory system can move blood around an animal's body much more quickly than an open circulatory system can.

FIGURE 17
Structure of an Earthworm
An earthworm's body is divided into more than 100 segments. Some organs are repeated in most of those segments. Other organs exist in only a few segments.
Interpreting Diagrams *Name an example of a body system that runs through all of the worm's segments.*

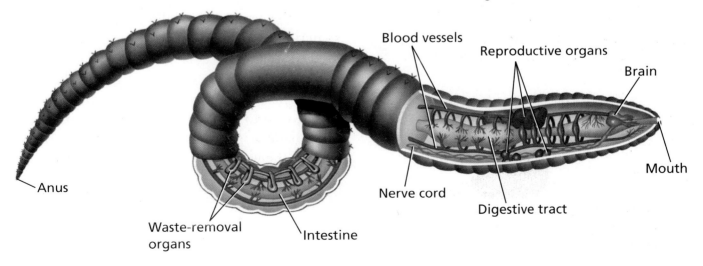

Blood vessels

Reproductive organs

Brain

Mouth

Anus

Nerve cord

Digestive tract

Waste-removal organs

Intestine

FIGURE 18
Comparing Mollusks

Although they don't look much alike at first, a snail, a clam, and a squid have the same basic body structures.

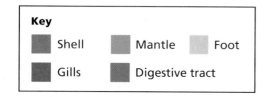

Key

■	Shell	■	Mantle	▪	Foot
■	Gills	■	Digestive tract		

Snail

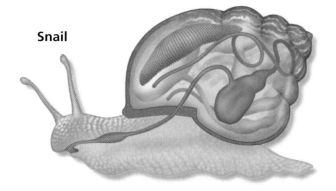

Clam

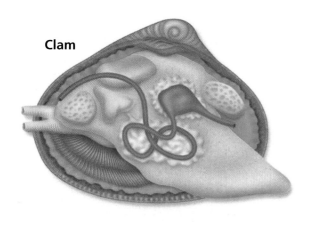

Squid

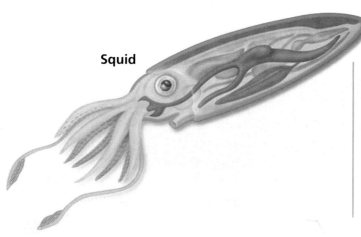

Characteristics of Mollusks

Clams, oysters, and scallops are all mollusks (phylum Mollusca). Snails and squids are mollusks, too. **Mollusks** are invertebrates with soft, unsegmented bodies that are often protected by a hard outer shell. All mollusks have the same basic structure. 🔹 **In addition to a soft body often covered by a shell, a mollusk has a thin layer of tissue called a mantle that covers its internal organs, and an organ called a foot.** In many mollusks, the mantle produces the hard shell. Depending on the type of mollusk, the foot has different functions—crawling, digging, or catching prey.

Body Structure Like segmented worms, mollusks have bilateral symmetry and a digestive system with two openings. However, unlike segmented worms, the body parts of mollusks are not usually repeated. Instead, the internal organs are located together in one area, as shown in Figure 18.

Circulatory System Most groups of mollusks have an **open circulatory system,** in which the blood is not always inside blood vessels. The heart pumps blood into a short vessel that opens into the body spaces containing the internal organs. The blood sloshes over the organs and returns eventually to the heart.

Obtaining Oxygen Most mollusks that live in water have **gills,** organs that remove oxygen from the water. The gills have tiny, hairlike structures called cilia and a rich supply of blood vessels. The cilia move back and forth, making water flow over the gills. The gills remove the oxygen from the water and the oxygen moves into the blood. At the same time, carbon dioxide, a waste gas, moves out of the blood and into the water.

 **Reading Checkpoint** Which organs of a mollusk obtain oxygen from water?

Diversity of Mollusks

Biologists classify mollusks into groups based on their physical characteristics. These characteristics include the presence of a shell, the type of foot, and the type of nervous system. 🔑 **The three major groups of mollusks are gastropods, bivalves, and cephalopods.**

Gastropods The **gastropods** include snails and slugs. Gastropods have a single shell or no shell at all. Some gastropods are herbivores, animals that eat only plants. Some are scavengers that eat decaying material. Still others are carnivores, animals that eat only other animals. No matter what food they eat, gastropods use an organ called a radula to obtain food. A **radula** (RAJ oo luh) is a flexible organ with tiny teeth.

A gastropod usually moves by creeping along on a broad foot. The foot may ooze a carpet of slippery mucus. The mucus makes it easier for a gastropod to move.

Bivalves Bivalves include oysters, clams, scallops, and mussels. **Bivalves** are mollusks that have two shells held together by hinges and strong muscles. Unlike gastropods, bivalves do not have radulas. Instead, most bivalves are filter feeders that strain tiny organisms from water. Most bivalves are herbivores, animals that eat plants.

Most adult bivalves don't move quickly. They stay in one place or use their foot to move very slowly.

Reading Checkpoint How do bivalves obtain food?

Lab zone Skills **Activity**

Classifying
While wading in a stream, you step on a small animal with a hard covering. As you examine the animal, you discover that it has a soft body inside its shell. It may be a mollusk. What characteristics would you look for to classify the animal into a group of mollusks?

FIGURE 19
The Radula of a Snail
Gastropods such as this land snail have an organ called a radula, which tears and scrapes up food. **Applying Concepts** *How is the structure of a radula related to its function?*

Mouth

Radula

Radula teeth

◆ **431**

FIGURE 20
A Cephalopod
An octopus is a cephalopod. In cephalopods, the foot forms tentacles.

Eye

Suckers

Tentacles

Video Field Trip
Discovery Channel School
Mollusks, Arthropods, and Echinoderms

Cephalopods Octopuses, squids, nautiluses, and cuttle-fishes are cephalopods. A **cephalopod** (SEF uh luh pahd) is an ocean-dwelling mollusk whose foot forms tentacles around its mouth. Some cephalopods lack shells. Cephalopods are the only mollusks with a closed circulatory system.

Cephalopods are carnivores. They use their muscular tentacles to capture prey. Large eyes and a complex nervous system also help them capture prey. Cephalopods have large brains and can remember things they have learned.

Section 3 Assessment

S 7.2.a, 7.5.a,
E-LA: Reading 7.1.4

Vocabulary Skill Use Clues to Determine Meaning Reread the paragraph on parasites, under Flatworms. What does *parasite* mean? What clues help you understand the meaning?

Reviewing Key Concepts

1. **a. Reviewing** What are the general characteristics of worms?
   b. Identifying In what two ways do worms reproduce?
   c. Explaining In hermaphrodite worms, how does fertilization usually take place?
2. **a. Listing** List the main phyla of worms.
   b. Comparing and Contrasting Contrast the ways the major worm phyla digest food.
   c. Applying Concepts A worm takes in food at its front end and expels undigested wastes from the other end. Can the worm be a flatworm? Explain.

3. **a. Listing** List the characteristics of a mollusk.
   b. Explaining How is a mollusk's mantle related to its shell?
4. **a. Identifying** What are three groups of mollusks?
   b. Classifying What are the characteristics of the three groups of mollusks?
   c. Comparing and Contrasting Contrast the functions of the foot in the three groups.

Lab zone **At-Home Activity**

Edible Mollusks Visit a supermarket with a family member and identify any mollusks that are being sold as food. Identify the parts of the mollusks that are used for food.

Earthworm Responses

S 7.5.b, 7.7.e

Problem

Do earthworms prefer dry or moist conditions?
Do they prefer light or dark conditions?

Skills Focus

observing, interpreting data

Materials

- plastic dropper • water • cardboard
- clock or watch • paper towels • flashlight
- 2 earthworms • storage container • tray

Procedure

1. Which environment do you think earthworms prefer—dry or moist? Record your hypothesis in your notebook.

2. Use the dropper to sprinkle water on the worms. Keep the worms moist at all times.

3. Fold a dry paper towel and place it on the bottom of one side of your tray. Fold a moistened paper towel and place it on the other side.

4. Moisten your hands. Then place the earthworms in the center of the tray. Make sure that half of each earthworm's body rests on the moist paper towel and half rests on the dry towel. Handle the worms gently.

5. Cover the tray with the piece of cardboard. After five minutes, remove the cardboard and observe whether the worms are on the moist or dry surface. Record your observations.

6. Repeat Steps 4 and 5.

7. Return the earthworms to their storage container. Moisten the earthworms with water.

8. Which do you think earthworms prefer— strong light or darkness? Record your hypothesis in your notebook.

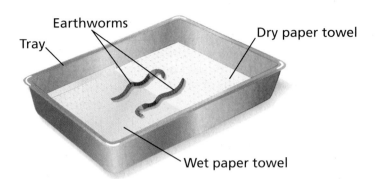

Earthworms

Tray

Dry paper towel

Wet paper towel

9. Cover the whole surface of the tray with a moistened paper towel.

10. Place the earthworms in the center of the tray. Cover half of the tray with cardboard. Shine a flashlight onto the other half.

11. After five minutes, note the locations of the worms. Record your observations.

12. Repeat Steps 10 and 11.

13. Moisten the earthworms and put them in the location designated by your teacher. Wash your hands after handling the worms.

Analyze and Conclude

1. **Observing** How did the earthworms respond to moisture? How did they respond to darkness?

2. **Interpreting Data** What organ in the earthworms' bodies directed their responses? If that organ were damaged, how might the earthworm's response have been different?

3. **Communicating** Write a description of how an earthworm moves. In your description, identify the type of tissue that enables an animal to move.

Design an Experiment

Do earthworms prefer a smooth or rough surface? Write your hypothesis. Then design an experiment to answer the question. *Obtain your teacher's permission before carrying out your investigation.*

Arthropods

CALIFORNIA
Standards Focus

S 7.2.a Students know the differences between the life cycles and reproduction methods of sexual and asexual organisms.

S 7.5.b Students know organ systems function because of the contributions of individual organs, tissues, and cells. The failure of any part can affect the entire system.

- What are the general characteristics of arthropods?
- What are the distinguishing structures of crustaceans, arachnids, centipedes and millipedes, and insects?

Key Terms

- arthropod
- exoskeleton
- molting
- antenna
- crustacean
- metamorphosis
- arachnid
- abdomen
- insect
- thorax
- complete metamorphosis
- pupa
- gradual metamorphosis
- nymph

Lab zone Standards **Warm-Up**

Will It Bend and Move?

1. Have a partner roll a piece of cardboard around your arm to form a tube that covers your elbow. Your partner should put three pieces of tape around the tube to hold it closed—one at each end and one in the middle.

2. With the tube in place, try to write your name on a piece of paper. Then try to scratch your head.

3. Keep the tube on your arm for 10 minutes. Observe how the tube affects your ability to do things.

Think It Over

Inferring Insects and many other animals have rigid skeletons on the outside of their bodies. Why do their skeletons need joints?

At dusk near the edge of a meadow, a grasshopper leaps through the grass. Nearby, a hungry spider waits in its web. The grasshopper leaps into the web. It's caught! As the grasshopper struggles to free itself, the spider rushes toward it. Quickly, the spider wraps the grasshopper in silk. The grasshopper cannot escape. Soon it will become a tasty meal for the spider.

The spider and grasshopper are both **arthropods,** or members of the arthropod phylum (phylum Arthropoda). Animals such as crabs, lobsters, centipedes, and scorpions are also arthropods.

FIGURE 21
A Spider at Work
This spider wraps its prey, a grasshopper, in silk. Both animals are arthropods.

FIGURE 22
Arthropod Characteristics
This Sally lightfoot crab shows the tough exoskeleton and the jointed appendages that are characteristic of arthropods.

Characteristics of Arthropods

All arthropods share specific characteristics. 🔑 **Arthropods are invertebrates that have an external skeleton, a segmented body, and jointed attachments called appendages.** Wings, mouthparts, and legs are all appendages. Jointed appendages are such a distinctive characteristic that arthropods are named for it. *Arthros* means "joint" in Greek, and *podos* means "foot" or "leg." Arthropods are classified into four major groups. 🔑 **The major groups of arthropods include crustaceans, arachnids, centipedes and millipedes, and insects.**

Arthropods share some characteristics with many other animals, too. They have bilateral symmetry, an open circulatory system, and a digestive system with two openings. In addition, most arthropods reproduce sexually.

Outer Skeleton Arthropods have a waxy, waterproof covering called an **exoskeleton,** or outer skeleton. It protects the animal and helps prevent evaporation of water. Water animals are surrounded by water, but land animals need a way to keep from drying out. Arthropods may have been the first animals to live on land. Their exoskeletons probably enabled them to do this because they keep the arthropods from drying out.

As an arthropod grows larger, its exoskeleton cannot expand. The growing arthropod is trapped within its exoskeleton, like a knight in armor that is too small. Arthropods solve this problem by occasionally shedding their exoskeletons and growing new ones that are larger. The process of shedding an outgrown exoskeleton is called **molting.** After an arthropod has molted, its new skeleton is soft for a time. During that time, the arthropod has less protection from danger than it does after its new skeleton has hardened.

 **What is an exoskeleton?**

FIGURE 23
A Molting Cicada
This cicada has just molted. You can see its old exoskeleton hanging on the leaf just below it.
Applying Concepts *Why must arthropods molt?*

Go Online
SciLinks NSTA

For: Links on arthropods
Visit: www.SciLinks.org
Web Code: scn-0222

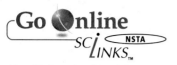

Segmented Body The bodies of arthropods are segmented. A segmented body plan is easiest to see in centipedes and millipedes, which have bodies made up of many identical-looking segments. You can also see segments on the tails of shrimp and lobsters. In some groups of arthropods, several body segments become joined into distinct sections. An arthropod may have up to three sections—a head, a midsection, and a hind section.

Jointed Appendages Just as your fingers are appendages attached to your palms, many arthropods have jointed appendages attached to their bodies. The joints in the appendages give the animal flexibility and enable it to move. Arthropod appendages tend to be highly specialized tools used for moving, obtaining food, reproducing, and sensing the environment. For example, arthropods use legs to walk and wings to fly. In addition, most arthropods have appendages called antennae (singular *antenna*). An **antenna** is an appendage attached to the head that contains sense organs.

Reading Checkpoint What is the function of an antenna?

Diversity of Arthropods

Scientists have identified more species of arthropods—over one million—than all other species of animals combined! There are probably many others that have not been discovered. Look at Figure 24 to compare some characteristics of the four major groups of arthropods.

FIGURE 24
Members of the largest arthropod groups differ in several characteristics.
Interpreting Tables *Which group of arthropods has no antennae?*

Comparisons of the Largest Arthropod Groups

Characteristic	Crustaceans	Arachnids	Centipedes and Millipedes	Insects
Number of body sections	2 or 3	2	2	3
Pairs of legs	5 or more	4	Many	3
Pairs of antennae	2	None	1	1

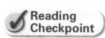

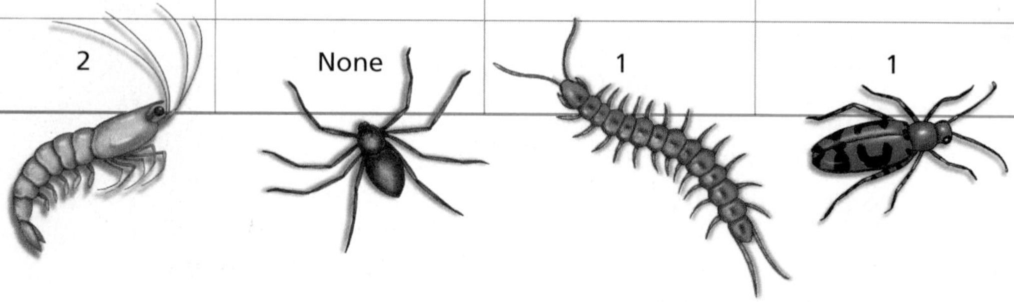

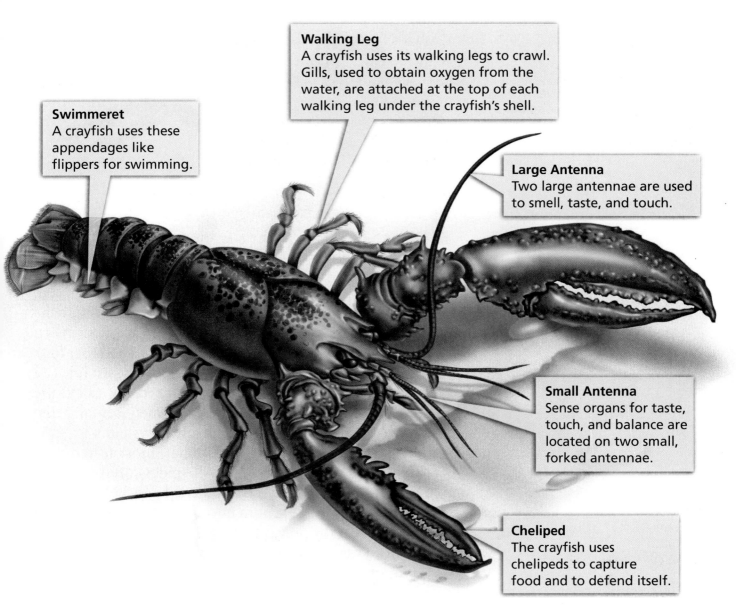

Swimmeret
A crayfish uses these appendages like flippers for swimming.

Walking Leg
A crayfish uses its walking legs to crawl. Gills, used to obtain oxygen from the water, are attached at the top of each walking leg under the crayfish's shell.

Large Antenna
Two large antennae are used to smell, taste, and touch.

Small Antenna
Sense organs for taste, touch, and balance are located on two small, forked antennae.

Cheliped
The crayfish uses chelipeds to capture food and to defend itself.

Crustaceans Crayfish, lobsters, shrimp, and crabs are all examples of **crustaceans** (krus TAY shunz). ⬤ **A crustacean is an arthropod that has two or three body sections, five or more pairs of legs, and two pairs of antennae.** Each crustacean body segment has a pair of legs or another appendage attached to it. The various types of appendages function differently, as you can see in Figure 25.

Crustaceans live in watery environments. Therefore, most use gills to obtain oxygen. The gills are protected by the crustacean's exoskeleton. Water containing oxygen reaches the gills as the crustacean moves along.

Most crustaceans, such as crabs and shrimp, begin their lives as tiny swimming larvae. Crustacean larvae develop into adults by metamorphosis. **Metamorphosis** (met uh MAWR fuh sis) is a process in which an animal's body undergoes dramatic changes in form during its lifetime.

FIGURE 25
Crayfish Appendages
A crayfish's appendages are as varied as the tools on a Swiss army knife. The appendages are adapted for different functions.
Interpreting Diagrams *What functions do the chelipeds serve?*

Arachnids Spiders, mites, ticks, and scorpions are the **arachnids** (uh RAK nidz) that people most often meet. 🔑 **Arachnids are arthropods with two body sections, four pairs of legs, and no antennae.** Their first body section is a combined head and midsection. The hind section, called the **abdomen,** is the other section. The abdomen contains the reproductive organs and part of the digestive system.

Spiders are probably the most familiar, most feared, and most fascinating kind of arachnid. All spiders are predators, and most of them eat insects. Spiders have hollow fangs through which they inject venom into their prey. Spider venom turns the tissues of the prey into mush. Later the spider uses its fangs like drinking straws, and sucks in the food.

In spite of what some people might think, spiders rarely bite people. When spiders do bite, their bites are often painful but rarely life-threatening. However, the bite of a brown recluse or a black widow may require hospital care.

Centipedes and Millipedes Centipedes and millipedes look something like earthworms. However, they are arthropods, not worms. 🔑 **Centipedes and millipedes are arthropods with two body sections and many pairs of legs.** The two body sections consist of a head with one pair of antennae, and a long abdomen with many segments.

Centipedes have one pair of legs attached to each segment. Some centipedes have more than 100 segments. In fact, the word *centipede* means "hundred feet." Millipedes, which may have more than 80 segments, have two pairs of legs on each segment. Though *millipede* means "thousand feet," millipedes don't have that many legs.

FIGURE 27
Centipede
Centipedes have many pairs of legs. **Interpreting Photographs**
How many pairs of legs does each segment of the centipede have?

 **Reading Checkpoint** **How many sections does an arachnid's body have?**

FIGURE 28

Structure of a Grasshopper
A grasshopper's body,
like that of every insect,
has three sections.

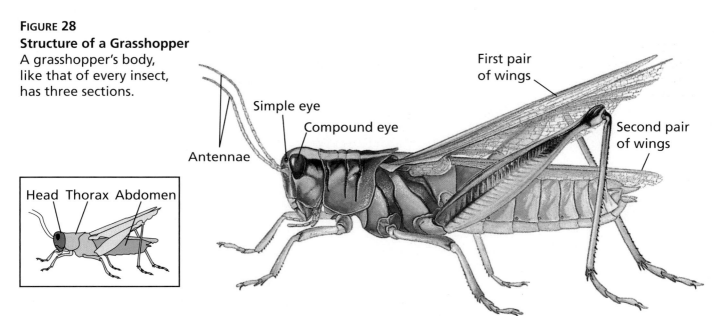

Characteristics of Insects

By far the most common of all the arthropods are the **insects.**
You can identify insects, like other arthropods, by counting
their body sections and legs. 🔑 **Insects are arthropods with
three body sections, six legs, one pair of antennae, and
usually one or two pairs of wings.** The three body sections are
the head, thorax, and abdomen, as you can see in Figure 28.

Head An insect's brain and most of its sense organs, such as the
eyes and antennae, are in its head. The brain, antennae, and eyes
are organs that are part of a well-developed nervous system. Each
organ, tissue, and cell in this system contributes to the function of
sensing the environment and directing body activities.

For example, insects usually have two large compound eyes,
which enable them to see their surroundings. These eyes contain
many lenses. Each lens is a structure that focuses light and forms
images. Compound eyes are especially keen at seeing movement.
Most insects also have simple eyes that can distinguish between
light and darkness.

Thorax An insect's midsection, or **thorax,** is the section to
which wings and legs are attached. Most insects can fly once
they are adults. Insects are the only invertebrates that can fly.

Abdomen Inside the abdomen are many of the insect's internal organs. Small holes on the outside of the abdomen lead to a
system of tubes inside the insect. These tubes allow air, which
contains oxygen, to enter the body. The oxygen in the air travels
directly to the insect's cells.

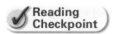 **Reading Checkpoint** What are the three sections of an insect's body?

Lab zone Skills **Activity**

Graphing
Use the data to make a
circle graph that shows the
percentage of total insect
species in each group. (See
the Skills Handbook.)

Insect Groups

Group	Number of Species
Ants, bees, and wasps	115,000
Beetles and weevils	350,000
Butterflies and moths	178,000
Flies and mosquitoes	110,000
Other insect groups	147,000

FIGURE 29
Insect Metamorphosis

Depending on the species, most insects develop into adults through complete metamorphosis or gradual metamorphosis.

1 Egg
Female fireflies lay their eggs in moist places. The eggs of fireflies glow in the dark.

2 Larva
The eggs hatch into larvae that feed on snails and slugs.

Complete Metamorphosis

4 Adult
When its development is complete, an adult firefly crawls out of its pupal case and unfurls its wings. Adult fireflies flash their light to attract mates.

3 Pupa
After a time, the firefly larva becomes a pupa. Inside the protective pupal case, wings, legs, and antennae form.

Insect Life Cycles

Insects hatch from eggs. They then develop through metamorphosis. 🔑 **Each insect species undergoes either complete metamorphosis or gradual metamorphosis.**

Complete Metamorphosis In Figure 29 you can see that an insect with **complete metamorphosis** has four different stages: egg, larva, pupa, and adult. Eggs hatch into larvae. The larvae, such as the caterpillars of butterflies, usually look something like worms. Larvae are specialized for eating and growing. After a time, a larva becomes a **pupa** (PYOO puh). Major changes in body structure are taking place in this stage, as the pupa becomes an adult insect. Beetles, butterflies, flies, and ants all undergo complete metamorphosis.

Gradual Metamorphosis In contrast, the second type of metamorphosis, called **gradual metamorphosis,** has no distinct larval stage. An egg hatches into a stage called a **nymph** (nimf), which usually looks like the adult insect without wings. A nymph may molt several times before becoming an adult. Grasshoppers, termites, cockroaches, and dragonflies go through gradual metamorphosis.

4 Adult
The adult grasshopper emerges from the final molt equipped with full-sized wings. Once its wings have hardened, the adult flies off to mate and begin the cycle again.

1 Egg
A female grasshopper uses the tip of her abdomen to jab holes in the soil where she lays her eggs.

Gradual Metamorphosis

2 Nymph
Eggs hatch into nymphs that look much like miniature adults, except that they have no wings, or only small ones.

3 Larger Nymph
A nymph feeds until its exoskeleton becomes too tight, and then it molts. The nymph molts four or five times before becoming an adult.

Section 4 Assessment

S 7.2.a, 7.5.b, E-LA: Reading 7.1.4

Vocabulary Skill Use Clues to Determine Meaning Find the Key Term *thorax* on page 439. What does *thorax* mean? What clues help you understand its meaning?

Reviewing Key Concepts

1. a. **Identifying** What are the characteristics of arthropods?
   b. **Explaining** What structure protects an arthropod's body from loss of water?
   c. **Relating Cause and Effect** Why does an insect's body need this protection?
2. a. **Listing** List the main groups of arthropods.
   b. **Interpreting Tables** Use Figure 24 to contrast the number of body sections in the major groups of arthropods.
   c. **Applying Concepts** In which section are most of an insect's sense organs located? What organ system are the sense organs a part of?

3. a. **Listing** List the stages of gradual metamorphosis and the stages of complete metamorphosis.
   b. **Interpreting Diagrams** Look at Figure 29. How are complete metamorphosis and gradual metamorphosis different?

Lab zone At-Home **Activity**

Bug Hunt Walk with a family member in your backyard or neighborhood. Search the undersides of leaves, under woodchips or rocks, and other likely places for insects. Show your family member what distinguishes an insect from other kinds of arthropods.

Invertebrates on Branches

S 7.3.d, 7.7.d

Problem

How can you construct a branching tree diagram to classify some invertebrates?

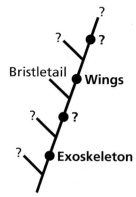

Bristletail — **Wings**

Exoskeleton

Common ancestor

Skills Focus

classifying, interpreting data

Materials

• index cards

Procedure

1. Review the explanation of a branching tree diagram in Chapter 7. Recall that in a branching tree diagram, the organism with none of the characteristics goes at the bottom of the tree. The organism with the greatest number of derived characteristics goes at the top.

2. Examine the incomplete branching tree diagram. Copy it in your notebook.

3. The table below lists characteristics of five invertebrates. Make a card for each animal that lists the characteristics of that animal. Then arrange the cards in order, beginning with the animal that has none of the characteristics and ending with the animal that has all the characteristics.

4. Use the data in the table and your cards to complete the branching tree diagram. Put the missing animals on their correct branches. Identify the missing characteristics.

5. You discover a fossil scorpion similar to the one in the photograph. The fossil animal has an exoskeleton but does not have three body sections. Mark on your copy of the branching tree diagram where the scorpion should go.

Analyze and Conclude

1. **Classifying** Which animal goes at the top of the diagram? How many of the listed characteristics does the animal have?

2. **Interpreting Data** Except for the earthworm, all the animals in the table belong to the same phylum. To which phylum do these animals belong?

3. **Drawing Conclusions** Which animal in the table is most closely related to the fossil scorpion? Explain how you know this.

4. **Communicating** Which two animals on the diagram are most distantly related? Write a paragraph in which you identify the data on which you base your conclusion.

More to Explore

Do research to learn some of the characteristics that are used to classify insects into groups. Write a report about what you have learned.

Characteristics of Some Invertebrates				
Invertebrate	Three Body Sections	Wings Present	Tiny Scales on Wings	Exoskeleton
Bristletail	Yes	No	No	Yes
Earthworm	No	No	No	No
Butterfly	Yes	Yes	Yes	Yes
Mosquito	Yes	Yes	No	Yes
Tarantula	No	No	No	Yes

Echinoderms

S 7.2.a Students know the differences between the life cycles and reproduction methods of sexual and asexual organisms.

S 7.5.b Students know organ systems function because of the contributions of individual organs, tissues, and cells. The failure of any part can affect the entire system.

What are the main characteristics of echinoderms?

What are the major groups of echinoderms?

Key Terms
- echinoderm
- endoskeleton
- water vascular system
- tube feet

Lab zone Standards **Warm-Up**

How Do Sea Stars Hold On?

1. Use a plastic dropper and water to model how a sea star moves and clings to surfaces. Fill the dropper with water, and then squeeze out most of the water.

2. Squeeze the last drop of water onto the inside of your arm. Then, while squeezing the bulb, touch the tip of the dropper into the water drop. With the dropper tip against your skin, release the bulb.

3. Hold the dropper by the tube and lift it slowly, paying attention to what happens to your skin.

Think It Over

Predicting Besides moving and clinging to surfaces, what might sea stars use their suction structures for?

While exploring a rocky beach one day, you see what looks like a dill pickle at the bottom of a tide pool. You think it might be a plant or a rock covered with green slime. But as you look more closely, the pickle begins to crawl very slowly. This amazing creature is a sea cucumber, a relative of sea stars.

Characteristics of Echinoderms

Sea cucumbers, sea stars, sea urchins, and sand dollars are all **echinoderms** (ee KY noh durmz), members of the phylum Echinodermata. **Echinoderms are invertebrates with an internal skeleton and a system of fluid-filled tubes called a water vascular system.** All echinoderms live in salt water.

Body Structure The skin of most echinoderms is stretched over an internal skeleton, or **endoskeleton,** made of hardened plates. These plates support the animal and give it a bumpy texture. Adult echinoderms have a unique kind of radial symmetry in which the body parts, usually in multiples of five, are arranged like spokes on a wheel.

Movement The internal organ system of fluid-filled tubes in echinoderms is called the **water vascular system.** You can see a sea star's water vascular system in Figure 30. Portions of the tubes in this system can contract, or squeeze together, forcing water into structures called **tube feet.** This process is something like moving water around in a water balloon by squeezing different parts of the balloon.

The ends of tube feet are sticky. When filled with water, they act like small, sticky suction cups. The stickiness and suction enable the tube feet to grip the surface beneath the echinoderm. Most echinoderms use their tube feet to move along slowly and to capture food.

Reproduction and Life Cycle Almost all echinoderms are either male or female. Eggs are usually fertilized in the water, after a female releases her eggs and a male releases his sperm. The fertilized eggs develop into tiny, swimming larvae that look very different from the adults. The larvae eventually undergo metamorphosis and become adult echinoderms.

Reading Checkpoint What are the functions of an echinoderm's tube feet?

FIGURE 30
A Water Vascular System

Echinoderms, such as this sea star, have a water vascular system that helps them move and catch food. **Interpreting Diagrams** *Where does water enter the water vascular system?*

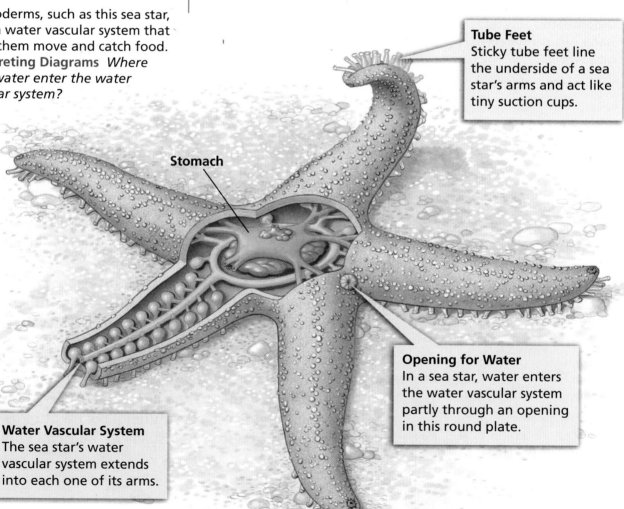

Stomach

Tube Feet
Sticky tube feet line the underside of a sea star's arms and act like tiny suction cups.

Opening for Water
In a sea star, water enters the water vascular system partly through an opening in this round plate.

Water Vascular System
The sea star's water vascular system extends into each one of its arms.

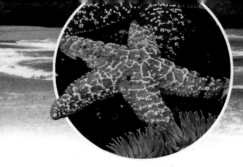

Sea Star

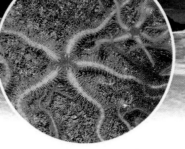

Brittle Star

Sea Urchin

Diversity of Echinoderms

🔑 **There are four major groups of echinoderms: sea stars, brittle stars, sea urchins, and sea cucumbers.** The members of these groups look quite different. They also have different ways of feeding and moving.

Sea stars are predators that eat mollusks, crabs, and even other echinoderms. Sea stars use their tube feet to move across the ocean floor. They also use their tube feet to capture prey. A sea star will grasp a clam with all five arms, and then pull the shells open. Then the sea star feeds on the clam's tissues.

A brittle star's arms are long and slender. To move, a brittle star waves its arms in a snakelike motion against the ocean floor. A brittle star uses its tube feet to catch food.

Sea urchins have no arms. Spines cover and protect their bodies, so they look something like a pincushion. To move, sea urchins use tube feet that extend out between the spines. They scrape and cut food with five toothlike structures.

Sea cucumbers look a little bit like the cucumbers you eat. With tube feet on their underside, sea cucumbers crawl along the ocean floor. They feed with a mouth surrounded by tentacles.

Sea Cucumber

FIGURE 31
Diversity of Echinoderms
Echinoderms are diverse in their appearance, but all have radial symmetry and are found in the ocean.

Section 5 Assessment

S 7.2.a, 7.5.b, E-LA: Writing 7.2.0, Reading 7.1.4

Vocabulary Skill Use Clues to Determine Meaning
Look at the definition of *endoskeleton* on page 443. What phrase in the sentence gives the meaning of *endoskeleton*?

🔑 **Reviewing Key Concepts**

1. a. **Reviewing** What characteristics do echinoderms have?
   b. **Summarizing** Explain how echinoderms reproduce.
   c. **Inferring** In echinoderms, could fertilization take place without water? Why or why not?
2. a. **Identifying** Identify the four major groups of echinoderms.
   b. **Comparing and Contrasting** Compare and contrast how sea stars and sea urchins feed.
   c. **Predicting** Would a sea star be able to eat clams without using its tube feet? Explain.

Writing in Science

Comparison Paragraph In a paragraph, compare and contrast how sea stars, brittle stars, and sea urchins move.

Study Guide

The BIG Idea The structures of animals' bodies enable them to obtain food and oxygen, keep internal conditions stable, move, and reproduce.

① What Is an Animal?

Key Concepts S 7.5.a

- The cells of most animals are organized into tissues, organs, and organ systems.
- Some major functions of animals are obtaining food and oxygen, keeping internal conditions stable, moving, and reproducing.
- Symmetry is a balanced arrangement of body parts that is characteristic of many animals.
- Animals are classified according to how they are related to other animals.

Key Terms

• anatomy • physiology • bilateral symmetry
• radial symmetry • vertebrate • invertebrate
• phylum

② Sponges and Cnidarians

Key Concepts S 7.2.a, 7.5.a

- Sponges are invertebrates that usually lack symmetry and never have tissues or organs.
- Cnidarians use stinging cells to capture food and defend themselves.

Key Terms

• larva • cnidarian • polyp • medusa

③ Worms and Mollusks

Key Concepts S 7.2.a, 7.5.a

- All worms are invertebrates that have long, narrow bodies without legs.
- Unlike cnidarians or flatworms, roundworms have a digestive system that is like a tube, open at both ends.
- Segmented worms have bodies made up of many linked sections called segments.
- In addition to a soft body often covered by a shell, a mollusk has a mantle and a foot.
- The three major groups of mollusks are gastropods, bivalves, and cephalopods.

Key Terms

• brain • parasite • host • anus
• closed circulatory system • mollusk
• open circulatory system • gill • gastropod
• radula • bivalve • cephalopod

④ Arthropods

Key Concepts S 7.2.a, 7.5.b

- Arthropods are invertebrates that have an external skeleton, a segmented body, and jointed attachments called appendages.
- The major groups of arthropods are crustaceans, arachnids, centipedes and millipedes, and insects.
- A crustacean is an arthropod that has two or three body sections, five or more pairs of legs, and two pairs of antennae.
- Arachnids are arthropods with two body sections, four pairs of legs, and no antennae.
- Insects have three body sections, six legs, one pair of antennae, and usually one or two pairs of wings.
- Each insect species undergoes either complete metamorphosis or gradual metamorphosis.

Key Terms

• arthropod • exoskeleton • molting
• antenna • crustacean • metamorphosis
• arachnid • abdomen • insect • thorax
• complete metamorphosis • pupa
• gradual metamorphosis • nymph

⑤ Echinoderms

Key Concepts S 7.2.a, 7.5.b

- Echinoderms are invertebrates with an internal skeleton and a system of fluid-filled tubes called a water vascular system.
- Groups of echinoderms include sea stars, brittle stars, sea urchins, and sea cucumbers.

Key Terms

• echinoderm • endoskeleton
• water vascular system • tube feet

Review and Assessment

Target Reading Skill

Take Notes To review part of Section 5, take notes on the text following the heading Movement. Copy the incomplete graphic organizer shown on the right. Complete it by answering the questions.

Questions	Notes: Movement
What is a water vascular system?	
What are tube feet?	

Reviewing Key Terms

Choose the letter of the best answer.

1. An animal without a backbone is called a(n)
   a. vertebrate.
   b. invertebrate.
   c. larva.
   d. parasite.

2. Which group of animals uses stinging cells to capture prey?
   a. vertebrates
   b. cnidarians
   c. sponges
   d. echinoderms

3. Which organ do most mollusks and crustaceans use to obtain oxygen?
   a. radula
   b. lungs
   c. gills
   d. legs

4. An arthropod's antennae are located on its
   a. head.
   b. thorax.
   c. abdomen.
   d. mantle.

5. At which stage of insect development do major changes in body structure occur?
   a. egg   **b.** larva
   c. pupa   **d.** adult

6. Echinoderms move by using structures called
   a. wings.   **b.** appendages.
   c. tube feet.   **d.** abdomens.

Complete the following sentences so that your answers clearly explain the key terms.

7. A sea anemone is a described as a **polyp** because its body is _____ .

8. Unlike the blood in an open circulatory system, the blood in a **closed circulatory system** _____ .

9. A gastropod has a **radula,** which is a(n) _____ .

10. An insect's body is protected by its **exoskeleton,** which is a(n) _____ .

11. Unlike **gradual metamorphosis,** complete metamorphosis has _____ .

Writing in Science

News Report As a television reporter, you are covering a story about a giant squid that has washed up on the local beach. Write a short news story describing the discovery. Be sure to describe how scientists classified the animal as a squid.

Video Assessment
Discovery Channel School
Mollusks, Arthropods, and Echinoderms

Review and Assessment

Checking Concepts

12. Explain the relationship among cells, tissues, and organs.

13. What are five key functions of animals?

14. Explain what a one-way digestive system is.

15. Describe the structure of a mollusk's gills.

16. Contrast the functions of an insect's compound eyes and simple eyes.

17. What is an endoskeleton? What is its function?

Thinking Critically

18. **Making Judgments** Suppose a book is called *Earth's Animals*. All the animals in the book are vertebrates. Is this title a good one? Explain your reasoning.

19. **Classifying** Classify each of the following animals as having radial symmetry, bilateral symmetry, or no symmetry: sea anemones, sponges, fishes, humans, and butterflies.

20. **Classifying** Which of the animals below is a roundworm? A sponge? A cnidarian? Describe the major characteristics shared by members of each phylum.

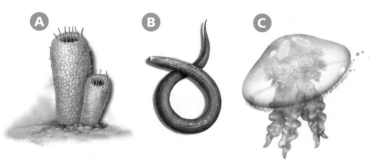

21. **Comparing and Contrasting** Compare and contrast bivalves and cephalopods.

22. **Applying Concepts** Explain why the development of a lion, which grows larger as it changes from a tiny cub to a 90-kg adult, is not metamorphosis.

23. **Applying Concepts** Some seafood restaurants serve a dish called soft-shelled crab. What do you think happened to the crab just before it was caught? Why is this process important?

24. **Classifying** Your friend said he found a dead insect that had two pairs of antennae and eight legs. Is this possible? Why or why not?

25. **Comparing and Contrasting** Compare and contrast centipedes and millipedes.

Applying Skills

Use the data table to answer Questions 26–28.
The following data appeared in a book on insects.

Flight Characteristics

Type of Insect	Wing Beats (per second)	Flight Speed (kilometers per hour)
Hummingbird moth	85	17.8
Bumblebee	250	10.3
Housefly	190	7.1

26. **Graphing** Use the data to make two bar graphs: one showing the three insect wing-beat rates and another showing the flight speeds.

27. **Interpreting Data** Which of the three insects has the highest wing-beat rate? Which insect flies the fastest?

28. **Drawing Conclusions** Based on the data, is there a relationship between the rate at which an insect beats its wings and the speed at which it flies? Explain. What factors besides wing-beat rate might affect flight speed?

Lab zone Standards Investigation

Performance Assessment Prepare a display to show how you set up your experiment and what your results were. Construct and display graphs to show the data you collected. Include pictures of the mealworms in each stage of development. Write your conclusion of how the experimental conditions affected the growth and development of the mealworms. Also suggest some possible explanations for your results.

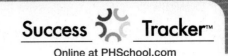
Choose the letter of the best answer.

1. What is the correct sequence in which a stinging cell reacts to the touch of another organism?
   A trigger brushes against prey, stinging cell fires, barbs snare prey
   B barbs snare prey, stinging cell fires, barbs release prey
   C prey is paralyzed, venom enters prey, stinging cell fires
   D tentacles pull prey to mouth, prey is ingested, stinging cell fires **S 7.5.b**

2. Which of the following is true of a one-way digestive system?
   A It is found in all parasites.
   B It has two openings.
   C It has one opening.
   D It is found in all parasites and has one opening. **S 7.5.a**

Use the diagram below and your knowledge of science to answer Question 3.

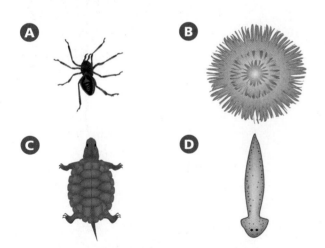

3. Of the four animals above, which have sense organs concentrated at one end of their bodies?
   A animals A and D
   B animals A, B, and D
   C animals B and D
   D animals A, C, and D **S 7.5.a**

4. Which of the following statements is true about gradual metamorphosis?
   A Gradual metamorphosis is a life cycle that involves asexual reproduction.
   B In gradual metamorphosis, a larva develops into a pupa.
   C In gradual metamorphosis, an egg hatches into a nymph.
   D Gradual metamorphosis has four distinct stages. **S 7.2.a**

Use the diagram below and your knowledge of science to answer Question 5.

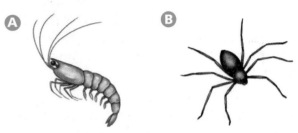

5. You are constructing a branching tree diagram that shows the relationship between animals A and B above. Which of the following characteristics could you use to place the two animals on different branches?
   A type of circulatory system
   B presence or absence of jointed appendages
   C type of digestive system
   D presence or absence of antennae **S 7.3.d**

6. Which of the following best describes the stages in the sexual life cycle of a sponge in the correct order?
   A larva, fertilization, egg and sperm, adult
   B adult, larva, egg and sperm, fertilization
   C adult, bud, bud breaks free
   D egg and sperm, fertilization, larva, adult **S 7.2.a**

Apply the
BIG Idea

7. Explain how a sea star's water vascular system enables the sea star to move. **S 7.5.b**

Chapter

12

Structure and Function of Vertebrates

Like all fishes, the fish in this school of "sweetlips" are vertebrates. ▶

Focus on the
BIG Idea

S 7.5.a

How does the structure of vertebrates help them to function ?

Check What You Know

Two friends are looking at fishes in an aquarium. One friend refers to the fishes as animals. The other friend argues that fishes aren't animals because they don't have four legs. Which friend is correct? Explain your answer.

Build Science Vocabulary

The images shown here represent some of the key terms in this chapter. You can use this vocabulary skill to help you understand the meaning of some key terms in this chapter.

Vocabulary Skill

Greek Word Origins

Some key terms in this chapter contain word parts whose origins are Greek. The table below lists some of the Greek words that key terms come from. Learning the meanings of these Greek words will help you understand and remember some key terms.

Greek Word	Meaning of Greek Word	Key Term
amphibios	living a double life	**amphibian** An animal that spends part of its life cycle on land and part in water
chordé	string, cord	**chordate** An animal that has a flexible rod that supports the animal's back
therme	heat	**endotherm** An animal that produces enough heat within its body to control its body temperature

Apply It!

1. How does the meaning of *amphibian* relate to the Greek word from which it comes?

2. Can you think of an English word besides *chordate* that might come from the Greek word *chordé*?

3. In the list of key terms on the next page, find another term besides *endotherm* that might come from the Greek word *therme*. Then look up the meaning of the key term and check how its meaning relates to the meaning of *endotherm*.

amphibian

mammal

reptile

fish

contour feather

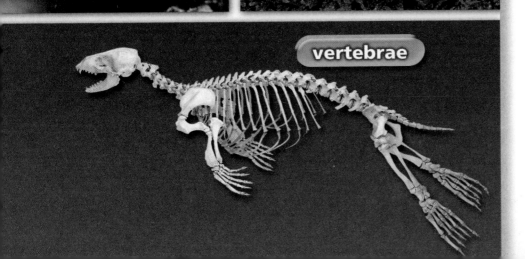

vertebrae

Chapter 12
Vocabulary

Build Science Vocabulary
Online
Visit: PHSchool.com
Web Code: cvj-3120

How to Read Science

 ## Compare and Contrast

When you compare and contrast, you examine similarities and differences between things. You can do this by using a table. Follow these steps to set up a compare/contrast table.

- List the characteristics to be compared across the top.
- List the items to be compared in the left column.
- Complete the table by filling in information about each characteristic.

Vertebrates can be divided into two groups—ectotherms and endotherms—depending on how their body temperatures are controlled. Study the table and then answer the questions.

Type of Body-Temperature Control	Characteristics of Body-Temperature Control	Groups With This Type of Temperature Control
Ectotherm	Body temperature changes, depending on the temperature of the environment.	Fishes, amphibians, reptiles
Endotherm	Body temperature stays about the same, no matter what the temperature of the environment.	Birds, mammals

Apply It!

1. Which vertebrate groups are ectotherms?

2. Which type of animal—ectotherm or endotherm—has a body temperature that is more affected by the temperature of the environment?

As you read, construct compare/contrast tables. For Section 2, compare the characteristics of jawless fishes, cartilaginous fishes, and bony fishes. For Section 6, compare the reproduction of monotremes, marsupials, and placental mammals.

Standards Investigation

Animal Adaptations

How does an animal capture food, escape from predators, or obtain oxygen? To help answer these questions, you will create models of three different animals and show how each is adapted to its environment.

Your Goal

To make three-dimensional models of a fish, an amphibian, and a reptile that show how each is adapted to carry out one life function in its environment

To complete this investigation, you must

- select one life function to show
- build a three-dimensional model of each type of animal, showing the adaptations each has for carrying out the function you selected
- make a poster that explains how each animal's adaptation is suited to its environment
- follow the safety guidelines in Appendix A

Plan It!

Pair up with a classmate and share what you already know about fishes, amphibians, and reptiles. Answer the following questions: Where do these animals live? How do they move around? How do they protect themselves?

Decide on the life function you will show. As you read about these types of animals, make your models showing the adaptations the animals have for carrying out the functions.

CALIFORNIA
Standards Focus

S 7.4.g Students know how to explain significant developments and extinctions of plant and animal life on the geologic time scale.

S 7.5.c Students know how bones and muscles work together to provide a structural framework for movement.

- What are the characteristics of chordates and vertebrates?

- How have scientists been able to infer the relationships of major groups of vertebrates?

- How do vertebrates differ in the way they control body temperature?

Key Terms
- chordate
- notochord
- vertebra
- ectotherm
- endotherm

Lab zone Standards Warm-Up

How Is an Umbrella Like a Skeleton?

1. Open an umbrella. Turn it upside down and examine how it is made.
2. Now close the umbrella and watch how the braces and ribs collapse.
3. Think of what would happen if you removed the ribs from the umbrella and then tried to use it during a rainstorm.

Think It Over

Inferring What is the function of the ribs of an umbrella? How are the ribs of the umbrella similar to the bones in your skeleton? How are they different?

Look backward in time, into an ocean 530 million years ago. There you see a strange-looking creature—a jawless fish—that is about as long as your index finger. The creature is swimming with a side-to-side motion, like a flag flapping in the wind. Its tail fin is broad and flat. Tiny armorlike plates cover its small body. Its eyes are set wide apart. If you could see inside the animal, you would notice that it has a backbone. You are looking at one of the earliest vertebrates, at home in an ancient sea.

Characteristics of Chordates

Vertebrates like the ancient jawless fish are a subgroup in the phylum Chordata. All members of this phylum are called **chordates** (KAWR dayts). **At some point in their lives, all chordates have three characteristics: a notochord, a nerve cord that runs down their back, and slits in their throat area.** Most chordates, including fishes, amphibians, and reptiles, are vertebrates. So are birds and mammals. But a few chordates, such as lancelets, are invertebrates.

Notochord The phylum name Chordata comes from the **notochord,** a flexible rod that supports a chordate's back. Some chordates, like the lancelet shown in Figure 1, have notochords all their lives. In contrast, in vertebrates, part or all of the notochord is replaced by a backbone.

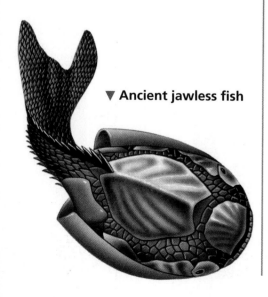

▼ Ancient jawless fish

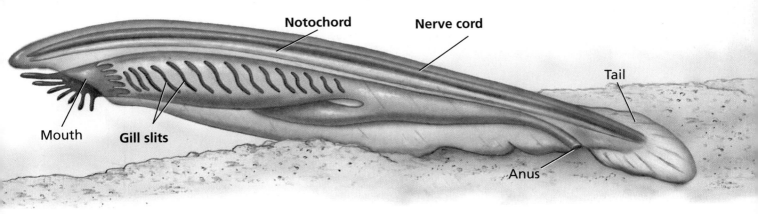

Notochord

Nerve cord

Tail

Mouth

Gill slits

Anus

Nerve Cord in Back

In addition to having a notochord, all chordates have a nerve cord that runs down their back. Your spinal cord is such a nerve cord. The nerve cord is the connection between the brain and the nerves, on which messages travel back and forth. Many other groups of animals—arthropods and segmented worms, for example—have nerve cords, but their nerve cords do not run down their backs.

Slits in Throat Area

At some point in their lives, chordates have slits in their throat area called pharyngeal (fuh RIN jee ul) slits, or gill slits. Some chordates, including fishes, keep these slits as part of their gills for their entire lives. But in many vertebrates, including humans, pharyngeal slits disappear before birth.

Reading Checkpoint What is a notochord?

FIGURE 1
Characteristics of a Lancelet
This lancelet shows the characteristics of a chordate: a notochord that helps support its body, a nerve cord down its back, and gill slits.

Characteristics of Vertebrates

Vertebrates have the characteristics shared by all chordates. In addition, vertebrates share certain other characteristics. **A vertebrate has a backbone that is part of an internal skeleton.** This internal skeleton, or endoskeleton, supports the body and allows it to move.

Backbone You can see in Figure 2 that a vertebrate's backbone, which is also called a spine, runs down the center of its back. The backbone is formed by many similar bones called **vertebrae** (singular *vertebra*). The vertebrae are lined up in a row like beads on a string. Joints, or movable connections between the vertebrae, give the spine flexibility. You can bend over and tie your shoes because your backbone has flexibility. Each vertebra has a hole in it that allows the spinal cord to pass through it. The spinal cord fits into the vertebrae like fingers fit into rings.

Backbone

FIGURE 2
The Backbone of a Lizard
The backbone of this gila monster has flexibility. **Predicting** *Could the backbone bend if it did not have joints?*

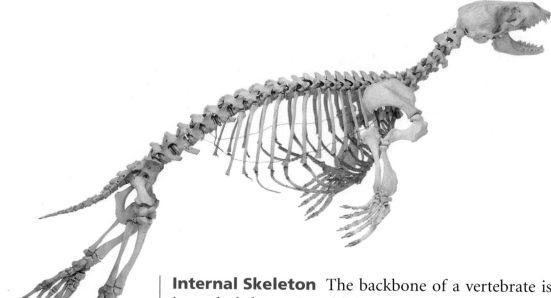

FIGURE 3
The Skeleton of a Seal
This seal's skeleton has adaptations for swimming. Long, flat bones support the flippers. The flat skull helps the seal move smoothly through the water.

Internal Skeleton The backbone of a vertebrate is part of its endoskeleton. In addition to the backbone, a vertebrate's endoskeleton includes the skull and ribs. Many vertebrates also have limb bones adapted for movement.

The endoskeleton gives the body shape. It also provides a framework to which muscles can attach. Together, bones and muscles enable a vertebrate's body to move. In addition, the endoskeleton protects internal organs. The skull protects the brain. The ribs protect the heart, lungs, and other organs.

Unlike an arthropod's exoskeleton, a vertebrate's endoskeleton grows as the animal grows. Therefore, the endoskeleton doesn't need to be replaced as the animal becomes larger. It also forms an internal frame that supports the body against the downward pull of gravity, while allowing easy movement. Because of their endoskeletons, vertebrates can grow bigger than animals with exoskeletons or no skeletons at all.

 **Reading Checkpoint** What are two functions of an endoskeleton?

Evolution of Vertebrates

The first tiny chordates swam in Earth's waters long before vertebrates appeared. Vertebrates probably evolved from an invertebrate chordate ancestor. ☞ **By studying fossils and other evidence, such as DNA, scientists have been able to infer the relationships of the major groups of vertebrates—fishes, amphibians, reptiles, birds, and mammals.** Figure 4 shows the probable order of vertebrate evolution.

Fossils show that the first vertebrates to live on Earth were probably fishes. Fishes appeared on Earth over 500 million years ago. Amphibians are descended from fishes. Then, amphibians gave rise to reptiles. Both mammals and birds are descended from reptiles. Birds were the latest group of vertebrates to arise.

Go Online
SciLINKS NSTA

For: Links on vertebrates
Visit: www.SciLinks.org
Web Code: scn-0231

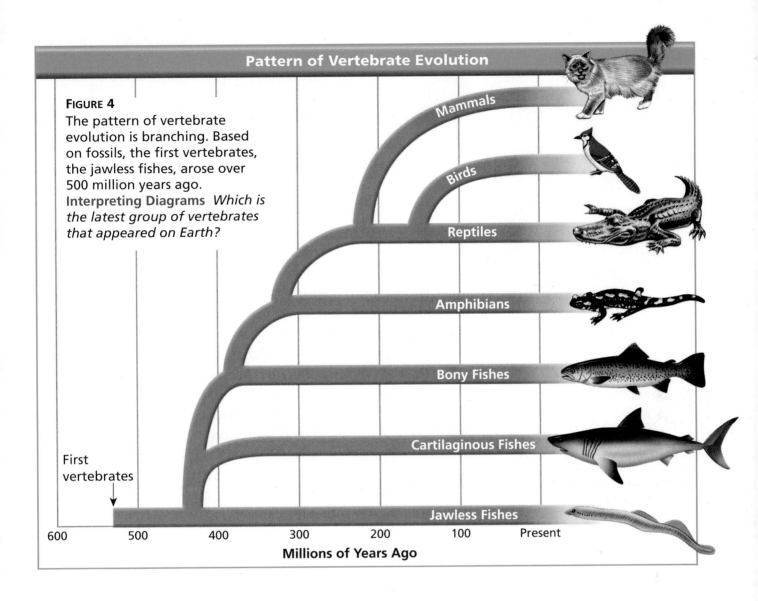

Pattern of Vertebrate Evolution

FIGURE 4

The pattern of vertebrate evolution is branching. Based on fossils, the first vertebrates, the jawless fishes, arose over 500 million years ago.
Interpreting Diagrams *Which is the latest group of vertebrates that appeared on Earth?*

Mammals

Birds

Reptiles

Amphibians

Bony Fishes

Cartilaginous Fishes

First vertebrates

Jawless Fishes

| 600 | 500 | 400 | 300 | 200 | 100 | Present |

Millions of Years Ago

Keeping Conditions Stable

One characteristic that differs among the major groups of vertebrates is the way they control their body temperature. 🔑 **The body temperature of most fishes, amphibians, and reptiles is close to the temperature of their environment. In contrast, birds and mammals have a stable body temperature that is often warmer than their environment.**

Ectotherms Fishes, amphibians, and reptiles are ectotherms. An **ectotherm** (EK toh thurm) is an animal whose body does not produce much internal heat. An ectotherm's body temperature changes depending on the temperature of its environment. For example, when a turtle is lying on a sunny riverbank, it has a higher body temperature than when it is swimming in a cool river. Ectotherms are sometimes called "coldblooded." This term is misleading because ectotherms' blood is often quite warm.

▼ **Emperor penguins**

Woma python ▶

FIGURE 5
Temperature Regulation
On a cool, sunny morning, a woma python raises its body temperature by basking in the sun. In contrast, an emperor penguin stays warm by producing internal heat.
Inferring Which animal is an endotherm?

Endotherms In contrast to a turtle, a beaver would have the same body temperature whether it is in cool water or on warm land. The beaver is an example of an **endotherm** (EN doh thurm)—an animal whose body regulates its own temperature by controlling the internal heat it produces. An endotherm's body temperature usually does not change much, even when the temperature of its environment changes. Birds and mammals, such as beavers, are endotherms.

Endotherms also have other adaptations, such as sweat glands and fur or feathers, for maintaining their body temperature. On hot days, some endotherms sweat. As the sweat evaporates, the animal is cooled. On cool days, fur or feathers keep endotherms warm. Because endotherms can keep their body temperatures stable, they can live in a greater variety of environments than ectotherms can.

Section 1 Assessment

S 7.4.g, 7.5.c,
E-LA: Reading 7.1.2

Vocabulary Skill Greek Word Origins The Greek word *ektos* means "outside." The Greek word *endon* means "within." How do these meanings relate to the meanings of *ectotherm* and *endotherm*?

Reviewing Key Concepts

1. a. **Listing** List three chordate characteristics.
   b. **Identifying** What characteristic do only vertebrates have?
   c. **Relating Cause and Effect** How does this characteristic give a vertebrate's body flexibility?
2. a. **Reviewing** What evidence indicates relationships among vertebrate groups?
   b. **Interpreting Data** Use Figure 4 to determine how many groups of fishes there are.
   c. **Sequencing** Which fish group appeared last?

3. a. **Summarizing** What is the difference between an ectotherm and an endotherm?
   b. **Making Generalizations** Would an ectotherm or an endotherm be more active on a cold night? Explain your answer.

Lab zone **At-Home Activity**

Bumpy Back Rub Have members of your family feel the tops of the vertebrae running down the center of their backs. Then have them feel the hard skull beneath the skin on their foreheads. Tell them about the functions of the backbone and skull.

A Model Backbone

S 7.5.b, 7.7.a, 7.7.c

Problem

Can you build a functional model of a backbone?

Skills Focus

making models, observing

Materials

- 20 pieces each of 3 different types of cylindrical dried pasta
- 120 cm of plastic lanyard or string

Procedure

1. Examine the properties of the materials. Begin by cutting a 1-foot section of string.

2. Choose a shape of pasta that you think would make good vertebrae and thread them onto the string to make a simple model of a backbone. **CAUTION**: *Do not eat any of the pasta or other food substance in this lab.*

3. Bend and twist your backbone model. Can it easily rotate and bend? Try to mimic the motions of several different vertebrates—for example, a snake, a frog, a horse, or a cat.

4. Using what you learned about the spinal column and the model you just constructed, design and build an improved model backbone for an imaginary vertebrate of your choice. Your model should have the following characteristics:
   - The backbone should be made of the materials approved by your teacher.
   - The backbone should be strong enough to protect the spinal cord.
   - The backbone should be highly flexible so that it can easily twist and rotate to match the motions of the vertebrate you chose.
   - As the backbone flexes, the bones should not rub directly together.
   - The backbone should also provide shock absorption for when the vertebrate jumps.

Analyze and Conclude

1. **Making Models** As you designed, built, and tested your model backbone, what problems did you encounter? How did you solve these problems?

2. **Observing** How are the pieces of pasta like vertebrae? How are they different?

3. **Communicating** Write a letter to a friend in which you describe how you designed and built a model backbone. Be sure to explain to your friend what you learned about backbones by doing this activity.

Design an Experiment

Write a procedure for an experiment to test the strength of the model backbone you constructed and to compare the strength to the models built by other students. Select appropriate tools to use. Do not perform the experiment until your teacher has approved your procedure.

CALIFORNIA
Standards Focus

S 7.5.b Students know that organ systems function because of the contributions of individual organs, tissues, and cells. The failure of any part can affect the entire system.

○ What are the characteristics of most fishes?

○ What are the major groups of fishes and how do they differ?

Key Terms

- fish
- cartilage
- swim bladder

Lab zone Standards **Warm-Up**

How Does Water Flow Over a Fish's Gills?

1. Closely observe a fish in an aquarium for a few minutes. Note how frequently the fish opens its mouth.

2. Notice the flaps on each side of the fish's head behind its eyes. Observe how the flaps open and close.

3. Observe the movements of the mouth and the flaps at the same time. Note any relationship between the movements of these two structures.

Think It Over

Observing What do the flaps on the sides of the fish do when the fish opens its mouth? What role do you think these two structures play in a fish's life?

In the warm waters of a coral reef, a large spotted fish called a graysby hovers in the water, barely moving. A smaller striped fish called a goby swims up to the graysby. Then, like a vacuum cleaner moving over a rug, the goby swims slowly over the larger fish, eating dead skin and tiny parasites. The goby even cleans inside the graysby's mouth and gills. Both fishes benefit from this cleaning. The graysby gets rid of unwanted materials, and the goby gets a meal.

Gobies cleaning a ▶ graysby

Water flow

Gills

Blood vessels in gills

Two-chambered heart

Blood vessels in body

Key
- Oxygen-rich blood
- Oxygen-poor blood

Characteristics of Fishes

Both the goby and the graysby are fishes. A **fish** is a vertebrate that lives in water and uses fins to move. 🔑 **In addition to living in water and having fins, most fishes are ectotherms, obtain oxygen through gills, and have scales.** Scales are thin, overlapping plates that cover the skin.

Fishes make up the largest group of vertebrates. Nearly half of all vertebrate species are fishes. In addition, fishes have been on Earth longer than any other kind of vertebrate.

Obtaining Oxygen A fish's respiratory and circulatory systems work together to deliver oxygen to body cells. Fishes get their oxygen from water. As a fish swims, it opens its mouth and takes a gulp of water. The water, which contains oxygen, moves through openings in the fish's throat region that lead to the gills. Gills, which look like tiny feathers, are the main organs in a fish's respiratory system. Gills have many blood vessels. As water flows over the gills, oxygen moves from the water into the fish's blood. At the same time, carbon dioxide, a waste product, moves out of the blood and into the water. After flowing over the gills, the water flows out of the fish through slits beneath the gills.

Circulatory System From the gills, the blood travels throughout the fish's body, supplying the body cells with oxygen. Like all vertebrates, fishes have a closed circulatory system. The heart of a fish has two chambers, or inner spaces. The heart of a fish pumps blood in one loop—from the heart to the gills, from the gills to the rest of the body, and back to the heart. You can trace this path in Figure 6.

FIGURE 6
Respiration and Circulation
Water flows into the mouth of this fish and then over its gills. Oxygen moves into the blood and is delivered to the cells of the fish.
Interpreting Diagrams *Where does oxygen get into the blood of a fish?*

▲ Skeleton

FIGURE 7
Fins of an Angelfish
The skeleton of a fish shows that the fins have bony support. The fins of this angelfish act like paddles as the fish moves through the water.

Movement Fins help fishes swim. Look at the fins on the angelfish in Figure 7. Each fin has a thin membrane stretched across bony supports. Like a canoe paddle, a fin provides a large surface to push against the water. The push allows for faster movement through the water. If you have ever swum wearing a pair of swim fins, you probably noticed how fast you moved through the water. Most of the movements of fishes are related to obtaining food, but some are related to reproduction.

Reproduction Like all vertebrates, fishes reproduce sexually. Most fishes have external fertilization. In external fertilization, the eggs are fertilized outside the female's body. The male hovers near the female and spreads a cloud of sperm over the eggs she releases. The young develop outside the female's body.

In contrast, some fishes, such as sharks and guppies, have internal fertilization. In internal fertilization, eggs are fertilized inside the female's body. The young develop inside her body. When the young fishes are mature enough to live on their own, she gives birth to them.

✓ Reading Checkpoint   **What is the structure of a fin?**

FIGURE 8
Trout Eggs
Young brook trout fish are developing in these eggs on the bottom of a stream.

Nervous System The nervous system and sense organs of fishes help them find food and avoid predators. Most fishes can see much better in water than you can. Keen senses of touch, smell, and taste also help fishes capture food. Some fishes, such as the catfish in Figure 9, have taste organs in unusual places.

Diversity of Fishes

Fishes are classified into three main groups based on the mouth structure and type of skeleton. ◷ **The major groups of fishes are jawless fishes, cartilaginous fishes, and bony fishes.**

Jawless Fishes Jawless fishes were the first vertebrates to appear on Earth. ◷ **Jawless fishes are unlike other fishes in that they have no jaws and no scales.** Jaws are hinged bony structures that allow animals to open and close their mouths. Instead of jaws, jawless fishes have mouths containing structures for scraping, stabbing, and sucking their food. Their skeletons are made of **cartilage,** a tissue that is more flexible than bone.

Hagfishes and lampreys are the only kinds of jawless fishes alive today. Hagfishes look like large, slimy worms. They crawl into the bodies of dead or dying fishes and use their rough tongues to scrape decaying tissues. Many lampreys are parasites of other fishes. They attach their mouths to healthy fishes and then suck in the tissues and blood of their victims. If you look at the lamprey's mouth in Figure 10, you can probably imagine the damage it can do.

 **Reading Checkpoint** What material makes up the skeleton of a jawless fish?

FIGURE 9
A Catfish
The whiskers of a catfish have many taste buds. To find food, the catfish drags its whiskers along muddy lake or river bottoms.

FIGURE 10
A Lamprey
Lampreys have eel-shaped bodies. They use sharp teeth and suction-cup mouths to feed on other fishes. *Classifying To which group of fishes do lampreys belong?*

▲ Mouth

FIGURE 11
Great White Shark and Ray
Both sharks and rays are cartilaginous fishes. Sharks such as the one below have sharp teeth. This ray lives on the ocean floor.

Cartilaginous Fishes Sharks, rays, and skates are cartilaginous (kahr tuh LAJ uh nuhs) fishes. ⬤ **The cartilaginous fishes have jaws and scales, and skeletons made of cartilage.** The pointed, toothlike scales that cover their bodies give their skin a rough texture.

Like all fishes, cartilaginous fishes obtain oxygen from water. Most sharks cannot pump water over their gills. Instead, they rely on swimming or currents to keep water moving across their gills. When sharks sleep, they position themselves in currents that send water over their gills. Rays and skates are not as active as sharks. They spend a lot of time on the ocean floor. During this time, they take in water through small holes behind their eyes. Water leaves through gill openings on the fishes' undersides.

Bony Fishes Most familiar kinds of fish, such as trout, tuna, and goldfish, are bony fishes. ⬤ **A bony fish has jaws, scales, a pocket on each side of the head that holds the gills, and a skeleton made of hard bones.** Each gill pocket is covered by a flap that opens to release water.

The major structures of a bony fish are shown in Figure 12. Notice that this bony fish has an organ called a **swim bladder,** which is an internal, gas-filled sac that helps the fish stay stable at different depths in the water. Gas levels in the swim bladder are adjusted after the fish reaches its desired depth. Because of this adjustment, the fish can stay at a depth without using a lot of energy.

Bony fishes make up about 95 percent of all fish species. They live in both salt water and fresh water. Some live in the dark depths of the ocean. Others thrive in light-filled waters, such as those around coral reefs.

 **Reading Checkpoint** Which organ helps a bony fish maintain its position in the water?

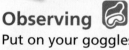

Observing 🥽

Put on your goggles and disposable gloves. Place a preserved bony fish on newspaper on your desk and examine it closely. Note its size and shape, and the number and locations of its fins. Lift the gill cover and observe the gills with a hand lens. Use your observations to make a diagram of the fish. Wash your hands when you are finished.

FIGURE 12
Structure of a Bony Fish

The yellow perch has the characteristics of a bony fish. **Interpreting Diagrams** *What are the functions of fins?*

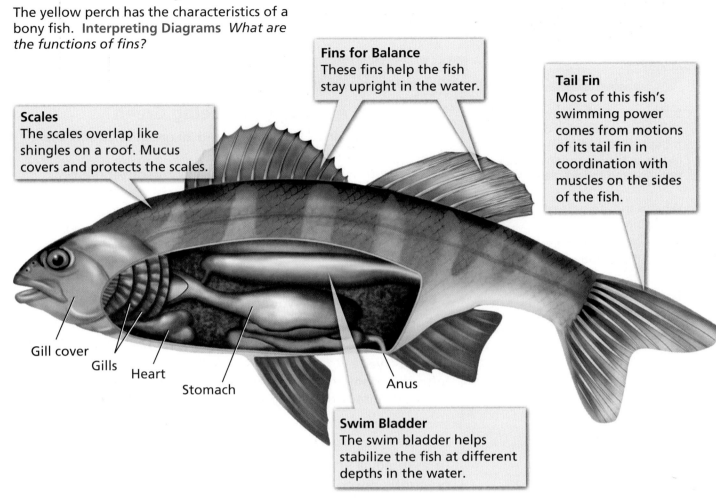

Fins for Balance
These fins help the fish stay upright in the water.

Tail Fin
Most of this fish's swimming power comes from motions of its tail fin in coordination with muscles on the sides of the fish.

Scales
The scales overlap like shingles on a roof. Mucus covers and protects the scales.

Gill cover

Gills

Heart

Stomach

Anus

Swim Bladder
The swim bladder helps stabilize the fish at different depths in the water.

Section 2 Assessment

S 7.5.b, E-LA: Writing 7.2.0, Reading 7.2.0

Target Reading Skill Compare and Contrast Use your compare/contrast chart about the different groups of fishes to help you answer Question 2.

Reviewing Key Concepts

1. a. **Reviewing** What are the main characteristics of fishes?
   b. **Explaining** What is the function of gills?
   c. **Applying Concepts** What would happen to a goldfish that could not open its mouth? Explain.
2. a. **Identifying** What are three major groups of fishes?
   b. **Classifying** Into which group of fishes would you classify a fish with jaws and a skeleton made of cartilage?
   c. **Comparing and Contrasting** How does shark reproduction differ from the reproduction of most fishes?

Writing in Science

Wanted Poster Design a "Wanted" poster for a lamprey. Present the lamprey as a "criminal of the ocean." Include the lamprey's physical characteristics, feeding habits, and any other details that will allow people to track down this fish.

CALIFORNIA
Standards Focus

S 7.5.a Students know plants and animals have levels of organization for structure and function, including cells, tissues, organs, organ systems, and the whole organism.

- What is the life cycle of an amphibian?
- How are adult amphibians adapted to living on land?

Key Terms
- amphibian
- tadpole
- lung
- atrium
- ventricle
- habitat

Lab zone · Standards **Warm-Up**

What's the Advantage of Being Green?

1. Count out 20 dried yellow peas and 20 green ones. Mix them up in a paper cup.
2. Cover your eyes. Have your partner gently scatter the peas onto a large sheet of green paper.
3. Uncover your eyes. Have your partner keep time while you pick up as many peas, one at a time, as you can find in 15 seconds.
4. When 15 seconds are up, count how many peas of each color you picked up.
5. Repeat Steps 2 through 4, but this time you scatter the peas and keep time while your partner picks up the peas.
6. Compare your results with those of your partner and your classmates.

Think It Over
Inferring Many frogs are green, as are their environments. What advantage does a frog have in being green?

In a pond, a frog lies in wait. In the air above the frog, a dragonfly approaches. Because the frog blends in with its surroundings, the dragonfly doesn't notice the frog. Zip! The frog's tongue shoots out, capturing the dragonfly.

Frogs and toads have camouflage that helps them obtain food and avoid predators. Most frogs and toads are green or brownish-green, making them hard to see in their environment. If you did the Standards Warm-Up, you learned that it is hard to see something green against a green background.

This green frog blends in with green duckweed in a pond. ▼

What Is an Amphibian?

A frog is one kind of amphibian. Toads and salamanders are other kinds. An **amphibian** (am FIB ee un) is a vertebrate that is ectothermic and spends its early life in water. Indeed, the word *amphibian* means "double life," and amphibians have exactly that. **After beginning their lives in water, most amphibians spend their adulthood on land, returning to water to reproduce.**

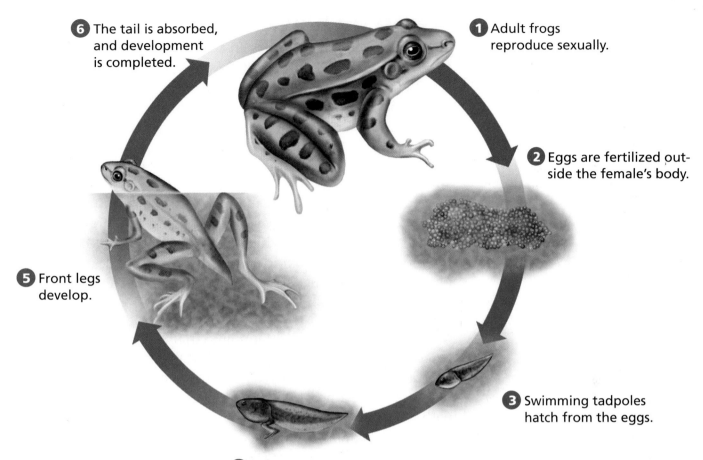

6 The tail is absorbed, and development is completed.

1 Adult frogs reproduce sexually.

2 Eggs are fertilized outside the female's body.

5 Front legs develop.

3 Swimming tadpoles hatch from the eggs.

4 Hind legs develop.

Reproduction and Development Eggs are fertilized internally in most salamanders and externally in most frogs and toads. Fertilized eggs develop in water. After a few days, larvae wriggle out of a jelly that coats the eggs and begin a free-swimming, fishlike life.

The larvae of most amphibians grow and eventually undergo metamorphosis. You can trace the process of frog metamorphosis in Figure 13. The larva of a frog or a toad is called a **tadpole.** Like fishes, tadpoles obtain oxygen through gills.

Unlike tadpoles, the larvae of salamanders look like adults. Most salamander larvae undergo a metamorphosis in which they lose their gills. However, the changes are not as dramatic as those that happen during a frog or toad's metamorphosis.

 **Reading Checkpoint** What is a frog larva called?

Diversity of Amphibians There are two major groups of amphibians. Salamanders form one group. Frogs and toads form the other. You can distinguish between the groups by the presence of a tail in the adults. Salamanders keep their tails in adulthood, while most frogs and toads do not.

FIGURE 13

Life Cycle of a Frog

During its metamorphosis from tadpole to adult, a frogs body undergoes a series of dramatic changes. **Applying Concepts** *How do these changes prepare a frog for living on land?*

For: More on the frog life cycle
Visit: PHSchool.com
Web Code: ced-2033

Living on Land

Once an amphibian becomes an adult and moves onto land, its survival needs change. It must now get its oxygen from the air, not the water. Fins no longer help it move. ⊜ **The respiratory and circulatory systems of adult amphibians are adapted for life on land. In addition, adult amphibians have adaptations for moving.**

Obtaining Oxygen Amphibian larvae use gills to obtain oxygen from the water. During metamorphosis, most amphibians lose their gills and develop lungs. **Lungs** are organs of air-breathing vertebrates in which oxygen moves from the air into the blood. Carbon dioxide moves from the blood into the air. Oxygen and carbon dioxide are also exchanged through the thin, moist skins of adult amphibians.

Circulatory System A tadpole's circulatory system has a single loop and a heart with two chambers, like that of a fish. In contrast, the circulatory system of many adult amphibians has two loops and a heart with three chambers. You can trace the path of blood through an adult amphibian in Figure 14. The two upper chambers of the heart, called **atria** (singular *atrium*), receive blood. One atrium receives oxygen-rich blood from the lungs, and the other receives oxygen-poor blood from the rest of the body. From the atria, blood moves into the lower chamber, the **ventricle,** which pumps blood out to the lungs and body. Oxygen-rich and oxygen-poor blood mix in the ventricle.

Go Online
active art

For: Respiration and Circulation activity
Visit: PHSchool.com
Web Code: cep-2032

Blood vessels in lungs

Three-chambered
heart

Right
atrium

Left
atrium

Ventricle

Blood vessels
in body

Key
- ■ Oxygen-rich blood
- ■ Oxygen-poor blood

FIGURE 14
Respiration and Circulation
This adult salamander has lungs and a double-loop circulatory system. **Interpreting Diagrams**
Why is the blood in the right atrium colored blue?

Movement A vertebrate that lives on land needs a strong skeleton to support its body. In addition, a land animal needs some way of moving. Fins work in water, but they don't work on land. Most adult amphibians have strong skeletons and muscular limbs adapted for moving on land.

Salamanders usually crawl. The legs of frogs and toads have adaptations for leaping. Leaping requires powerful hind-leg muscles and a skeleton that can absorb the shock of landing.

Amphibians in Danger Worldwide, amphibian populations are decreasing. One reason is the destruction of amphibian habitats. An animal's **habitat** is the environment in which it lives. When a swamp is filled in or a forest is cut, an area that was moist becomes drier. Few amphibians can survive for long in dry, sunny areas.

But amphibians are declining even in areas where their habitats have not been damaged. Because their skins are delicate and their eggs lack shells, amphibians are especially sensitive to changes in their environment. Poisons in the environment, such as pesticides and other chemicals, can pollute the waters that amphibians need to live and reproduce.

FIGURE 15
Golden Frog
Golden frogs, like the one shown here, are rarely seen anymore in their native habitat—the rain forests of Panama.
Relating Cause and Effect *What are two possible causes for the decrease in the number of golden frogs?*

 **Reading Checkpoint** **What is a habitat?**

Section 3 Assessment

S 7.5.a, E-LA: Reading 7.1.2, Writing 7.2.0

Vocabulary Skill Greek Word Origins In the Greek word *amphibios,* the word part *bios* means "life." What do you think the word part *amphi-* means?

Reviewing Key Concepts

1. **a. Defining** What is an amphibian?
   b. Sequencing Describe a frog's life cycle, beginning with the egg.
   c. Comparing and Contrasting Contrast the ways in which tadpoles and adult frogs obtain oxygen.
2. **a. Reviewing** What are three adaptations of adult amphibians for living on land?
   b. Sequencing How does blood move in the circulatory system of an adult amphibian? (*Hint:* Start with blood leaving the ventricle of the heart and going to the lungs.)

c. Interpreting Diagrams How is an adult amphibian's circulatory system different from that of a fish? Use Figure 6 and Figure 14 to help answer this question.

Writing in Science

Web Site Design the home page of a Web site that introduces people to amphibians. First, come up with a catchy title for your Web site. Then, design your home page, the first page people will see. Consider these questions as you come up with your design: What information will you include? What will the illustrations or photos show? What links to specific topics relating to amphibians will you have?

Reptiles

CALIFORNIA
Standards Focus

S 7.3.e Students know that extinction of a species occurs when the environment changes and the adaptive characteristics of a species are insufficient for its survival.

S 7.5.a Students know plants and animals have levels of organization for structure and function, including cells, tissues, organs, organ systems, and the whole organism.

- What adaptations allow reptiles to live on land?
- What are the characteristics of each of the three main groups of reptiles?
- What environmental change may have caused the extinction of the dinosaurs?

Key Terms
- reptile
- kidney
- urine
- amniotic egg

Lab zone Standards **Warm-Up**

How Do Snakes Feed?

1. To model how a snake feeds, stretch a sock cuff over a grapefruit "prey" by first pulling on one side and then on the other. Work the grapefruit down into the "stomach." A snake's jawbones can spread apart like the sock cuff.

2. Remove the grapefruit and put a rubber band around the sock about 8 centimeters below the opening. The rubber band represents the firmly joined jawbones of a lizard. Now try to repeat Step 1.

Think It Over
Inferring What is the advantage of having jawbones?

The king cobra of Southeast Asia is the world's longest venomous snake. It can grow to more than 4 meters long. When it encounters a predator, a king cobra flattens its neck and rears up. Its ropelike body sways back and forth, and its tongue flicks in and out.

A king cobra's fearsome behavior in response to a predator contrasts with the gentle way it treats its eggs. King cobras are one of the few snakes that build nests. The female builds a nest of grass and leaves on the forest floor. She lays her eggs inside the nest and guards them until they hatch.

◀ **King cobra**

Adaptations for Life on Land

Like other reptiles, king cobras lay their eggs on land rather than in water. A **reptile** is an ectothermic vertebrate that has lungs and scaly skin. In addition to snakes such as the king cobra, lizards, turtles, and alligators are also reptiles. Unlike amphibians, reptiles can spend their entire lives on dry land.

The ancestors of modern reptiles were the first vertebrates adapted to life completely out of water. Reptiles get their oxygen from air and breathe entirely with lungs. Reptiles that live in water, such as sea turtles, evolved from reptiles that lived on land. So, even though sea turtles live in water, they still breathe with lungs and come ashore to lay eggs.

You can think of a land animal as a pocket of water held within a bag of skin. To thrive on land, an animal must have adaptations that keep the water within the "bag" from evaporating in the dry air. **The skin, kidneys, and eggs of reptiles are adapted to conserve water.**

Skin and Kidneys Unlike amphibians, which have thin, moist skin, reptiles have dry, tough skins covered with scales. This scaly skin protects reptiles and helps keep water in their bodies. Another adaptation that helps keep water inside a reptile's body is its **kidneys,** which are organs that filter wastes from the blood. The wastes are then excreted in a watery fluid called **urine.** The kidneys of reptiles concentrate the urine so that the reptiles lose very little water.

 **Reading Checkpoint** What are two functions of a reptile's skin?

For: More on reptiles
Visit: PHSchool.com
Web Code: ced-2034

An Egg With a Shell Reptiles have internal fertilization and lay their eggs on land. While still inside a female's body, fertilized eggs are covered with membranes and a leathery shell. Unlike an amphibian's egg, a reptile's egg has a shell and membranes that protect the embryo and help keep it from drying out. An egg with a shell and internal membranes that keep the embryo moist is called an **amniotic egg** (am nee AHT ik). Pores in the shell let oxygen gas in and carbon dioxide gas out.

Look at Figure 17 to see the membranes of a reptile's egg. One membrane holds a liquid that surrounds the embryo. The liquid protects the embryo and keeps it moist. A second membrane holds the yolk, or food for the embryo. A third membrane holds the embryo's wastes. Oxygen and carbon dioxide are exchanged across the fourth membrane.

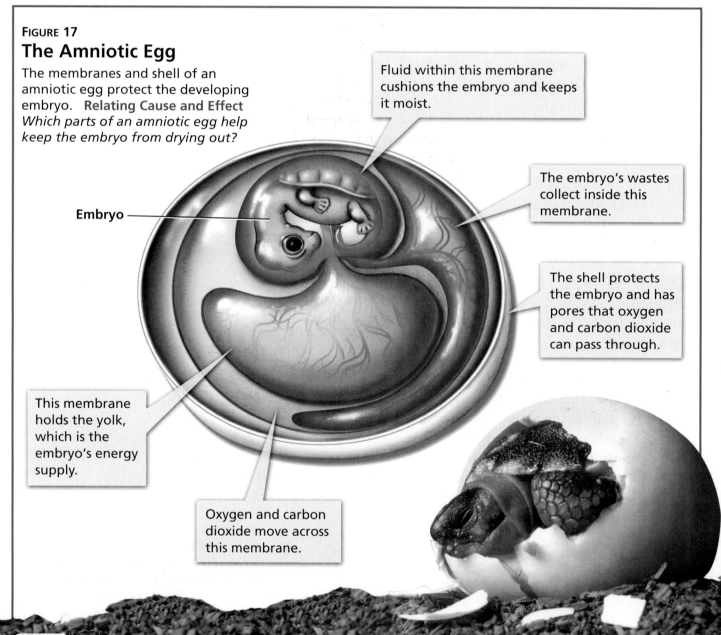

FIGURE 17
The Amniotic Egg
The membranes and shell of an amniotic egg protect the developing embryo. **Relating Cause and Effect** *Which parts of an amniotic egg help keep the embryo from drying out?*

Fluid within this membrane cushions the embryo and keeps it moist.

The embryo's wastes collect inside this membrane.

The shell protects the embryo and has pores that oxygen and carbon dioxide can pass through.

Embryo

This membrane holds the yolk, which is the embryo's energy supply.

Oxygen and carbon dioxide move across this membrane.

FIGURE 18
An Egg-Eating Snake
The jawbones of this snake's skull have moved to let the snake swallow an egg.
Making Generalizations *How are snakes different from lizards?*

Diversity of Reptiles

Reptiles that are alive today include lizards, snakes, and turtles. The dinosaurs are reptiles that are now extinct.

Lizards and Snakes Most reptiles alive today are either lizards or snakes. ⬭ **Both lizards and snakes are reptiles that have skin covered with overlapping scales.** As they grow, they shed their skin and scales, replacing the worn ones with new ones. Lizards differ from snakes in an obvious way. Lizards have four legs and snakes have streamlined bodies with no legs. Snakes move by contracting bands of muscles that are connected to their ribs and backbones.

A few lizards are herbivores that eat leaves. Most lizards, however, are carnivores that capture their prey by jumping at it. While some large lizards eat frogs and birds, most smaller lizards hunt insects.

All snakes are carnivores. Most snakes feed on small animals, such as mice, but some eat large prey. If you did the Standards Warm-Up, you learned that a snake's jawbones can spread wide apart. In addition, the bones of a snake's skull can move to let the snake swallow an animal larger in diameter than itself. Snakes capture their prey in different ways. For example, some snakes have long, curved front teeth for hooking slippery prey. Other snakes, such as rattlesnakes and copperheads, have venom glands attached to hollow teeth called fangs. When these snakes bite their prey, venom flows down through the fangs and enters the prey.

 **Reading Checkpoint** **How do rattlesnakes capture prey?**

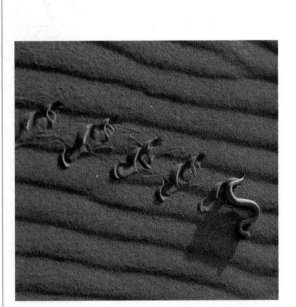

FIGURE 19
A Sidewinder Snake
The sidewinder snake lifts loops of its body off the desert sand as it moves along. Only a small part of its body touches the sand at one time.

Alligators and Crocodiles If you walk along a lake in Florida, you just might see an alligator swimming silently in the water. Most of its body lies beneath the surface, but you can see its large, bulging eyes above the surface. Alligators, crocodiles, and their relatives are the largest living reptiles. The American alligator can grow to be more than 5 meters long.

Both alligators and crocodiles are large, carnivorous reptiles that care for their young. So, how do you tell an alligator from a crocodile? Alligators have broad, rounded snouts, with only a few teeth visible when their mouths are shut. In contrast, crocodiles have pointed snouts, with most of their teeth visible when their mouths are shut. Alligators and crocodiles are carnivores that often hunt at night.

Science and **History**

Discovering Vertebrate Fossils

People have been discovering fossils since ancient times. Here are some especially important fossil discoveries.

**1677
Dinosaur-Bone Illustration**
Robert Plot, the head of a museum in England, published a book that had an illustration of a huge fossilized thighbone. Plot thought that the bone belonged to a giant human, but it probably was the thighbone of a dinosaur.

1811 Sea Reptile
Along the cliffs near Lyme Regis, England, 12-year-old Mary Anning discovered the fossilized remains of the giant sea reptile now called *Ichthyosaurus*. Mary became one of England's first professional fossil collectors.

**1822
Dinosaur Tooth**
In a quarry near Lewes, England, Mary Ann Mantell discovered a strange-looking tooth embedded in stone. Her husband Gideon drew the picture of the tooth shown here. The tooth belonged to the dinosaur *Iguanodon*.

| 1670 | 1760 | 1820 |

Unlike most reptiles, crocodiles and alligators care for their eggs and newly hatched young. The female lays her eggs in a nest of rotting plants. The female stays near the nest. From time to time, she comes out of the water and crawls over to the nest to keep it moist. After the tiny young hatch, the female scoops them up in her huge mouth. She carries the young from the nest to a nursery area in the water, where they will be safer.

For as long as a year after young alligators have hatched, the female stays near her young. The young alligators make gulping quacks when they are alarmed. When their mother hears her young quack, she rushes toward them. She protects her young until they can feed and protect themselves.

Reading Checkpoint How can you tell an alligator from a crocodile?

Writing in Science

Research and Write If you could interview the person who discovered one of the fossils, what questions would you ask about the fossil and how it was found? Write a list of those questions. Then use reference materials to try to find the answers to some of them.

**1861
Bird Bones**
A worker in a stone quarry in Germany found *Archaeopteryx*, a feathered, birdlike animal that also had many reptile characteristics.

**1902
*Tyrannosaurus***
A tip from a local rancher sent Barnum Brown, a fossil hunter, to a barren, rocky area near Jordan, Montana. There Brown found the first relatively complete skeleton of *Tyrannosaurus rex.*

1964 *Deinonychus*
In Montana, paleontologist John Ostrom discovered the remains of a small dinosaur, *Deinonychus*. This dinosaur was probably a predator that could move rapidly. This fossil led scientists to hypothesize that dinosaurs may have been endotherms.

**1991
Dinosaur Eggs in China**
Digging beneath the ground, a farmer on Green Dragon Mountain in China uncovered what may be the largest nest of fossil dinosaur eggs ever found. A paleontologist chips carefully to remove one of the eggs from the rock.

| 1880 | 1940 | 2000 |

Math Analyzing Data

The Sex Ratio of Newly Hatched Alligators

The temperature of the developing eggs of the American alligator affects the sex ratio of the young. (Sex ratio is the number of females compared with the number of males.) The graph on the right shows the numbers of young of each sex that hatched from eggs in which the young developed at different temperatures.

1. **Reading Graphs** At which temperature(s) did only females hatch?

2. **Drawing Conclusions** What effect does the temperature of developing eggs have on the sex of the baby alligators?

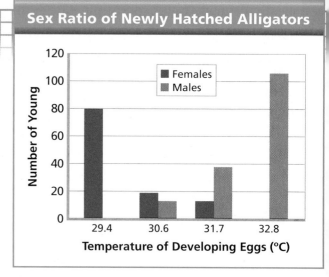

Sex Ratio of Newly Hatched Alligators

3. **Calculating** If 100 eggs developed at 31.7°C, about how many of the young would be male?

Turtles Turtles live in the ocean, in fresh water, and on land. Turtles that live on land are commonly called "tortoises." 🔑 **A turtle is a reptile whose body is covered by a protective shell that includes the ribs and the backbone.** The bony plates of the shell are covered by large scales made from the same material as the skin's scales. Some turtles have shells that can cover the whole body. Most turtles can draw the head, legs, and tail inside the shell for protection. Turtle shells may be hard or as soft as pancakes.

Turtles feed in a variety of ways, but all have a sharp-edged beak instead of teeth for tearing food. Some turtles are carnivores, such as the largest turtles, the leatherbacks. Leatherbacks feed mainly on jellyfishes. The leatherbacks' tough skin protects them from the effects of the stinging cells. Other turtles, such as the Galápagos tortoise, are herbivores. They feed mainly on cacti, using their beaks to scrape off the prickly spines before swallowing the cactus.

 Reading Checkpoint What are turtles that live on land called?

FIGURE 20
A Galápagos Tortoise
The Galápagos tortoise lives on land, where it eats mainly cacti.

Extinct Reptiles—The Dinosaurs

Millions of years ago, huge turtles and fish-eating reptiles swam in the oceans. Flying reptiles soared through the skies. Snakes and lizards basked on warm rocks. And there were dinosaurs of every description. Some dinosaurs were the largest land animals that ever lived. Unlike today's reptiles, some dinosaurs may have been endothermic.

Dinosaurs were the earliest vertebrates that had legs positioned directly beneath their bodies. This adaptation allowed them to move more easily than animals such as salamanders and lizards, whose legs stick out from the sides of their bodies. Most herbivorous dinosaurs, such as *Brachiosaurus*, walked on four legs. Most carnivores, such as the huge *Tyrannosaurus rex*, ran on two legs.

Dinosaurs became extinct, or disappeared from Earth, about 65 million years ago. **Climate change may have caused the extinction of dinosaurs and other organisms.** Scientists hypothesize that Earth became much cooler because huge clouds of dust and gases blocked sunlight. As you learned in Chapter 8, volcanoes or the impact of a huge object from space may have caused the clouds. Lack of sunlight would have caused the death of many plants—and the animals that depended on the plants. The dinosaurs did not have adaptations that let them survive.

FIGURE 21
Brachiosaurus
Brachiosaurus grew to be more than 22.5 meters long—longer than two school buses put together end to end. **Inferring** *What advantage did a long neck give Brachiosaurus?*

Section 4 Assessment

S 7.3.e, 7.5.a, E-LA: Writing 7.2.5, Reading 7.1.2

Vocabulary Skill Greek Word Origins
Tyrannosaurus comes from the Greek words *tyrannos,* meaning "a cruel ruler," and *sauros,* meaning "lizard." How do these Greek words relate to the characteristics of *Tyrannosaurus rex*?

Reviewing Key Concepts

1. a. Defining What is a reptile?
 b. Explaining What are three adaptations that allow reptiles to survive on land?
 c. Predicting What might happen to a reptile egg if part of its shell were removed?
2. a. Identifying What are the three main groups of reptiles?
 b. Classifying A gecko is a small reptile that has no shell protecting its body. It uses its legs to climb trees. Into which reptile group would you classify the gecko?
 c. Inferring How do you think a gecko captures its prey? Explain your answer.
3. a. Reviewing When did the dinosaurs become extinct?
 b. Relating Cause and Effect What may have caused the dinosaurs to become extinct?

Writing in Science

Product Label Write a "packaging label" that will be pasted onto the eggshell of a reptile. Include on your label a list of the contents of the shell and a one-paragraph description of the egg's ability to survive in a dry environment.

CALIFORNIA
Standards Focus

S 7.5.a Students know plants and animals have levels of organization for structure and function, including cells, tissues, organs, organ systems, and the whole organism.

🔑 What are the main characteristics of birds?

Key Terms
- bird
- contour feather
- down feather
- crop
- gizzard

Lab zone Standards **Warm-Up**

What Are Feathers Like?

1. 🐾 Observe the overall shape and structure of a feather. Then use a hand lens to examine the many hairlike barbs that project out from the feather's central shaft.

2. Gently separate two barbs in the middle of the feather. Rub the separated edges with your fingertip. How do they feel?

3. Use the hand lens to examine the edges of the two separated barbs. Draw a diagram of what you observe.

4. Rejoin the two separated barbs by gently pulling outward from the shaft. Then wash your hands.

Think It Over
Observing Once the barbs have been separated, is it easy to rejoin them? How might this be an advantage to the bird?

One day in 1861, in a limestone quarry in what is now Germany, Hermann von Meyer was inspecting rocks. Meyer, a fossil hunter, spotted something dark in a rock. It was the blackened imprint of a feather! Excited, he began searching for a fossil of an entire bird. He eventually found it—a skeleton surrounded by the imprint of many feathers. The fossil was given the scientific name *Archaeopteryx* (ahr kee AHP tur iks), meaning "ancient winged thing."

Paleontologists now think that *Archaeopteryx* lived about 145 million years ago. *Archaeopteryx* didn't look much like the birds you know. It looked more like a reptile with wings. Unlike any modern bird, *Archaeopteryx* had a long, bony tail and a mouth full of teeth. But, unlike a reptile, it had feathers and wings. Paleontologists think that *Archaeopteryx* and modern birds descended from some kind of reptile. Many scientists think that birds descended from dinosaurs.

◀ **A model of *Archaeopteryx***

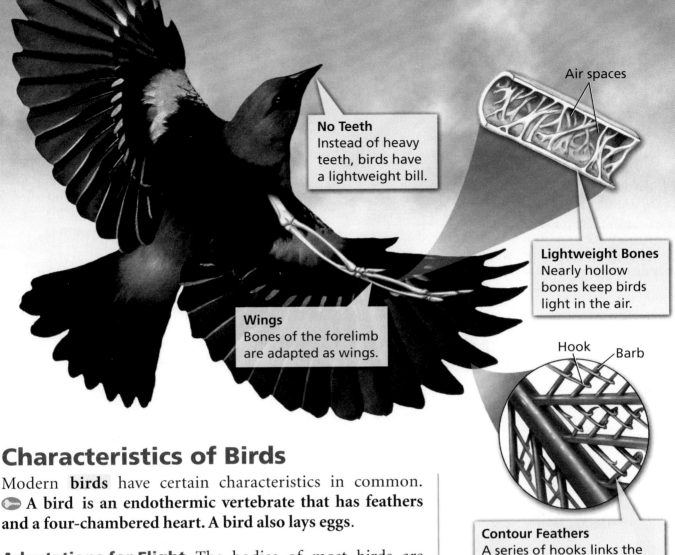

No Teeth
Instead of heavy teeth, birds have a lightweight bill.

Air spaces

Lightweight Bones
Nearly hollow bones keep birds light in the air.

Wings
Bones of the forelimb are adapted as wings.

Hook   Barb

Contour Feathers
A series of hooks links the barbs of a feather together, keeping the feather smooth.

Characteristics of Birds

Modern **birds** have certain characteristics in common. 🔑 **A bird is an endothermic vertebrate that has feathers and a four-chambered heart. A bird also lays eggs.**

Adaptations for Flight The bodies of most birds are adapted for flight, as shown in Figure 22. Many of a bird's bones are nearly hollow, making the bird lightweight. In addition, the bones of a bird's forelimbs form wings. Flying birds have large chest muscles that move the wings. Finally, feathers help birds fly. Birds are the only animals with feathers.

Feathers are not all the same. If you have ever picked up a feather, it was probably a contour feather. A **contour feather** is one of the large feathers that give shape to a bird's body. The long contour feathers that extend beyond the body on the wings and tail are called flight feathers. When a bird flies, these feathers help it balance and steer. You can see in Figure 22 that a contour feather consists of a central shaft and many projections, called barbs. Hooks hold the barbs together.

In addition to contour feathers, birds have short, fluffy **down feathers** that are specialized to trap heat and keep the bird warm. Down feathers are found right next to the bird's skin, at the base of the contour feathers. Down feathers are soft and flexible, unlike contour feathers.

✓ **Reading Checkpoint** How are the structures of contour feathers and down feathers different?

FIGURE 22
Adaptations for Flight
The bodies of most birds have adaptations for flight.
Interpreting Diagrams *What are two adaptations that make birds light?*

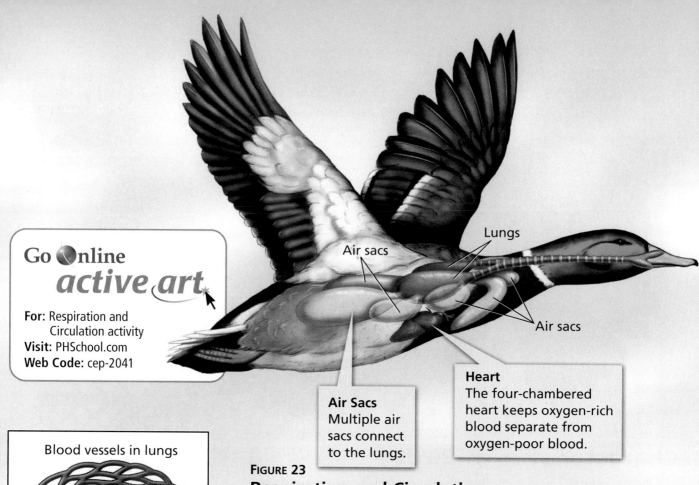

Go Online
active art

For: Respiration and Circulation activity
Visit: PHSchool.com
Web Code: cep-2041

Lungs

Air sacs

Air sacs

Air Sacs
Multiple air sacs connect to the lungs.

Heart
The four-chambered heart keeps oxygen-rich blood separate from oxygen-poor blood.

FIGURE 23

Respiration and Circulation

Air sacs and a four-chambered heart help birds obtain oxygen and move it to their cells.
Applying Concepts *Why is a four-chambered heart efficient?*

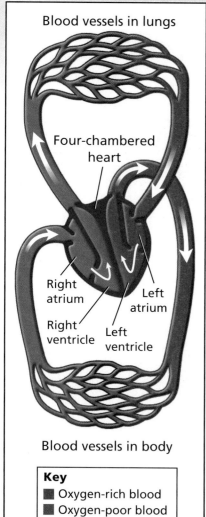

Blood vessels in lungs

Four-chambered heart

Right atrium

Left atrium

Right ventricle

Left ventricle

Blood vessels in body

Key
■ Oxygen-rich blood
■ Oxygen-poor blood

Obtaining Oxygen Flying uses a lot of energy. Therefore, cells must receive plenty of oxygen to release the energy contained in food. Birds have a highly efficient way to get oxygen into their bodies and to their cells. Birds have a system of air sacs in their bodies that connects to the lungs. The air sacs enable birds to obtain more oxygen from each breath of air than other animals can.

The circulatory systems of birds are also efficient at getting oxygen to the cells. Birds have hearts with four chambers—two atria and two ventricles. Trace the path of blood through a bird's two-loop circulatory system in Figure 23. The right side of a bird's heart pumps oxygen-poor blood to the lungs, where oxygen is picked up. Oxygen-rich blood returns to the left side of the heart, which pumps it to the cells.

The advantage of a four-chambered heart over a three-chambered heart is that oxygen-rich blood does not mix with oxygen-poor blood. Therefore, blood carried to the cells of the body has plenty of oxygen.

Obtaining Food Birds must obtain a lot of food to provide the energy needed for flight. To capture, grip, and handle food, birds mainly use their bills. Bills are shaped to help birds feed quickly and efficiently. For example, the pointy, curved bill of a hawk acts like a meat hook to pull off bits of its prey. In contrast, a duck's bill acts like a kitchen strainer, separating out seeds and tiny animals from muddy pond water.

After a bird eats its food, digestion begins. Each organ in a bird's digestive system is adapted to process food. Many birds have an internal storage tank, or **crop,** for storing food inside the body after swallowing it. Find the crop in Figure 24. The crop is connected to the stomach.

A bird's stomach has two parts. In the first part, food is bathed in chemicals that begin to break it down. Then the food moves to a thick-walled, muscular part of the stomach called the **gizzard.** The gizzard squeezes and grinds the partially digested food. Birds do not have teeth. The gizzard does the same grinding function for birds that your teeth do for you. The gizzard may contain small stones that the bird has swallowed. These stones help grind the food by rubbing against it and crushing it.

 **Reading Checkpoint** What is a gizzard?

Video Field Trip
Discovery Channel School
Birds and Mammals

FIGURE 24
Digestive System of a Hawk
Some birds like this hawk have a crop and a gizzard. The crop stores food, and the gizzard crushes food. **Interpreting Diagrams** *Does food reach the crop or the gizzard first?*

Crop
The crop stores food before it enters the stomach.

Gizzard
The gizzard is a thick-walled muscular part of the stomach that squeezes and grinds the food.

Down Feather ▶

FIGURE 25
Keeping Warm
A pine grosbeak puffs out its feathers to trap air in the layer of down feathers next to its skin. Down feathers help keep birds warm.

Try This **Activity**

"Eggs-amination"

1. Observe the surface of a chicken egg with a hand lens. Then gently crack the egg into a bowl. Do not break the yolk.
2. Note the membrane attached to the inside of the shell. Then look at the blunt end of the egg. What do you see?
3. Fill one part of the eggshell with water. What do you observe?
4. Find the egg yolk. What is its function?
5. Look for a small white spot on the yolk. This marks the spot where the embryo would have developed if the egg had been fertilized.
6. Wash your hands with soap.

Observing Draw a labeled diagram of the egg that names each structure and describes its function.

Keeping Conditions Stable Like all animals, birds use their food for energy. You know that birds need energy for flight. Because birds are endotherms, they also need a lot of energy to maintain their body temperature. Each day, an average bird eats food equal to about a quarter of its body weight. When people say, "You're eating like a bird," they usually mean that you're eating very little. But if you were actually eating as much as a bird does, you would be eating huge meals. You might be eating as many as 100 hamburger patties in one day!

To maintain their body temperature, birds use feathers as well as energy from food. As you read earlier, down feathers are specialized to trap heat. They are found right next to a bird's skin. In Figure 25, you can see what a down feather looks like. Unlike contour feathers, down feathers are soft and flexible. So, they mingle and overlap, trapping air. Air is a good insulator—a material that does not conduct heat well and therefore helps prevent heat from escaping. By trapping a blanket of warm air next to the bird's skin, down feathers slow the rate at which the skin loses heat. In effect, down feathers cover a bird in lightweight long underwear.

✓ **Reading Checkpoint** Why do birds need a lot of food?

Reproduction and Caring for Young Like reptiles, birds have internal fertilization and lay eggs. Bird eggs are similar to reptile eggs. However, the shells of bird eggs are harder. In most bird species, the female lays the eggs in a nest that has been prepared by one or both parents.

Bird eggs will only develop at a temperature close to the body temperature of the parent bird. Thus, a parent bird usually incubates the eggs by sitting on them to keep them warm. In some species, incubating the eggs is the job of just one parent. For example, female robins incubate their eggs. In other species, such as pigeons, the parents take turns incubating the eggs. Chicks may take from 12 to 80 days to develop, depending on the species.

When it is ready to hatch, a chick pecks its way out of the eggshell. Some newly hatched chicks, such as ducks, chickens, and partridges, are covered with down and can run about soon after they have hatched. Other chicks, such as baby blue jays and robins, are featherless, blind, and so weak they can barely lift their heads to beg for food. Most parent birds feed and protect their young at least until they are able to fly.

FIGURE 26
Parental Care
The partridge chicks (left) find their own food from the day they hatch. In contrast, the blue jay chicks (above) are featherless, blind, and totally dependent on their parents for food for several weeks.

Section 5 Assessment

S 7.5.a, E-LA: Reading 7.1.2

Vocabulary Skill Greek Word Origins *Archaeopteryx* comes from the Greek words *archaios,* meaning "ancient," and *pteron,* meaning "wing." How do these Greek words relate to the characteristics of *Archaeopteryx*?

Reviewing Key Concepts

1. **a. Identifying** What characteristics do birds share?
   b. Explaining How is a bird's body adapted for flight?
   c. Relating Cause and Effect Why do birds need so much oxygen? What adaptation helps them obtain oxygen?
2. **a. Reviewing** How does a parent bird usually incubate its eggs?
   b. Explaining Why is the incubating process necessary for the development of birds?

Lab zone At-Home **Activity**

Count Down Look for products in your home that contain down feathers. What common purpose do these items have? Explain to a family member how down feathers function on a bird.

Mammals

S 7.2.a Students know the differences between the life cycles and reproduction methods of sexual and asexual organisms.

S 7.5.a Students know plants and animals have levels of organization for structure and function, including cells, tissues, organs, organ systems, and the whole organism.

🔑 What characteristics do all mammals share?

🔑 What are the main groups of mammals and how do they differ in their reproduction?

Key Terms
- mammal
- mammary gland
- diaphragm
- monotreme
- marsupial
- gestation period
- placental mammal
- placenta

Lab zone Standards **Warm-Up**

What Are Mammals' Teeth Like?

1. 🖐️ Wash your hands before you begin. Then, with a small mirror, examine the shapes of your teeth. Observe the incisors (the front teeth); the pointed canine teeth; the premolars behind the canine teeth; and the molars, which are the large teeth in the very back.

2. Compare and contrast the structures of the different kinds of teeth.

3. Use your tongue to feel the cutting surfaces of the different kinds of teeth in your mouth.

4. Bite off a piece of cracker and chew it. Observe the teeth that you use to bite and chew. Wash your hands when you are finished.

Think It Over

Inferring What is the advantage of having teeth with different shapes?

High in the Himalaya Mountains of Tibet, several yaks inch their way, single file, along a narrow cliff path. The cliff plunges thousands of meters to the valley below, so one false step can mean disaster. But the sure-footed yaks, carrying heavy loads of grain, slowly but steadily cross the cliff and make their way through the mountains.

People who live in the mountains of central Asia have depended on yaks for thousands of years. Not only do yaks carry materials for trade, they also pull plows and provide milk. Mountain villagers weave blankets from yak hair and make shoes and ropes from yak hides.

The yak is a member of the group of vertebrates called **mammals.** Today about 4,000 different species of mammals exist. Some, like the yak and wildebeest, you may never have seen. But others, such as dogs, cats, and mice, are very familiar to you. What characteristics do mammals share?

▲ **Himalayan yak**

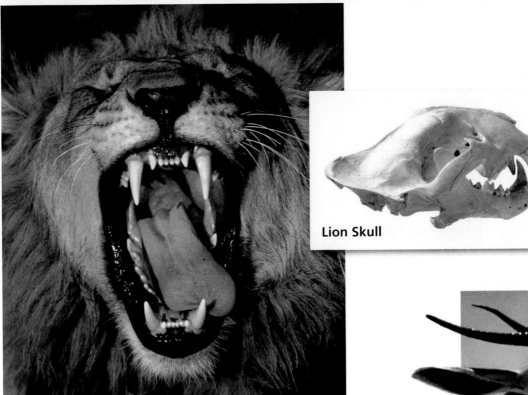

Lion Skull

Springbok Skull

Characteristics of Mammals

All mammals are endothermic vertebrates that have a four-chambered heart and skin covered with fur or hair. Most mammals are born alive, and every young mammal is fed with milk produced by organs in its mother's body. These organs are called **mammary glands.** The word *mammal,* in fact, comes from the term *mammary.*

Obtaining Food In addition to their other characteristics, most mammals have teeth. Their teeth are adapted to chew their food, breaking it into small bits that make digestion easier. Most mammals have teeth with four different shapes. If you did the Standards Warm-Up, you observed these shapes. Incisors are flat-edged teeth used to bite off and cut food. Canines are pointed teeth that stab food and tear into it. Premolars and molars have broad, flat upper surfaces for grinding and shredding food.

The size, shape, and hardness of a mammal's teeth reflect its diet. For example, the canines of carnivores are especially large and sharp. Large carnivores, such as the lion in Figure 27, use their canines to hold their prey while they kill it. In contrast, herbivores, such as a springbok, have molars for grinding and mashing plants.

FIGURE 27
Teeth of Different Shapes
Lions have sharp, pointed canines. Springboks have broad molars.
Inferring *What kind of diet does each of these mammals eat?*

 **Reading Checkpoint** Which teeth stab and tear into food?

FIGURE 28
Fur and Hair
A hippo has hardly any hair. In contrast, a wolf has a thick coat of fur.
Inferring *What can you infer about the environment each animal lives in?*

Insulated Mammals

Discover whether or not fat is an effective insulator.

1. Put on a pair of rubber gloves.
2. Spread a thick coating of solid white shortening on the outside of one of the gloves. Leave the other glove uncoated.
3. Put both hands in a bucket or sink filled with cold water.

Inferring Which hand got cold faster? Explain how this activity relates to mammalian adaptations.

Obtaining Oxygen To release energy, food must combine with oxygen inside cells. Therefore, a mammal must have an efficient way to get oxygen into the body and to the cells that need it. Like reptiles and birds, all mammals breathe with lungs. Mammals breathe in and out because of the combined action of rib muscles and a large muscle called the **diaphragm** (DY uh fram). The diaphragm is located at the bottom of the ribs. The lungs have a huge, moist surface area where oxygen can move into the blood.

Like birds, mammals have a four-chambered heart and a two-loop circulatory system. This efficient system takes oxygen to the cells.

Keeping Conditions Stable Like birds, mammals are endotherms. They need the energy in food to keep a steady internal temperature. In addition, all mammals have fur or hair at some point in their lives that helps them keep their internal temperature stable. Each strand of fur or hair is composed of dead cells strengthened with the same tough material that strengthens feathers. The amount of fur or hair that covers a mammal's skin varies greatly. In general, animals that live in cold regions, like the wolf shown in Figure 28, have more fur than animals that live in warmer environments.

Fur is not the only adaptation that allows mammals to live in cold climates. Mammals also have a layer of fat beneath their skin. Like fur and feathers, fat is an insulator.

Movement Like all vertebrates, mammals have a musculoskeletal system, which consists of muscles and bones working together. Each muscle consists of a bundle of fibers that are muscle cells. When muscles pull on bones, they make the bones move. Energy for this movement is supplied by the action of mitochondria in muscle cells.

Mammals have adaptations that allow them to move in more ways than members of any other group of vertebrates. Most mammals walk or run on four limbs, but some have specialized ways of moving. For example, kangaroos hop. Bats have wings adapted from their front limbs. The front limbs of whales, dolphins, and other sea mammals are adapted as flippers for swimming. These specialized ways of moving allow mammals to survive in many habitats.

Nervous System A mammal's nervous system coordinates its movements. In addition, the nervous system receives information about the environment. The brains of mammals enable them to learn, remember, and behave in complex ways. For example, in order for squirrels to eat nuts, they must crack the nutshell to get to the meat inside. Squirrels learn to use different methods to crack different kinds of nuts, depending on where the weak point in each kind of shell is located.

The senses of mammals are highly developed and adapted for the ways a species lives. Tarsiers, which are active at night, have huge eyes that let them see in the dark. Bats use keen hearing to navigate and catch prey. Dogs, cats, and bears often use smell to track their prey.

FIGURE 29
A Swinging Orangutan
This young orangutan can grasp branches with its limbs and swing from place to place.

 **Reading Checkpoint** What are three ways that mammals can move?

FIGURE 30
The Senses of Seals
Seals can see under water in near darkness. Their long whiskers help them obtain food by detecting the movements of their prey.

FIGURE 31
A Spiny Anteater
The young of this spiny anteater, a monotreme, hatch from eggs.

Diversity of Mammals

Mammals are a very diverse group. ⬤ **The three main groups of mammals are monotremes, marsupials, and placental mammals. The groups differ in how they reproduce and how their young develop.**

Monotremes Egg-laying mammals are called **monotremes** (MAHN oh treemz). There are just three species of monotremes—two species of spiny anteaters and the duck-billed platypus. A female spiny anteater lays one to three leathery-shelled eggs directly into a pouch on her belly. After the young hatch, they stay in the pouch for six to eight weeks. There they drink milk that seeps out of pores on the mother's skin. In contrast, the duck-billed platypus lays her eggs in an underground nest. The tiny young feed by lapping at the milk that oozes from slits onto the fur of their mother's belly.

Marsupials Koalas, kangaroos, and opossums are some of the better-known marsupials. **Marsupials** (mahr SOOP ee ulz) are mammals whose young are born at an early stage of development, and they usually continue to develop in a pouch on their mother's body.

Marsupials have a very short **gestation period,** the length of time between fertilization and birth. For example, opossums have a gestation period of about 13 days. Newborn marsupials are tiny—some opossums are less than 1 centimeter long at birth! When they are born, marsupials are blind, hairless, and pink. They crawl along the wet fur of their mother's belly until they reach her pouch. Once inside, they find one of her nipples and attach to it. They remain in the pouch until they have grown enough to peer out of the pouch opening.

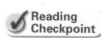
Reading Checkpoint What is a marsupial?

FIGURE 32
Kangaroos
This gray kangaroo, a marsupial, carries her offspring in a pouch.
Classifying *How do marsupials differ from monotremes?*

Placental Mammals Unlike a monotreme or a marsupial, a **placental** (pluh SEN tal) **mammal** develops inside its mother's body until its body systems can function independently. The name of this group comes from the **placenta,** an organ in pregnant female mammals that passes materials between the mother and the developing embryo. Food and oxygen pass from the mother to her young. Wastes pass from the young to the mother, who eliminates them. An umbilical cord connects the young to the mother's placenta. Most mammals, including humans, are placental mammals. Gestation periods of placental mammals are generally longer than those of marsupials. Usually, the larger the placental mammal, the longer the gestation period. The gestation period for an elephant, for example, averages about 21 months, but for a mouse, it's only about 20 days.

Placental mammals are classified into groups on the basis of characteristics such as how they eat and how their bodies move. You can see the diversity of placental mammals in Figure 34 on the next page.

 **Reading Checkpoint** What is a placenta?

FIGURE 33 Mother and Baby Giraffe
This baby giraffe, a placental mammal, feeds on milk produced by its mother.

Reviewing Math: Algebra and Functions 7.1.5

Math ▶ Analyzing Data

Mammal Diversity

This circle graph shows the percentage of species of some types of mammals.

1. **Reading Graphs** What percentage of species are bats?

2. **Calculating** What percentage of species are not bats?

3. **Graphing** Suppose you used the data shown in the circle graph to make a bar graph. Which bar would be tallest?

4. **Predicting** What total should all the percentages in the pie chart add up to? Do you have to add the percentages to obtain your answer? Explain.

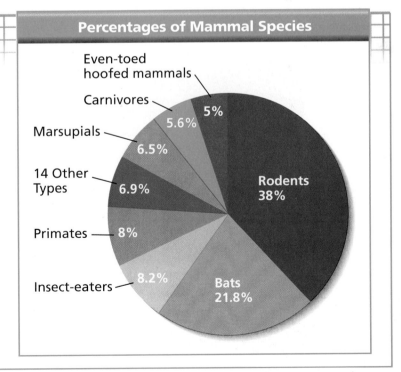

Percentages of Mammal Species

- Even-toed hoofed mammals — 5%
- Carnivores — 5.6%
- Marsupials — 6.5%
- 14 Other Types — 6.9%
- Primates — 8%
- Insect-eaters — 8.2%
- Bats 21.8%
- Rodents 38%

FIGURE 34
Diversity of Placental Mammals

From tiny moles to huge elephants, placental mammals are diverse. They are grouped on the basis of how they eat and move as well as other characteristics.

Rabbits and Hares ▶
Leaping mammals like this black-tailed jack rabbit have long hind legs specialized for spectacular jumps. Rabbits and hares have long, curved incisors for gnawing.

Carnivores ▶
This river otter belongs to the group known as carnivores. Dogs, raccoons, and seals are other members of this group. Most carnivores have large canine teeth and clawed toes that help them catch and eat their prey.

Marine Mammals ▲
Whales, manatees, and these Atlantic spotted dolphins are ocean-dwelling mammals with a body shape adapted for swimming.

Rodents ▶
Rodents are gnawing mammals such as mice, rats, beavers, and the capybaras shown here. The incisor teeth of most rodents keep growing throughout their lives but are constantly worn down by gnawing.

Mammals With Trunks ▲
Elephants' noses are long trunks that they use for collecting food and water.

Insect-Eaters ▲
Moles and their relatives have sharp cutting surfaces on all of their teeth. This star-nosed mole spends much of its time searching for prey with its sensitive, tentacled snout.

◄ Flying Mammals
The wings of bats are made of a thin skin that stretches from their wrists to the tips of their long finger bones.

◄ Toothless Mammals
Armadillos, such as the one shown here, are toothless mammals. So are sloths. Although a few members of this group have small teeth, most have none.

Primates ▼
This group of mammals with large brains and eyes that face forward includes humans, monkeys, and apes such as this chimpanzee.

Hoofed Mammals ▲
Some mammals with hooves have an even number of toes and some have an odd number of toes. Cows, deer, and pigs all have an even number of toes. Horses and zebras have an odd number of toes.

FIGURE 35
Parental Care by Dall's Sheep
Young mammals usually require much parental care. On a rocky slope in Alaska, this Dall's sheep, a placental mammal, keeps a close watch on her lamb.

Caring for Young Whether a monotreme, a marsupial, or a placental mammal, young mammals are usually quite helpless for a long time after being born. Many are born without a coat of insulating fur. Their eyes are often sealed and may not open for weeks. For example, black bear cubs are surprisingly tiny when they are born. The blind, nearly hairless cubs have a mass of only 240 to 330 grams—about the same mass as a grapefruit. The mass of an adult black bear, in contrast, ranges from about 120 to 150 kilograms—about 500 times as much as a newborn cub!

Young mammals usually stay with their mother or both parents for an extended time. After black bear cubs learn to walk, they follow their mother about for the next year, learning how to be a bear. They learn things that are important to their survival, such as which mushrooms and berries are good to eat and how to rip apart a rotten log and find good-tasting grubs within it. During the winter, when black bears go through a period of inactivity, the young bears stay with their mother. The following spring, she will usually force them to live independently.

Reading Checkpoint Why are most young mammals dependent on one or both parents after they are born?

Section 6 Assessment

S 7.2.a, 7.5.a,
E-LA: Reading 7.2.0

 **Target Reading Skill** Compare and Contrast Use your compare/contrast table to help you answer Question 2.

Reviewing Key Concepts

1. a. **Defining** What characteristics do mammals share?
   b. **Describing** Describe the adaptation that most mammals have for obtaining food.
   c. **Relating Cause and Effect** What enables mammals to live in colder environments than reptiles? Explain.
2. a. **Reviewing** What are the three main groups of mammals?
   b. **Explaining** How do these groups differ in their manner of reproduction?
   c. **Comparing and Contrasting** Why might scientists consider monotremes to be a link between reptiles and mammals?

Lab zone At-Home **Activity**

Mammals' Milk With a family member, examine the nutrition label on a container of whole milk. What types of nutrients does whole milk contain? Discuss why milk is an ideal source of food for young, growing mammals.

Keeping Warm

S 7.5.b, 7.7.c

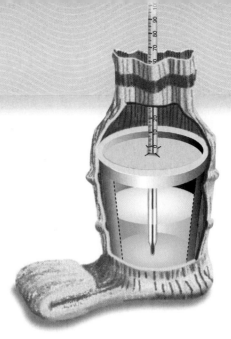

Problem

Wool products are made from the hair of mammals, such as sheep. Do wool products provide insulation from the cold? How well does wool insulate when it is wet?

Skills Focus

graphing, interpreting data

Materials

- tap water, hot   • scissors   • beaker, 1-L
- 3 thermometers   • clock or watch
- graph paper   • a pair of wool socks
- tap water, room temperature
- 3 containers, 250-mL, with lids

Procedure

1. Put one container into a dry woolen sock. Soak a second sock with water at room temperature, wring it out so it's not dripping, and then slide the second container into the wet sock. Both containers should stand upright. Leave the third container uncovered.

2. Create a data table in your notebook, listing the containers in the first column. Provide four more columns in which to record the water temperatures during the experiment.

3. Use scissors to carefully cut a small "X" in the center of each lid. Make the X just large enough for a thermometer to pass through.

4. Fill a beaker with about 800 mL of hot tap water. Then pour hot water nearly to the top of each of the three containers. **CAUTION:** *Avoid spilling hot water on yourself or others.*

5. Place a lid on each of the containers, and insert a thermometer into the water through the hole in each lid. Gather the socks around the thermometers above the first two containers so that the containers are completely covered.

6. Immediately measure the temperature of the water in each container, and record it in your data table. Take temperature readings every 5 minutes for at least 15 minutes.

Analyze and Conclude

1. **Graphing** Graph your results using a different color to represent each container. Graph time in minutes on the horizontal axis and temperature on the vertical axis.

2. **Interpreting Data** Compare the temperature changes in the three containers. Relate your findings to the insulation characteristics of mammal skin coverings.

3. **Communicating** Suppose a company claims that its wool socks keep you warm even if they get wet. Do your findings support this claim? Write a letter to the company explaining why or why not.

Design an Experiment

Design an experiment to compare how wool's insulating properties compare with those of other natural materials (such as cotton) or manufactured materials (such as acrylic). Obtain your teacher's permission before carrying out your investigation.

Go Online PHSchool.com
For: Data sharing
Visit: PHSchool.com
Web Code: ced-2043

Chapter 12 Study Guide

The BIG Idea

Vertebrates have endoskeletons that include backbones. Backbones provide support and enable movement.

① What Is a Vertebrate?

Key Concepts   S 7.4.g, 7.5.c

- Chordates have a notochord, a nerve cord that runs down their back, and slits in their throat area.
- A vertebrate has a backbone that is part of an internal skeleton.
- By studying fossils and other evidence, scientists infer the relationships between vertebrate groups.
- The body temperature of most fishes, amphibians, and reptiles is close to that of their environment. In contrast, birds and mammals have a stable body temperature.

Key Terms
- chordate • notochord • vertebra
- ectotherm • endotherm

② Fishes

Key Concepts   S 7.5.b

- In addition to living in water and having fins, most fishes are ectotherms, obtain oxygen through gills, and have scales.
- The major groups of fishes are jawless fishes, cartilaginous fishes, and bony fishes.
- Jawless fishes have no jaws and no scales.
- Cartilaginous fishes have jaws and scales, and skeletons made of cartilage.
- A bony fish has jaws, scales, a pocket on each side of the head that holds the gills, and a skeleton made of hard bone.

Key Terms
- fish • cartilage • swim bladder

③ Amphibians

Key Concepts   S 7.5.a

- After beginning their lives in water, most amphibians spend their adulthood on land, returning to water to reproduce.
- The respiratory and circulatory systems of adult amphibians are adapted for life on land.

Key Terms
- amphibian • tadpole • lung • atrium
- ventricle • habitat

④ Reptiles

Key Concepts   S 7.3.e, 7.5.a

- The skin, kidneys, and eggs of reptiles are adapted to conserve water.
- Both lizards and snakes are reptiles that have skin covered with overlapping scales.
- Both alligators and crocodiles are large, carnivorous reptiles that care for their young.
- A turtle is a reptile with a protective shell that includes the ribs and the backbone.
- Climate changes may have caused the extinction of dinosaurs and other organisms.

Key Terms
- reptile • urine • kidney • amniotic egg

⑤ Birds

Key Concepts   S 7.5.a

- A bird is an endothermic vertebrate that has feathers and a four-chambered heart. A bird also lays eggs.

Key Terms
- bird • contour feather • down feather
- crop • gizzard

⑥ Mammals

Key Concepts   S 7.2.a, 7.5.a

- All mammals are endothermic vertebrates that have a four-chambered heart and skin covered with fur or hair. Most mammals are born alive, and every young mammal is fed with milk.
- There are three main groups of mammals—monotremes, marsupials, and placental mammals. The groups differ in how their young develop.

Key Terms
- mammal • mammary gland • diaphragm
- monotreme • marsupial • gestation period
- placental mammal • placenta

Review and Assessment

Target Reading Skill

Compare and Contrast Complete the compare/contrast table below, which compares the circulatory systems of four vertebrate groups.

Vertebrate Group	Number of Loops in Circulatory System	Number of Chambers in Heart
Fishes	one	a. _____?_____
Adult amphibians	b. _____?_____	c. _____?_____
Birds	d. _____?_____	e. _____?_____
Mammals	f. _____?_____	four

Reviewing Key Terms

Choose the letter of the best answer.

1. Vertebrates are a subgroup of
   a. chordates.
   b. fishes.
   c. amphibians.
   d. reptiles.

2. A fish
   a. is an endotherm.
   b. has fins.
   c. has lungs.
   d. has a three-chambered heart.

3. A reptile
   a. is an endotherm.
   b. lays eggs.
   c. has a swim bladder.
   d. has a thin skin.

4. The gizzard of a bird
   a. stores air.
   b. removes oxygen from air.
   c. helps a bird fly.
   d. grinds food.

5. A monotreme differs from a placental mammal because the monotreme
   a. has fur.
   b. has a placenta.
   c. lays eggs.
   d. feeds its young with milk.

Complete the following sentences so that your answers clearly explain the key terms.

6. At some point, all chordates have a **notochord,** which is a(n) _____ .

7. The life cycles of **amphibians** are different from those of most vertebrates because amphibians _____ .

8. Unlike an amphibian's eggs, a reptile's **amniotic eggs** have _____ .

9. A **contour feather** functions to _____ .

10. The **placenta** is an organ whose function is to _____ .

Writing in Science

Cause and Effect Paragraph Which adaptations improve a bird's ability to fly? Write a paragraph in which you describe the adaptations that enable a bird to fly. Be sure to include a topic sentence.

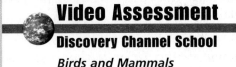

Video Assessment
Discovery Channel School
Birds and Mammals

Review and Assessment

Checking Concepts

11. What evidence has enabled scientists to infer the order in which vertebrate groups evolved?

12. How do fishes reproduce?

13. Describe the adaptations of an adult amphibian for obtaining oxygen from the air.

14. Explain how the structure of a reptile's egg protects the embryo inside.

15. Describe the position of dinosaurs' legs on their bodies. How did this give dinosaurs an advantage?

16. What adaptations help a bird obtain enough oxygen for flight?

17. How does the structure of an incisor relate to its function?

18. Describe how mammals breathe in and out.

Thinking Critically

19. **Relating Cause and Effect** Explain why an endoskeleton allows vertebrates to grow larger than animals without endoskeletons.

20. **Interpreting Diagrams** How does blood move in the circulatory system shown below?

Key
■ Oxygen-rich blood
■ Oxygen-poor blood

21. **Classifying** A museum has a vertebrate fossil that is over 500 million years old. To which group—fishes, amphibians, reptiles, birds, or mammals—does the fossil most likely belong? Explain your answer.

22. **Comparing and Contrasting** Compare temperature regulation in ectotherms and endotherms.

Applying Skills

Use the graph to answer Questions 23–25.

A scientist performed an experiment on five goldfishes to test the effect of water temperature on "breathing rate"—the rate at which the fishes open and close their gill covers. The graph shows the data that the scientist obtained at four different temperatures.

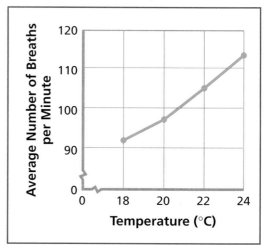

Fish Breathing Rate at Different Temperatures

23. **Controlling Variables** Identify the manipulated variable and the responding variable in this experiment.

24. **Interpreting Data** How does the breathing rate at 18°C compare to the breathing rate at 22°C?

25. **Drawing Conclusions** Based on the data shown, what is the relationship between water temperature and fish breathing rate?

Lab zone Standards Investigation

Performance Assessment Display your models in a creative and interesting way—for example, show the models in action and show details of the animals' habitats. Also display your poster. List all the adaptations you learned from your classmates' presentations. How did constructing a three-dimensional model help you understand the characteristics of these groups?

Choose the letter of the best answer.

1. Which of the following is the order in which vertebrate groups appeared on Earth, beginning with the group that appeared earliest?
   A amphibians, fishes, birds, reptiles, mammals
   B fishes, birds, reptiles, amphibians, mammals
   C birds, fishes, mammals, amphibians, reptiles
   D fishes, amphibians, reptiles, mammals, birds   **S 7.4.g**

2. The dinosaurs probably became extinct because they lacked adaptations to survive
   A attacks by predators.
   B disease.
   C in a cool climate.
   D in a warm climate.   **S 7.3.e**

Use the diagram below to answer Question 3.

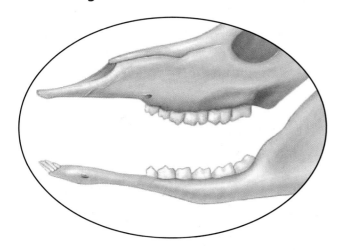

3. In the diagram above, the front of the mouth faces left. What is the most likely function of the large teeth in the center of the mouth?
   A grinding food
   B killing prey
   C biting food
   D cutting and tearing food   **S 7.5.a**

4. Suppose a bony fish injured its swim bladder. The fish would probably have difficulty
   A digesting food.
   B regulating its body temperature.
   C staying stable at different depths.
   D obtaining oxygen from water.   **S 7.5.b**

Use the table below to answer Question 5.

Characteristics of Observed Animals

Animal	Skeleton	Scales	Outer Covering of Egg
1	Bone	None	Clear jelly
2	Bone	Yes	Leathery shell
3	Bone	Yes	Thin, moist membrane
4	Cartilage	Yes	No eggs observed

5. A scientist observed four different animals and recorded her data in the table shown above. Which of the animals most likely reproduces by means of amniotic eggs?
   A Animal 1
   B Animal 2
   C Animal 3
   D Animal 4   **S 7.2.a**

6. Which of the following organs together enable all vertebrates to move from place to place?
   A crop and gizzard
   B lungs and fins
   C bones and muscles
   D air sacs and kidneys   **S 7.5.c**

7. All vertebrates reproduce
   A sexually.
   B asexually.
   C by means of internal fertilization.
   D by means of external fertilization.   **S 7.2.a**

Apply the BIG Idea

8. Describe the structure of a vertebrate's backbone and explain how this structure gives flexibility to a vertebrate's body.   **S 7.5.a**

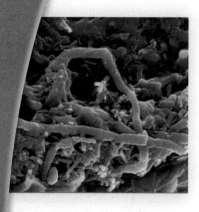

Chapter 9
Viruses, Bacteria, Protists, and Fungi

The BIG Idea

Organisms in different domains and kingdoms display varying levels of organization, from single cells to more complex structures.

- What is the structure of a virus?
- How do the cells of bacteria differ from those of eukaryotes?
- What are the characteristics of animal-like, plantlike, and funguslike protists?
- What characteristics do fungi share?

Chapter 10
Structure and Function of Plants

The BIG Idea

The structure of plants enables them to obtain water and nutrients, make food, grow, develop, and reproduce.

- What do plants need to live successfully on land?
- What characteristics do the three groups of seedless vascular plants share?
- What characteristics do seed plants share?

Chapter 11
Structure and Function of Invertebrates

The BIG Idea

The structures of animal's bodies enable them to obtain food and oxygen, keep internal conditions stable, move, and reproduce.

- What are four major functions of animals?
- What are the main characteristics of cnidarians?
- What are the main characteristics of worms?
- What are the distinguishing structures of insects, crustaceans, arachnids, centipedes, and millipedes?

Chapter 12
Structure and Function of Vertebrates

The BIG Idea

Vertebrates have endoskeletons that include backbones. Backbones provide support and enable movement.

- What are the characteristics of chordates and vertebrates?
- What adaptations allow reptiles to live on land?
- What are the main characteristics of birds?
- What characteristics do all mammals share?

Unit 3 Assessment

The circle graphs compare the number of species in each group of organisms. These graphs include only the species that scientists have named and described. There may be millions more species that have yet to be discovered or described! Keep in mind that the graphs include only the number of species, not the total number of organisms. For example, there are relatively few named species of bacteria, but there are more bacteria on Earth than any other kind of organism.

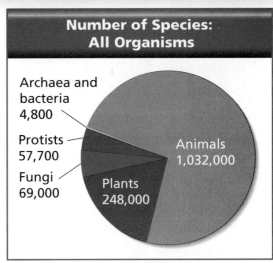

Number of Species: All Organisms

Archaea and bacteria 4,800
Protists 57,700
Fungi 69,000
Plants 248,000
Animals 1,032,000

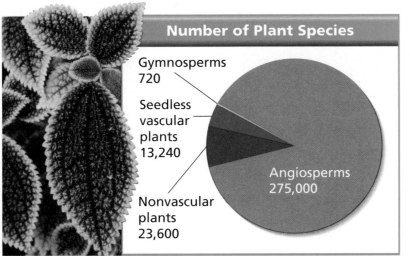

Number of Plant Species

Gymnosperms 720
Seedless vascular plants 13,240
Nonvascular plants 23,600
Angiosperms 275,000

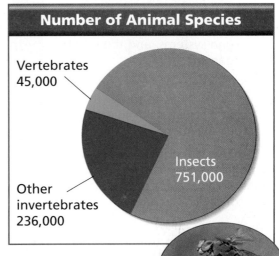

Number of Animal Species

Vertebrates 45,000
Other invertebrates 236,000
Insects 751,000

1. Look at the graph that compares all organisms. How do the cells of organisms in the smallest group differ from those in other groups? *(Chapter 9)*
   a. They have cell walls.
   b. They are prokaryotic.
   c. They have no genetic material.
   d. They have more than one nucleus.

2. What is the role of vascular tissue in plants? *(Chapter 10)*
   a. performing photosynthesis
   b. preventing water loss
   c. producing sperm and egg cells
   d. transporting water and food

3. Which statement is true of the animals in the largest group? *(Chapter 11)*
   a. They reproduce asexually.
   b. They have internal skeletons.
   c. They have external skeletons.
   d. They have radial symmetry.

4. Which of the following is found only in vertebrates? *(Chapter 12)*
   a. bony endoskeleton
   b. closed circulatory system
   c. brain and nerves
   d. bilateral symmetry

5. **Summary** Choose one plant, one animal, and one protist. Summarize how each organism reproduces.

Bones and Muscles

No matter your age or ability level, playing sports is fun and healthful. ▶

Focus on the
BIG Idea

S 7.6.i

How do the physical principles of forces and machines relate to the functions of your muscles and skeleton?

Check What You Know

A cat sleeps on one end of a seesaw, while a mouse crouches on the other end. The cat wakes up and walks away. How will the forces acting on the ends change? How will the forces change if the cat runs across the board toward the mouse?

Build Science Vocabulary

The images shown here represent some of the Key Terms in this chapter. You can use this vocabulary skill to help you understand the meaning of some Key Terms in this chapter.

Vocabulary Skill

Latin Word Origins

Many English words come from Latin. In Chapter 2 you learned that the Latin prefix re- means "back" or "against." In this chapter you will learn the term *resistance*. Resistance comes from the Latin prefix *re-* and the Latin word *sistere*, which means "to stand." So *resistance* means "the act of standing against." The table below shows Latin words that are sources of some Key Terms in this chapter.

Latin Word	Meaning of Latin Word	Key Term
in-	not	**involuntary muscle** Type of muscle that is not under a person's conscious control
ligare	to tie	**ligament** Connective tissue that holds bones together
porus	a tiny opening or hole	**osteoporosis** A condition in which bones lose minerals, develop larger openings than normal bones, and become weak
resistere	to place against	**resistance force** The force that a lever exerts against an object
voluntas	free will	**voluntary muscle** Type of muscle that is under a person's conscious control

Apply It!

1. How does the meaning of the Latin word *ligere* help you to understand what a ligament is?

2. What two key terms in the table come from the Latin word *voluntas*? What does this Latin word mean?

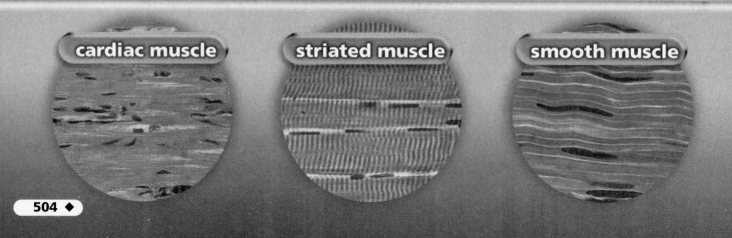

cardiac muscle   striated muscle   smooth muscle

work

joint

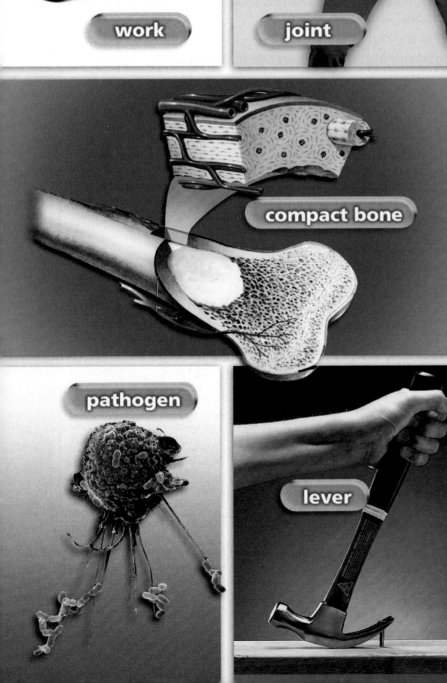

compact bone

pathogen

lever

Chapter 13 Vocabulary

How to Read Science

Take Notes

When you take notes, you write important ideas in shortened form.

1. Use a red or blue heading as the title of your notes.
2. Create a two-column note-taking organizer similar to the sample below. In the left column, write questions about the text that follows the heading. The questions should ask for important information.
3. Write the answers in the right column.
4. Write a summary statement that expresses the main idea.

See the sample notes below on part of Section 1 of this chapter.

Questions	Notes: Cells
What is a cell?	The basic unit of structure and function in a living thing
What is the structure of a cell?	See Figure 1. Cell membrane—outside boundary of cell Nucleus—directs cell's activities; contains DNA, which contains information determining cell's structure and function Cytoplasm—everything inside cell except nucleus; contains organelles
What are the functions of cells?	Carry on processes that let organisms live, grow, and reproduce
	Summary Statement: Organisms are made of cells. Cells carry on important functions in organisms.

Apply It!

1. Review the notes in the right column. What are two important ideas found in the notes?

2. According to the summary, what is the main idea of this text?

3. As you read Section 1, take notes on the rest of the section. When you read Section 3, take notes on the whole section.

Standards Investigation

A Not-So-Simple Machine

S 7.5.c, 7.6.h

A prosthesis is an artificial device that replaces a human body part. Designing artificial replacements, such as prosthetic hands, can be a challenging task. This is because even a simple act, such as picking up a pen, involves a complex interaction of body parts. If you study the movements of your hand, you may see how some of its movements are like simple machines, such as levers and hinges. You can use the physical principles behind these and other simple machines to build a prosthetic hand.

Your Goal

To design, build, and test a replacement for a human hand

Your prosthesis must

- grasp and lift a variety of objects
- be activated by pulling a cord or string
- spring back when the cord is released
- be built following the safety guidelines in Appendix A

Plan It!

Before you design your prosthetic hand, study the human hand. Watch how the fingers move to pick up objects. Make a list of tools, machines, or other devices that mimic the ability of the hand to pick up objects. Examples include tongs, tweezers, pliers, and chopsticks. Then, choose materials for your hand and sketch your design. When your teacher has approved your design, build and test your prosthetic hand.

Organ Systems and Homeostasis

CALIFORNIA
Standards Focus

S 7.5.a Students know plants and animals have levels of organization for structure and function, including cells, tissues, organs, organ systems, and the whole organism.

- What are the levels of organization in the body?
- What systems are in the human body, and what are their functions?
- What is homeostasis?

Key Terms

- muscle tissue
- nervous tissue
- connective tissue
- epithelial tissue
- organ system
- digestion
- kidney
- nephron
- urinary bladder
- pathogen
- antibody
- immunity
- homeostasis
- stress

Lab zone Standards **Warm-Up**

How Does Your Body Respond?

1. Stack one book on top of another one.

2. Lift the two stacked books in front of you so the lowest book is about level with your shoulders. Hold the books in this position for 30 seconds. While you are performing this activity, note how your body responds. For example, how do your arms feel at the beginning and toward the end of the 30 seconds?

3. Balance one book on the top of your head. Walk a few steps with the book on your head.

Think It Over
Inferring List all the parts of your body that worked together as you performed the activities in Steps 1 through 3.

The bell rings—lunchtime! You hurry down the noisy halls to the cafeteria. The unmistakable aroma of hot pizza makes your mouth water. At last, you balance your tray of pizza and salad while you pay the cashier. You look around the cafeteria for your friends. Then, you walk to the table, sit down, and begin to eat.

Think about how many parts of your body were involved in the simple act of getting and eating your lunch. Every minute of the day, whether you are eating, studying, walking, or even sleeping, your body is busy. Each part of the body has a specific function, or job. And all the different parts of your body usually work together so smoothly that you don't even notice them.

This smooth functioning is due partly to the way in which the body is organized. **The levels of organization in the human body consist of cells, tissues, organs, and organ systems.** The smallest unit of organization is the cell. The next largest unit is tissue; then, organs. Finally, the organ system is the largest unit of organization.

Cells

From the cell theory, you know that a cell is the basic unit of structure and function in a living thing. Complex organisms are composed of many cells in the same way a brick building is composed of many bricks. The human body contains about 100 trillion cells.

Structures of Cells Most animal cells, including those in the human body, have a structure similar to the cell in Figure 1. You may recall that the cell forms the outside boundary of the cell. Inside the cell is a large structure called the nucleus, which directs the cell's activities. The nucleus also contains DNA—the information that determines the cell's form and function. When the cell divides, or reproduces, this information is passed along to the newly formed cells. The material within a cell apart from the nucleus is the cytoplasm. The cytoplasm is made of a clear, jellylike substance containing many cell structures called organelles.

Functions of Cells Cells carry on processes that keep organisms alive. Inside cells, for example, molecules from digested food undergo cellular respiration that releases energy for the body's activities. Cells also grow and reproduce. And they get rid of waste products that result from these activities.

Reading Checkpoint What is the function of the nucleus?

Lab zone Try This **Activity**

How Is a Book Organized?

In this activity, you will analyze the levels of organization in a book.

1. Examine this textbook to see how it is subdivided—into chapters, sections, and so on.

2. Make a concept map that shows this pattern of organization. Place the largest subdivision at the top of the map and the smallest at the bottom.

3. Compare the levels of organization in this textbook to those in the human body.

Making Models Which level of organization in the textbook represents cells? Which represents tissues? Organs? Organ systems?

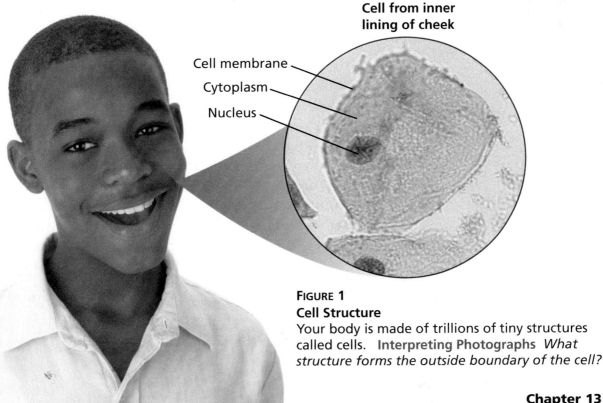

Cell from inner lining of cheek

Cell membrane

Cytoplasm

Nucleus

FIGURE 1
Cell Structure
Your body is made of trillions of tiny structures called cells. **Interpreting Photographs** *What structure forms the outside boundary of the cell?*

FIGURE 2

Types of Tissues

Your body contains four kinds of tissues: muscle, nervous, connective, and epithelial.
Comparing and Contrasting *How is the function of nervous tissue different from that of epithelial tissue?*

Muscle Tissue
Every movement you make depends on muscle tissue. The muscle tissue shown here allows your body to move.

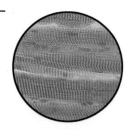

Nervous Tissue
Nervous tissue, such as the brain cells shown here, enables you to see, hear, and think.

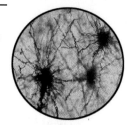

Connective Tissue
Connective tissue, such as the bone shown here, connects and supports parts of your body.

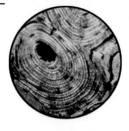

Epithelial Tissue
Epithelial tissue, such as the skin cells shown here, covers the surfaces of your body and lines your internal organs.

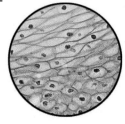

Tissues

The next largest unit of organization in your body is a tissue—a group of specialized cells that perform the same function. The human body contains four basic types of tissue. Look at Figure 2 as you read about each type.

Like the muscle cells that form it, **muscle tissue** can contract, or shorten. By doing this, muscle tissue makes parts of your body move. While muscle tissue carries out movement, **nervous tissue** directs and controls the process. Nervous tissue carries electrical messages back and forth between the brain and other parts of the body. Another type of tissue, **connective tissue,** provides support for your body and connects all its parts. Bone tissue and fat are connective tissues.

The surfaces of your body, inside and out, are covered by **epithelial tissue** (ep uh THEE lee ul). Some epithelial tissue, such as your skin, protects the delicate structures that lie beneath it. The lining of your digestive system consists of epithelial tissue that allows you to digest and absorb the nutrients in your food.

 **Reading Checkpoint** **What is the job of muscle tissue?**

Organs and Organ Systems

The stomach, heart, brain, and lungs are all organs. Recall that an organ is a structure that is composed of different kinds of tissue and does specific jobs. For example, your heart pumps blood through your body. The heart contains all four kinds of tissue—muscle, nervous, connective, and epithelial. Each tissue contributes to the organ's overall job of pumping blood.

Each organ in your body is part of a system. An **organ system** is a group of organs that work together to perform a major function. **The human body has 11 organ systems. The integumentary, skeletal, and muscular systems provide structure and allow movement. The circulatory, respiratory, digestive, excretory, immune, and reproductive systems carry out the processes of life. The nervous and endocrine systems provide control over body processes.** The next five pages describe the major functions of these systems. Remember that for each system to function, its organs and tissues must work together. And so must its cells.

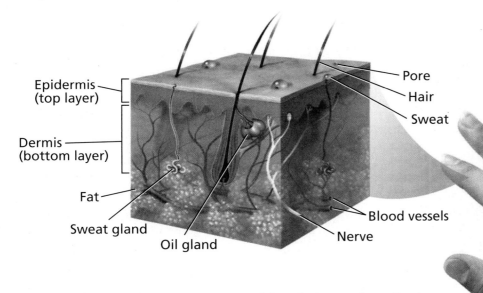

Epidermis (top layer)

Dermis (bottom layer)

Fat

Sweat gland

Oil gland

Pore

Hair

Sweat

Blood vessels

Nerve

The Integumentary System Your skin, hair, and nails make up your body's covering, or integumentary system. Figure 3 shows the structure of human skin. The cells and tissues of your skin work together to create a barrier that protects your body from injury and disease-causing bacteria and viruses. Skin also helps regulate your body temperature and keeps your cells from drying out. Your skin works with other systems, too. As part of your excretory system, skin helps remove waste when you perspire. Skin works with your nervous system to give you information about your environment.

FIGURE 3
The Skin
In some ways, the skin is the body's largest organ. It accounts for about 15 percent of body weight, heavier than any internal organ. In an adult of average size, the skin covers a surface area of about 1.5 or 2 square meters.

The Skeletal System Your skeletal system is made up of all the bones in your body and other connective tissues. The skeletal system supports the body and gives it structure. It also protects your body's organs. For example, hard rib bones shield your heart and lungs from damage. Your bones consist of hard, compact layers of tissue. Different kinds of specialized tissue provide structure, produce blood cells, and store important minerals, such as calcium. Connective tissue attaches one bone to another and forms joints that allow movement.

The Muscular System Most of your muscles work to move your body by pulling on your skeleton. These muscles, called skeletal muscles, usually work only when you want them to. Other muscles work involuntarily—that is, when you don't think about them. Together, your muscles and bones are sometimes called the musculoskeletal system. Each muscle cell contains mitochondria, which release energy for muscles to work. These muscle cells are combined into bundles of fibers, which work together during movement. Fiber bundles are then combined into muscle groups that move your bones. For example, the biceps is a muscle group that helps move your arm.

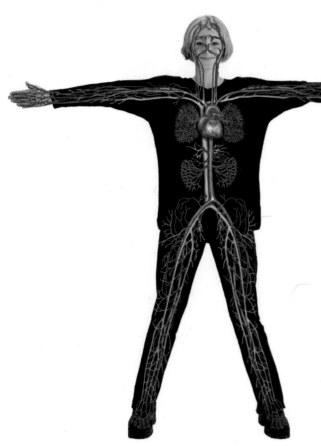

▲ **Circulatory System**

The Circulatory System Your circulatory system serves as a transportation network. It carries food and oxygen to all the cells of your body. It also collects the wastes that must be removed. Tube-like vessels transport these materials in the form of a mixture of cells and fluid that is called blood.

The circulatory system is powered by the pumping of your heart. Blood vessels that carry blood away from the heart are called arteries. Vessels that carry blood toward the heart are called veins. These vessels consist of epithelial tissue that lines their inner walls and connective tissue that covers their outer surfaces. Involuntary muscle tissue within the vessel walls helps move the blood as it circulates. The smallest and thinnest blood vessels—called capillaries—connect the arteries and veins. Capillaries reach every cell, delivering and collecting the materials transported by the blood.

The Respiratory System Take a deep breath. You can feel your lungs fill with air. The lungs are the main organs of your respiratory system, which takes in oxygen and disposes of carbon dioxide. (Recall that your cells use oxygen for cellular respiration. Carbon dioxide is a waste product in this process.)

When you breathe, air moves into your lungs through a set of branching passageways. These passageways end in clusters of tissue that are surrounded by capillaries. There, oxygen crosses into the blood and is then distributed through the body by the circulatory system.

Air moves in and out of your body as a result of the actions of muscles in your chest. You can sometimes control the action of these muscles. But not for long. Soon your respiratory system starts working on its own again.

The Digestive System Have you had anything to eat today? Food provides your body with materials for growing and for repairing tissues. Food also provides energy for everything you do. **Digestion** is the breakdown of food into small molecules the body can use. The digestive system does this job.

FIGURE 4
Blowing Bubbles
The respiratory system moves air in and out of the lungs.

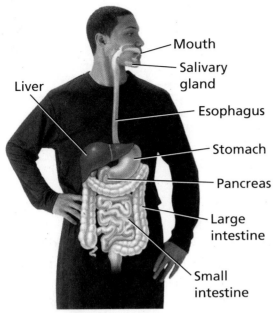

Liver
Mouth
Salivary gland
Esophagus
Stomach
Pancreas
Large intestine
Small intestine

▲ **Digestive System**

Kidney
Ureter
Urinary bladder
Urethra

▲ **Excretory System**

Figure 5 shows most of the organs of the digestive system. Food enters the body through your mouth and gradually moves through the system. Epithelial tissues in the stomach and small intestine produce chemicals called enzymes that help digest the food. Involuntary muscle tissue churns the food and keeps it moving.

Meanwhile, bile produced by the liver and enzymes from the pancreas help break down the food in the small intestine even more. Specialized cells in the lining of the small intestine then absorb the nutrients into the bloodstream. When the left-over material moves into the large intestine, water is removed and the solid waste material passes out of the body.

The Excretory System Your body produces excess water and waste from the activities in cells and from the breakdown of some materials in the digestive system. The excretory system, shown in Figure 5, removes these wastes from your bloodstream.

Your two **kidneys** are the major organs of the excretory system. Each kidney contains about 1 million specialized structures called **nephrons** that act as tiny filtering factories. These structures remove both wastes and needed materials from the blood. Then, the needed materials are returned to the bloodstream, and the wastes are combined with water to create urine. Urine flows from the kidneys to the **urinary bladder,** where it is stored until it leaves the body through the urethra.

 **Reading Checkpoint** What is the function of the kidneys?

FIGURE 5
Materials in the Body
The digestive system breaks down materials needed by the body. The excretory system removes wastes. **Interpreting Diagrams** *What structure carries food from the mouth to the stomach?*

Lab zone Try This **Activity**

Break Up!
Model the breakup of fats in the small intestine.

1. Fill two plastic jars half full of water. Add a few drops of oil to each jar.
2. Add about ¼ spoonful of baking soda to one jar.
3. Stir the contents of both jars. Record your observations.

Observing In which jar did the oil begin to break up? What type of substance does the baking soda represent?

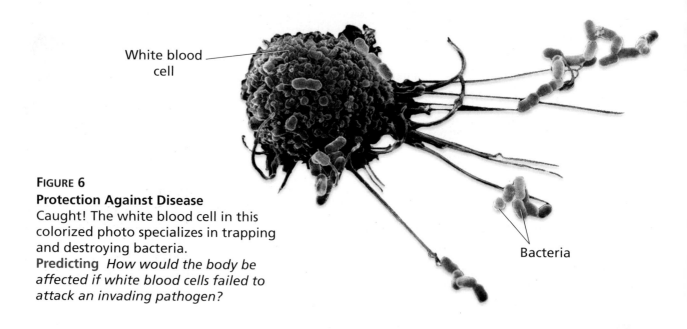

White blood cell

Bacteria

FIGURE 6
Protection Against Disease
Caught! The white blood cell in this colorized photo specializes in trapping and destroying bacteria.
Predicting *How would the body be affected if white blood cells failed to attack an invading pathogen?*

The Immune System Your immune system protects your body from disease-causing bacteria and viruses, or **pathogens.** Specialized white blood cells target and destroy these pathogens. An example of one kind of white blood cell is shown in Figure 6. Its captures and destroys bacteria that could cause infection. Other white blood cells specialize in identifying specific types of viruses. These white blood cells recognize different marker molecules on the surface of the viruses. In some cases, the white blood cells attack and destroy these viruses. In other cases, white blood cells activate different cells that make **antibodies**—proteins that help destroy pathogens. The antibodies bind to the marker molecules on the pathogens, causing them to clump together. These clumps are then destroyed by white blood cells like the one in the figure.

After an infection, your immune system "remembers" the pathogen and can produce antibodies more quickly if you are exposed again. This ability to destroy pathogens before they can cause disease is called **immunity.**

The Reproductive System The reproductive systems of males and females contain organs that produce sex cells. Recall that sex cells carry information in the form of DNA. When these cells combine, the DNA can direct the development of a new individual. The organs of the reproductive system also produce chemicals that regulate the physical development of maturing bodies. In mature females, for example, these chemicals make pregnancy and the delivery of a baby possible.

✓ **Reading Checkpoint** **What is the function of the immune system?**

Sight

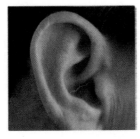
Hearing

Touch

Taste

Smell

FIGURE 7
Senses of Your Nervous System
Your eyes, ears, skin, mouth, and nose contain nerve cells that transmit information to your brain about the world around you.

The Nervous System You can think, move, hear music, and do much more because of your nervous system. The nervous system takes in information from your environment and from within your body. It processes this information and commands the body to respond. For example, you might sense that it is too warm and decide to take off your coat. In this case, you actually think about what to do. But in many other ways, your nervous system functions automatically.

The nervous system includes the brain and spinal cord. Specialized nerve cells make up these two organs. These nerve cells also reach from the spinal cord to all parts of your body. Nerve cells transmit information between the parts of your body and the spinal cord and brain.

The Endocrine System The systems in your body constantly make adjustments to maintain the internal conditions you need to live and function. Your endocrine system helps regulate the activities of the organs and organ systems by releasing hormones. Hormones are chemicals that change the activity in your body's cells. Each hormone affects a specific group of cells or an organ in a particular way.

The endocrine system consists of a collection of glands—specialized tissues that produce and release hormones. Your endocrine glands are located in different places throughout your body. These glands release their hormones into your bloodstream, where the circulatory system carries them to the targeted tissues. Complex processes regulate the amount of every hormone in your body. The levels can go up or down, depending on signals from other glands or from your brain.

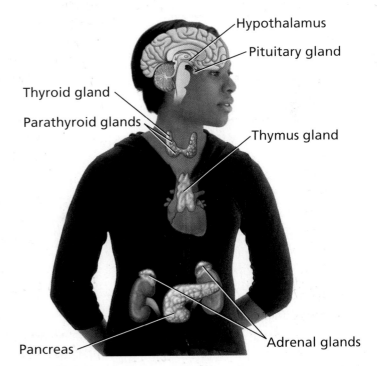
Hypothalamus
Pituitary gland
Thyroid gland
Parathyroid glands
Thymus gland
Pancreas
Adrenal glands

FIGURE 8
Some Glands of the Endocrine System
The endocrine glands produce hormones, which are then released into the bloodstream.
Interpreting Diagrams *Which glands are located in the throat?*

Go Online
*Sci*LINKS™ NSTA

For: Links on body systems
Visit: www.SciLinks.org
Web Code: scn-0411

Homeostasis

The different organ systems work together and depend on one another. When you ride a bike, you use your muscular and skeletal systems to steer and push the pedals. But you also need your nervous system to direct your arms and legs to move. Your respiratory, digestive, and circulatory systems work together to fuel your muscles with the energy they need. And your circulatory, respiratory, and excretory systems remove the wastes produced while your muscles are hard at work.

All the systems of the body work together to maintain **homeostasis** (hoh mee oh STAY sis), the body's tendency to keep an internal balance. **Homeostasis is the process by which an organism's internal environment is kept stable in spite of changes in the external environment.**

Homeostasis in Action To see homeostasis in action, all you have to do is take your temperature when the air is cold. Then, take it again in an overheated room. No matter what the temperature of the air around you, your internal body temperature will be close to 37°C. Of course, if you become sick, your body temperature may rise. But when you are well again, it returns to 37°C.

Maintaining Homeostasis Your body has various ways of maintaining homeostasis. For example, when you are too warm, you sweat. Sweating helps to cool your body. On the other hand, when you are cold, you shiver. Shivering occurs when your muscles rapidly contract and relax. This action produces heat that helps keep you warm. Both of these processes help your body regulate your temperature and maintain homeostasis.

FIGURE 9
Maintaining Homeostasis
Regardless of the surrounding temperature, your body temperature remains fairly constant at about 37°C. Sweating (left) and shivering (right) help regulate your body temperature.
Applying Concepts *What is the term for the body's tendency to maintain a stable internal environment?*

Stress and Homeostasis Sometimes, things can happen to disrupt homeostasis. As a result, your heart may beat more rapidly or your breathing may increase. These reactions of your circulatory and respiratory systems are signs of stress. **Stress** is the reaction of your body to potentially threatening, challenging, or disturbing events.

Think about what happens when you leave the starting line in a bike race. As you pedal, your heart beats faster and your breathing increases. What is happening in your body? First, your endocrine system releases a chemical called adrenaline into your bloodstream. Adrenaline gives you a burst of energy and prepares your body to take action.

As you pedal, your muscles work harder and require more oxygen. Oxygen is carried by the circulatory system, so your heart beats even faster to move more blood to your muscles. Your breath comes faster and faster, too, so that more oxygen can get into your body. Your body is experiencing stress.

If stress is over quickly, your body soon returns to its normal state. Think about the bike race again. After you cross the finish line, you continue to breathe hard for the next few minutes. Soon, however, your breathing and heart rate return to normal. The level of adrenaline in your blood returns to normal. Thus, homeostasis is restored after just a few minutes of rest.

FIGURE 10
Stress
Your body reacts to stress, such as the start of a bike race, by releasing adrenaline and carrying more oxygen to body cells.

 **Reading Checkpoint** What is stress?

Section 1 Assessment

S 7.5.a, E-LA: Reading 7.2.0, Writing 7.2.5

Target Reading Skill Take Notes Review your notes for this section. What are two important ideas that you noted under Organs and Organ Systems?

Reviewing Key Concepts

1. a. **Identifying** List the four levels of organization in the human body from smallest to largest. Give an example of each level.
   b. **Comparing and Contrasting** What is the difference between tissues and organs?
2. a. **Listing** List the 11 main systems of the human body.
   b. **Describing** Next to the name of each system, write a phrase that describes its function.

3. a. **Defining** What is homeostasis?
   b. **Explaining** How does stress affect homeostasis?
   c. **Relating Cause and Effect** Describe what happens inside your body as you give an oral report in front of your class.

Writing in Science

Summary Write a paragraph that explains what body systems are involved when you prepare a sandwich and then eat it. Be sure to begin your paragraph with a topic sentence and include supporting details.

2 The Skeletal System

S 7.5.c Students know how bones and muscles work together to provide a structural framework for movement.

S 7.6.h Students know how to compare joints in the body (wrist, shoulder, thigh) with structures used in machines and simple devices (hinge, ball-and-socket, and sliding joints).

- What are the functions of the skeleton?
- What role do joints play in the body?
- What are the characteristics of bone, and how can you keep your bones strong and healthy?

Key Terms
- skeleton
- vertebrae
- joint
- ligament
- cartilage
- compact bone
- spongy bone
- marrow
- osteoporosis

Lab zone Standards **Warm-Up**

Hard as a Rock?

1. Your teacher will give you a rock and a leg bone from a cooked turkey or chicken.
2. Use a hand lens to examine both the rock and the bone.
3. Gently tap both the rock and the bone on a hard surface.
4. Pick up each object to feel how heavy it is.
5. Wash your hands. Then make notes of your observations.

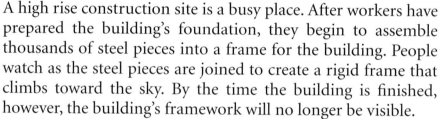

Think It Over

Observing Based on your observations, why do you think bones are sometimes compared to rocks? List some ways in which bones and rocks are similar and different.

A high rise construction site is a busy place. After workers have prepared the building's foundation, they begin to assemble thousands of steel pieces into a frame for the building. People watch as the steel pieces are joined to create a rigid frame that climbs toward the sky. By the time the building is finished, however, the building's framework will no longer be visible.

Like a building, you also have an inner framework, but it isn't made up of steel. Your framework, or **skeleton**, is made up of all the bones in your body. The number of bones in your skeleton, or skeletal system, depends on your age. A newborn has about 275 bones. An adult, however, has about 206 bones. As a baby grows, some of the bones in the body fuse together. For example, as you grew, some of the bones in your skull fused together.

Functions of the Skeletal System

Just as a building could not stand without its frame, you would collapse without your skeleton. **Your skeleton has five major functions. It provides shape and support, enables you to move, protects your organs, produces blood cells, and stores minerals and other materials until your body needs them.**

Shape and Support Your skeleton determines the shape of your body, much as a steel frame determines the shape of a building. The backbone, also called the vertebral or spinal column, is the center of the skeleton. Locate the backbone in Figure 11. Notice that the bones in the skeleton are in some way connected to this column. If you move your fingers down the center of your back, you can feel the 26 small bones, or **vertebrae** (VUR tuh bray) (singular: *vertebra*), that make up your backbone. Bend forward at the waist and feel the bones adjust as you move. Each individual vertebra is like a bead on a string. Just as a beaded necklace is flexible and able to bend, so too is your vertebral column. If your backbone were just one bone, you would not be able to bend or twist.

Reading Checkpoint Why is the vertebral column considered the center of the skeleton?

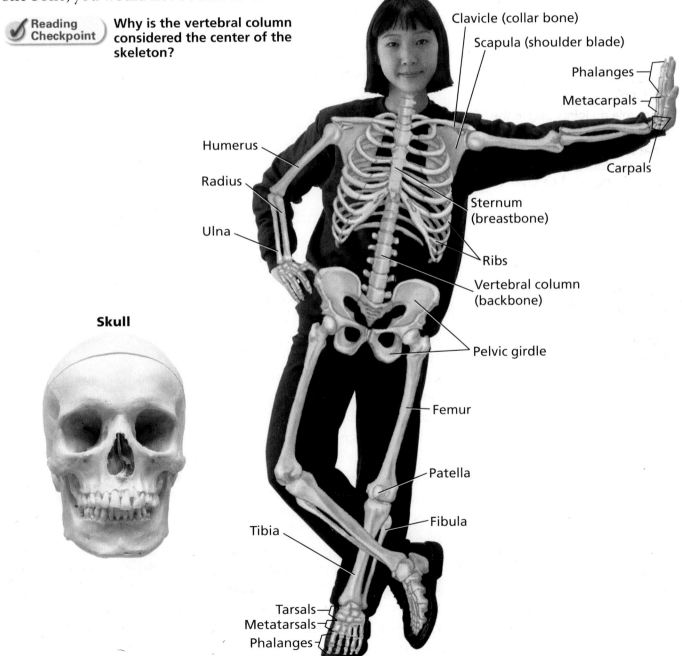

FIGURE 11
The Skeleton
The skeleton provides a framework that supports and protects many other body parts. **Comparing and Contrasting** *In what ways is the skeleton like the steel framework of a building? In what ways is it different?*

Clavicle (collar bone)

Scapula (shoulder blade)

Phalanges

Metacarpals

Carpals

Humerus

Radius

Ulna

Sternum (breastbone)

Ribs

Vertebral column (backbone)

Pelvic girdle

Skull

Femur

Patella

Fibula

Tibia

Tarsals

Metatarsals

Phalanges

Movement and Protection Your skeleton allows you to move. Most of the body's bones are associated with muscles. The muscles pull on the bones to make the body move. Bones also protect many of the organs in your body. For example, your skull protects your brain, and your breastbone and ribs form a protective cage around your heart and lungs.

Production and Storage of Substances Some of your bones produce substances that your body needs. You can think of the long bones of your arms and legs as factories that make certain blood cells. Bones also store minerals such as calcium and phosphorus. When the body needs these minerals, the bones release small amounts of them into the blood.

Joints of the Skeleton

Suppose that a single long bone ran the length of your leg. How would you get out of bed or run for a bus? Luckily, your body contains many small bones rather than fewer large ones. A **joint** is a place in the body where two bones come together. ◯ **Joints allow bones to move in different ways.** There are two kinds of joints—immovable joints and movable joints.

Go Online
active art

For: Movable Joints activity
Visit: PHSchool.com
Web Code: cep-4012

FIGURE 12
Movable Joints

Without movable joints, your body would be as stiff as a board. The different kinds of joints allow your body to move in a variety of ways. Comparing and Contrasting *How is the movement of a hinge joint different from that of a ball-and-socket joint?*

Hinge Joint
A hinge joint allows forward or backward motion. Your knee is a hinge joint that allows you to bend and straighten your leg. Your elbow is also a hinge joint.

Ball-and-Socket Joint
Ball-and-socket joints allow the greatest range of motion. The ball-and-socket joint in your shoulder allows you to swing your arm freely in a circle. Your hips also have ball-and-socket joints.

Immovable Joints Some joints in the body connect bones in a way that allows little or no movement. These joints are called immovable joints. The bones of the skull are held together by immovable joints.

Movable Joints Most joints in the body are movable joints. Movable joints allow the body to make a wide range of movements. Look at Figure 12 to see the variety of movements that these joints make possible. Notice how some joints move much like a simple machine. For example, your knee makes the same motion as a door hinge.

The bones in movable joints are held together by strong connective tissues called **ligaments.** Most joints have a second type of connective tissue, called **cartilage** (KAHR tuh lij), which is more flexible than bone. Cartilage covers the ends of the bones and keeps them from rubbing against each other. For example, in the knee, cartilage acts as a cushion that keeps your femur (thighbone) from rubbing against the bones of your lower leg. In addition, a fluid lubricates the ends of the bones, allowing them to move smoothly over each other.

 **Reading Checkpoint** How are movable joints held together?

Lab zone Skills Activity

Classifying
Perform these activities.

- Move your arm in a circle.
- Push open a door.
- Lift a book from a desk.
- Kneel down.
- Wave your hand.
- Twist your head from side to side.

Determine which type of movable joint or joints is involved in performing each activity. Give a reason to support your classifications.

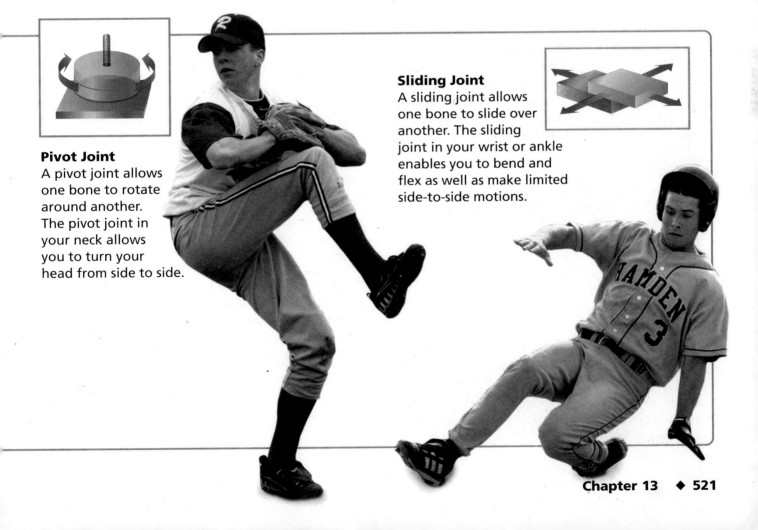

Pivot Joint
A pivot joint allows one bone to rotate around another. The pivot joint in your neck allows you to turn your head from side to side.

Sliding Joint
A sliding joint allows one bone to slide over another. The sliding joint in your wrist or ankle enables you to bend and flex as well as make limited side-to-side motions.

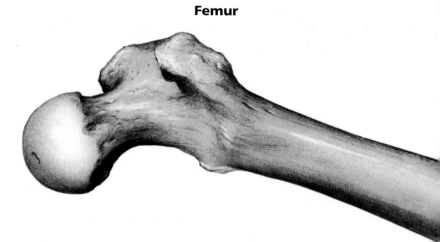

Femur

FIGURE 13

Bone Structure

The most obvious feature of a long bone, such as the femur, is its long shaft. Running through the compact bone tissue within the shaft is a system of canals. The canals bring materials to the living bone cells.
Interpreting Diagrams *What different tissues make up the femur?*

Lab zone **Try This Activity**

Soft Bones?

In this activity, you will explore the role that calcium plays in bones.

1. Put on protective gloves. Soak one clean chicken bone in a jar filled with water. Soak a second clean chicken bone in a jar filled with vinegar. (Vinegar causes calcium to dissolve out of bone.)

2. After one week, put on protective gloves and remove the bones from the jars.

3. Compare how the two bones look and feel. Note any differences between the two bones.

Drawing Conclusions Based on your results, explain why it is important to consume a diet that is high in calcium.

Bones—Strong and Living

When you think of a skeleton, you may think of the paper cutouts that are used as decorations at Halloween. Many people connect skeletons with death. The ancient Greeks did, too. The word *skeleton* actually comes from a Greek word meaning "a dried body." The bones of your skeleton, however, are not dead at all. ⬤ **Bones are complex living structures that undergo growth and development.**

Bone Structure Figure 13 shows the structure of the femur, or thighbone. The femur, which is the body's longest bone, connects the pelvic bones to the lower leg bones. Notice that a thin, tough membrane covers all of the bone except the ends. Blood vessels and nerves enter and leave the bone through the membrane. Beneath the bone's outer membrane is a layer of **compact bone,** which is hard and dense, but not solid. As you can see in Figure 13, small canals run through the compact bone. These canals carry blood vessels and nerves from the bone's surface to the living cells within the bone.

Just inside the femur's compact bone is a layer of spongy bone. Like a sponge, **spongy bone** has many small spaces within it. This structure makes spongy bone tissue lightweight but strong. Spongy bone is also found at the ends of the bone.

The spaces in many bones contain a soft, connective tissue called **marrow.** There are two types of marrow—red and yellow. Red bone marrow produces most of the body's blood cells. As a child, most of your bones contained red bone marrow. As a teenager, only the ends of your femurs, skull, hip bones, and sternum (breastbone) contain red marrow. Your other bones contain yellow marrow. This marrow stores fat that can serve as an energy reserve.

 **Reading Checkpoint**   **What are the two types of bone marrow?**

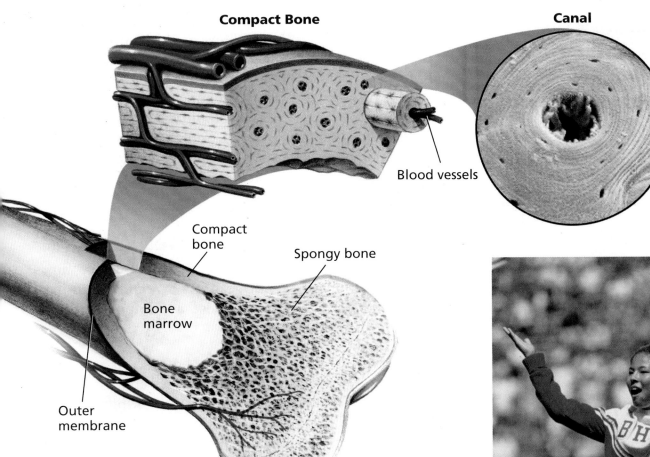

Compact Bone

Canal

Blood vessels

Compact bone

Spongy bone

Bone marrow

Outer membrane

Bone Strength The structure of bone makes it both strong and lightweight. Bones are so strong that they can absorb more force without breaking than can concrete or granite rock. Yet, bones are much lighter than these materials. In fact, only about 20 percent of an average adult's body weight is bone.

Have you ever heard the phrase "as hard as a rock"? Most rock is hard because it is made up of minerals that are packed tightly together. In a similar way, bones are hard because they contain minerals—primarily phosphorus and calcium.

Bone Growth Bones are alive—they contain cells and tissues, such as blood and nerves. Because they are alive, bones also form new bone tissue as you grow. Even after you are grown, bone tissue continues to form within your bones. For example, every time you play soccer or basketball, some of your bones absorb the force of your weight. They respond by making new bone tissue.

Sometimes, new bone tissue forms after an accident. If you break a bone, for example, new bone tissue forms to fill the gap between the broken ends of the bone. In fact, the healed region of new bone may be stronger than the original bone!

▲ You can jump up and down or turn cartwheels without breaking bones.

Video Field Trip

Discovery Channel School

Bones, Muscle, and Skin

Bone Development Try this activity: Move the tip of your nose from side to side with your fingers. Notice that the tip of your nose is not stiff. That is because it contains cartilage. As an infant, much of your skeleton was cartilage. Over time, most of the cartilage was replaced with hard bone tissue.

The replacement of cartilage by bone tissue usually is complete by the time you stop growing. You've seen, however, that not all of your body's cartilage is replaced by bone. Even in adults, many joints contain cartilage that protects the ends of the bones.

Taking Care of Your Bones

Because your skeleton performs so many necessary functions, it is important to keep it healthy. **A combination of a balanced diet and regular exercise are important for a lifetime of healthy bones.**

Diet One way to help ensure healthy bones is to eat a well-balanced diet. A well-balanced diet includes enough calcium and phosphorus to keep your bones strong while they are growing. Meats, whole grains, and leafy green vegetables are all good sources of both calcium and phosphorus. Dairy products, including yogurt, are good sources of calcium.

Exercise Another way to build and maintain strong bones is to get plenty of exercise. During activities such as running, skating, or dancing, your bones support the weight of your entire body. These weight-bearing activities help your bones grow stronger and denser. To prevent injuries while exercising, be sure to wear appropriate safety equipment, such as a helmet and pads.

 **Reading Checkpoint** What are two ways to keep your bones healthy?

FIGURE 14
Caring for Your Bones
Exercising regularly and eating a balanced diet help to keep your bones strong and healthy.

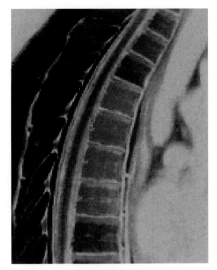

Healthy Spine

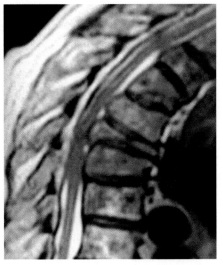

Spine With Osteoporosis

FIGURE 15
Osteoporosis
Without enough calcium in the diet, a person's bones weaken. These photos show how the shape and structure of vertebrae in a healthy spine compare with those in a person with osteoporosis.
Relating Cause and Effect
What can you do to prevent osteoporosis?

Osteoporosis As people become older, their bones begin to lose some of the minerals they contain. Mineral loss can lead to **osteoporosis** (ahs tee oh puh ROH sis), a condition in which the body's bones become weak and break easily. You can see the effect of osteoporosis in Figure 15. Evidence indicates that regular exercise throughout life and a diet with enough calcium can help prevent osteoporosis. If you eat enough calcium-rich foods now, you may help prevent osteoporosis later in life.

Section 2 Assessment

S 7.5.c, 7.6.h,
E-LA: Reading 7.1.2

Vocabulary Skill Latin Word Origins The Greek word *osteon* means "bone." What does the Latin word *porus* mean? How do these two word parts combine to produce the meaning of *osteoporosis*?

Reviewing Key Concepts

1. a. **Listing** What are five functions of the skeleton?
   b. **Explaining** How does the skeleton protect the body?
   c. **Predicting** How would your life be different if your backbone were just one long bone?
2. a. **Naming** What are four types of movable joints?
   b. **Comparing and Contrasting** Compare immovable joints with movable joints.
   c. **Classifying** Which of your movable joints are ball-and-socket joints?
3. a. **Identifying** What are three layers within the femur?

   b. **Relating Cause and Effect** How does the structure of bones make them both strong and lightweight?
   c. **Applying Concepts** How do a well-balanced diet and weight-bearing exercise help keep bones strong?

Lab zone At-Home Activity

Model Joints Choose two examples of movable joints from Figure 12. Ask a family member to perform separate movements that involve one joint and then the other. Make drawings to represent the joints and bones involved in each movement. Use the drawings to explain to your family how the motions of the two joints differ.

CALIFORNIA
Standards Focus

S 7.5.c Students know how bones and muscles work together to provide a structural framework for movement.

What types of muscles are found in the body?

Why do skeletal muscles work in pairs?

Key Terms

- involuntary muscle
- voluntary muscle
- skeletal muscle
- tendon
- striated muscle
- smooth muscle
- cardiac muscle

Go Online
PHSchool.com

For: More on muscle types
Visit: PHSchool.com
Web Code: ced-4014

Lab zone Standards Warm-Up

How Do Muscles Work?

1. Grip a spring-type clothespin with the thumb and index finger of your writing hand. Squeeze the clothespin open and shut as quickly as possible for two minutes. Count how many times you can squeeze the clothespin before your muscles tire.

2. Rest for one minute. Then, repeat Step 1.

Think It Over
Predicting What do you think would happen if you repeated Steps 1 and 2 with your other hand? Give a reason for your prediction. Then, test your prediction.

A rabbit becomes still when it senses danger. The rabbit sits so still that it doesn't seem to move a muscle. Could you sit without moving any muscles? Saliva builds up in your mouth. You swallow. You need to breathe. Your chest expands to let air in. All of these actions involve muscles. It is impossible to sit absolutely still without muscle movement.

There are about 600 muscles in your body. Muscles have many functions. For example, they keep your heart beating, pull your mouth into a smile, and move the bones of your skeleton. The girl doing karate on the next page uses many of her muscles to move her arms, legs, hands, feet, and head. Other muscles expand and contract her chest and allow her to breathe.

Types of Muscle

Some of your body's movements, such as smiling, are easy to control. Other movements, such as the beating of your heart, are impossible to control completely. That is because some of your muscles are not under your conscious control. Those muscles are called **involuntary muscles.** Involuntary muscles are responsible for such essential activities as moving food along the digestive tract and controlling the size of an eye's pupil.

The muscles that are under your conscious control are called **voluntary muscles.** Smiling, turning a page in a book, and getting out of your chair when the bell rings are all actions controlled by voluntary muscles.

🔑 **Your body has three types of muscle tissue—skeletal muscle, smooth muscle, and cardiac muscle. Only skeletal muscle is voluntary. Smooth muscle and cardiac muscle are involuntary.** In Figure 16, you see a magnified view of each type of muscle in the body. Both skeletal and smooth muscles are found in many places in the body. Cardiac muscle is found only in the heart. Each muscle type performs specific functions in the body.

FIGURE 16
Types of Muscle

Your body has three types of muscle tissue: skeletal muscle, smooth muscle, and cardiac muscle. **Classifying** *Which type of muscle is found only in the heart?*

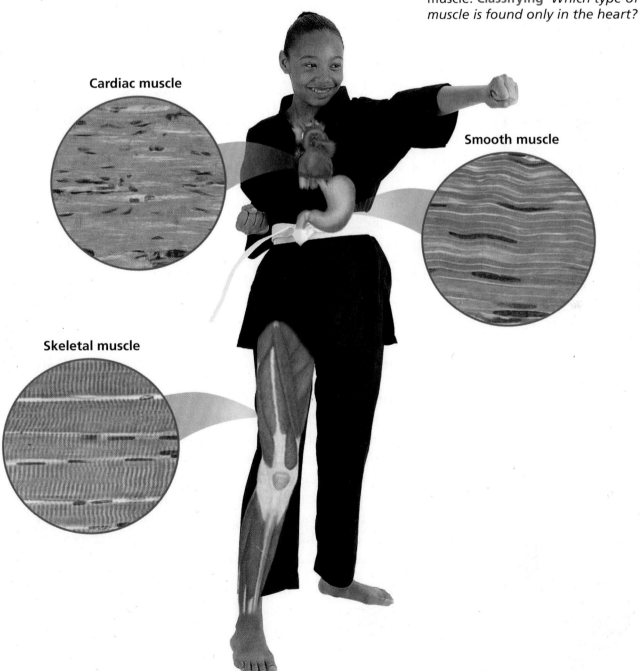

Cardiac muscle

Smooth muscle

Skeletal muscle

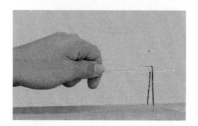
Skeletal Muscle Every time you type on a computer keyboard, shoot a basketball, or walk across a room, you are using skeletal muscles. As their name suggests, **skeletal muscles** are attached to the bones of your skeleton. These muscles provide the force that moves your bones. At each end of a skeletal muscle is a tendon. A **tendon** is a strong connective tissue that attaches muscle to bone. Skeletal muscle cells appear banded, or striated. For this reason, skeletal muscle tissue is sometimes called **striated** (STRY ay tid) **muscle.**

Because you have conscious control of skeletal muscles, they are classified as voluntary muscles. One characteristic of skeletal muscles is that they react very quickly. Think about what happens during a swim meet. Immediately after the starting gun sounds, a swimmer's leg muscles push the swimmer off the block into the pool. However, another characteristic of skeletal muscles is that they tire quickly. By the end of the race, the swimmer's muscles are tired and need a rest. If you did the Standards Warm-Up at the start of this section, you felt the effects of tired muscles in your fingers.

Smooth Muscle The inside of many internal organs, such as the stomach and blood vessels, contain **smooth muscles.** Smooth muscles are involuntary muscles. They work automatically to control certain movements inside your body, such as those involved in digestion. For example, as the smooth muscles of your stomach contract, they produce a churning action. The churning mixes the food with chemicals, and helps to digest the food.

Unlike skeletal muscles, smooth muscle cells are not striated. Smooth muscles behave differently than skeletal muscles, too. Smooth muscles react more slowly and tire more slowly.

Cardiac Muscle The tissue called **cardiac muscle** is found only in your heart. Cardiac muscle has some characteristics in common with both smooth muscle and skeletal muscle. Like smooth muscle, cardiac muscle is involuntary. Like skeletal muscle, cardiac muscle cells are striated. However, unlike skeletal muscle, cardiac muscle does not get tired. It can contract repeatedly. A specialized group of nerve cells within the heart sends out signals that cause the cardiac muscle to contract. You call those repeated contractions heartbeats.

Reading Checkpoint Where is smooth muscle found?

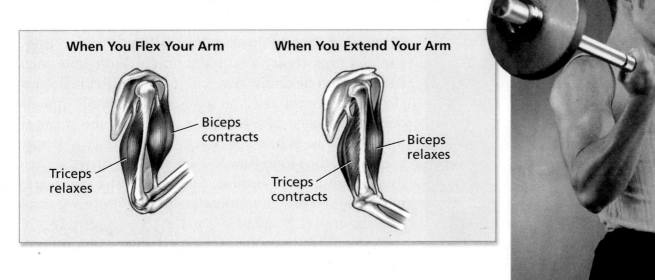

When You Flex Your Arm

Biceps contracts

Triceps relaxes

When You Extend Your Arm

Biceps relaxes

Triceps contracts

Muscles at Work

Has anyone ever asked you to "make a muscle"? If so, you probably tightened your fist, bent your arm at the elbow, and made the muscles in your upper arm bulge. Like other skeletal muscles, the muscles in your arm do their work by contracting, becoming shorter and thicker. Muscles work in coordination with the skeletal system and the nervous system. First, messages from the nervous system cause a muscle to contract. Then the shortened muscle pulls on the attached bone, causing it to move. 🔑 **Because muscle cells can only move bones by contracting, skeletal muscles must work in pairs. While one muscle contracts, the other muscle in the pair relaxes to its original length.**

Muscles Work in Pairs The coordinated contraction and relaxation of different muscles allows you, for instance, to bend your arm. Figure 17 shows this action. The biceps muscle on the upper arm contracts. This motion bends, or flexes, your arm at the elbow. The angle between the bones in your forearm (the radius and ulna) and the bone in your upper arm (the humerus) then decreases. Your biceps muscle bulges as it shortens. You "make a muscle." As the biceps contracts, the triceps on the back of the upper arm relaxes and extends.

To move the weight down, the biceps and triceps also work together. This time, the triceps muscle contracts. The action causes the angle between your upper arm bone and lower arm bone to increase. In other words, our arm straightens. At the same time, the biceps relaxes and extends to its original length.

When you lift a weight, the biceps moves your arm. But the triceps is important, too. It helps keep the motion smooth and controlled, protecting the elbow joint from a sudden, strong contraction. When you extend your arm, the biceps smoothes the motion. The flexing and extending of your arm is a good example of how muscles work in coordinated pairs.

FIGURE 17
Muscle Pairs
Because muscles can only contract, or shorten, they must work in pairs. To bend the arm at the elbow, the biceps contracts while the triceps returns to its original length. **Interpreting Diagrams** *What happens to each muscle to straighten the arm?*

FIGURE 18
Preventing Muscle Injuries
When you warm up before exercising, you increase the flexibility of your muscles.

Muscular Strength and Flexibility Regular exercise is important for maintaining both muscular strength and flexibility. Exercise makes individual muscle cells grow in size. As a result, the whole muscle becomes thicker. The thicker a muscle is, the stronger the muscle is. When you warm up thoroughly before exercising, the blood flow to your muscles increases and they become more flexible. Stretching after you warm up helps prepare your muscles for the more vigorous exercise or play ahead.

Sometimes, despite taking proper precautions, muscles can become injured. A muscle strain, or pulled muscle, can occur when muscles are overworked or overstretched. Tendons can also be overstretched or partially torn. After a long period of exercise, a skeletal muscle can cramp. When a muscle cramps, the entire muscle contracts strongly and stays contracted. If you injure a muscle or tendon, it is important to follow medical instructions and to rest the injured area so it can heal.

 **Reading Checkpoint** What are two ways to prepare the muscles for exercise?

Section 3 Assessment

S 7.5.c, E-LA: Reading 7.2.0, Writing 7.2.0

Target Reading Skill Take Notes Review your notes for this section. What are two important ideas that you noted under Muscles at Work?

Reviewing Key Concepts

1. a. **Identifying** What are the three types of muscle tissue?
   b. **Comparing and Contrasting** How do voluntary and involuntary muscles differ? Give an example of each type of muscle.
   c. **Predicting** The muscles that move your fingers are attached to the bones in your fingers by tendons. Suppose one of the tendons in a person's index finger were cut. How would it affect movement in the finger?

2. a. **Identifying** Where might you find muscle pairs?
   b. **Describing** Describe how the muscles in your upper arm work together to bend and straighten your arm.
   c. **Applying Concepts** When exercising to build muscular strength, why is it important to exercise both muscles in a muscle pair equally?

Writing in Science

Comparison Paragraph Write a paragraph comparing smooth muscle tissue and skeletal muscle tissue. Include whether these muscle tissues are voluntary or involuntary, where they are found and what their functions are. In addition, describe what you might expect to see if you looked at these muscle tissues under a microscope.

A Look Beneath the Skin

S 7.5.c, 7.7.d

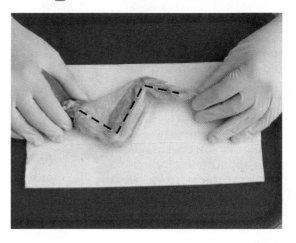

Problem

What are some characteristics of skeletal muscles? How do skeletal muscles work?

Skills Focus

observing, inferring, classifying

Materials

- water
- paper towels
- scissors
- dissecting tray
- uncooked chicken wing, treated with bleach

Procedure

1. Put on goggles, an apron, and protective gloves. **CAUTION:** *Wear gloves whenever you handle the chicken.*

2. Your teacher will give you a chicken wing. Rinse it well with water, dry it with paper towels, and place it in a dissecting tray.

3. Carefully extend the wing to find out how many major parts it has. Draw a diagram of the external structure. Label the upper arm, elbow, lower arm, and hand (wing tip).

4. Use scissors to remove the skin. Cut only through the skin. **CAUTION:** *Cut away from your body and your classmates.*

5. Examine the muscles, which are the bundles of pink tissue around the bones. Find the two groups of muscles in the upper arm. Hold the arm down at the shoulder, and alternately pull on each muscle group. Observe what happens.

6. Find the two groups of muscles in the lower arm. Hold down the arm at the elbow, and alternately pull on each muscle group. Then, make a diagram of the wing's muscles.

7. Find the tendons—shiny white tissue at the ends of the muscles. Notice what parts the tendons connect. Add the tendons to your diagram.

8. Remove the muscles and tendons. Find the ligaments, which are the whitish ribbon-shaped structures between bones. Add them to your diagram.

9. Dispose of the chicken parts according to your teacher's instructions. Wash your hands.

Analyze and Conclude

1. **Observing** How does a chicken wing move at the elbow? How does the motion compare to how your elbow moves? What type of joint is involved?

2. **Inferring** What happened when you pulled on one of the arm muscles? What muscle action does the pulling represent?

3. **Classifying** Categorize the muscles you observed as smooth, cardiac, or skeletal.

4. **Communicating** Why is it valuable to record your observations with accurate diagrams? Write a paragraph in which you describe what your diagrams show.

More to Explore

Use the procedures from this lab to examine an uncooked chicken thigh and leg. Compare how the chicken leg and a human leg move. *Obtain your teacher's permission before carrying out your investigation.*

Machines and the Body

CALIFORNIA
Standards Focus

S 7.6.h. Students know how to compare joints in the body (wrist, shoulder, thigh) with structures used in machines and simple devices (hinge, ball-and-socket, and sliding joints).

S 7.6.i. Students know how levers confer mechanical advantage and how the application of this principle applies to the musculoskeletal system.

- How are force and work related?
- How does a lever make work easier?
- How do bones and muscles function as levers in the body?

Key Terms

- force
- work
- machine
- lever
- fulcrum
- effort force
- effort distance
- resistance force
- resistance distance
- mechanical advantage
- effort arm
- resistance arm

Lab zone Standards **Warm-Up**

Are You an Eating Machine?

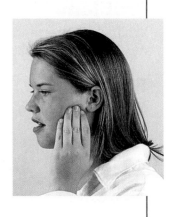

1. Using your front teeth, bite off a piece of a cracker.
2. Now chew the cracker. Pay attention to how your lower jaw moves. Touch your jaw just in front of your ear, as shown in the photo. As you chew, push in slightly on your jaw so that you can feel how it moves. If the movement is still not clear, try opening your mouth wide while you feel the back of the jaw.

Think It Over
Inferring When you bite and chew, the back of your jaw moves less than your teeth. Why is that?

A fresh load of soil for your school's garden has been dumped too far from the garden. To move the soil, you might use simple machines such as a lever, shovel, or wheelbarrow to make the job easier. As you work in the garden, you may also lift handfuls of soil by bending your arm and using your hand just like a shovel. Many bones and muscles of the human body act like the simple machine known as a lever.

FIGURE 19
Using Machines
Shovels and rakes make the work of these students easier.

Force and Work

To understand how parts of your body act like machines, you first need to know about two concepts: force and work.

Force A **force** is a push or a pull on an object. A force is described by its strength, or magnitude, and the direction in which it acts. If you push on a door, you exert a force in a different direction than if you pull on the door.

The standard unit for the magnitude of a force is the newton (N). An arrow can represent the direction and strength of a force. The arrow points in the direction of the force. The longer the arrow is drawn, the greater the force's strength.

Work You do **work** when you exert a force on an object that causes the object to move some distance in the same direction as the force. 🔑 **You can calculate the amount of work done on an object by multiplying force times distance.**

> **Work = Force × Distance**

You can use this formula to calculate the amount of work you do to lift a plant. When you lift an object, the upward force must be at least equal to the object's weight. So, to lift a plant that weighs 50 newtons by a distance of 0.5 meter requires 25 newton-meters (N•m) of work. The • symbol means that the units are multiplied.

> **Work = 50 N × 0.5 m = 25 N•m**

But what can you do if an object weighs more than the amount of force you can exert? For example, what if you wanted to lift a piano up a flight of stairs? You would need to use a machine. A **machine** is a device that allows you to do work in a way that is easier or more effective.

✓ **Reading Checkpoint** How can you calculate work?

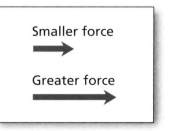

FIGURE 20
Representing Forces
Arrows tell you how the strengths of different forces compare. A force arrow points in the direction of a force.

FIGURE 21
Amount of Work
When you lift a plant, you do work. You do more work when you lift a heavier plant the same distance.
Relating Cause and Effect
Why does it take more work to lift the heavier plant?

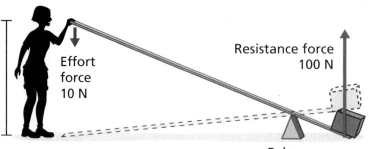

The girl pushes down with a small force over a long distance.

Effort distance 1 m

Effort force 10 N

Resistance force 100 N

The lever changes the small force to a larger force, and the crate moves up a short distance.

Resistance distance 0.1 m

Fulcrum

FIGURE 22
A Simple Machine
A lever is a simple machine that makes lifting heavy objects easier. **Applying Concepts** *Why does the girl place the fulcrum close to the crate?*

FIGURE 23
Pulling Out a Nail
A hammer acts as a lever when you use it to pull a nail from a board. The hammer changes the direction and amount of force you exert, so the nail is easier to remove.

Effort force

Resistance force

Levers

Have you ever played pick-up sticks? If so, you are already familiar with a simple machine called a lever. A **lever** is a rigid rod that is free to rotate around a fixed pivot point. The fixed point that a lever rotates around is called the **fulcrum.** You can use a lever to turn a small force into a large force so you can lift a piano.

Levers were probably used in prehistoric times. But the first person to explain how levers work was Archimedes, a mathematician of ancient Greece.

Force and Work in Levers To understand levers, look at Figure 22. The girl is using a lever to lift a crate that weighs 100 newtons. She places the fulcrum close to the crate and stands far away from the fulcrum, on the other side. She applies a force on the lever of 10 newtons over a distance of 1 meter. In this way, she can lift the 100-N crate 0.1 meter. The work done on each side of the lever is equal, but the girl has to apply less force than she would need without a lever. ⊙ **A lever makes work easier by changing the amount of force exerted, the distance over which the force is exerted, or the direction of the force.**

The force that you exert on a lever is called the **effort force.** The distance you push down is the **effort distance.** In contrast, the force that a lever exerts on an object is called the **resistance force,** and the distance the lever pushes up on an object is the **resistance distance.**

In Figure 22, the girl applies a small effort force on the lever, which becomes a larger resistance force on the crate. A small force that is applied over a long distance can create a larger force over a short distance.

When you apply an effort force over an effort distance, you are doing work on the lever. In turn, the lever applies a resistance force over a resistance distance and does work on an object. The work you do on the lever equals the work the lever does on the object.

The relationship between the work done on a lever and the work that the lever does on an object can be written as this formula.

$$\frac{\text{Effort}}{\text{force}} \times \frac{\text{Effort}}{\text{distance}} = \frac{\text{Resistance}}{\text{force}} \times \frac{\text{Resistance}}{\text{distance}}$$

If you know any three values in the formula, you can calculate the fourth value, as shown in the Sample Problem below.

 Math **Sample Problem**

Math: **Measurement and Geometry 7.1.3**

Calculating Effort Distance

Suppose you need to move a boulder. Using a wooden plank as a lever and a log for the fulcrum, you plan to lift the boulder 0.05 m and then let it roll away. The boulder weighs 240 N and you can exert 80 N of force. How far will you have to push down on your end of the lever to lift the boulder?

1 **Read and Understand**
What information are you given?

   Resistance force = 240 N

   Resistance distance = 0.05 m

   Effort force = 80 N

2 **Plan and Solve**
What quantity are you trying to calculate?

   Effort distance = ■

What formula contains the given quantities and the unknown quantity?

$$\frac{\text{Effort}}{\text{force}} \times \frac{\text{Effort}}{\text{distance}} = \frac{\text{Resistance}}{\text{force}} \times \frac{\text{Resistance}}{\text{distance}}$$

Perform the calculation.

$$80 \text{ N} \times \frac{\text{Effort}}{\text{distance}} = 240 \text{ N} \times 0.05 \text{ m}$$

$$80 \text{ N} \times \frac{\text{Effort}}{\text{distance}} = 12 \text{ N} \cdot \text{m}$$

$$\frac{\text{Effort}}{\text{distance}} = \frac{12 \text{ N} \cdot \text{m}}{80 \text{ N}} = 0.15 \text{ m}$$

3 **Look Back and Check**
Does your answer make sense?
An effort distance of 0.15 m is more than the resistance distance of 0.05 m. This answer makes sense because your effort force is less than the resistance force.

Math **Practice**

1. **Calculating Effort Force** A friend who weighs 400 N is sitting on the end of a seesaw. You push down a distance of 0.5 m on the opposite end, which lifts your friend a distance of 0.1 m. How much effort force did you apply?

2. **Calculating Resistance Force** In order to lift a box, you push down 0.75 m on a lever with an effort force of 100 N. If the box moves up 0.25 m, how much does the box weigh?

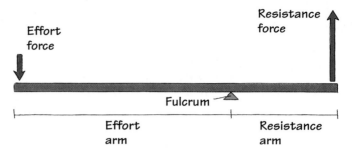

FIGURE 24
The Law of the Lever
A lever's effort arm is the distance from the fulcrum to the effort force. A lever's resistance arm is the distance from the fulcrum to the resistance force.

Mechanical Advantage If you compare the effort force to the resistance force, you can find the advantage of using a lever. A lever's **mechanical advantage** is the number of times a lever increases a force exerted on it. The mechanical advantage of a lever is equal to the ratio of resistance force to the effort force.

$$\text{Mechanical advantage} = \frac{\text{Resistance force}}{\text{Effort force}}$$

In the sample problem on the previous page, an effort force of 80 newtons was exerted to move a 240-newton boulder. The lever's mechanical advantage is 240 newtons divided by 80 newtons, or 3. The lever tripled the effort force.

The Law of the Lever Have you ever balanced a metal spoon on your finger? If so, you have experience with the law of the lever. The spoon is a lever, and your finger acts as the fulcrum. To make the spoon balance, your finger has to be closer to the heavier, bowl end of the spoon than to the other end.

Figure 24 shows how a lever may be balanced when the effort force and resistance force are different. Notice that the fulcrum is not in the middle. The distance from the fulcrum to the effort force is called the **effort arm.** The distance from the fulcrum to the resistance force is the **resistance arm.** The law of the lever states, that for a lever to be balanced, the effort force times the effort arm must be equal to the resistance force times the resistance arm.

Different Classes of Levers There are three classes of levers. These are defined by the location of the fulcrum relative to the effort force and the resistance force. In a first-class lever, the fulcrum is between the effort force and the resistance force. In a second-class lever, the resistance force is between the effort force and the fulcrum. In a third-class lever, the effort force is between the resistance force and the fulcrum. Figure 25 shows examples of all three classes of levers.

 **Reading Checkpoint** How many different classes of levers are there?

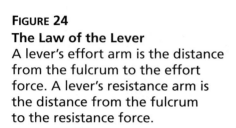

Video Field Trip
Discovery Channel School
Bones, Muscles, and Skin

FIGURE 25

Three Classes of Levers

The three classes of levers differ in the positions of the fulcrum, effort force, and resistance force. **Applying Concepts** *Which type of lever always has a mechanical advantage less than 1?*

First-Class Levers

First-class levers always change the direction of the effort force. If the fulcrum is closer to the resistance force, these levers also increase force. If the fulcrum is closer to the effort force, these levers also increase distance. Other examples include scissors, pliers, and seesaws.

Second-Class Levers

These levers increase force, but do not change the direction of the effort force. Other examples include doors, nutcrackers, and bottle openers.

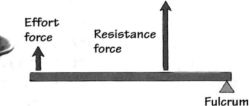

Third-Class Levers

These levers increase distance, but do not change the direction of the effort force. Other examples include fishing poles, shovels, and baseball bats.

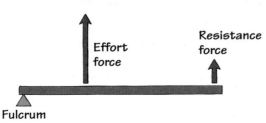

Math ▸ Analyzing Data

Mechanical Advantage

The effort force and resistance force for three different levers are shown in the graph.

1. **Reading Graphs** What variable is plotted on the horizontal axis?

2. **Interpreting Data** If an 80-N effort force is exerted on Lever 2, what is the resistance force?

3. **Calculating** Calculate the mechanical advantage of Lever 2.

4. **Drawing Conclusions** Which lever produces the greatest resistance force when an effort force of 20 N is exerted? Of 40 N? Which lever has the greatest mechanical advantage?

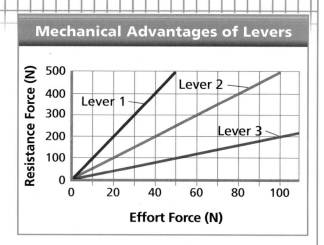

Mechanical Advantages of Levers

Machines in the Body

Now that you know how levers work, you can see how parts of your body act like levers. When you move your legs, hips, hands, or head, you are using a lever system to perform the movement. Most of the machines in your body are levers that consist of bones and muscles.

Joints as Machine Structures In Section 2, you learned about the joints of the human skeleton. ◯ **Many of the body's movable joints are actually fulcrums. The joints in the body act as pivot points for the bones. The bones act as levers, and muscles provide the force.** The thigh joint, the wrist joint, the shoulder joint, the knee joint, and the elbow joint are examples of fulcrums for third-class levers in the body.

The thigh joint, also known as the hip joint, is an example of a ball-and-socket joint. Your thigh bone, or femur, has a rounded end that fits into a hole of the bone that is your pelvic girdle. Another example of a ball-and-socket joint is your shoulder.

Your wrist is an example of a sliding joint, where one bone slides over another bone. Your elbow and your knee are examples of hinge joints. These joints function like the hinges on a door.

For: Links on work
Visit: www.SciLinks.org
Web Code: scn-1341

 **Reading Checkpoint** What kind of joint is the wrist?

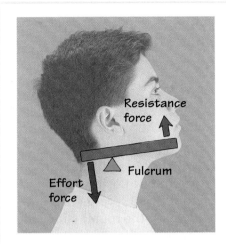

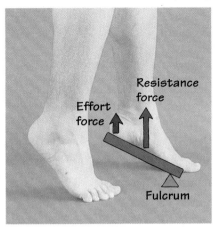

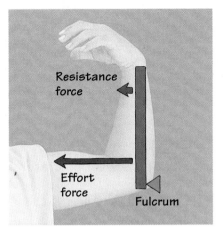

First-Class Lever The joint at the top of your neck is the fulcrum of a first-class lever. The muscles in the back of your neck provide the effort force. The resistance force is used to tilt your head back.

Second-Class Lever The ball of your foot is the fulcrum of a second-class lever. The muscle in the calf of your leg provides the effort force. The resistance force is used to raise your body.

Third-Class Lever Your elbow is the fulcrum of a third-class lever. Your biceps muscle provides the effort force. The resistance force is used to lift your arm.

Bones and Muscles as Lever Systems The most common type of lever in your body is the third-class lever. But your body also has first-class and second-class levers. You can see examples of all three classes of levers in Figure 26. In each case, the effort force is applied at the point where a muscle attaches to a bone. The bone serves as the lever, and the resistance force is the force exerted by the bone. This force may be used for many things, such as chewing, running, or lifting a glass of water.

FIGURE 26
Levers in the Body
You don't need to look further than your own body to find machines. Three different types of levers are responsible for many of your movements.

Section 4 Assessment

S 7.6.h, 7.6.i
E-LA: Reading 7.1.2

Vocabulary Skill Latin Word Origins
Remember that the Latin word *resistere* means "to place against." How does this meaning help you understand the key term *resistance force*?

Reviewing Key Concepts

1. **a. Defining** What is a force?
   b. Comparing and Contrasting How is work different from force?
   c. Measuring How is the value for a distance measurement important in calculating work done on an object?
2. **a. Reviewing** What is a lever, and how is a lever useful?
   b. Explaining What is the mechanical advantage of a lever?
   c. Comparing and Contrasting How does a first-class lever differ from a second-class lever?

3. **a. Listing** Name three joints that act as fulcrums for levers in the body.
   b. Applying Concepts For one of the joints you listed above, explain how the joint functions as a fulcrum when you move.

Math Practice

4. **Calculating** With an effort force of 50 N, Archimedes pushes a lever down. On the other side of the fulcrum, a statue that weighs 5,000 N rises 0.01 m. How far down did Archimedes push the lever?
5. **Calculating** A lever has an effort force of 40 N and a resistance force of 80 N. What is its mechanical advantage?

Using Your Leverage

 S 7.6.h, 7.6.i, 7.7.a

Problem

Is the law of the lever accurate?

Skills Focus

calculating, predicting, interpreting data

Materials

- meter stick • set of hooked weights
- set of weight holders
- 3 spring scales (5-N, 10-N, 20-N)
- plastic fulcrum or other pivoted support

Procedure

PART 1 First-Class Lever

1. Copy the data table onto a separate piece of paper. Label the data table *First-Class Lever*.

2. Place the meter stick with its center resting on the fulcrum so that it is balanced evenly. Make sure the left end is above the table and the right end hangs over the edge.

3. Choose a position on the meter stick to the left of the fulcrum. Record the distance from the fulcrum to that position as the resistance arm. Hang the lightest hooked weight at that position. The meter stick should tilt until that side is resting on the table. Record the value of the hooked weight in newtons as the resistance force.
   (*Hint:* A mass of 1 gram weighs 0.01 newtons, so you can convert grams to newtons by multiplying the mass by 0.01.)

4. Choose a position on the meter stick to the right of the fulcrum. Record the distance from the fulcrum to that position as the effort arm. Using the 5-N spring scale at that position, pull down on the meter stick until it is horizontal with the table. Record the reading on the spring scale in newtons as the effort force.

5. Repeat the experiment four more times with four different hooked weights. Record your data in the table. If necessary, use a larger spring scale for heavier weights.

PART 2 Second-Class Lever

6. Draw a new data table on a separate piece of paper. Label the table *Second-Class Lever*.

7. Balance the meter stick from its center by hanging it on the 5-N spring scale. Record the weight of the meter stick in newtons. You will need this value because the weight of the meter stick adds to the resistance force.

8. Place the meter stick with one end resting on the fulcrum and the other end resting on the table.

9. Choose the 50-cm mark as the resistance arm. Hang the lightest hooked weight at that position. Record the resistance force in newtons as the sum of the weights of the meter stick (from Step 7) and the hooked weight. (Recall that you can convert grams to newtons by multiplying the mass by 0.01.)

▼ Part 1

▼ Part 2

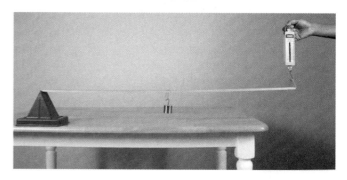

Data Table							
Trial #	Resistance Arm (cm)	Resistance Force (N)	Effort Arm (cm)	Effort Force (N)	RA × RF (N·cm)	EA × EF (N·cm)	Mechanical Advantage
1							
2							
3							
4							
5							

10. Choose the 100-cm mark at the free end of the meter stick as the effort arm. Using the 5-N spring scale at that position, lift the meter stick until it is horizontal with the table. Record the reading on the spring scale in newtons as the effort force.

11. Repeat the experiment four more times with four different hooked weights. Record all your data. If necessary, use a larger spring scale for heavier weights.

Analyze and Conclude

1. **Calculating** In each data table, calculate the value of the resistance arm times the resistance force and the value of the effort arm times the effort force. Record the results in the appropriate place on each data table.

2. **Interpreting Data** How do your calculations in Question 1 compare to the law of the lever as it is stated on page 536?

3. **Calculating** Calculate and record the mechanical advantage of the lever for each trial.

4. **Interpreting Data** Did the two classes of levers have the same mechanical advantage? If so, why? If not, which type of lever had the greater mechanical advantage? Why?

5. **Predicting** How can you balance a first-class lever using a 100-gram hooked weight and a 200-gram hooked weight? Explain. With your teacher's permission, test your prediction.

6. **Communicating** Many sports such as tennis and baseball use equipment that extends the arm. The racquet or bat is made of material that is strong, but lightweight. Suppose you work for a company that produces racquets or bats. Write an advertisement describing your product. In the advertisement, explain how the racquet or bat acts as a lever to make the work of hitting the ball easier.

More to Explore

Repeat the experiment with a third-class lever. Hang the weight at the end of the meter stick, and pull up with the spring scale at the center of the meter stick. Remember to take into account the weight of the meter stick as you did for the second-class lever. This time, however, the weight of the stick opposes your effort force and must be subtracted from the value on the spring scale. Does the third-class lever give you the same results as the second-class lever? Explain.

The BIG Idea When muscles contract, they exert a force that pulls on a bone and makes it move. Many bones act as levers by rotating around a joint that acts as a fulcrum.

① Organ Systems and Homeostasis

Key Concepts — S 7.5.a

- The levels of organization in the body consist of cells, tissues, organs, and organ systems.

- The human body has 11 organ systems. The integumentary, skeletal, and muscular systems provide structure and allow movement. The circulatory, respiratory, digestive, excretory, immune, and reproductive systems carry out the processes of life. The nervous and endocrine systems provide control over body processes.

- Homeostasis is the process by which an organism's internal environment is kept stable in spite of changes in the external environment.

Key Terms

muscle tissue	nephron
nervous tissue	urinary bladder
connective tissue	pathogen
epithelial tissue	antibody
organ system	immunity
digestion	homeostasis
kidney	stress

② The Skeletal System

Key Concepts — S 7.5.c, 7.6.h

- Your skeleton provides shape and support, enables you to move, protects your organs, produces blood cells, and stores minerals and other materials until your body needs them.

- Joints allow bones to move in different ways.

- Bones are complex living structures that undergo growth and development.

- A balanced diet and regular exercise are important for a lifetime of healthy bones.

Key Terms

skeleton	compact bone
vertebrae	spongy bone
joint	marrow
ligament	osteoporosis
cartilage	

③ The Muscular System

Key Concepts — S 7.5.c

- Your body has three types of muscle tissue—skeletal, smooth, and cardiac.

- Skeletal muscles work in pairs. While one muscle contracts, the other muscle in the pair relaxes to its original length.

Key Terms

involuntary muscle	striated muscle
voluntary muscle	smooth muscle
skeletal muscle	cardiac muscle
tendon	

④ Machines and the Body

Key Concepts — S 7.6.h, 7.6.i

- How are force and work related?

- How does a lever make work easier?

- How do bones and muscles function as levers in the body?

Key Terms

force	effort distance
work	resistance force
machine	resistance distance
lever	mechanical advantage
fulcrum	effort arm
effort force	resistance arm

Review and Assessment

⟳ Target Reading Skill

Take Notes To help you review part of Section 2, take notes on the text following the heading Joints of the Skeleton (pages 520-521). The notes have been started for you at the right.

Questions	Notes: Joints of the Skeleton
What is a joint?	A place in the body where two bones come together
What is the function of joints?	

Reviewing Key Terms

Choose the letter of the best answer.

1. Which type of body tissue covers the surfaces of the body?
   a. muscle tissue
   b. nervous tissue
   c. connective tissue
   d. epithelial tissue

2. A soft, connective tissue found inside some bones is
   a. cytoplasm.
   b. marrow.
   c. cartilage.
   d. osteoporosis.

3. Muscles that help the bones move are
   a. cardiac muscles.
   b. smooth muscles.
   c. skeletal muscles.
   d. involuntary muscles.

4. The force you apply to a lever is called the
   a. effort force.
   b. resistance force.
   c. effort distance.
   d. resistance distance.

5. The distance from the fulcrum to the resistance force in a lever is called the
   a. effort distance.
   b. resistance distance.
   c. effort arm.
   d. resistance arm.

Complete the following sentences so that your answers clearly explain the Key Terms.

6. The mouth, stomach, and small intestine are organs that function in **digestion,** which involves _____ .

7. Strong connective tissue found at the ends of bones is called **cartilage,** which is important because _____ .

8. Smooth muscles are also called **involuntary muscles** because _____ .

9. A **lever** is a type of machine, which is useful because _____ .

10. A lever can increase **mechanical advantage,** which is _____ .

Writing in Science

Descriptive Paragraph Pretend you are a writer for a science magazine for children. Write a few paragraphs that compare the characteristics of cartilage with the characteristics of bones. Be sure to explain the advantages of both types of materials.

Video Assessment
Discovery Channel School
Bones, Muscles, and Skin

Review and Assessment

Checking Concepts

11. Explain the relationship among cells, tissues, organs, and organ systems.

12. List the four kinds of movable joints. Describe the type of movement each joint allows.

13. How does eating a well-balanced diet and exercising regularly contribute to healthy bones?

14. Explain how skeletal muscles work in pairs.

15. What three things can a lever do to make work easier?

16. Describe a third-class lever in your body. Locate the effort force, the resistance force, and the fulcrum.

Thinking Critically

17. Inferring In addition to bone, cartilage, and fat, scientists classify blood as a connective tissue. Explain why.

18. Making Generalizations How is homeostasis important to survival?

19. Comparing and Contrasting Explain how the structure of compact bone and spongy bone relate to the function of a bone, such as your femur.

20. Predicting If smooth muscle had to be controlled consciously, what problems could you foresee in day-to-day living?

21. Making Judgments Suppose a member of your running team suggests eliminating "warm-up time" because it takes too much time away from practice. Do you think this suggestion is a good idea? Why or why not?

22. Applying Concepts How does the law of the lever explain why the seesaw pictured below stays balanced?

Math Practice

23. Calculating You use a lever to lift a 100-N box onto a shelf. If you push down an effort distance of 1.5 m using an effort force of 60 N, how high will the box rise? (*Hint:* In this problem, the box's weight is equal to the resistance force.)

Applying Skills

Use the diagram to answer Questions 24–26.

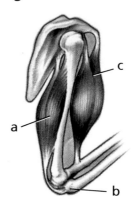

24. Classifying Which structure in the diagram is the triceps? Which is the biceps?

25. Predicting How will the shape of each muscle change if the arm in the diagram is extended?

26. Interpreting Diagrams Which structure in the diagram serves as the fulcrum for extending the arm?

Lab zone Standards Investigation

Performance Assessment Before testing your prosthetic hand, explain to your classmates how and why you designed the hand the way you did. When you test the hand, observe how it picks up objects. How does it compare with a real human hand? How could you improve the function of your prosthetic hand?

Choose the letter of the best answer.

1. Which of the following represents the smallest level of organization in the body?
   A cardiac muscle tissue
   B the heart
   C a muscle cell
   D the circulatory system   **S 7.5.a**

2. The muscles that you use to lift a book are
   A cardiac muscles.
   B smooth muscles.
   C involuntary muscles.
   D skeletal muscles.   **S 7.5.c**

Use the graph to answer Question 3.

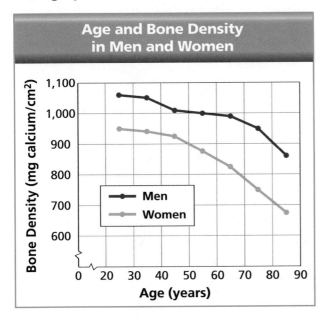

Age and Bone Density in Men and Women

3. Which of the following statements is true according to the graph shown above?
   A The bones of women are more dense than the bones of men.
   B The bones of men contain less calcium than do the bones of women.
   C The bone density of both men and women decreases as they age.
   D An average 55-year-old woman has stronger bones than an average 55-year-old man.
          S 7.5.a

4. Which skeletal joint functions most like the machine shown below?

   A neck
   B knee
   C wrist
   D shoulder   **S 7.6.h**

5. Which statement describes what happens when you bend your arm at the elbow?
   A The biceps contracts and the triceps relaxes.
   B The triceps contracts and the biceps relaxes.
   C Both the biceps and the triceps contract.
   D Only the triceps functions.
          S 7.5.c

6. To open a door, you push on the part of the door that is farthest from the hinges. Why would it be harder to open the door if you pushed on its center?
   A You would have to apply a larger effort force.
   B You would have to apply a larger resistance force.
   C The door is a first-class lever.
   D You would be increasing the effort arm.
          S 7.6.i

🔑 Apply the
BIG Idea

7. A shovel is a type of lever that has a greater effort force than resistance force. Explain why a shovel is still useful. What class of lever is the shovel? Identify an example of how this class of lever is used in the body.   **S 7.6.h, 7.6.i**

Chapter 14

Circulation and Respiration

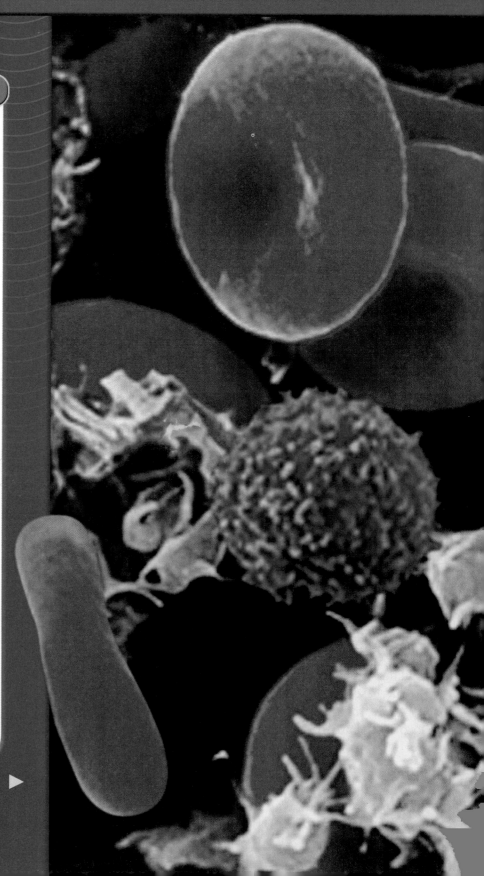

Blood cells travel in blood vessels to all parts of the body. ▶

Video Preview
Discovery Channel School
Circulation

Focus on the
BIG Idea

S 7.5.b

What are the major functions of the circulatory and respiratory systems?

Check What You Know

Suppose you are blowing up balloons for a sports rally at school. How is the air you take into your lungs different from the air you blow into a balloon? Explain how this difference occurs.

Build Science Vocabulary

The images shown here represent some of the key terms in this chapter. You can use this vocabulary skill to help you understand the meaning of some key terms in this chapter.

Vocabulary Skill

High-Use Academic Words

High-use academic words are words that are used frequently in classrooms. You and your teachers use these words when you discuss the subjects you study. Look for these words in this chapter.

Word	Definition	Example Sentence
detect (dee TEKT) p. 553	*v.* To find out or discover	Lisa searched in the grass, trying to <u>detect</u> a four-leaf clover.
regulate (REG yuh layt) p. 563	*v.* To control, direct, or govern according to rule	A small device <u>regulates</u> the temperature in the building.
complex (Kahm PLEKS) p. 571	*adj.* Not simple; involved, complicated	The inside of a computer has a <u>complex</u> network of wires.
contribute (kun TRIB yoot) p. 584	*v.* To give or provide; to bring about a result	Physical activity can <u>contribute</u> to your good health.

Apply It!

Choose the word that best completes the sentence.

1. The doctor used several tests to _____ the disease.

2. One group of cells in the heart help _____ the rate at which the heart beats.

3. Blood is a _____ tissue that has several parts.

4. Air pollution can _____ to problems with breathing.

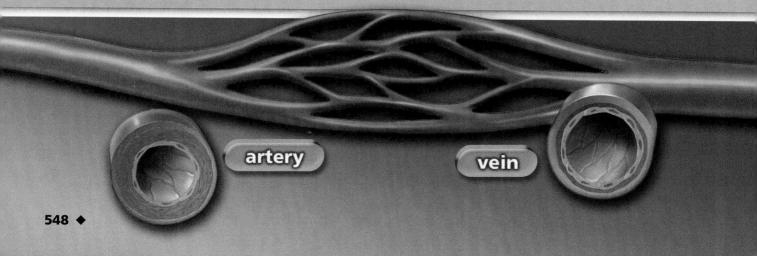

artery

vein

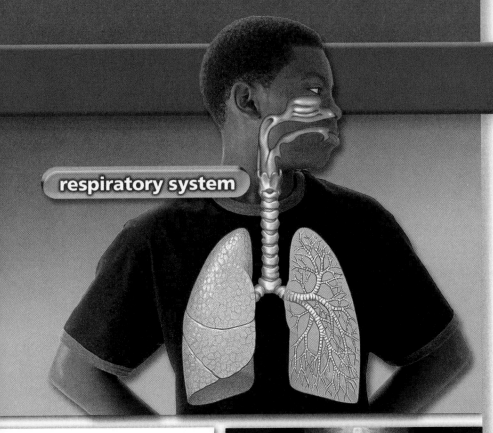

respiratory system

valve

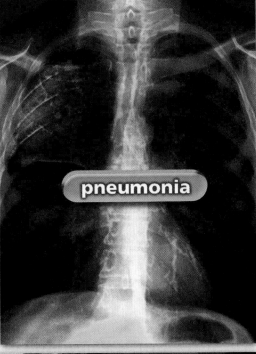

pneumonia

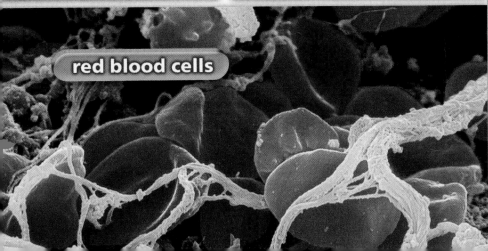

red blood cells

Section 1 (page 552)

cardiovascular system
heart
atrium
pacemaker
ventricle
valve
artery
capillary

vein
aorta
coronary artery
pulse
diffusion
pressure
blood pressure

Section 2 (page 563)

plasma
red blood cell
hemoglobin
white blood cell
platelet

shock
lymphatic system
lymph
lymph node

Section 3 (page 570)

respiration
mucus
cilia
pharynx
trachea
bronchi

lungs
alveoli
diaphragm
larynx
vocal cords

Section 4 (page 580)

atherosclerosis
heart attack
hypertension
stroke
emphysema

bronchitis
asthma
suffocation
pneumonia

Build Science Vocabulary
Online
Visit: PHSchool.com
Web Code: cvj-4140

How to Read Science

Sequence

Sequence is the order in which events happen. Often science textbooks describe a sequence of events. Sometimes the text uses signal words like *first, second,* and *then* to show a sequence. Look for the sequence of events in the paragraph below.

> Blood flows through the body in something like a figure eight. In the <u>first</u> loop, blood travels from the heart to the lungs and <u>then</u> back to the heart. In the <u>second</u> loop, blood is pumped from the heart throughout the body and then returns to the heart <u>again</u>.

Apply It!

In your notebook, complete the flowchart below by showing the sequence of the second loop.

Blood Flow

Blood travels from the heart to the lungs.

↓

Blood travels from the lungs back to the heart.

↓

↓

Standards Investigation

Travels of a Red Blood Cell

Every day, you travel from home to school and back home again. Your travel path makes a loop, or circuit, ending where it began. In this chapter, you'll learn how your blood also travels in circuits. In this investigation, you'll create a display to show how blood cells circulate and function throughout the body.

Your Goal

To design and construct a display showing a complete journey of a red blood cell through the human body

Your display must

- show a red blood cell that leaves from the heart and returns to the same place
- show where the exchange of oxygen and carbon dioxide takes place
- provide written descriptions of the circuits made by the red blood cell
- be designed following the safety guidelines in Appendix A

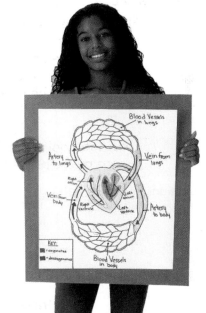

Plan It!

Preview the chapter and find diagrams that show the heart, red blood cells, and the pathway of blood throughout the body. Then discuss the kinds of displays you could use, including a three-dimensional model, posters, a series of drawings, a flip book, or a video animation. Write down any content questions you'll need to answer.

The Body's Transport System

CALIFORNIA

Standards Focus

S 7.5.a Students know plants and animals have levels of organization for structure and function, including cells, tissues, organs, organ systems, and the whole organism.

S 7.6.j Students know that contractions of the heart generate blood pressure and that heart valves prevent backflow of blood in the circulatory system.

- What are the functions of the cardiovascular system?
- What is the function and structure of the heart?
- What path does blood take through the cardiovascular system?
- What are the functions and structures of arteries, capillaries, and veins?

Key Terms

- cardiovascular system
- heart • atrium • pacemaker
- ventricle • valve • artery
- capillary • vein • aorta
- coronary artery • pulse
- diffusion • pressure
- blood pressure

Lab zone Standards **Warm-Up**

How Hard Does Your Heart Work?

1. Every minute, your heart beats about 75 to 85 times. With each beat, it pumps about 60 milliliters of blood. Can you work as hard and fast as your heart does?

2. Cover a table or desk with newspapers. Place two large plastic containers side by side on the newspapers. Fill one with 2.5 liters of water, which is about the volume of blood that your heart pumps in 30 seconds. Leave the other container empty.

3. With a plastic cup that holds about 60 milliliters, transfer water as quickly as possible into the empty container, trying not to spill any. **CAUTION:** *Wipe up spills on the floor immediately.* Have a partner time you for 30 seconds. As you work, count how many transfers you make in 30 seconds.

4. Multiply your results by 2 to find the number of transfers in 1 minute.

Think It Over

Inferring Compare your performance with the number of times your heart beats every minute. What do your results tell you about the strength and speed of a heartbeat?

Late at night, a truck rolls through the darkness. Loaded with fresh fruits and vegetables, the truck is headed for a city supermarket. The driver steers off the interstate and onto a smaller highway. Finally, after driving through narrow city streets, the truck reaches its destination. As dawn breaks, store workers unload the cargo. At the same time, a garbage truck removes yesterday's trash and drives off down the road.

The Cardiovascular System

Like the roads that link all parts of the country, your body has a "highway" network, called the cardiovascular system, that links all parts of your body. The **cardiovascular system,** also called the circulatory system, consists of the heart, blood vessels, and blood. **The cardiovascular system carries needed substances to cells and carries waste products away from cells. In addition, blood contains cells that fight disease.**

Delivering Needed Materials Most substances that need to get from one part of the body to another are carried by blood. For example, blood carries oxygen from your lungs to your other body cells. Blood also transports the glucose your cells use to produce energy.

Removing Waste Products The cardiovascular system picks up wastes from cells. For example, when cells break down glucose, they produce carbon dioxide as a waste product. The carbon dioxide passes from the cells into the blood. The cardiovascular system then carries carbon dioxide to the lungs, where it is exhaled.

Fighting Disease The cardiovascular system also transports cells that attack disease-causing microorganisms. This process can help keep you from becoming sick. If you do get sick, these disease-fighting blood cells will detect and kill the microorganisms and help you get well.

✓ **Reading Checkpoint** How does the cardiovascular system help fight disease?

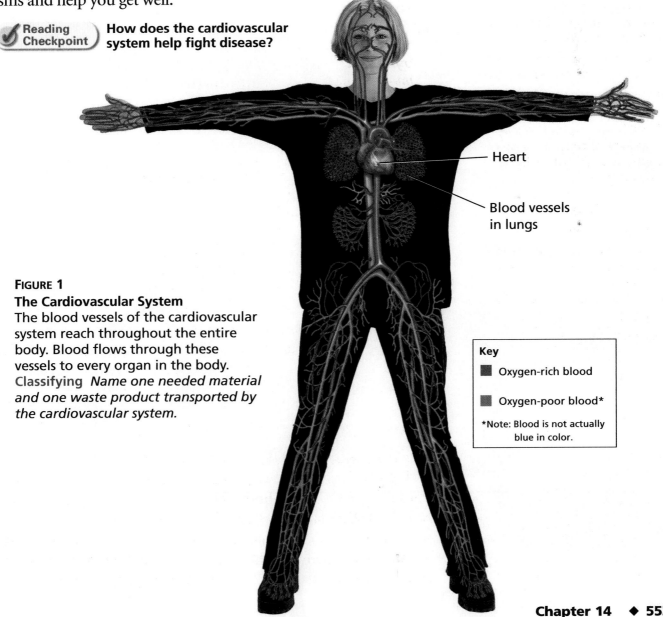

Heart

Blood vessels in lungs

FIGURE 1
The Cardiovascular System
The blood vessels of the cardiovascular system reach throughout the entire body. Blood flows through these vessels to every organ in the body. Classifying *Name one needed material and one waste product transported by the cardiovascular system.*

Key
■ Oxygen-rich blood
■ Oxygen-poor blood*
*Note: Blood is not actually blue in color.

The Heart

Without the heart, blood wouldn't go anywhere. The **heart** is a hollow, muscular organ that pumps blood throughout the body. ☛ **Each time the heart beats, it pushes blood through the blood vessels of the cardiovascular system.**

Your heart, shown in Figure 2, is about the size of your fist. It is located in the center of your chest. The heart lies behind the sternum (breastbone) and inside the rib cage. It is made of cardiac muscle tissue, which can contract over and over without getting tired.

FIGURE 2
The Heart

Every second of your life, your heart pumps blood through your body. In a year, the heart pumps enough blood to fill more than 30 competition-size swimming pools.

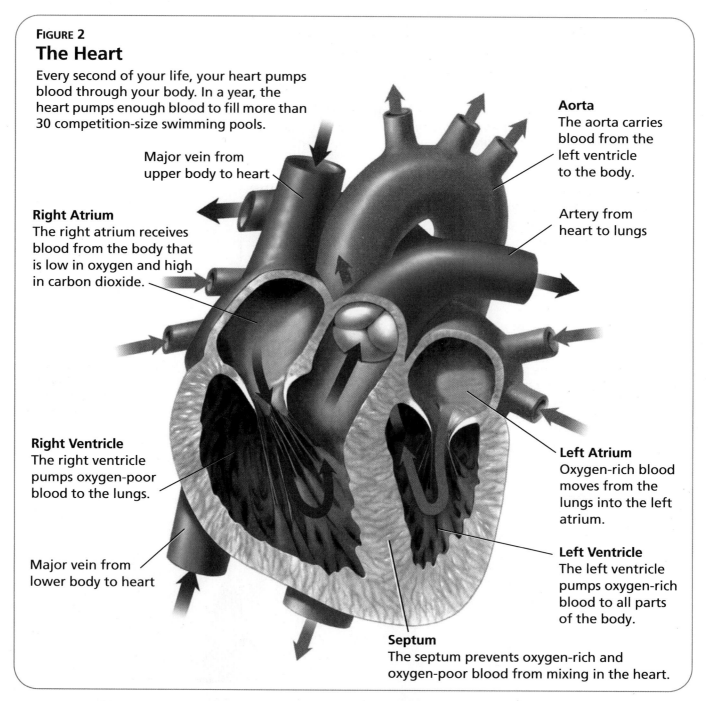

Major vein from upper body to heart

Aorta
The aorta carries blood from the left ventricle to the body.

Right Atrium
The right atrium receives blood from the body that is low in oxygen and high in carbon dioxide.

Artery from heart to lungs

Right Ventricle
The right ventricle pumps oxygen-poor blood to the lungs.

Left Atrium
Oxygen-rich blood moves from the lungs into the left atrium.

Major vein from lower body to heart

Left Ventricle
The left ventricle pumps oxygen-rich blood to all parts of the body.

Septum
The septum prevents oxygen-rich and oxygen-poor blood from mixing in the heart.

The Heart's Structure The heart has a right side and a left side. 👄 **The right side of the heart is completely separated from the left side by a wall of tissue called the septum. Each side has two compartments, or chambers—an upper chamber and a lower chamber.** Each of the two upper chambers, called an **atrium** (AY tree um) (plural *atria*), receives blood that comes into the heart. Located in the right atrium is a group of heart cells called the **pacemaker,** which sends out signals that make the heart muscle contract.

Each lower chamber, called a **ventricle,** pumps blood out of the heart. The atria are separated from the ventricles by valves. A **valve** is a flap of tissue that prevents blood from flowing backward. Valves are also located between the ventricles and the large blood vessels that carry blood away from the heart.

How the Heart Works The action of the heart has two main phases. In one phase, the heart muscle relaxes and the heart fills with blood. In the other phase, the heart muscle contracts and pumps blood forward. A heartbeat, which sounds something like *lub-dup*, can be heard during the pumping phase.

When the heart muscle relaxes, blood flows into the chambers. Then, the atria contract, squeezing blood out of the atria, through the valves, and into the ventricles. Next, the ventricles contract. This contraction closes the valves between the atria and ventricles, making the *lub* sound and squeezing blood into large blood vessels. As the valves between the ventricles and the blood vessels snap shut, they make the *dup* sound.

When muscle cells in the ventricles contract, they exert a force on the blood. A force is a push or a pull. The force exerted by the ventricles pushes blood out of your heart and into blood vessels. The contraction of the left ventricle exerts much more force than the contraction of the right ventricle.

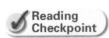
Reading Checkpoint What is the role of the pacemaker?

FIGURE 3
Open and Closed Heart Valves
As blood flows out of the heart and toward the lungs, it passes through a valve like the one in the photograph. **Applying Concepts** *What is the function of a closed heart valve?*

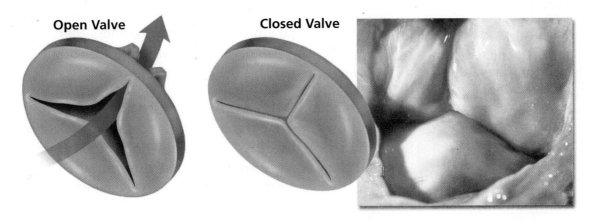

Open Valve   Closed Valve

A Two-Loop System

After leaving the heart, blood travels in blood vessels through the body. Your body has three kinds of blood vessels—arteries, capillaries, and veins. **Arteries** are blood vessels that carry blood away from the heart. From the arteries, blood flows into tiny, narrow vessels called **capillaries.** In the capillaries, substances are exchanged between the blood and body cells. From capillaries, blood flows into **veins,** blood vessels that carry blood back to the heart.

Pattern of Blood Flow The overall pattern of blood flow through the body is something like a figure eight. The heart is at the center where the two loops cross. **In the first loop, blood travels from the heart to the lungs and then back to the heart. In the second loop, blood is pumped from the heart throughout the body and then returns again to the heart.** The heart is really two pumps, one on the right and one on the left. The right side pumps blood to the lungs, and the left side pumps blood to the rest of the body.

Blood travels in only one direction. If you were a drop of blood, you could start at any point and eventually return to the same point. The entire trip would take less than a minute. As you read about the path that blood takes through the cardiovascular system, trace the path in Figure 5.

Loop One: To the Lungs and Back When blood from the body flows into the right atrium, it contains little oxygen but a lot of carbon dioxide. This oxygen-poor blood is dark red. The blood then flows from the right atrium into the right ventricle. Then, the ventricle pumps the oxygen-poor blood into the arteries that lead to the lungs.

As blood flows through the lungs, large blood vessels branch into smaller ones. Eventually, blood flows through tiny capillaries that are in close contact with the air that comes into the lungs. The air in the lungs has more oxygen than the blood in the capillaries, so oxygen moves from the lungs into the blood. For the same reason, carbon dioxide moves in the opposite direction—from the blood into the lungs. As the blood leaves the lungs, it is now rich in oxygen and poor in carbon dioxide. This blood, which is bright red, flows to the left side of the heart and will be pumped through the second loop.

Loop Two: To the Body and Back The second loop begins as the left atrium fills with oxygen-rich blood coming from the lungs. The blood then moves into the left ventricle. From the left ventricle, the blood is pumped into the **aorta** (ay AWR tuh), the largest artery in the body.

Eventually, after passing through branching arteries, blood flows through tiny capillaries in different parts of your body, such as your brain, liver, and legs. These vessels are in close contact with body cells. Oxygen moves out of the blood and into the body cells. At the same time, carbon dioxide passes from the body cells and into the blood. This blood, which is low in oxygen, then flows back to the right atrium of the heart through veins, completing the second loop.

FIGURE 5
Direction of Blood Flow
Blood circulates through the body in two loops, with the heart at the center. Loop one goes from the heart to the lungs and back. Loop two circulates blood throughout the rest of the body.
Interpreting Diagrams *Where does the blood that enters the left atrium come from?*

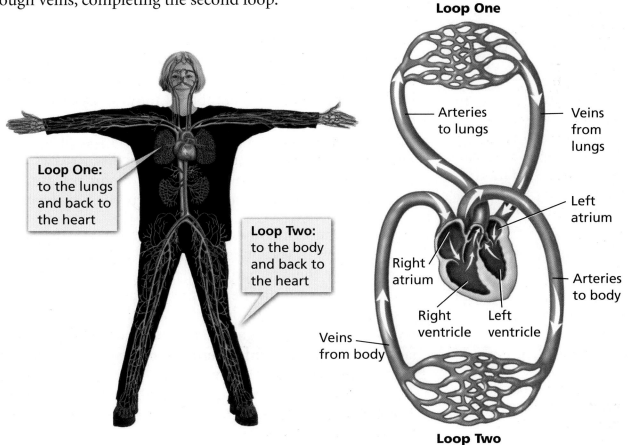

Loop One: to the lungs and back to the heart

Loop Two: to the body and back to the heart

Loop One

Arteries to lungs

Veins from lungs

Left atrium

Right atrium

Arteries to body

Right ventricle

Left ventricle

Veins from body

Loop Two

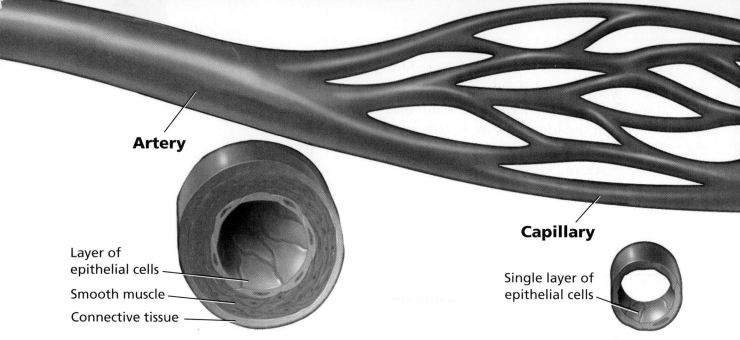

Artery

Layer of
epithelial cells

Smooth muscle

Connective tissue

Capillary

Single layer of
epithelial cells

FIGURE 6
Artery, Capillary, and Vein
The walls of arteries and veins
have three layers. The walls of
capillaries are only one cell
thick. **Relating Cause and Effect**
*How does material get from
inside capillaries to body cells?*

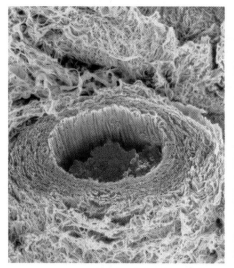

▲ The artery wall appears as a
thick pink band surrounding a
clump of red blood cells.

Arteries

🔑 **When blood leaves the heart, it travels through arteries.**
The right ventricle pumps blood into the arteries that go to the
lungs. The left ventricle pumps blood into the aorta. Smaller
arteries branch off the aorta. The first branches, called the
coronary arteries, carry blood to the heart itself. Other
branches carry blood to the brain, intestines, and other organs.
Each artery branches into smaller and smaller arteries.

Artery Structure 🔑 **The walls of arteries are generally
very thick. In fact, artery walls consist of three cell layers.** The
innermost layer, which is made up of epithelial cells, is smooth.
This smooth surface enables blood to flow freely. The middle
layer consists mostly of muscle tissue. The outer wall is made
up of flexible connective tissue. Because of this layered structure, arteries have both strength and flexibility. Arteries are able
to withstand the enormous pressure of blood as it is pumped
by the heart and to expand and relax between heartbeats.

Pulse If you lightly touch the inside of your wrist, you can
feel the artery in your wrist rise and fall repeatedly. This **pulse**
is caused by the alternating expansion and relaxation of the
artery wall. Every time the heart's ventricles contract, they send
a spurt of blood out through all the arteries in your body. As
this spurt travels through the arteries, it pushes the artery walls
and makes them expand. After the spurt passes, the artery walls
relax and become narrower again.

When you count the number of times an artery pulses
beneath your fingers, you are counting heartbeats. By taking your
pulse rate, you can determine how fast your heart is beating.

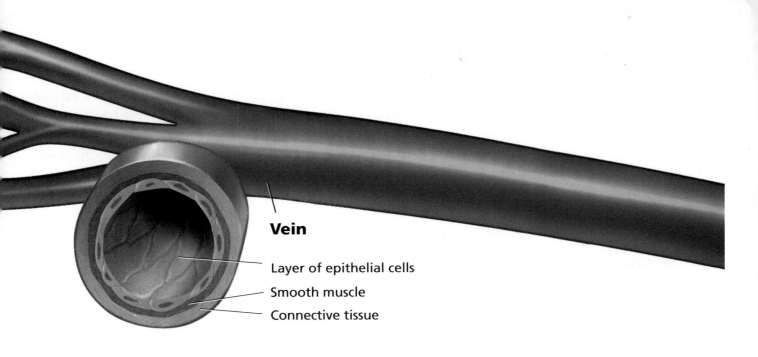

Vein

Layer of epithelial cells

Smooth muscle

Connective tissue

Regulating Blood Flow The layer of muscle in an artery acts as a control gate, adjusting the amount of blood sent to different organs. When the muscle contracts, the opening in the artery becomes smaller. When the muscle relaxes, the opening becomes larger. For example, after you eat, your stomach and intestines need a greater blood supply for digestion. The arteries leading to those organs open wider, and more blood flows through them. In contrast, when you are running, your stomach and intestines need less blood than the muscles in your legs. The arteries leading to the digestive organs become narrower, decreasing the blood flow to these organs.

 **Reading Checkpoint** What causes your pulse?

Capillaries

Eventually, blood flows from small arteries into the tiny capillaries. ⬭ **In the capillaries, materials are exchanged between the blood and the body's cells. Capillary walls are only one cell thick.** Thus, materials can pass easily through them. Materials such as oxygen and glucose pass from the blood, through the capillary walls, to the cells. Cellular waste products travel in the opposite direction—from cells, through the capillary walls, and into the blood.

One way that materials are exchanged between the blood and body cells is by diffusion. **Diffusion** is the process by which molecules move from an area of higher concentration to an area of lower concentration. For example, glucose is more highly concentrated in the blood than it is in the body cells. Therefore, glucose diffuses from the blood into the body cells.

Math Skills

Calculating a Rate

A rate is the speed at which something happens. When you calculate a rate, you compare the number of events with the time period in which they occur. Here's how to calculate the pulse rate of a person whose heart beats 142 times in 2 minutes.

1. Write the comparison as a fraction.

$$\frac{142 \text{ heartbeats}}{2 \text{ minutes}}$$

2. Divide the numerator and the denominator by 2.

$$\frac{142 \div 2}{2 \div 2} = \frac{71}{1}$$

The person's pulse rate is 71 heartbeats per minute.

Practice Problem Calculate your pulse rate if your heart beats 170 times in 2.5 minutes.

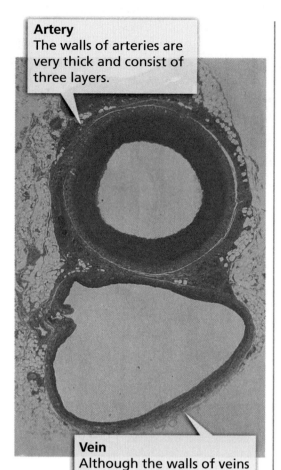

Artery
The walls of arteries are very thick and consist of three layers.

Vein
Although the walls of veins also consist of three layers, they are much thinner than the walls of arteries.

FIGURE 7
Artery and Vein
In this photo, you can compare the wall of an artery (top) with the wall of a vein (bottom).
Comparing and Contrasting *Where is the pushing force of the heart greater—in arteries or in veins?*

Veins

After blood moves through capillaries, it enters larger blood vessels called veins, which carry blood back to the heart. The walls of veins, like those of arteries, have three layers, with muscle in the middle layer. However, the walls of veins are generally much thinner than those of arteries.

By the time blood flows into veins, the pushing force of the heart has much less effect than it did in the arteries. Several factors help move blood through veins. First, because many veins are located near skeletal muscles, the contraction of the muscles helps push the blood along. For example, as you run or walk, the skeletal muscles in your legs contract and squeeze the veins in your legs. Second, larger veins in your body have valves in them that prevent the backflow of blood. Third, breathing movements, which exert a squeezing pressure against veins in the chest, also force blood toward the heart.

Reading Checkpoint **How do skeletal muscles help move blood in veins?**

Blood Pressure

Suppose that you are washing a car. You attach the hose to the faucet and turn on the faucet. The water flows out in a slow, steady stream. Then, while your back is turned, your little brother turns the faucet on all the way. Suddenly, the water spurts out rapidly, and the hose almost jumps out of your hand.

As water flows through a hose, it pushes against the walls of the hose, creating pressure on its inner surface. **Pressure** is force per unit area. It can be measured in various units. When your brother turned on the faucet all the way, the additional water flow increased the pressure exerted on the inside of the hose. The extra pressure made the water spurt out of the nozzle faster.

What Causes Blood Pressure? Blood traveling through blood vessels resembles water moving through a hose. Blood exerts a force, called **blood pressure,** against the walls of the blood vessels. Blood pressure is caused by the force with which the ventricles contract. This action increases the pressure on the blood and forces it through the vessels. In general, as blood moves away from the heart, blood pressure decreases. The blood flowing through your arteries exerts the highest pressure. Blood pressure in your capillaries and veins is much lower than in your arteries.

Measuring Blood Pressure Blood pressure can be measured with an instrument called a sphygmomanometer (sfig moh muh NAHM uh tur). A cuff is wrapped around the upper arm. Air is pumped into the cuff until the blood flow through the artery is stopped. As the pressure is released, the examiner listens to the pulse and records two numbers. Blood pressure is expressed in millimeters of mercury (mmHg). The first number is a measure of the blood pressure while the heart's ventricles contract and pump blood into the arteries. The second number, which is lower, measures the blood pressure while the ventricles relax. The two numbers are expressed as a fraction: the contraction pressure over the relaxation pressure.

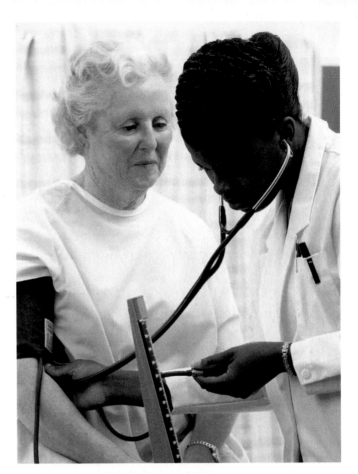

FIGURE 8
Measuring Blood Pressure
Blood pressure can be measured with a sphygmomanometer. A typical blood pressure reading for a healthy person is 120/80 or lower.

Section 1 Assessment

S 7.5.a, 7.6.j, E-LA: Reading 7.2.0, Math: 7.1.3

⟳ **Target Reading Skill** Sequence Describe the path of blood from the lungs to the heart, through the heart, and then out of the heart to the rest of the body.

🔑 **Reviewing Key Concepts**

1. **a. Reviewing** What does the cardiovascular system consist of?
   b. Classifying What three functions does the cardiovascular system perform?
2. **a. Identifying** What function does the heart perform?
   b. Summarizing What are the four chambers of the heart? What structures separate one chamber from another?
   c. Predicting What would happen if the valve between the right atrium and the right ventricle did not work properly?
3. **a. Identifying** Where does blood returning from the body enter the heart?
   b. Sequencing Where does the blood move next?

4. **a. Describing** What roles do arteries, capillaries, and veins play in the cardiovascular system?
   b. Comparing and Contrasting How are the structures of arteries, capillaries, and veins similar? How are they different?

Math ▶ **Practice**

Before a run, you take your pulse rate for 30 seconds and count 29 beats. Immediately after the run, you count 63 beats in 30 seconds.

5. **Calculating a Rate** What was your pulse rate per minute before the run?
6. **Calculating a Rate** What was your pulse rate immediately after the run?

Skills Lab

Heart Beat, Health Beat

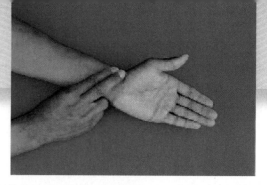

 S 7.5.a, 7.7.c

Problem

How does physical activity affect your pulse rate?

Skills Focus

graphing, interpreting data, drawing conclusions

Materials

• graph paper
• watch with second hand or heart rate monitor

Procedure

1. Predict how your pulse rate will change as you go from resting to being active, then back to resting again. Then, copy the data table into your notebook.

2. Locate your pulse by placing the index and middle finger of one hand on your other wrist at the base of your thumb. Move the two fingers slightly until you feel your pulse. If you are using a heart rate monitor, see your teacher for instructions.

3. Work with a partner for the rest of this lab. Begin by determining your resting pulse rate. Count the number of beats in your pulse for exactly 1 minute while your partner times you. Record your resting pulse rate in your data table. **CAUTION:** *Do not complete the rest of this lab if there is any medical reason why you should avoid physical activities.*

Data Table	
Activity	**Pulse Rate**
Resting	
Walking	
Running	
Resting after exercise (1 min)	
Resting after exercise (3+ min)	

4. Walk in place for 1 minute while your partner times you. Stop and immediately take your pulse for 1 minute. Record the number in your data table.

5. Run in place for 1 minute. Take your pulse again, and record the result.

6. Sit down right away, and have your partner time you as you rest for 1 minute. Then, take your pulse rate again.

7. Have your partner time you as you rest for 3 more minutes. Then take your pulse rate again and record it.

Analyze and Conclude

1. **Graphing** Use the data you obtained to create a bar graph of your pulse rate under the different conditions you tested.

2. **Interpreting Data** What happens to the pulse rate when the physical activity has stopped?

3. **Inferring** What can you infer about the heartbeat when the pulse rate increases?

4. **Drawing Conclusions** What conclusion can you draw about the relationship between physical activity and heart function?

5. **Communicating** How could you improve the accuracy of your pulse measurements? Write a paragraph in which you discuss this question in relation to the steps you followed in your procedure.

Design an Experiment

Design an experiment to determine whether the resting pulse rates of adults, teens, and young children differ. *Obtain your teacher's permission before carrying out your investigation.*

For: Data sharing
Visit: PHSchool.com
Web Code: ced-4032

Blood and Lymph

CALIFORNIA
Standards Focus

S 7.5.a Students know plants and animals have levels of organization for structure and function, including cells, tissues, organs, organ systems, and the whole organism.

S 7.5.b Students know organ systems function because of the contributions of individual organs, tissues, and cells. The failure of any part can affect the entire system.

- What are the components of blood?
- What determines the type of blood that a person can receive in a transfusion?
- What are the structures and functions of the lymphatic system?

Key Terms
- plasma
- red blood cell
- hemoglobin
- white blood cell
- platelet
- shock
- lymphatic system
- lymph
- lymph node

Lab zone Standards Warm-Up

What Kinds of Cells Are in Blood?

1. Obtain a microscope slide of human blood. Look at the slide under the microscope, first under low power and then under high power.
2. Look carefully at the different kinds of cells that you see.
3. Make several drawings of each kind of cell. Use red pencil for the red blood cells.

Think It Over

Observing How many kinds of cells did you see? How do they differ from one another?

While riding your bike through the neighborhood, you take a tumble and scrape your knee. Your knee begins to sting, and you notice blood oozing from the wound. You go inside to clean the wound. As you do, you wonder, "Just what is blood?"

Blood

Blood may seem like just a plain red liquid, but it is actually a complex tissue that has several parts. **Blood is made up of four components: plasma, red blood cells, white blood cells, and platelets.** About 45 percent of the volume of blood is cells. The rest is plasma.

Plasma Most of the materials transported in the blood travel in the plasma. **Plasma** is the liquid part of the blood. Water makes up 90 percent of plasma. The other 10 percent is dissolved materials. Plasma carries nutrients, such as glucose, fats, vitamins, and minerals. Plasma also carries chemical messengers that direct body activities such as the uptake of glucose by your cells. In addition, many wastes produced by cell processes are carried away by plasma.

Protein molecules give plasma its yellow color. There are three groups of plasma proteins. One group helps to regulate the amount of water in blood. The second group, which is produced by white blood cells, helps fight disease. The third group of proteins interacts with platelets to form blood clots.

Red Blood Cells Without red blood cells, your body could not use the oxygen that you breathe in. **Red blood cells** take up oxygen in the lungs and deliver it to cells elsewhere in the body. Red blood cells, like most blood cells, are produced in bone marrow. Under a microscope, these cells look like disks with pinched-in centers. Because of their pinched shape, red blood cells are thin in the middle and can bend and twist easily. This flexibility enables them to squeeze through narrow capillaries.

A red blood cell is made mostly of **hemoglobin** (HEE muh gloh bin), which is an iron-containing protein that binds chemically to oxygen molecules. When hemoglobin combines with oxygen, the cells become bright red. Without oxygen, the cells are dark red. Thus, blood leaving the heart through the aorta is bright red, whereas blood returning from the body to the heart through veins is dark red. Hemoglobin picks up oxygen in the lungs and releases it as blood travels through capillaries in the rest of the body. Hemoglobin also picks up some of the carbon dioxide produced by cells. However, most of the carbon dioxide is carried by plasma. The blood carries the carbon dioxide to the lungs, where it is released from the body.

Mature red blood cells have no nuclei. Without a nucleus, a red blood cell cannot reproduce or repair itself. Mature red blood cells live only about 120 days. Every second, about 2 million red blood cells in your body die. Fortunately, your bone marrow produces new red blood cells at the same rate.

Reading Checkpoint What is hemoglobin?

White Blood Cells Like red blood cells, white blood cells are produced in bone marrow. **White blood cells** are the body's disease fighters. Some white blood cells recognize disease-causing organisms, such as bacteria, and alert the body that it has been invaded. Other white blood cells produce chemicals to fight the invaders. Still others surround and kill the organisms.

White blood cells are different from red blood cells in several important ways. There are fewer of them—only about one white blood cell for every 500 to 1,000 red blood cells. White blood cells are also larger than red blood cells. In addition, white blood cells contain nuclei. Most white blood cells can live for months or even years.

FIGURE 9
Parts of Blood
Blood consists of liquid plasma, red blood cells, white blood cells, and platelets.
Observing *Describe the shape of a red blood cell.*

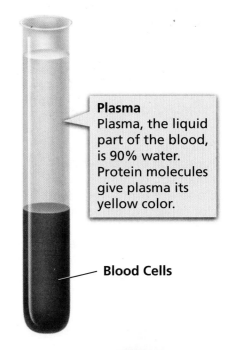

Plasma
Plasma, the liquid part of the blood, is 90% water. Protein molecules give plasma its yellow color.

— **Blood Cells**

Red Blood Cells
Oxygen is carried throughout your body by red blood cells. Your blood contains more red blood cells than any other kind of cell.

White Blood Cells
By finding and destroying disease-causing organisms, white blood cells fight disease.

Platelets
When you cut yourself, platelets help form the blood clot that stops the bleeding. Platelets aren't really whole cells. Instead, they are small pieces of cells and do not have nuclei.

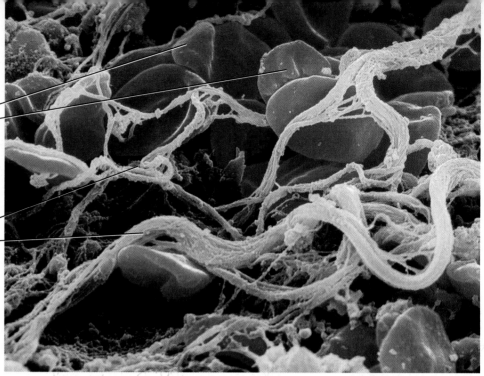

Red blood cells

Fibrin

FIGURE 10
Formation of a Blood Clot
When you cut your skin, a blood clot forms. The blood clot consists of blood cells trapped in a fiber net.
Relating Cause and Effect *How is this net of fibers produced?*

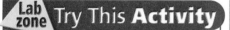

Caught in the Web

In this activity, you will model part of the process by which a blood clot forms.

1. Cover the opening of a sturdy plastic cup with a piece of cheesecloth. Use a rubber band to hold the cheesecloth in place.
2. Put some water, paper clips, and coins in another cup.
3. Carefully pour the water, coins, and paper clips into the middle of the cheesecloth.

Making Models The paper clips and coins represent blood cells. What does the cheesecloth represent? What starts the production of the substance that the cheesecloth represents?

Platelets When you scraped your knee, blood oozed out of the wound. After a short time, however, a blood clot formed, stopping the blood flow. **Platelets** (PLAYT lits) are cell fragments that play an important part in forming blood clots.

When a blood vessel is cut, platelets collect and stick to the vessel at the site of the wound. The platelets release chemicals that start a chain reaction. This series of reactions eventually produces a protein called fibrin (FY brin). Fibrin gets its name from the fact that it weaves a net of tiny fibers across the cut in the blood vessel. Look at Figure 10 to see how the fiber net traps the blood cells. As more and more platelets and blood cells become trapped in the net, a blood clot forms. A scab is a dried blood clot on the skin surface.

Blood Volume An adult of average size has about 5 liters of blood. In contrast, an infant has a blood volume less than one tenth of that! You and your classmates have blood volumes that may range from below 2.5 liters to above 4 liters. If you lose a small amount of blood from a minor injury, your blood volume is not greatly affected. Your body recovers quickly. However, sometimes a person may suffer greater blood loss from a major injury or during surgery. This loss of blood volume is dangerous because it can send the body into shock. **Shock** is the failure of the circulatory system to provide an adequate supply of oxygen-rich blood to all parts of the body. Other causes of shock include heart failure, infection, and emotional trauma. If not treated, shock may cause death.

 **Reading Checkpoint** **What is the role of platelets?**

Blood Types

If a person loses a lot of blood—either from a wound or during surgery—he or she may be given a blood transfusion. A blood transfusion is the transfer of blood from one person to another. Most early attempts at blood transfusion failed, but no one knew why until the early 1900s. At that time, Karl Landsteiner, an Austrian American physician, tried mixing blood samples from pairs of people. Sometimes the two blood samples blended smoothly. In other cases, however, the red blood cells clumped together. This clumping accounted for the failure of many blood transfusions. If clumping occurs within the body, it clogs the capillaries and may lead to death.

Marker Molecules Landsteiner went on to discover that there are four major types of blood—named A, B, AB, and O. Blood types are determined by proteins known as marker molecules that are on the red blood cells. If your blood type is A, you have the A marker. If your blood type is B, you have the B marker. People with type AB blood have both A and B markers. People with type O blood have neither A nor B markers.

Your plasma contains clumping proteins that recognize red blood cells with "foreign" markers (not yours) and make those cells clump together. For example, if you have blood type A, your blood contains clumping proteins that are anti-B. That is, they act against cells with B markers. So, if you receive a transfusion of type B blood, your clumping proteins will make the "foreign" type B cells clump together.

Landsteiner's work led to a better understanding of transfusions. ◯ **The marker molecules on your red blood cells determine your blood type and the type of blood that you can safely receive in transfusions.** Figure 11 shows which transfusions are safe for each blood type.

Go Online
SciLINKS NSTA

For: Links on blood
Visit: www.SciLinks.org
Web Code: scn-0433

FIGURE 11
Blood Types and Their Markers
The chemical markers on a person's red blood cells determine the types of blood he or she can safely receive in a transfusion.
Interpreting Tables *What types of blood can be given safely to a person with blood type AB?*

Blood Types and Their Markers				
Blood Type Characteristic	**Blood Type A**	**Blood Type B**	**Blood Type AB**	**Blood Type O**
Marker Molecules on Red Blood Cells				
Clumping Proteins	anti-B	anti-A	no clumping proteins	anti-A and anti-B
Blood Types That Can Be Safely Received in a Transfusion	A and O	B and O	A, B, AB, and O	O

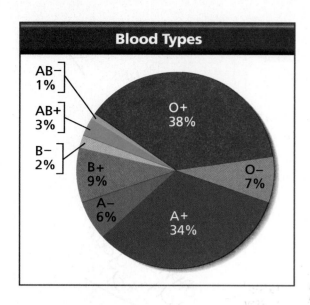

Blood Types

AB−
1%

AB+
3%

B−
2%

B+
9%

A−
6%

A+
34%

O+
38%

O−
7%

FIGURE 12
Blood Types in the Population
This circle graph shows the percentage of each blood type found in the population of the United States.
Calculating *What percentage of the population is Rh negative?*

Safe Transfusions A person with type A blood can receive transfusions of either type A or type O blood. Neither of these two blood types has B markers. Thus they would not be recognized as foreign by the clumping proteins in type A blood. A person with type AB blood can receive all blood types in transfusions because type AB blood has no clumping proteins.

If you ever receive a transfusion, your blood type will be checked first. Then, donated blood that you can safely receive will be found. This process is called cross matching. You may have heard a doctor on a television show give the order to "type and cross." The doctor wants to find out what blood type the patient has and then cross match it with donated blood.

Rh Factor Landsteiner also discovered the presence of another protein on red blood cells, which he called Rh factor. About 85 percent of the people he tested had this protein, and about 15 percent lacked it. Like the A, B, AB, and O blood types, the presence of Rh factor is determined by a marker on the red blood cells. If your blood type is Rh positive, you have the Rh marker. If your blood type is Rh negative, you lack the marker on your cells. If you are Rh negative and ever received Rh positive blood, you would develop Rh clumping proteins in your plasma. This situation is potentially dangerous.

 **Reading Checkpoint** Where is the Rh marker found?

The Lymphatic System

As blood travels through the capillaries in the cardiovascular system, some of the fluid leaks out. It moves through the walls of capillaries and into surrounding tissues. This fluid carries materials that the cells in the tissues need.

After bathing the cells, this fluid moves into your body's drainage system, called the **lymphatic system** (lim FAT ik). See Figure 13 on the next page. ☛ **The lymphatic system is a network of veinlike vessels that returns the fluid to the bloodstream.** The lymphatic system acts something like rain gutters after a rainstorm, carrying the excess fluid away.

Lymph Once the fluid is inside the lymphatic system, it is called **lymph.** Lymph consists of water and dissolved materials, such as glucose. It also contains some white blood cells that have left the capillaries.

The lymphatic system has no pump, so lymph moves slowly. Lymphatic vessels, which are part of the cardiovascular system, connect to large veins in the chest. Lymph empties into these veins, and the fluid once again becomes part of the blood plasma.

Lymph Nodes As lymph flows through the lymphatic system, it passes through small knobs of tissue called lymph nodes. The **lymph nodes** filter lymph, trapping bacteria and other disease-causing microorganisms in the fluid. When the body is fighting an infection, the lymph nodes enlarge. If you've ever had "swollen glands" when you've been sick, you've actually had swollen lymph nodes.

 **Reading Checkpoint** What is lymph?

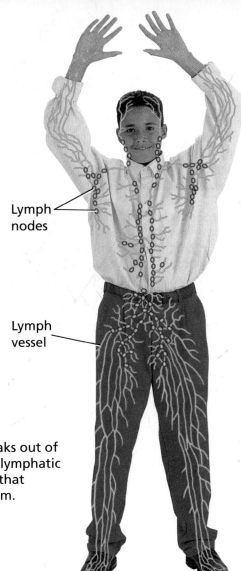

Lymph nodes

Lymph vessel

FIGURE 13
The Lymphatic System
Some of the liquid part of blood leaks out of blood vessels. This liquid enters the lymphatic system, a system of veinlike vessels that returns the liquid to the bloodstream.

Section 2 Assessment

S 7.5.a, 7.5.b, E-LA: Reading 7.1.0

Vocabulary Skill High-Use Academic Words
Explain why it is important for white blood cells to be able to *detect* disease-causing organisms.

Reviewing Key Concepts

1. a. **Listing** Name the four components of blood. Identify whether each is a cell, a part of a cell, or a liquid.
   b. **Summarizing** Briefly describe what happens to stop the bleeding when you cut yourself.
   c. **Relating Cause and Effect** People with the disorder hemophilia do not produce the protein fibrin. Explain why hemophilia is a serious disorder.
2. a. **Reviewing** What is a marker molecule?
   b. **Explaining** Explain why a person with type O blood cannot receive a transfusion of type A blood.

   c. **Predicting** Can a person with type AB, Rh negative blood safely receive a transfusion of type O, Rh negative blood? Explain.
3. a. **Identifying** Where does lymph come from?
   b. **Sequencing** What happens to lymph after it travels through the lymphatic system?

Lab zone At-Home **Activity**

What's Your Blood Type? If possible, find out your blood type. Explain to family members the types of blood you can receive and to whom you can donate blood. Create a chart to help with your explanation.

The Respiratory System

S 7.5.a Students know plants and animals have levels of organization for structure and function, including cells, tissues, organs, organ systems, and the whole organism.

S 7.5.b Students know organ systems function because of the contributions of individual organs, tissues, and cells. The failure of any part can affect the entire system.

- What are the functions of the respiratory system?
- What structures does air pass through as it travels to the lungs?
- What happens during gas exchange and breathing?

Key Terms

- respiration
- mucus
- cilia
- pharynx
- trachea
- bronchi
- lungs
- alveoli
- diaphragm
- larynx
- vocal cords

Lab zone Standards Warm-Up

How Big Can You Blow Up a Balloon?

1. Take a normal breath, then blow as much air as possible into a balloon. Twist the end and hold it closed. Have your partner measure around the balloon at its widest point.
2. Let the air out of the balloon. Repeat Step 1 and calculate the average of the two measurements.
3. Compare your results with those of your classmates. The bigger the circumference, the greater the volume of air exhaled.

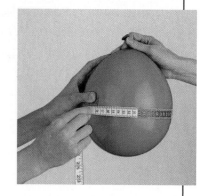

Think It Over

Inferring What factors might affect the volume of air a person can exhale?

Jerry, the main character in Doris Lessing's story "Through the Tunnel," is on vacation at the seaside. Day after day, he watches some older boys dive into deep water on one side of a huge rock. The boys mysteriously reappear on the other side. Jerry figures out that there must be an underwater tunnel in the rock. He finds the tunnel beneath the water and decides to swim through it. Once inside, though, he is terrified. The walls are slimy, and rocks scrape his body. He can barely see where he is going. But worst of all, Jerry has to hold his breath for far longer than ever before. The author describes Jerry this way: "His head was swelling, his lungs were cracking."

Hold your breath!

Respiratory System Functions

No one can go for very long without breathing. Your body cells need oxygen, and they get that oxygen from the air you breathe. ▸ **The respiratory system moves oxygen from the outside environment into the body. It also removes carbon dioxide and water from the body.**

Taking in Oxygen The oxygen your body needs comes from the atmosphere—the mixture of gases that blankets Earth. Your body doesn't use most of the other gases in the air you breathe in. When you exhale, most of the air goes back into the atmosphere.

Oxygen is needed for the energy-releasing chemical reactions that take place inside your cells. Like a fire, which cannot burn without oxygen, your cells cannot "burn" enough fuel to keep you alive without oxygen. The process in which oxygen and glucose undergo a complex series of chemical reactions inside cells is called **respiration.** Respiration, which is also called cellular respiration, is different from breathing. Breathing refers to the movement of air into and out of the lungs. Respiration, on the other hand, refers to the chemical reactions inside cells. As a result of respiration, your cells release the energy that fuels growth and other cell processes.

Removing Carbon Dioxide and Water In addition to the release of energy, respiration produces carbon dioxide and water. Your respiratory system eliminates the carbon dioxide and some of the water through your lungs.

Math: Statistics, Data Analysis, and Probability 7.1.0

Math ▸ Analyzing Data

The Air You Breathe

The air you breathe in contains several different gases, shown in the circle graph on the left. The air you breathe out contains the same gases, but in the amounts shown in the circle graph on the right.

1. **Interpreting Data** Based on the data, which gas is used by the body? Explain.

2. **Drawing Conclusions** Compare the percentage of carbon dioxide in inhaled air with the percentage in exhaled air. How can you account for the difference?

3. **Inferring** Explain why the percentage of nitrogen is the same in both inhaled air and exhaled air.

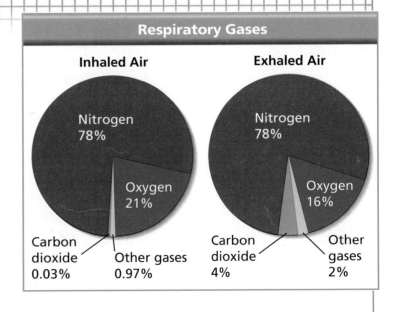

Respiratory Gases

Inhaled Air
- Nitrogen 78%
- Oxygen 21%
- Carbon dioxide 0.03%
- Other gases 0.97%

Exhaled Air
- Nitrogen 78%
- Oxygen 16%
- Carbon dioxide 4%
- Other gases 2%

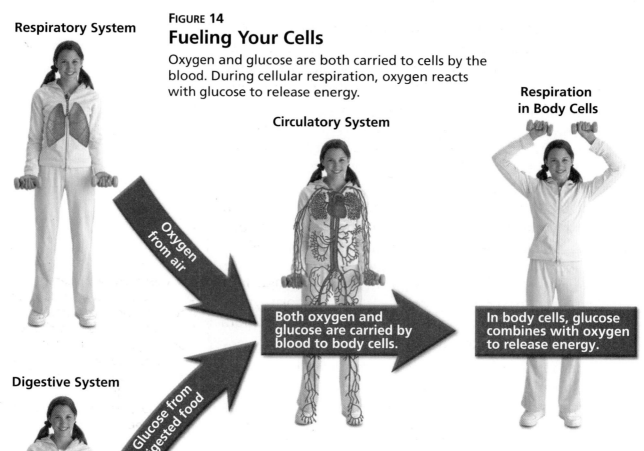

Respiratory System

FIGURE 14
Fueling Your Cells

Oxygen and glucose are both carried to cells by the blood. During cellular respiration, oxygen reacts with glucose to release energy.

Circulatory System

Respiration in Body Cells

Oxygen from air

Glucose from digested food

Both oxygen and glucose are carried by blood to body cells.

In body cells, glucose combines with oxygen to release energy.

Digestive System

Systems Working Together The respiratory system is just one of the body systems that makes respiration possible. As you can see in Figure 14, respiration could not take place without the digestive and circulatory systems as well. Your respiratory system brings oxygen into your lungs. Meanwhile, your digestive system absorbs glucose from the food you eat. Then, your circulatory system carries both the oxygen and the glucose to your cells, where respiration occurs.

The Path of Air

If you look toward a window on a bright day, you may see tiny particles dancing in the air. These particles include such things as floating grains of dust, plant pollen, and ash from fires. Though you can't see them, air also contains microorganisms. Some of these microorganisms can cause diseases in humans. When you breathe in, all these materials enter your body along with the air.

However, most of these materials never reach your lungs. On its way to the lungs, air passes through a series of structures that filter and trap particles. These organs also warm and moisten the air. **As air travels from the outside environment to the lungs, it passes through the following structures: nose, pharynx, trachea, and bronchi.** It takes air only a few seconds to complete the route from the nose to the lungs.

The Nose Air enters the body through the nose and then moves into spaces called the nasal cavities. Some of the cells lining the nasal cavities produce **mucus**—a thick, sticky liquid that moistens the air and keeps the lining from drying out. Mucus also traps particles such as dust.

Cells that line the nasal cavities have **cilia** (SIL ee uh), tiny hairlike extensions that move together in a sweeping motion. Cilia sweep mucus into the throat, where you swallow it. Stomach acid destroys the mucus, and everything trapped in it.

Some particles and bacteria can irritate the lining of your nose or throat, causing you to sneeze. The powerful force of a sneeze shoots the particles out of your nose and into the air.

The Pharynx Next, air enters the **pharynx** (FAR ingks), or throat. The pharynx is the only part of the respiratory system that is shared with another system—the digestive system. Both the nose and the mouth connect to the pharynx.

Reading Checkpoint What is the role of cilia?

FIGURE 15
The Respiratory System
On its path from outside the body into the lungs, air passes through several structures that clean, warm, and moisten it. Once in the lungs, the oxygen in the air can enter your bloodstream. *Classifying Which part of the respiratory system is also part of the digestive system?*

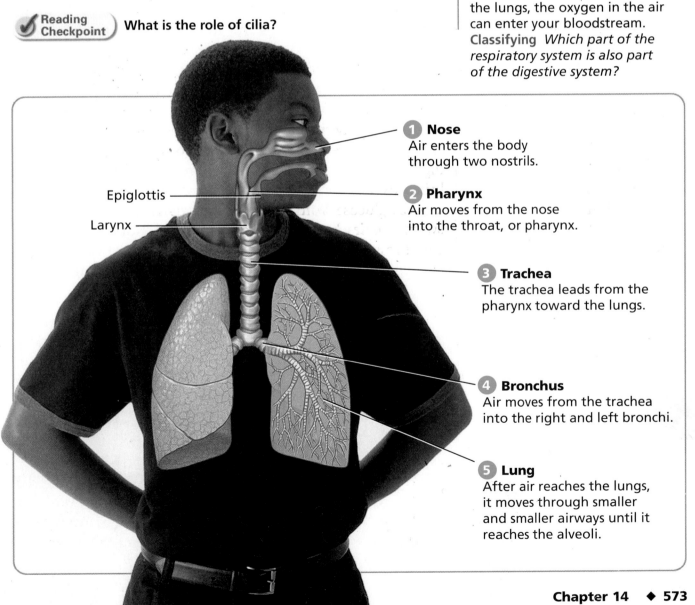

Epiglottis

Larynx

1 Nose
Air enters the body through two nostrils.

2 Pharynx
Air moves from the nose into the throat, or pharynx.

3 Trachea
The trachea leads from the pharynx toward the lungs.

4 Bronchus
Air moves from the trachea into the right and left bronchi.

5 Lung
After air reaches the lungs, it moves through smaller and smaller airways until it reaches the alveoli.

The Trachea From the pharynx, air moves into the **trachea** (TRAY kee uh), or windpipe. You can feel your trachea if you gently run your fingers down the center of your neck. The trachea feels like a tube with a series of ridges. The firm ridges are rings of cartilage that strengthen the trachea and keep it open.

The trachea, like the nose, is lined with cilia and mucus. The cilia in the trachea sweep upward, moving mucus toward the pharynx, where it is swallowed. The trachea's cilia and mucus continue the cleaning and moistening of air that began in the nose. If particles irritate the lining of the trachea, you cough. A cough, like a sneeze, sends the particles into the air.

Normally, only air—not food—enters the trachea. If food does enter the trachea, the food can block the opening and prevent air from getting to the lungs. When that happens, a person chokes. Fortunately, food rarely gets into the trachea. The epiglottis, a small flap of tissue that folds over the trachea, seals off the trachea while you swallow.

The Bronchi and Lungs Air moves from the trachea to the **bronchi** (BRAHNG ky) (singular *bronchus*), the passages that direct air into the lungs. The **lungs** are the main organs of the respiratory system. The left bronchus leads into the left lung, and the right bronchus leads into the right lung. Inside the lungs, each bronchus divides into smaller and smaller tubes in a pattern that resembles the branches of a tree.

At the end of the smallest tubes are structures that look like bunches of grapes. The "grapes" are **alveoli** (al VEE uh ly) (singular *alveolus*), tiny sacs of lung tissue specialized for the movement of gases between air and blood. Notice in Figure 16 that each alveolus is surrounded by a network of capillaries. It is here that the blood picks up its cargo of oxygen from the air.

✓ Reading Checkpoint **How is food prevented from entering the trachea?**

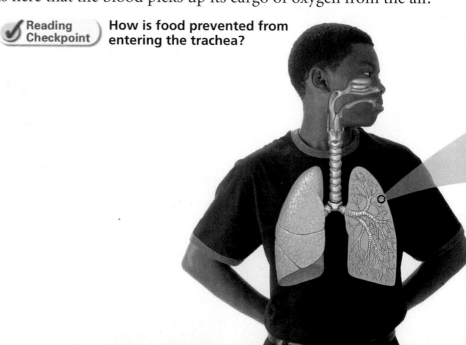

Gas Exchange

Because the walls of both the alveoli and the capillaries are very thin, certain materials can pass through them easily. **After air enters an alveolus, oxygen passes through the wall of the alveolus and then through the capillary wall into the blood. Carbon dioxide and water pass from the blood into the alveoli. This whole process is known as gas exchange.**

How Gas Exchange Occurs Gas exchange occurs as the circulatory and respiratory systems work together. *Pulmonary* means, "having to do with the lungs." Pulmonary circulation carries blood from the heart to the lungs and back. On the way to the lungs, blood has little oxygen. But it has a lot of carbon dioxide. In the capillaries around the alveoli, oxygen attaches to the hemoglobin in the red blood cells. At the same time, carbon dioxide moves from the blood and into the alveoli. As a result of pulmonary circulation, the blood that returns to the heart is rich in oxygen and poor in carbon dioxide.

FIGURE 16
Gas Exchange in the Alveoli

During gas exchange, oxygen moves from the alveoli into the blood and carbon dioxide moves from the blood into the alveoli.
Interpreting Diagrams *How is the structure of the alveoli important for gas exchange?*

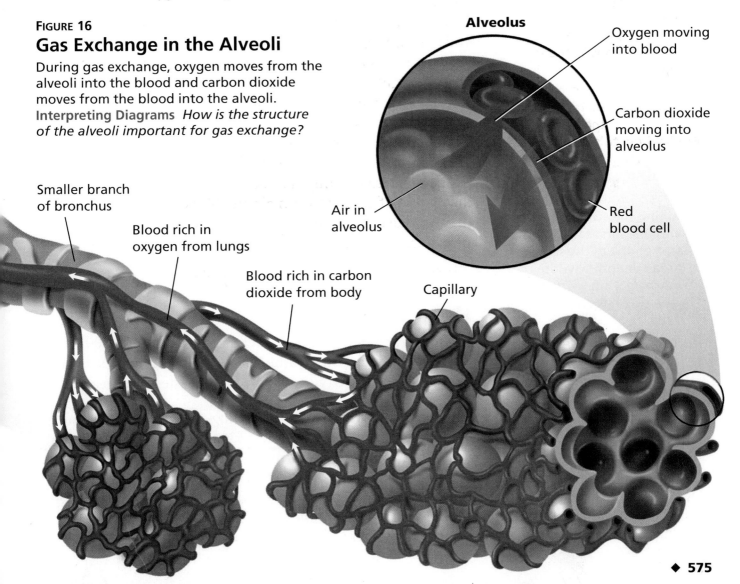

Alveolus

Oxygen moving into blood

Carbon dioxide moving into alveolus

Air in alveolus

Red blood cell

Smaller branch of bronchus

Blood rich in oxygen from lungs

Blood rich in carbon dioxide from body

Capillary

◆ 575

FIGURE 17
Oxygen for Activities
The huge surface area of the alveoli supplies the oxygen these trombone players need to march and play.

Surface Area

Surface area refers to the total area of all of the surfaces of a three-dimensional object. Consider a cube, which has six equal sides. Each side measures 2 cm by 2 cm.

1. To find the surface area of the cube, first calculate the area of one of the six sides:
Area = length × width
= 2 cm × 2 cm = 4 cm²
Each side has an area of 4 cm².

2. Next, add the areas of the six sides together to find the total surface area:
4 cm² + 4 cm² + 4 cm² + 4 cm² + 4 cm² + 4 cm² = 24 cm²
The surface area of the cube is 24 cm².

Practice Problem Calculate the surface area of a cube whose side measures 3 cm.

Surface Area for Gas Exchange Your lungs can absorb a large amount of oxygen because of the large surface area of the alveoli. An adult's lungs contain about 300 million alveoli. If you opened the alveoli and spread them out on a flat surface, you would have a surface area of about 70 square meters.

The huge surface area of the alveoli enables the lungs to absorb a large amount of oxygen. The lungs can, therefore, supply the oxygen that people need—even when they are performing strenuous activities. When you play a wind instrument or a fast-paced game of basketball, you have your alveoli to thank.

Your lungs are not the only organs that provide a large surface area in a relatively small space. The small intestine of your digestive system contains specialized structures that increase the surface available to absorb food molecules.

Reading Checkpoint What gases are exchanged across the alveoli?

How You Breathe

In an average day, you may breathe more than 20,000 times. The rate at which you breathe depends on your body's need for oxygen. The more oxygen you need, the faster you breathe.

Muscles for Breathing Breathing, like other body movements, is controlled by muscles. Figure 18 shows the structure of the chest, including the muscles that enable you to breathe. Notice that the lungs are surrounded by the ribs, which have muscles attached to them. At the base of the lungs is the **diaphragm** (DY uh fram), a large, dome-shaped muscle that plays an important role in breathing.

The Process of Breathing  When you breathe, the actions of your rib muscles and diaphragm cause your chest to expand or contract. As a result, air flows in or out.

Here's what happens when you inhale, or breathe in. The rib muscles contract, lifting the chest wall upward and outward. At the same time, the diaphragm contracts and moves downward. The combined action of these muscles makes the chest cavity larger. The same amount of air now occupies a larger space, causing the pressure of the air inside your lungs to decrease. This change means that the pressure of air inside the chest cavity is lower than the pressure of the atmosphere pushing on the body. Because of this difference in air pressure, air rushes into your chest, in the same way that air is sucked into a vacuum cleaner.

When you exhale, or breathe out, the rib muscles and diaphragm relax. This reduces the size of the chest cavity. This decrease in size squeezes air out of the lungs, the way squeezing a container of ketchup pushes ketchup out of the opening.

Reading Checkpoint What muscles cause the chest to expand during breathing?

FIGURE 18

The Breathing Process

When you inhale, the diaphragm moves downward and pressure in the lungs decreases, causing air to flow in. When you exhale, the diaphragm moves upward and the pressure in the lungs increases, pushing the air out.
Interpreting Diagrams *How does the movement of the diaphragm affect the size of the chest cavity?*

Go Online
active art

For: The Breathing Process activity
Visit: PHSchool.com
Web Code: cep-4041

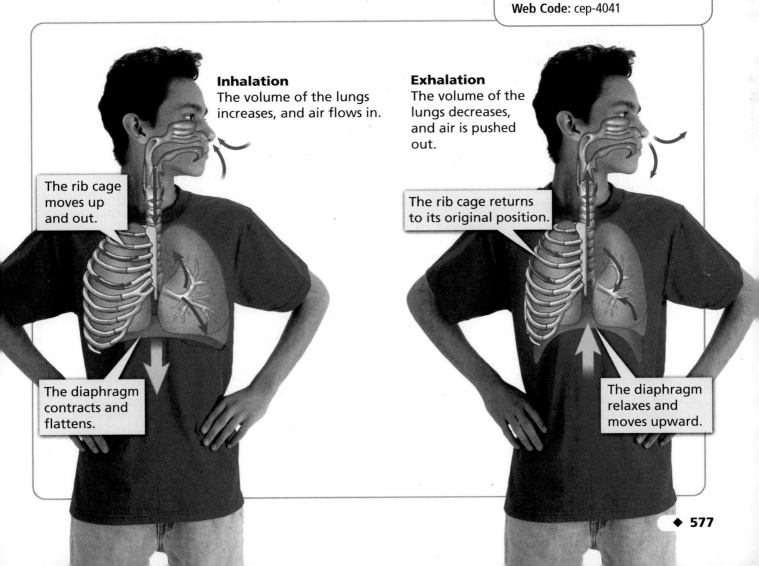

Inhalation
The volume of the lungs increases, and air flows in.

Exhalation
The volume of the lungs decreases, and air is pushed out.

The rib cage moves up and out.

The rib cage returns to its original position.

The diaphragm contracts and flattens.

The diaphragm relaxes and moves upward.

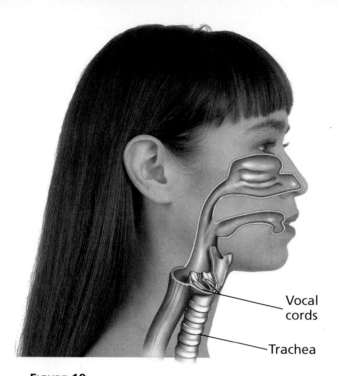

Vocal cords

Trachea

FIGURE 19
The Vocal Cords
Air moving over the vocal cords causes them to vibrate and produce sound.
Interpreting Diagrams *Where are the vocal cords located?*

Relating Breathing and Speaking The air that moves out of your lungs as you breathe also helps you speak. The **larynx** (LAR ingks), or voice box, is located in the top part of the trachea, underneath the epiglottis. Place your fingers on your Adam's apple, which sticks out from the front of your neck. You can feel some of the cartilage that makes up the larynx. Two **vocal cords,** folds of connective tissue that produce your voice, stretch across the opening of the larynx.

If you've ever let air out of a balloon while stretching its neck, you've heard the squeaking sound that the air makes. The neck of the balloon is something like your vocal cords. If you look at Figure 19 you can see that the vocal cords have a slit-like opening between them. When you speak, muscles make the vocal cords contract, narrowing the opening. Air from the lungs rushes through this opening. The movement of the vocal cords makes the air molecules vibrate, or move rapidly back and forth. This vibration creates a sound—your voice.

Section 3 Assessment

S 7.5.a, 7.5.b, E-LA: Reading 7.2.0, Math: 7.2.4

Target Reading Skill Sequence Construct a flowchart showing the sequence of events that happens when you breathe in. In the first box write "Rib muscles and diaphragm contract."

Reviewing Key Concepts

1. a. **Listing** What are the functions of the respiratory system?
   b. **Comparing and Contrasting** Explain the difference between respiration and breathing.
   c. **Predicting** How might respiration in your body cells be affected if your respiratory system did not work properly?

2. a. **Identifying** Name the structures of the respiratory system.
   b. **Sequencing** Describe the path that a molecule of oxygen takes as it moves from the air outside your body into the alveoli.
   c. **Relating Cause and Effect** In a healthy person, how do coughing and sneezing protect the respiratory system?

3. a. **Reviewing** What three substances are exchanged in the alveoli?
   b. **Explaining** What happens to the carbon dioxide in the blood when it flows through the capillaries in the alveoli?
   c. **Applying Concepts** How would gas exchange be affected at the top of a tall mountain, where air pressure is lower and there is less oxygen than at lower elevations? Explain.

Math Practice

4. **Surface Area** A cube measures 4 cm × 4 cm on a side. Find its surface area.

5. **Surface Area** Suppose you cut up the cube into eight smaller cubes, so that each cube is 2 cm × 2 cm on a side. If the larger cube represents a lung, and the smaller cubes represent alveoli, which would provide a larger surface area for oxygen exchange?

A Breath of Fresh Air

S 7.5.b, 7.7.d

Problem

What causes your body to inhale and exhale air?

Skills Focus

making models, observing, drawing conclusions

Materials

- small balloon
- large balloon
- scissors
- transparent plastic bottle with narrow neck

Procedure

1. In your notebook, explain how you think air gets into the lungs during the breathing process.

2. Cut off and discard the bottom of a small plastic bottle. Trim the cut edge so there are no rough spots.

3. Stretch a small balloon; then blow it up a few times to stretch it further. Insert the round end of the balloon through the mouth of the bottle. Then, with a partner holding the bottle, stretch the neck of the balloon and pull it over the mouth of the bottle.

4. Stretch a large balloon; then blow it up a few times to stretch it further. Cut off and discard the balloon's neck.

5. Have a partner hold the bottle while you stretch the remaining part of the balloon over the bottom opening of the bottle, as shown in the photo.

6. Use one hand to hold the bottle firmly. With the knuckles of your other hand, push upward on the large balloon, causing it to form a dome. Remove your knuckles from the balloon, letting the balloon flatten. Repeat this procedure a few times. Observe what happens to the small balloon. Record your observations in your notebook.

Analyze and Conclude

1. **Making Models** Make a diagram of the completed model in your notebook. Add labels to show which parts of your model represent the chest cavity, diaphragm, lungs, and trachea.

2. **Observing** In this model, what is the position of the "diaphragm" just after you have made the model "exhale"? What do the lungs look like just after you have exhaled?

3. **Drawing Conclusions** In this model, how does the "diaphragm" move? How do these movements of the "diaphragm" affect the "lungs"?

4. **Communicating** Write a paragraph describing how this model shows that pressure changes are responsible for breathing.

More to Explore

How could you improve on this model to show more closely what happens in the chest cavity during the process of breathing? *Obtain your teacher's permission before carrying out your investigation.*

Cardiovascular and Respiratory Diseases

CALIFORNIA
Standards Focus

S 7.5.b Students know organ systems function because of the contributions of individual organs, tissues, and cells. The failure of any part can affect the entire system.

- What are some diseases of the cardiovascular system?

- How may tobacco smoke affect the body?

- What are some respiratory diseases that result from infections or other physical conditions?

Key Terms
- atherosclerosis
- heart attack
- hypertension
- stroke
- emphysema
- bronchitis
- asthma
- suffocation
- pneumonia

Lab zone Standards **Warm-Up**

Which Foods Are "Heart Healthy"?

1. Your teacher will give you an assortment of foods. If they have nutrition labels, read the labels.
2. Sort the foods into three groups. In one group, put those foods that you think are good for your cardiovascular system. In the second group, put foods that you think might damage your cardiovascular system if eaten often. Place foods you aren't sure about in the third group.

Think It Over
Forming Operational Definitions How did you define a "heart-healthy" food?

Shortly after sunrise, when most people are just waking up, a team of rowers is already out on the river. Rhythmically, with perfectly coordinated movement, the rowers pull on the oars, making the boat glide swiftly through the water. Despite the chilly morning air, sweat glistens on the rowers' faces and arms. Inside their chests, their hearts are pounding and their lungs are working hard. Oxygen-rich blood speeds to the arm and chest muscles that power the oars. Without healthy circulatory and respiratory systems, the rowers cannot do their best.

FIGURE 20
Exercising for Health
Strenuous exercise, such as rowing, requires a healthy cardiovascular system. In turn, exercise keeps the cardiovascular system healthy.

Healthy, unblocked artery

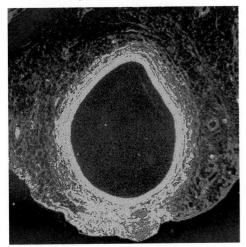

Partially blocked artery

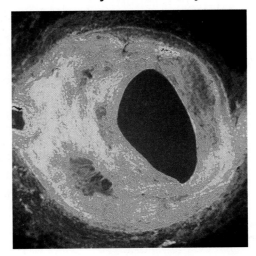

FIGURE 21
Effect of Atherosclerosis
The artery on the right shows atherosclerosis, which is caused by deposits of fat on the artery walls.
Relating Cause and Effect
What kind of diet can lead to atherosclerosis?

Cardiovascular Diseases

Cardiovascular health is important for all people, not just for athletes. Cardiovascular disease ranks as the leading cause of death in the United States today. ⚷ **Diseases of the cardiovascular system include atherosclerosis and hypertension.**

Atherosclerosis Compare the photos of the two arteries in Figure 21. The healthy artery has a large space in the center through which blood can flow easily. The artery on the right, in contrast, has a much smaller space. This artery exhibits **atherosclerosis** (ath uh roh skluh ROH sis), a condition in which an artery wall thickens as a result of the buildup of fatty materials. One of these fatty materials is cholesterol, a waxy substance. Atherosclerosis results in a reduced flow of blood in the affected artery.

Atherosclerosis can develop in the coronary arteries, which supply blood to the heart muscle. The muscle cells then receive less blood and, therefore, less oxygen. This condition may lead to a heart attack. A **heart attack** occurs when blood flow to part of the heart muscle is blocked. Cells die where the muscle does not receive sufficient blood and oxygen. This permanently damages the heart and may cause death. If a person who suffers a heart attack lives, the heart may remain badly weakened. The heart's ventricles may no longer contract normally, and the heart fails to pump enough blood to the body.

Treatment for atherosclerosis usually includes a low-fat diet, a moderate exercise program, and medications. Some people may need surgery to unclog blocked arteries.

 **Reading Checkpoint** How is cholesterol related to atherosclerosis?

Go Online

SciLINKS NSTA

For: Links on cardiovascular problems
Visit: www.SciLinks.org
Web Code: scn-0434

Hypertension High blood pressure, or **hypertension** (hy pur TEN shun), is a disorder in which a person's blood pressure is consistently higher than normal—usually defined as greater than 140/90. Hypertension makes the heart work harder. It also may damage the walls of blood vessels. Over time, the heart and arteries can be severely harmed by hypertension. People with hypertension often have no clear symptoms to warn them of the danger until damage is severe. For this reason, hypertension is sometimes called the "silent killer." Like atherosclerosis, treatment for hypertension includes regular exercise, careful food choices, and medications.

• Tech & Design in History •

Advances in Cardiovascular Medicine

Scientists today have an in-depth understanding of how the cardiovascular system works and how to treat cardiovascular problems. This timeline describes some of the advances in cardiovascular medicine.

1958
Artificial Pacemaker
Electrical engineer Earl Baaken developed an external pacemaker to correct irregular heartbeats. A small electric generator connected to the pacemaker generated electric pulses that regulated heart rate. The first pacemakers had a fixed rate of 70 to 75 pulses per minute.

1961
Heart Valve Replacement
The first successful artificial heart valve was inserted into a patient's heart by surgeons Albert Starr and M. L. Edwards in Oregon. The valve was a rubberlike ball inside a stainless steel cage.

1930s–1940s
Blood Banks
Charles Drew demonstrated that emergency blood transfusions could be done with plasma if whole blood was not available. During World War II, Drew established blood banks for storing donated blood. His work helped save millions of lives on and off the battlefield.

1930	1940	1950	1960

Stroke Sometimes atherosclerosis and hypertension may lead to a stroke. A **stroke** is the death of brain tissue that can result when a blood vessel in the brain is either blocked by a clot or bursts. For example, sometimes blood clots form in vessels that are affected by atherosclerosis. A clot that breaks free may travel to a blood vessel in the brain, blocking the flow of blood. Such a blockage prevents needed gas exchange between the blood and brain cells, which can result in paralysis or permanent brain damage. Sometimes a blood vessel in the brain can become weakened. If so, hypertension can cause the vessel to burst, flooding the brain with blood and damaging cells.

Writing in Science

Research and Write
Research one of the scientists in the timeline using print and electronic resources. Imagine that you are on a committee that has chosen this scientist to receive an award. Write the speech you would give at the award ceremony, explaining the scientist's contributions.

1967
First Heart Transplant
Christiaan Barnard, a South African surgeon, performed the first transplant of a human heart. Louis Washkanksky, the man who received the heart, lived for only 18 days after the transplant. But Barnard's work paved the way for future successes in transplanting hearts and other organs.

1977
Angioplasty
The first coronary balloon angioplasty was performed by Andreas Gruentizig and a team of surgeons in San Francisco. A balloon is inserted into the coronary artery and inflated, thus opening the artery. In 2001, more than two million angioplasties were performed worldwide.

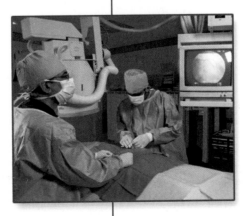

2001
Replacement Heart
The first replacement heart was implanted by a team of surgeons in Louisville, Kentucky. Unlike the first artificial heart, the Jarvik-7, the replacement heart has its own internal batteries. The patient does not have to be "plugged in" to an external power source. The first patient to receive the replacement heart lived for more than 500 days.

| 1970 | 1980 | 1990 | 2000 |

Lung of a nonsmoker

FIGURE 23
Deadly chemicals in tobacco
smoke can damage body systems
or interfere with their function.

Three Deadly Chemicals in Tobacco Smoke	
Tar	A dark, sticky substance that coats cilia making them clump together
Carbon Monoxide	A colorless, odorless gas that binds to hemoglobin in red blood cells taking the place of oxygen
Nicotine	An addictive drug that increases heart rate and blood pressure

Health Problems and Smoking

You may know that smoking tobacco is unhealthy. With each puff, a smoker inhales more than 4,000 chemicals. Three of the most deadly chemicals in tobacco smoke are listed in Figure 23. They are tar, carbon monoxide, and nicotine.

Tobacco smoke causes health problems in several ways. For example, tar-coated cilia can't sweep away mucus. Thus, many smokers have a frequent cough. The mucus buildup also limits space for airflow. As a result, oxygen intake decreases. Lack of oxygen may also cause long-term or heavy smokers to be short of breath during even light exercise.

🔑 **Tobacco smoke damages the respiratory system and strains the circulatory system, resulting in such diseases as emphysema, cancer, and chronic bronchitis.** The respiratory and circulatory systems work together to get oxygen to body cells. A failure of any part of either system means other parts of both systems must work harder. Serious health problems can result from long-term smoking. Every year in the United States, more than 400,000 people die from smoking-related illnesses. That's one out of every five deaths. Tobacco smoke is the most important preventable cause of major illness and death.

You read earlier about atherosclerosis. This thickening of an artery wall from the buildup of fatty materials can lead to a heart attack. The chemicals from tobacco smoke cause added harm. Some of these chemicals get into the blood and are absorbed by the blood vessels. The chemicals irritate the walls of the vessels. This irritation contributes to the buildup of fatty material on the vessel walls. Compared to nonsmokers, smokers are more than twice as likely to have heart attacks.

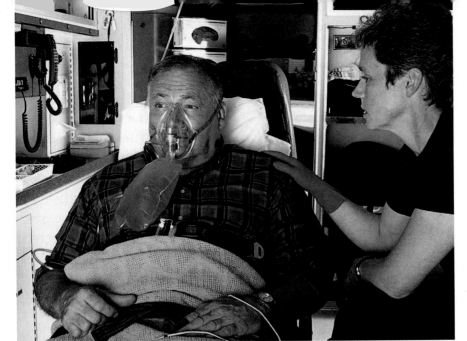

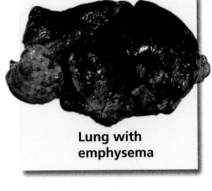

Lung with emphysema

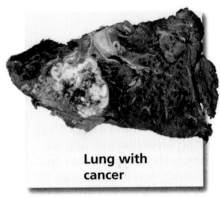

Lung with cancer

FIGURE 24

Effects of Smoking on the Lungs
Over time, smoking damages the lungs and leads to serious health problems. **Comparing and Contrasting** *Compare the diseased lungs below to the lung of a nonsmoker shown on the opposite page.*

Emphysema The chemicals in tobacco smoke damage lung tissue as well as breathing passages. **Emphysema** (em fuh SEE muh) is a serious disease that destroys lung tissue and causes breathing difficulties. About 90 percent of the people who suffer from emphysema are smokers. People with emphysema do not get enough oxygen and cannot adequately eliminate carbon dioxide. Therefore, they are always short of breath. Some people with emphysema even have trouble blowing out a match. Unfortunately, the damage caused by emphysema is permanent, even if a person stops smoking.

Lung Cancer About 140,000 Americans die each year from lung cancer caused by smoking. Nonsmoking-related lung cancer is much less common. Cigarette smoke contains more than 50 different chemicals that cause cancer. Cancerous growths, or tumors, take away space in the lungs that are used for gas exchange. Unfortunately, lung cancer is rarely detected early, when treatment would be most effective.

Chronic Bronchitis Bronchitis (brahng KY tis) is an irritation of the breathing passages in which the small passages become narrower than normal and may be clogged with mucus. People with bronchitis have difficulty breathing. If the irritation continues over a long time, it is called chronic bronchitis. Chronic bronchitis can cause permanent damage to the breathing passages. It is often accompanied by infection with disease-causing microorganisms. Chronic bronchitis is five to ten times more common in heavy smokers than in nonsmokers.

Reading Checkpoint How does emphysema affect a person's lungs?

Respiratory Diseases

Respiratory diseases—also called pulmonary diseases—have causes other than smoking. **Diseases such as asthma, colds, influenza, and pneumonia are caused by infections or other physical conditions.** Like smoking-related diseases, other respiratory diseases can affect the function of the circulatory system. For example, a pulmonary infection may reduce the amount of oxygen that can be absorbed in the lungs. The heart must pump blood harder and faster. Breathing may become harder, too.

Asthma More than 20 million Americans suffer from a respiratory condition called asthma. **Asthma** (AZ muh) is a disorder in which the airways in the lungs narrow significantly. This narrowing causes wheezing, coughing, and shortness of breath.

Figure 25 compares the airways in a healthy person with the airways in a person who has asthma. During an asthma attack, the muscles around the airways tighten, making the airways narrower. At the same time, the inner walls of the airways become inflamed. That is, they become irritated, red, swollen, and warm. They also secrete mucus. The mucus clogs the airways and makes breathing even more difficult.

Asthma attacks may be triggered by many factors. These include tobacco smoke, air pollution, strong odors, heavy exercise, and respiratory infections. Other triggers are allergies to pollen, mold, dust and pets. People with asthma require medicines to open affected airways and reduce inflammation. Someone having a severe asthma attack may need emergency care to prevent suffocation. **Suffocation** occurs when there is insufficient gas exchange in the lungs. If this happens, not enough oxygen gets to vital organs and the person could die.

FIGURE 25
Effects of Asthma on Airways
During an asthma attack, air passages become narrow and breathing is more difficult.
Applying Concepts *What must happen to the muscles around the air passages for an asthma sufferer to begin to feel relief?*

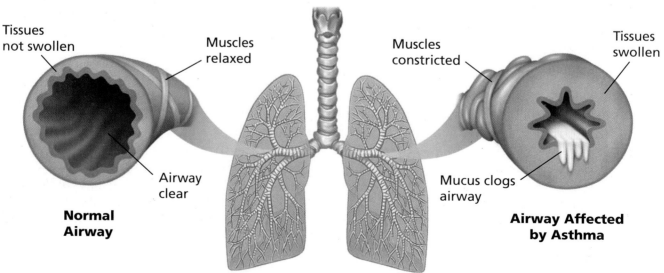

Tissues not swollen

Muscles relaxed

Muscles constricted

Tissues swollen

Airway clear

Mucus clogs airway

Normal Airway

Airway Affected by Asthma

Colds, Influenza, and Pneumonia Have you ever had a cold? Colds are the most common respiratory infection that people get. No doubt you know the symptoms of a typical cold. They include a sore throat, runny nose, cough, and stuffy head and chest. Most people recover quickly from colds.

Influenza, also known as "the flu," has symptoms like those of a cold, plus high fever and muscle aches. The flu usually feels worse than a cold. It can last longer, and it is more dangerous. In infants, the elderly, and people with heart and lung diseases, influenza can lead to pneumonia. **Pneumonia** (noo MOHN yuh) is an infection that causes fluid to collect in the alveoli, decreasing the lungs' ability to take in oxygen and remove carbon dioxide. If the infection is severe, breathing may be difficult. In the worst cases, insufficient gas exchange in the lungs can lead to suffocation and death.

 **Reading Checkpoint** What is suffocation?

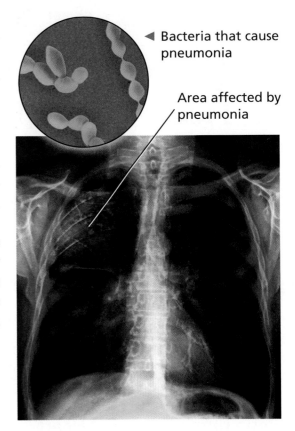

◀ Bacteria that cause pneumonia

Area affected by pneumonia

FIGURE 26
Pneumonia
Bacteria or viruses can cause pneumonia. Doctors may diagnose the disease by looking at an X-ray of the affected lung.

Section 4 Assessment

S 7.5.b, E-LA: Reading 7.1.0

Vocabulary Skill High-Use Academic Words
Use what you know about the meaning of *contribute* to answer Question 2.b below.

Reviewing Key Concepts

1. a. **Defining** What is atherosclerosis? What is hypertension?
   b. **Relating Cause and Effect** How do atherosclerosis and hypertension affect the heart?
   c. **Sequencing** Describe the sequence of events in which atherosclerosis may lead to a stroke.
2. a. **Listing** What are three harmful substances in tobacco smoke?
   b. **Describing** How does smoking contribute to emphysema and atherosclerosis?
   c. **Inferring** What would be the effect on the circulatory system if a person were to quit smoking?

3. a. **Listing** Name three respiratory diseases that are caused by infections.
   b. **Making Generalizations** What do the effects of asthma and pneumonia have in common with those of emphysema and chronic bronchitis?

Lab zone **At-Home Activity**

Warning Labels With a family member, make a list of the warning statements found on cigarette labels. What health problems and chemicals found in tobacco smoke do the labels identify? Summarize the information you find to share with the class.

Heart-Lung Machines

S 7.5.b

What if you were too tired to make it through the day? What if walking up stairs left you out of breath and dizzy? These are symptoms that a person with a damaged heart may experience. A severely damaged heart may require surgery. While the heart is being repaired, blood must continue to circulate through the body around the heart. One way to bypass the heart during surgery is by using a heart-lung machine.

Repairing a Damaged Heart

A heart-lung machine takes over the functions of the heart and the lungs when the heart is stopped during heart surgery. Surgeons insert one tube into the right atrium and a second tube into the aorta. Oxygen-poor blood flows into the heart-lung machine from the right atrium. Within the machine, carbon dioxide is removed, oxygen is added, the blood is filtered, and the blood's temperature is regulated. The filtered, oxygen-rich blood is then pumped through the second tube into the aorta, without flowing through the patient's heart. Once the surgical procedure is over, doctors disconnect the machine and restart the heart.

Oxygen-poor blood to machine

Oxygen-rich blood from machine

Heart-lung machine in use for open heart surgery ▶

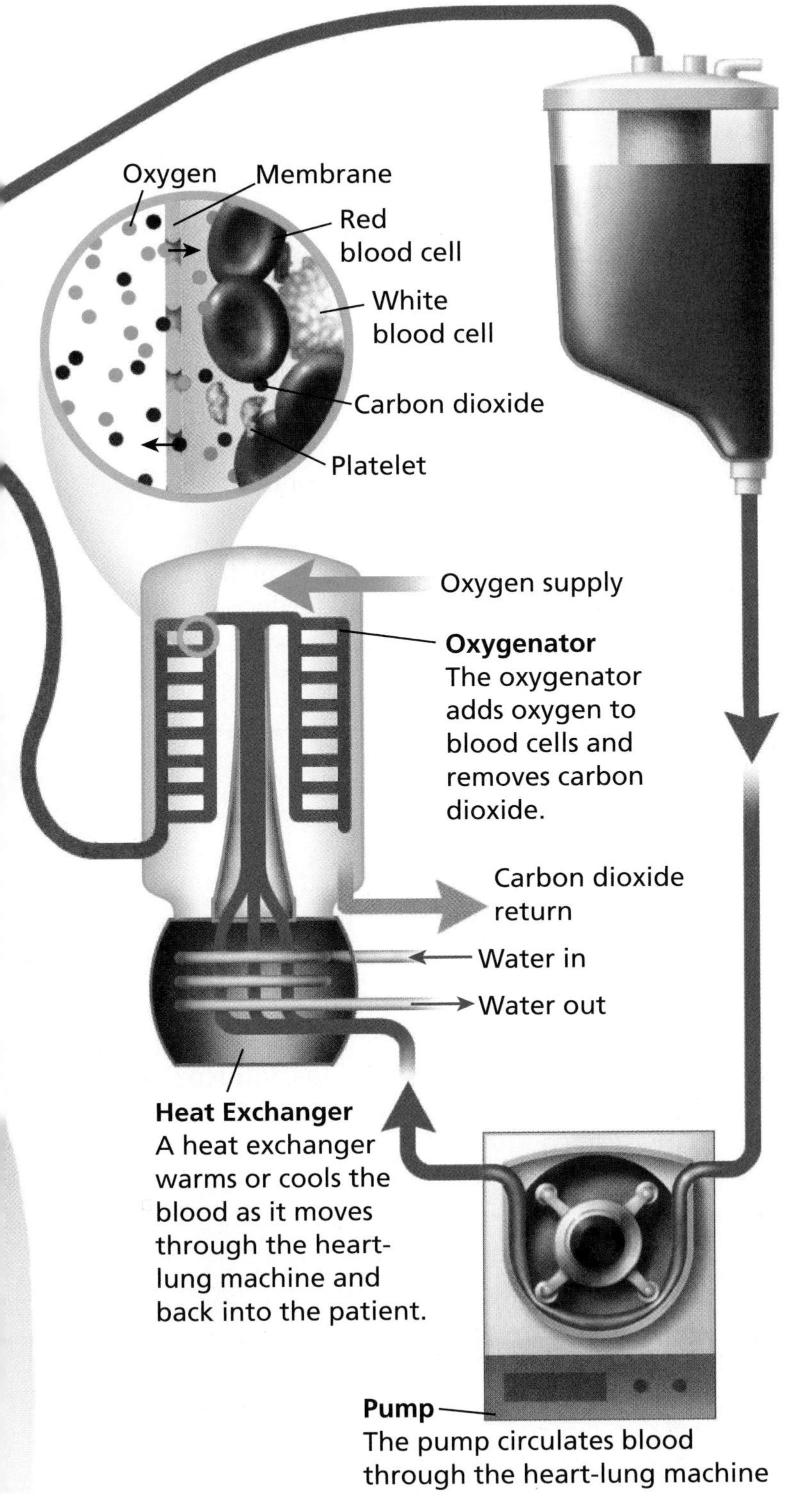

Reservoir
The reservoir acts as a storage chamber for the blood and provides a constant supply and pressure to the pump.

Oxygen   Membrane
Red blood cell
White blood cell
Carbon dioxide
Platelet

Oxygen supply

Oxygenator
The oxygenator adds oxygen to blood cells and removes carbon dioxide.

Carbon dioxide return

Water in
Water out

Heat Exchanger
A heat exchanger warms or cools the blood as it moves through the heart-lung machine and back into the patient.

Pump
The pump circulates blood through the heart-lung machine and back into the patient.

Missing a Beat?

Heart valve repair and replacement, heart transplants, and coronary bypass surgery are a few of the surgeries that may use a heart-lung machine. Heart-lung machines have been credited with saving nearly one million lives around the world each year.

However, like all technologies, heart-lung machines pose certain risks. Use of the heart-lung machine has been associated with an increased risk of bleeding, stroke, kidney and lung problems, and memory loss. As with any surgical procedure, patients must consider the trade-offs.

Weigh the Impact

1. Identify the Need
What is the purpose of a heart-lung machine?

2. Research
Use print and electronic resources to research the success rate of bypass surgery using a heart-lung machine. Then research steps that patients might take to prevent the need for bypass surgery.

3. Write
Write a paragraph on steps patients might take to prevent the need for bypass surgery. Use your research and notes.

Go Online
PHSchool.com

For: More on heart-lung machines
Visit: PHSchool.com
Web Code: ceh-4030

🔑 The **BIG Idea** The circulatory and respiratory systems move blood through the body and enable the exchange of gases.

① The Body's Transport System

🗝 **Key Concepts** 🖊 S 7.5.a, 7.6.j

- The cardiovascular system carries substances to cells and away from cells. In addition, blood contains cells that fight disease.

- The heart pushes blood through the cardiovascular system. The two sides of the heart are separated by the septum. Each side has an upper chamber and a lower chamber.

- Blood circulates in two loops. First, it travels from the heart to the lungs and then back to the heart. Second, it is pumped from the heart to the body and then it returns to the heart.

- Blood leaves the heart through arteries. Materials are exchanged between the blood and the body's cells in the capillaries. Veins carry blood back to the heart.

Key Terms
- cardiovascular system • heart • atrium
- pacemaker • ventricle • valve • artery
- capillary • vein • aorta • coronary artery
- pulse • diffusion • pressure • blood pressure

② Blood and Lymph

🗝 **Key Concepts** 🖊 S 7.5.a, 7.5.b

- Blood is made up of four components: plasma, red blood cells, white blood cells, and platelets.

- Marker molecules on red blood cells determine blood type and the type of blood that you can safely receive in transfusions.

- The lymphatic system is a network of vein-like vessels that returns the fluid to the bloodstream.

Key Terms
- plasma • red blood cell • hemoglobin
- white blood cell • platelet • shock
- lymphatic system • lymph • lymph node

③ The Respiratory System

🗝 **Key Concepts** 🖊 S 7.5.a, 7.5.b

- The respiratory system moves oxygen from the outside environment into the body. It also removes carbon dioxide and water.

- As air travels from the outside environment to the lungs, it passes through the following structures: nose, pharynx, trachea, and bronchi.

- Oxygen passes through the walls of the alveoli and then through the capillary walls into the blood. Carbon dioxide and water pass from the blood into the alveoli.

- When you breathe, the actions of your rib muscles and diaphragm cause your chest to expand or contract. Thus, air flows in or out.

Key Terms
- respiration • mucus • cilia • pharynx
- trachea • bronchi • lungs • alveoli
- diaphragm • larynx • vocal cords

④ Cardiovascular and Respiratory Diseases

🗝 **Key Concepts** 🖊 S 7.5.b

- Diseases of the cardiovascular system include atherosclerosis and hypertension.

- Tobacco smoke damages the respiratory system, resulting in such diseases as emphysema, cancer, and chronic bronchitis.

- Diseases such as asthma, colds, influenza, and pneumonia are caused by infections or other physical conditions.

Key Terms
- atherosclerosis
- heart attack
- hypertension
- stroke
- emphysema
- bronchitis
- asthma
- suffocation
- pneumonia

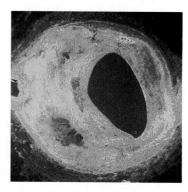

Review and Assessment

⊙ Target Reading Skill

Sequence Copy the flowchart below. Use it to describe the path of air through the body. End with air entering the alveoli.

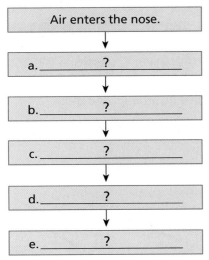

Path of Air

Air enters the nose.

↓

a. _____ ?

↓

b. _____ ?

↓

c. _____ ?

↓

d. _____ ?

↓

e. _____ ?

Reviewing Key Terms

Choose the letter of the best answer.

1. The heart's larger pumping chambers are called
   a. ventricles.
   b. atria.
   c. valves.
   d. arteries.

2. The alternating expansion and relaxation of the artery that you feel in your wrist is your
   a. pulse.
   b. coronary artery.
   c. blood pressure.
   d. plasma.

3. Blood components that transport oxygen in the body are
   a. platelets.
   b. red blood cells.
   c. white blood cells.
   d. plasmas.

4. The exchange of gases between the blood and the air takes place in the
   a. trachea.
   b. diaphragm.
   c. bronchi.
   d. alveoli.

5. Which of the following diseases causes less oxygen to be taken into the body from the air?
   a. emphysema
   b. stroke
   c. hypertension
   d. atherosclerosis

Complete the following sentences so that your answers clearly explain the key term.

6. **Blood pressure** is exerted by the blood on the walls of blood vessels as a result of _____.

7. The protein **hemoglobin** that is present in red blood cells enables the blood to carry oxygen because _____.

8. Air comes into the lungs as a result of the actions of the **diaphragm** and chest muscles, which _____.

9. Fluid that is carried by the lymphatic system is called **lymph**, which consists of _____.

10. A **heart attack** can result in the death of some heart muscle cells because_____.

Writing in Science

Letter Write a letter to a friend describing what you do to stay active. For example, do you participate in team sports, jog, or take long walks with your dog? Include in your letter additional ways you can be even more active.

Video Assessment
Discovery Channel School
Circulation

Review and Assessment

Checking Concepts

11. Contrast the forces with which the right and left ventricles contract. How does this relate to each ventricle's function?

12. A red blood cell is moving through an artery in your leg. Describe the path that the blood cell will follow back to your heart. Identify the chamber of the heart to which it will return.

13. How is a capillary's structure adapted to its function?

14. Explain the difference between breathing and respiration.

15. Explain how the alveoli provide a large surface area for gas exchange in the lungs.

16. How does a heart attack affect the body?

Thinking Critically

17. Predicting Some babies are born with an opening between the left and right ventricles of the heart. How would this heart defect affect the ability of the cardiovascular system to deliver oxygen to body cells?

18. Making Judgments What process is shown in the diagram below? What role do changes in air pressure play in this process?

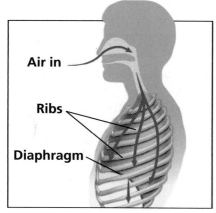

19. Applying Concepts Describe how the buildup of mucus in air passages affects breathing.

20. Making Judgments Do you think that drugstores, which sell medicines, should also sell cigarettes and other tobacco products? Why or why not?

Math Practice

21. Calculating a Rate The veterinarian listens to your cat's heart and counts 30 beats in 15 seconds. What is your cat's heart rate?

22. Surface Area Which has a greater surface area, a cube that is 2 cm × 2 cm on a side, or eight cubes that are each 1 cm × 1 cm on a side? Show your work.

Applying Skills

Use the graph to answer Questions 23–25.

The graph below shows how average blood pressure changes as men and women grow older.

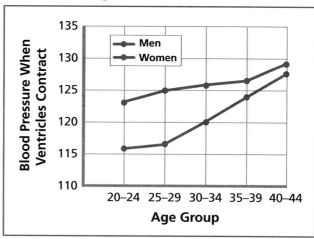

Changes in Blood Pressure

23. Interpreting Data At age 20, who is likely to have higher blood pressure—men or women?

24. Drawing Conclusions In general, what happens to blood pressure as people age?

25. Predicting Do you think that there is some age at which both men and women have about the same blood pressure? Use the graph lines to explain your prediction.

Lab zone Standards Investigation

Performance Assessment You should now be ready to present your display. Make sure it is clear and accurate, and be ready to answer questions from classmates.

Choose the letter of the best answer.

1. The most important function of the cardiovascular system is to
   A transport needed materials to body cells and remove wastes.
   B provide structural support for the lungs.
   C generate blood pressure so the arteries and veins do not collapse.
   D produce blood and lymph.

   S 7.5.a

2. The correct sequence of organs through which air travels when it is breathed into the body is
   A pharynx, nose, trachea, bronchi.
   B nose, trachea, pharynx, bronchi.
   C nose, pharynx, bronchi, trachea.
   D nose, pharynx, trachea, bronchi.

   S 7.5.a

3. When valves in the heart or blood vessels fail to function,
   A the pumping of blood stops.
   B a backflow of blood occurs.
   C the heart stops.
   D the blood pressure decreases.

   S 7.5.b

4. Blood pressure results from the
   A contraction of the diaphragm.
   B exchange of gases between the blood and body cells.
   C build up of fatty materials in artery walls.
   D contraction of the ventricles in the heart that forces blood into blood vessels.

   S 7.6.j

5. Which of the following conditions may result from insufficient gas exchange in the lungs?
   A suffocation
   B heart attack
   C stroke
   D atherosclerosis

   S 7.5.b

6. Which of the following pairs of structures work together to control inhaling and exhaling?
   A lungs and rib muscles
   B diaphragm and rib muscles
   C diaphragm and bronchi
   D trachea and lungs

   S 7.5.a

Use the table below and your knowledge of science to answer Questions 7 and 8.

Blood Types		
Blood Type	**Marker Molecules**	**Clumping Proteins**
A	A	anti-B
B	B	anti-A
AB	A and B	none
O	none	anti-A and anti-B

7. A person who has type O blood can safely receive blood from a person with
   A type O blood.
   B type A blood.
   C type AB blood.
   D type B blood.

   S 7.5.b

8. A person who has type O blood can safely donate blood to a person with
   A type AB blood.
   B type O blood.
   C types A, B, AB, or O blood.
   D type A or type B blood.

   S 7.5.b

Apply the
BIG Idea

9. The delivery of oxygen to body cells and the removal of carbon dioxide from body cells depend on the functions of both the circulatory system and the respiratory system. In a paragraph, explain how functions in both of these systems are affected when gas exchange in the lungs is reduced. Give specific details in describing changes that may occur.

   S 7.5.b

CALIFORNIA Standards Preview

S 7.5 The anatomy and physiology of plants and animals illustrate the complementary nature of structure and function. As a basis for understanding this concept:

b. Students know organ systems function because of the contributions of individual organs, tissues, and cells. The failure of any part can affect the entire system.

g. Students know how to relate the structures of the eye and ear to their functions.

S 7.6 Physical principles underlie biological structures and functions. As a basis for understanding this concept:

b. Students know that for an object to be seen, light emitted by or scattered from it must be detected by the eye.

S 7.7 Scientific progress is made by asking meaningful questions and conducting careful investigations. As a basis for understanding this concept and addressing the content in the other three strands, students should develop their own questions and perform investigations. Students will:

c. Communicate the logical connection among hypotheses, science concepts, tests conducted, data collected, and conclusions drawn from scientific evidence.

Without your nervous system, a sport ▶ like windsurfing would be impossible!

Focus on the
BIG Idea

How do organs and other structures enable the nervous system to function?

Check What You Know

You smell a delicious aroma. You walk into the kitchen and see a bag of popcorn in the microwave. You hear some kernels still popping. Then you think to yourself, "Snack time!" Which body systems enabled you to smell, walk, see, hear, and think? How did each system play a part in your response?

Build Science Vocabulary

The images shown here represent some of the Key Terms in this chapter. You can use this vocabulary skill to help you understand the meaning of some key terms in this chapter.

Suffixes

A suffix is a word part that is added to the end of a word to change its meaning. For example, the Anglo-Saxon suffix *-ness* means "state of." When this suffix is added to the adjective *dark,* it forms the noun *darkness.* Darkness means "the state of being dark."

The table below lists some common suffixes and explains their meanings. The table also gives you an example that uses the suffix. You can use the meanings of these suffixes to help understand the meanings of some key terms.

Suffix	Meaning of Suffix	Example and Meaning of Example
-ant	A person or thing that	**Pollutant** Something that pollutes or makes dirty
-ism	Action or practice of	**Criticism** Action of judging the value of something
-ness	Condition of; state of	**Sickness** Condition of being sick
-ous	Having; full of	**Disastrous** Full of disaster

Apply It!

1. What is the suffix in the word *nearsightedness*? What does the suffix mean?

2. The word *stimulate* means "to increase activity." Predict the meaning of *stimulant.* Revise your definition as needed after you read Section 5.

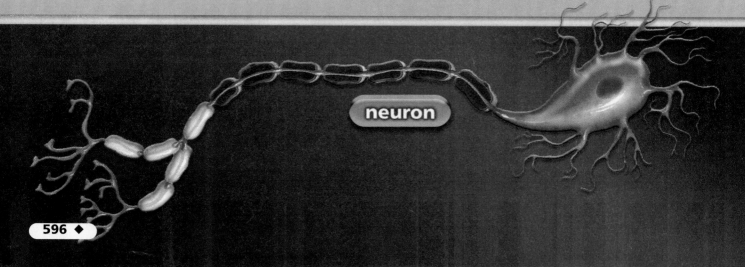

neuron

Chapter 15 Vocabulary

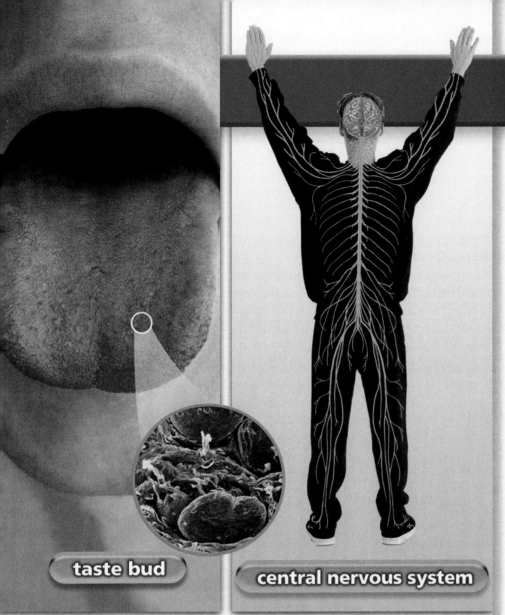

taste bud

central nervous system

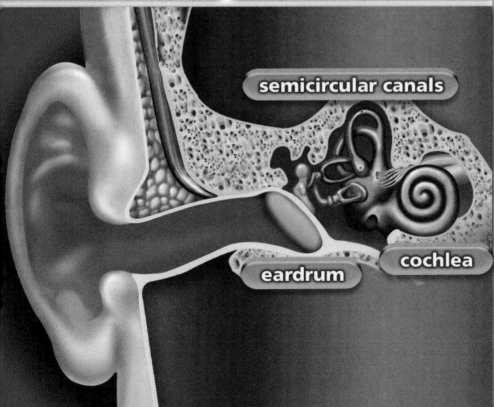

semicircular canals

eardrum

cochlea

Interactive Textbook

Build Science Vocabulary
Online
Visit: PHSchool.com
Web Code: cvj-4150

How to Read Science

Identify Main Ideas

The main idea in a paragraph or section is the most important idea. Headings and the boldface key concept statements can often help you identify main ideas. The details in a paragraph or section support the main idea. Details are usually specific facts and examples that help readers understand the main idea.

Look for the main idea and details in the paragraph below. Then copy the graphic organizer in your notebook and complete it.

> **Depressants** Depressants are drugs that slow down the activity of the central nervous system. When people take depressants, their muscles relax and they may feel sleepy. They may fail to respond normally. For example, depressants may prevent people from responding quickly to the danger of an onrushing car.

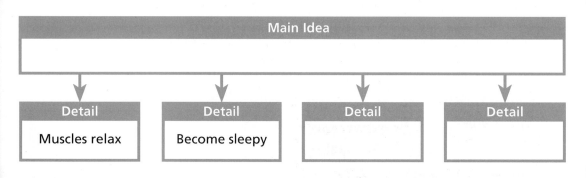

Main Idea

Detail	Detail	Detail	Detail
Muscles relax	Become sleepy		

Apply It!

1. What is the heading of the paragraph? What does it tell you about the main idea?

2. Choose one detail. Explain how it supports the main idea.

In this chapter, look for the main ideas in paragraphs. Also try to identify the main ideas for the text following each heading.

S 7.5.g

Sense and Nonsense

An optical illusion is a picture or other visual effect that tricks you into seeing something incorrectly. In this investigation, you'll discover how your senses sometimes can be fooled by illusions.

Your Goal

To demonstrate how different people respond to illusions

To complete this investigation you must

- try out a variety of optical illusions as well as some illusions that involve the senses of hearing or touch
- select one or more illusions and set up an experiment to monitor people's responses to the illusions
- learn why the illusions fool the senses
- follow the safety guidelines in Appendix A

Plan It!

In a small group, discuss illusions that you know about. Look in books to learn about others. Which illusions would make an interesting experiment? How could you set up such an experiment at a science fair? Find out how your nervous system allows you to sense your environment. For example, which structures are involved in observing the optical illusion below? Use this chapter and other print or electronic resources to learn how these structures function when people are fooled by illusions.

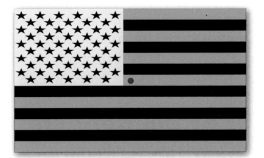

Stare for 30 seconds at the red dot in the center of the flag. Then stare at the dot in the white box for a few seconds. Did you see an illusion?

How the Nervous System Works

CALIFORNIA
Standards Focus

S 7.5.b Students know organ systems function because of the contributions of individual organs, tissues, and cells. The failure of any part can affect the entire system.

- What are the functions of the nervous system?
- What is the structure of a neuron and what kinds of neurons are found in the body?
- How do nerve impulses travel from one neuron to another?

Key Terms
- stimulus
- response
- neuron
- nerve impulse
- dendrite
- axon
- nerve
- sensory neuron
- interneuron
- motor neuron
- synapse

Lab zone Standards **Warm-Up**

How May Systems Work Together?

1. Trace the outline of a penny in twelve different places on a piece of paper.
2. Number the circles 1 through 12. Write the numbers randomly, in no particular order.
3. Now, pick up the penny again. Put it in each circle, one after another, in numerical order, starting at 1 and ending at 12.

Think It Over

Inferring Make a list of all the sense organs, muscle movements, and thought processes used in this activity. Compare your list with your classmates' lists. Which organ systems were working together? What organ system coordinated all the different processes involved in this task?

The ball whizzes toward the soccer goalie. She lunges for the ball, and in one swift movement blocks it from entering the net. To tend goal, soccer players need excellent coordination and keen vision. In addition, they must remember what they have learned from years of practice.

Whether or not you play soccer, you too need coordination, memory, and the ability to learn. Your nervous system carries out all these functions. The nervous system includes the brain, spinal cord, and nerves that run throughout the body. It also includes sense organs, such as the eyes and ears.

Functions of the Nervous System

The Internet lets people gather information from anywhere in the world with the click of a button. Like the Internet, your nervous system is a communications network. But it is much more efficient than the Internet.

The nervous system receives information about what is happening both inside and outside your body. It also directs the way in which your body responds to this information. In addition, your nervous system helps maintain homeostasis. Without your nervous system, you could not move, think, feel pain, or taste a spicy taco.

Receiving Information Because of your nervous system, you are aware of what is happening in the environment around you. For example, you know that a fly is buzzing around your head, that the wind is blowing, or that a friend is telling a funny joke. Your nervous system also checks conditions inside your body, such as the level of your blood pressure.

Responding to Information Any change or signal in the environment that can make an organism react is called a **stimulus** (STIM yoo lus) (plural: *stimuli*). A buzzing fly is a stimulus. After your nervous system analyzes the stimulus, it causes a response. A **response** is what your body does in reaction to a stimulus—you swat at the fly.

Some nervous system responses, such as swatting a fly, are voluntary, or under your control. However, many processes necessary for life, such as the beating of your heart, are controlled by involuntary actions of the nervous system.

Maintaining Homeostasis The nervous system helps maintain homeostasis by directing the body to respond appropriately to the information it receives. For example, when you need energy, your nervous system prompts you to feel hungry and then eat. This action maintains homeostasis by supplying your body with the nutrients and energy it needs.

Reading Checkpoint What is a stimulus?

FIGURE 1
The Nervous System at Work
The zooming soccer ball is a stimulus. The goalie responds by lunging toward the ball and blocking the shot.
Interpreting Diagrams *How does the goalie's nervous system help her body maintain homeostasis?*

Receiving Information
The goalie's eyes receive information that a soccer ball is zooming toward her.

Responding to Information
The nervous system causes a response, and the goalie reaches out to block the shot.

Maintaining Homeostasis
The goalie's nervous system adjusts her breathing and heart rate to meet her energy needs throughout the game.

FIGURE 2
Structure of a Neuron
A neuron has one axon and many dendrites that extend from the cell body.

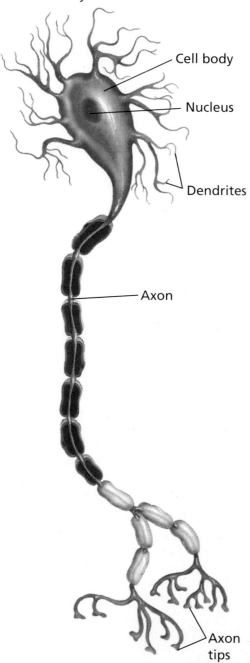

The Neuron

Your nervous system includes various organs, tissues, and cells. For example, your brain is an organ, and the nerves running throughout your body are tissues. The cells that carry information through your nervous system are called **neurons** (NOO rahnz), or nerve cells. The message that a neuron carries is called a **nerve impulse.**

The Structure of a Neuron The structure of a neuron enables it to carry nerve impulses. **A neuron has a large cell body that contains the nucleus, threadlike extensions called dendrites, and an axon.** The **dendrites** carry impulses toward the neuron's cell body. The **axon** carries impulses away from the cell body. Find the dendrites and axon in Figure 2. Nerve impulses begin in a dendrite, next move toward the cell body, and then move down the axon. A neuron can have many dendrites, but it has only one axon. An axon, however, can have more than one tip, so the impulse can go to more than one other cell.

Axons and dendrites are sometimes called nerve fibers. Nerve fibers are often arranged in parallel bundles covered with connective tissue, something like a package of uncooked spaghetti wrapped in cellophane. A bundle of nerve fibers is called a **nerve.**

Kinds of Neurons **Three kinds of neurons are found in the body—sensory neurons, interneurons, and motor neurons.** Figure 3 shows how these three kinds of neurons work together.

A **sensory neuron** picks up stimuli from the internal or external environment and converts each stimulus into a nerve impulse. The impulse travels along the sensory neuron until it reaches an interneuron, usually in the brain or spinal cord. An **interneuron** is a neuron that carries nerve impulses from one neuron to another. Some interneurons pass impulses from sensory neurons to motor neurons. A **motor neuron** sends an impulse to a muscle or gland, and the muscle or gland reacts in response.

 **Reading Checkpoint** **What is the function of an axon?**

How a Nerve Impulse Travels

Every day of your life, billions of nerve impulses travel through your nervous system. Each of those nerve impulses begins in the dendrites of a neuron. The impulse moves rapidly toward the neuron's cell body and then down the axon until it reaches the axon tip. A nerve impulse travels along the neuron in the form of electrical and chemical signals. Nerve impulses can travel as fast as 120 meters per second!

FIGURE 3

The Path of a Nerve Impulse

When you hear your phone ring, you pick it up to answer it. Many sensory neurons, interneurons, and motor neurons are involved in this action.

Interpreting Diagrams *To where does the impulse pass from the sensory neurons?*

Receptors in ear

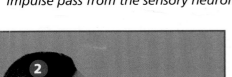

1 Sensory Neuron

Nerve impulses begin when receptors pick up stimuli from the environment. Receptors in the ear pick up the sound of the phone ringing. The receptors trigger nerve impulses in sensory neurons.

2 Interneuron

From the sensory neurons, the nerve impulse passes to interneurons in the brain. Your brain interprets the impulses from many interneurons and makes you realize that the phone is ringing. Your brain also decides that you should answer the phone.

Muscle in hand

3 Motor Neuron

Impulses then travel along thousands of motor neurons. The motor neurons send the impulses to muscles. The muscles carry out the response, and you reach for the phone.

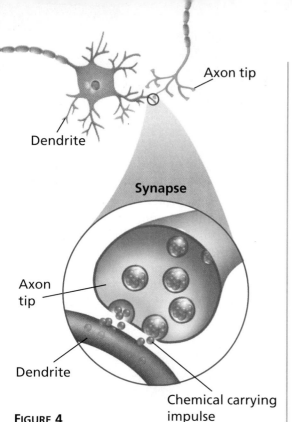

FIGURE 4
The Synapse
When a nerve impulse reaches the tip of an axon, chemicals are released into the gap at the synapse. The chemicals carry the nerve impulse across the gap.

Axon tip

Dendrite

Synapse

Axon tip

Dendrite

Chemical carrying impulse

The Synapse What happens when a nerve impulse reaches the axon tip at the end of a neuron? At that point, the impulse can pass to the next structure. Sometimes the structure is the dendrite of another neuron. Other times, the structure is a muscle or a cell in another organ, such as a sweat gland. The junction where one neuron can transfer an impulse to another structure is called a **synapse** (SIN aps).

How an Impulse Is Transferred Figure 4 shows a synapse between the axon tip of one neuron and the dendrite of another neuron. Notice that a small gap separates these two structures. ● **For a nerve impulse to be carried along at a synapse, it must cross the gap between the axon and the next structure. The axon tips release chemicals that carry the impulse across the gap.**

You can think of the gap at a synapse as a river, and an axon as a road that leads up to the riverbank. The nerve impulse is like a car traveling on the road. To get to the other side, the car has to cross the river. The car gets on a ferry boat, which carries it across the river. The chemicals that the axon tips release are like the ferry, carrying the nerve impulse across the gap.

Section 1 Assessment

S 7.5.b, E-LA: Reading: 7.2.0

● **Target Reading Skill** **Identify Main Ideas**
Reread the text following the heading Functions of the Nervous System (pages 600–601). Note that the Key Concept is the main idea. List three details that support this main idea.

● **Reviewing Key Concepts**

1. a. **Listing** What are three functions of the nervous system?
   b. **Describing** Give an example of a stimulus and describe how the nervous system produces a response.
   c. **Predicting** Your heart rate is controlled by involuntary actions of the nervous system. What would life be like if your heartbeat were under voluntary control?
2. a. **Identifying** Identify the three kinds of neurons that are found in the nervous system.
   b. **Explaining** How do the three kinds of neurons interact to carry nerve impulses?

   c. **Comparing and Contrasting** How do sensory neurons and motor neurons differ?
3. a. **Reviewing** What is a synapse?
   b. **Sequencing** Outline the steps by which a nerve impulse reaches and then crosses the gap at a synapse.

Lab zone **At-Home Activity**

Pass the Salt, Please During dinner, ask a family member to pass the salt to you. Observe what your family member then does. Explain that the words you spoke were a stimulus and that the family member's reaction was a response. Describe which structures of the nervous system detect stimuli and enable a response.

Design Your Own Lab

Ready or Not!

S 7.5.b, 7.7.c

Problem

Do people's reaction times vary at different times of the day?

Skills Focus

developing hypotheses, controlling variables, drawing conclusions

Material

• meter stick

Procedure

PART 1 Observing a Response to a Stimulus

1. Have your partner hold a meter stick with the zero end about 50 cm above a table.

2. Get ready to catch the meter stick by positioning the top of your thumb and forefinger just at the zero position, as shown in the photograph.

3. Your partner should drop the meter stick without any warning. Using your thumb and forefinger only (no other part of your hand), catch the meter stick as soon as you can. Record the distance in centimeters that the meter stick fell. This distance is a measure of your reaction time.

PART 2 Designing Your Experiment

4. With your partner, discuss how you can use the activity from Part 1 to find out whether people's reaction times vary at different times of day. Consider the questions below. Then, write up your experimental plan.
   • What hypothesis will you test?
   • What variables do you need to control?
   • How many people will you test? How many times will you test each person?

5. Submit your plan for your teacher's review. Make any changes your teacher recommends. Create a data table to record your results. Then, perform your experiment.

Analyze and Conclude

1. **Inferring** In this lab, what is the stimulus? What is the response? Is the response voluntary or involuntary? Explain.

2. **Drawing Conclusions** Which body systems were involved in people's reactions?

3. **Developing Hypotheses** What hypothesis did you test in Part 2?

4. **Controlling Variables** In Part 2, why was it important to control all variables except the time of day?

5. **Drawing Conclusions** Based on your results in Part 2, do people's reaction times vary at different times of the day? Explain.

6. **Communicating** Write a paragraph to explain why you can use the distance on the meter stick as a measure of reaction time.

More to Explore

Do you think people can do arithmetic problems more quickly and accurately at certain times of the day? Design an experiment to investigate this question. *Obtain your teacher's permission before carrying out your investigation.*

Divisions of the Nervous System

S 7.5.b Students know organ systems function because of the contributions of individual organs, tissues, and cells. The failure of any part can affect the entire system.

- What are the structures and functions of the central nervous system?
- What are the structures and functions of the peripheral nervous system?
- What is a reflex?
- What are two ways in which the nervous system can be injured?

Key Terms

- central nervous system
- peripheral nervous system
- brain
- spinal cord
- cerebrum
- cerebellum
- brain stem
- somatic nervous system
- autonomic nervous system
- reflex
- concussion

Lab zone Standards **Warm-Up**

How Does Your Knee React?

1. Sit on a table or counter so that your legs dangle freely. Make sure that your partner is not directly in front of your legs.

2. Have your partner use the side of his or her hand to tap one of your knees gently just below the kneecap. Observe what happens to your leg. Note whether you have any control over your reaction.

3. Change places with your partner. Repeat Steps 1 and 2.

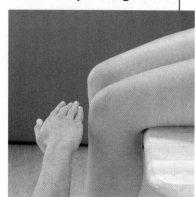

Think It Over

Inferring When might it be an advantage for your body to react very quickly and without your conscious control?

You are standing at a busy street corner, waiting to cross the street. A traffic cop blows his whistle and waves his arms energetically. For the heavy traffic to move smoothly, there needs to be a traffic cop and responsive drivers. The traffic cop coordinates the movements of the drivers, and they steer the cars safely through the intersection.

Similarly, your nervous system has two divisions that work together. The **central nervous system** consists of the brain and spinal cord. The **peripheral nervous system** (puh RIF uh rul) includes all the nerves located outside of the central nervous system. The central nervous system is like a traffic cop. The peripheral nervous system is like the drivers and pedestrians.

The traffic cop keeps everybody moving.

Central Nervous System

You can see the central and peripheral nervous systems in Figure 5. ⬤ **The central nervous system is the control center of the body. It includes the brain and spinal cord.** All information about what is happening in the world inside or outside your body is brought to the central nervous system. The **brain,** located in the skull, is the part of the central nervous system that controls most functions in the body. The **spinal cord** is the thick column of nervous tissue that links the brain to most of the nerves in the peripheral nervous system.

Most impulses from the peripheral nervous system travel through the spinal cord to get to the brain. Your brain then directs a response. The response usually travels from the brain, through the spinal cord, and then to the peripheral nervous system.

For example, here is what happens when you reach under the sofa to find a lost quarter. Your fingers move over the floor, searching for the quarter. When your fingers finally touch the quarter, the stimulus of the touch triggers nerve impulses in sensory neurons in your fingers. These impulses travel through nerves of the peripheral nervous system to your spinal cord. Then the impulses race up to your brain. Your brain interprets the impulses, telling you that you've found the quarter. Your brain starts nerve impulses that move down the spinal cord. From the spinal cord, the impulses travel through motor neurons in your arm and hand. The impulses in the motor neurons cause your fingers to grasp the quarter.

 **Reading Checkpoint** What are the parts of the central nervous system?

Go Online
active art

For: Nervous System activity
Visit: PHSchool.com
Web Code: cep-4062

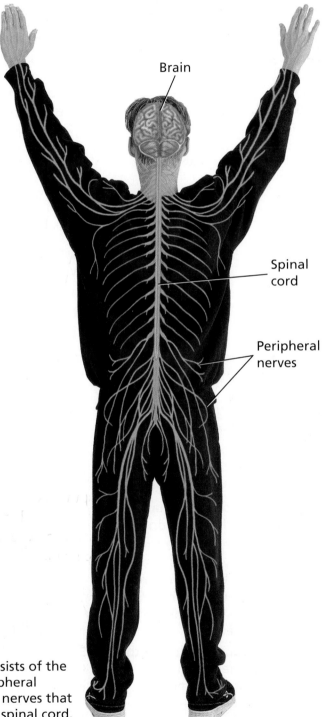

Brain

Spinal cord

Peripheral nerves

FIGURE 5
The Nervous System
The central nervous system consists of the brain and spinal cord. The peripheral nervous system includes all the nerves that branch out from the brain and spinal cord.

The Brain and Spinal Cord

Your brain contains about 100 billion neurons, all of which are interneurons. Each of those neurons may receive messages from up to 10,000 other neurons and may send messages to about 1,000 more! Three layers of connective tissue cover the brain. The space between the middle layer and innermost layer is filled with a watery fluid. The skull, the layers of connective tissue, and the fluid all help protect the brain from injury.

🔑 **There are three main regions of the brain that receive and process information. These are the cerebrum, the cerebellum, and the brain stem.** Find each in Figure 6.

Cerebrum The largest part of the brain is called the cerebrum. The **cerebrum** (suh REE brum) interprets input from the senses, controls movement, and carries out complex mental processes such as learning and remembering. Because of your cerebrum, you can locate your favorite comic strip in the newspaper, read it, and laugh at its funny characters.

The cerebrum is divided into a right and a left half. The right half sends impulses to skeletal muscles on the left side of the body. In contrast, the left half controls the right side of the body. When you reach with your right hand for a pencil, the messages that tell you to do so come from the left half of the cerebrum. In addition, each half of the cerebrum controls slightly different kinds of mental activity. The right half is usually associated with creativity and artistic ability. The left half is usually associated with mathematical skills, language, and logical thinking.

As you can see in Figure 6, certain areas of the cerebrum are associated with smell, touch, taste, hearing, and vision. Other areas control movement, speech, written language, and abstract thought. Different tissues in the cerebrum carry out different functions.

Cerebellum and Brain Stem The second largest part of your brain is the cerebellum. The **cerebellum** (sehr uh BEL um) coordinates muscle action and balance. When you walk, the impulses that move your feet start in your cerebrum. However, your cerebellum gives you the muscular coordination and sense of balance that keep you from falling down.

The **brain stem,** which lies beneath the cerebrum and cerebellum, controls your body's involuntary actions—those that occur automatically. For example, neurons in the brain stem regulate your breathing and help control your heartbeat.

 **Reading Checkpoint** What actions does the brain stem control?

FIGURE 6
The Brain

Each of the three main parts of the brain—the cerebrum, cerebellum, and brain stem—carries out more than one specific function.

Interpreting Diagrams *What are three functions of the cerebrum?*

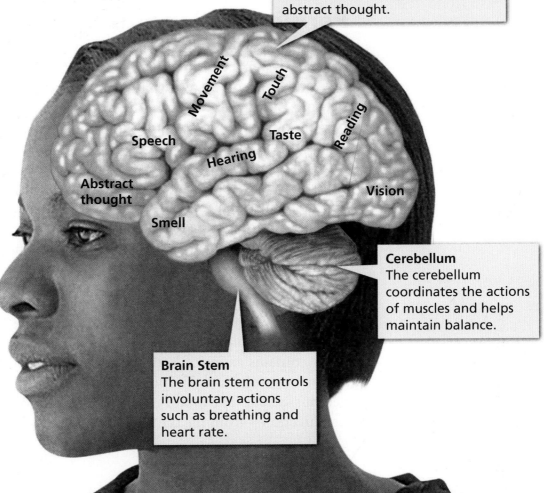

Cerebrum
The cerebrum is the largest part of the brain. Different areas of the cerebrum control such functions as movement, the senses, speech, and abstract thought.

Movement

Touch

Reading

Speech

Taste

Hearing

Abstract thought

Vision

Smell

Cerebellum
The cerebellum coordinates the actions of muscles and helps maintain balance.

Brain Stem
The brain stem controls involuntary actions such as breathing and heart rate.

Top View of Cerebrum

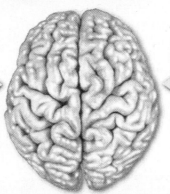

Left Half
The left half of the cerebrum is associated with mathematical and logical thinking.

Right Half
The right half of the cerebrum is associated with creativity and artistic ability.

The Spinal Cord ● **The spinal cord is the link between your brain and the peripheral nervous system.** Run your fingers down the center of your back to feel the bones of the vertebral column. The vertebral column surrounds and protects the spinal cord. The layers of connective tissue that surround and protect the brain also cover the spinal cord. Like the brain, the spinal cord is further protected by a watery fluid.

Peripheral Nervous System

The second division of the nervous system is the peripheral nervous system. ● **The peripheral nervous system consists of a network of nerves that branch out from the central nervous system and connect it to the rest of the body. The peripheral nervous system is involved in both involuntary and voluntary actions.**

A total of 43 pairs of nerves make up the peripheral nervous system. Twelve pairs originate in the brain. The other 31 pairs—the spinal nerves—begin in the spinal cord. One nerve in each pair goes to the left side of the body, and the other goes to the right. As you can see in Figure 7, spinal nerves leave the spinal cord through spaces between the vertebrae.

How Spinal Nerves Function A spinal nerve is like a two-lane highway. Impulses travel on a spinal nerve in two directions—both to and from the central nervous system. Each spinal nerve contains axons of both sensory and motor neurons. The sensory neurons carry impulses from the body to the central nervous system. The motor neurons carry impulses in the opposite direction—from the central nervous system to the body.

FIGURE 7
The Spinal Nerves
The spinal nerves, which connect to the spinal cord, emerge from spaces between the vertebrae. Each spinal nerve consists of both sensory and motor neurons.

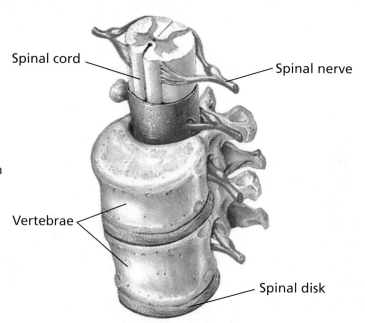

Spinal cord

Spinal nerve

Vertebrae

Spinal disk

FIGURE 8
Somatic and Autonomic Nervous Systems
The somatic nervous system controls voluntary actions. The autonomic nervous system controls involuntary actions. **Classifying** *Which system helps regulate the artist's heartbeat?*

Actions Controlled by the Somatic Nervous System
- Hands shape the clay.
- Foot turns the wheel.
- Mouth smiles.

Actions Controlled by the Autonomic Nervous System
- Heartbeat is regulated.
- Breathing rate is kept steady.
- Body temperature remains constant.

Somatic and Autonomic Systems The nerves of the peripheral nervous system can be divided into two groups, the somatic (soh MAT ik) and autonomic (awt uh NAHM ik) nervous systems. The nerves of the **somatic nervous system** control voluntary actions such as using a fork or tying your shoes. In contrast, nerves of the **autonomic nervous system** control involuntary actions. For example, the autonomic nervous system regulates the contractions of the smooth muscles that adjust the diameter of blood vessels.

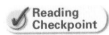 **Reading Checkpoint** **What kinds of actions are controlled by the autonomic nervous system?**

Reflexes

Imagine that you are watching an adventure movie. The movie is so thrilling that you don't notice a fly circling above your head. When the fly zooms right in front of your eyes, however, your eyelids immediately blink shut. You didn't decide to close your eyes. The blink, which is a **reflex,** is a response that happened automatically. **A reflex is an automatic response that occurs very rapidly and without conscious control. Reflexes help to protect the body.** If you did the Standards Warm-Up on page 606, you observed another reflex.

Lab zone Try This **Activity**

You Blinked!
Can you make yourself *not* blink? Find out in this activity.

1. Put on safety goggles.
2. Have your partner stand across from you and gently toss ten cotton balls, one at a time, toward your goggles. Your partner should not give you any warning before a toss.
3. Count the number of times you blink and the number of times you don't blink.

Interpreting Data Compare the two numbers. Why is blinking considered a reflex? What structure protects your eye when you blink?

A Reflex Pathway As you have learned, the contraction of skeletal muscles is usually controlled by the brain. However, in some reflex actions, skeletal muscles contract with the involvement of the spinal cord only—not the brain.

Figure 9 shows the reflex action that occurs when you touch a sharp object. When your finger touches the object, sensory neurons send impulses to the spinal cord. The impulses may then pass to interneurons in the spinal cord. From there the impulses pass directly to motor neurons in your arm and hand. The muscles then contract, and your hand jerks up and away from the sharp object. By removing your hand quickly, this reflex protects you from getting badly cut.

Signaling the Brain At the same time that some nerve impulses make your arm muscles contract, other nerve impulses travel up your spinal cord to your brain. When these impulses reach your brain, your brain interprets them. You then feel a sharp pain in your finger.

It takes longer for the pain impulses to get to the brain and be interpreted than it does for the reflex action to occur. By the time you feel the pain, you have already moved your hand away.

Reading Checkpoint What is an example of a reflex?

FIGURE 9

A Reflex Action

If you touch a sharp object, your hand immediately jerks away. This action, which is known as a reflex, happens automatically. Follow the numbered steps to understand how a reflex happens.
Sequencing *Do you pull your hand away before or after you feel the pain? Explain.*

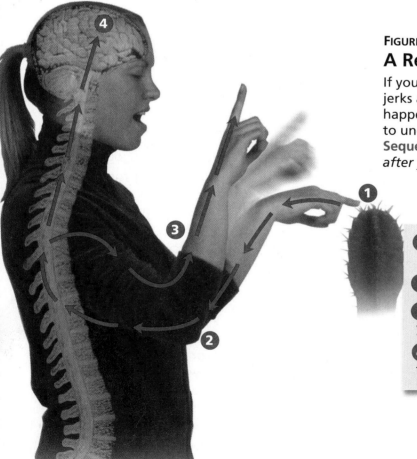

1 Sensory neurons in your fingertip detect a pain stimulus.

2 Nerve impulses travel to your spinal cord.

3 Nerve impulses return to motor neurons in your hand, and you pull your hand away.

4 As you pull your hand away, nerve impulses travel to your brain. You feel the pain.

Nervous System Injuries

The nervous system can suffer injuries that interfere with its functioning. ⊙ **Concussions and spinal cord injuries are two ways in which the central nervous system can be damaged.**

FIGURE 10
Protecting the Nervous System
You can help protect yourself from a spinal cord injury by wearing a seatbelt when you travel in a car.

Concussions A **concussion** is a bruiselike injury of the brain. A concussion occurs when the soft tissue of the brain collides against the skull. Concussions can happen when you bump your head in a hard fall, in an automobile crash, or during a contact sport such as football.

With most concussions, you may have a headache for a short time, but the injured tissue heals by itself. However, with more serious concussions, you may lose consciousness, experience confusion, or feel drowsy after the injury. To decrease your chances of getting a brain injury, wear a helmet during activities in which you risk bumping your head.

Spinal Cord Injuries Spinal cord injuries occur when the spinal cord is cut or crushed. As a result, axons in the injured region are damaged, so they fail to carry impulses. This type of injury usually results in paralysis, which is the loss of movement in some part of the body. Car crashes are the most common cause of spinal cord injuries.

 **What is paralysis?**

Section 2 Assessment

S 7.5.b, E-LA: Reading: 7.1.2
Writing:7.2.0

Vocabulary Skill Suffixes In the term *nervous system*, the word *nervous* contains the suffix *-ous*. What does this suffix mean? How does it relate to the meaning of *nervous system*?

⊙ **Reviewing Key Concepts**

1. a. **Listing** What two structures are part of the central nervous system?
   b. **Describing** Describe the functions of the three main regions of the brain.
   c. **Relating Cause and Effect** What symptoms might indicate that a person's cerebellum has been injured?
2. a. **Identifying** What are the two groups of nerves into which the peripheral nervous system is divided?
   b. **Comparing and Contrasting** How do the functions of the two groups of peripheral nerves differ?

3. a. **Defining** What is a reflex?
   b. **Sequencing** Trace the pathway of a reflex in the nervous system.
   c. **Inferring** How do reflexes help protect the body from injury?
4. a. **Reviewing** What is a concussion?
   b. **Applying Concepts** How can you reduce your risk of concussion?

Writing in Science

Comparison Paragraph Write two paragraphs in which you compare the functions of the left and right halves of the cerebrum. Discuss what kinds of mental activities each half controls as well as which side of the body it controls.

Sight and Hearing

CALIFORNIA
Standards Focus

S 7.5.g Students know how to relate the structures of the eye and ear to their functions.

S 7.6.b Students know that for an object to be seen, light emitted by or scattered from it must be detected by the eye.

🔑 How do your eyes enable you to see?

🔑 How do you hear and maintain your sense of balance?

Key Terms

- cornea • pupil • iris • lens
- retina • rods • cones • optic nerve • eardrum • hammer
- anvil • stirrup • cochlea
- semicircular canals

Lab zone Standards **Warm-Up**

Can You See Everything With One Eye?

1. Write an X and an O on a sheet of paper. The O should be about 5 cm to the right of the X.
2. Hold the sheet of paper at arm's length.
3. Close or cover your left eye. Stare at the X with your right eye.
4. Slowly move the paper toward your face while staring at the X. What do you notice?
5. Repeat the activity, keeping both eyes open. What difference do you notice?

Think It Over

Posing Questions Write two questions about vision that you could investigate using the X and the O.

The pitcher goes into her windup, keeping her eye on the strike zone. The batter watches the pitcher release the ball and then swings. Crack! She drops the bat and sprints toward first base. From your seat, you watch the ball travel toward the outfield. Will it be a base hit? The left fielder watches the ball speed toward her. It's over her head for a double!

Players and spectators alike followed the first rule of baseball: Keep your eye on the ball. As the ball moves near and far, your eyes must adjust continuously to keep it in focus. Fortunately, this change in focus happens automatically.

Video Field Trip
Discovery Channel School

The Nervous System

Keep your eye on the ball! ▶

FIGURE 11
The Eye

The eye is a complex organ that senses light. **Interpreting Diagrams** *What structure adjusts the size of the pupil?*

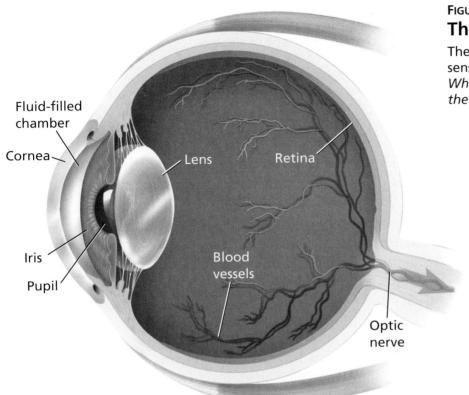

Fluid-filled chamber

Cornea

Lens

Retina

Iris

Pupil

Blood vessels

Optic nerve

Pupil in Bright Light

Pupil in Dim Light

Vision

Your eyes are the sense organs that enable you to see the objects in your environment. 🔑 **Your eyes respond to the stimulus of light. They convert that stimulus into impulses that your brain interprets, enabling you to see.**

How Light Enters Your Eye Light rays from an object enter the eye through the structures shown in Figure 11. First, the light strikes the **cornea** (KAWR nee uh), the clear tissue that covers the front of the eye. The light then passes through a fluid-filled chamber behind the cornea and reaches the pupil. The **pupil** is the opening through which light enters the eye.

You may have noticed that people's pupils change size when they go from a dark room into bright sunshine. In bright light, the pupil becomes smaller. In dim light, the pupil becomes larger. The size of the pupil is adjusted by muscles in the iris. The **iris** is a circular structure that surrounds the pupil and regulates the amount of light entering the eye. Together, the iris and the pupil act much like the aperture of a camera. The iris also gives the eye its color.

Go **O**nline
active art

For: Virtual Dissection of the Eye activity
Visit: PHSchool.com
Web Code: cvp-4153

Reading Checkpoint What is the function of the iris?

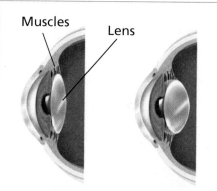

Muscles   Lens

Seeing Far Away
The muscles relax, making the lens thin.

Seeing Close Up
The muscles contract, making the lens thick.

FIGURE 12
Focusing the Lens
Muscles change the shape of the lens, allowing the eye to focus on objects at different distances.
Applying Concepts *What structures does light pass through before it reaches the lens?*

How Light Is Focused Light rays enter the eye through the cornea. The cornea transforms the diverging rays that come from an object into converging rays. Then the light passes through the pupil and strikes the lens. The **lens** is a flexible structure that focuses light. The lens of your eye functions something like the lens of a camera. Because of the way in which the lens of the eye bends the light rays, the image it produces is upside down and reversed. Muscles that attach to the lens adjust its shape, producing an image that is in focus.

How You See an Image After passing through the lens, the focused light rays pass through a transparent, jellylike fluid. Then the rays strike the **retina** (RET 'n uh), a sheet of light-sensitive cells that lines the back of the eye. The retina, which has the same job as a film or video chip in a camera, contains about 130 million receptor cells. These cells respond to light. There are two types of receptors: rods and cones. **Rod cells** work best in dim light and enable you to see black, white, and shades of gray. In contrast, **cone cells** work best in bright light and enable you to see colors. This difference between rods and cones explains why you see colors best in bright light, but you see only shadowy gray images in dim light.

The rods and cones send electrical impulses to the brain through a short, thick nerve called the **optic nerve.** One optic nerve comes from the left eye and the other one comes from the right eye. The brain interprets the signals. First, it turns the reversed image right-side up. Then the brain combines the images from each eye. You see a single image.

Seeing in Depth Unlike many animals, humans have both eyes in the front of the head. Both your eyes look forward. However, you see a slightly different image with your right eye than you do with your left eye. Your brain compares the images from your two eyes. This comparison gives you three-dimensional vision. That is, you can judge how close or how far away an object is.

Reading Checkpoint   **What enables humans to see in three dimensions?**

Lab zone Try This Activity

Working Together
Discover how your two eyes work together.

1. With your arms fully extended, hold a drinking straw in one hand and a pipe cleaner in the other.
2. With both eyes open, try to insert the pipe cleaner into the straw.
3. Now close your right eye. Try to insert the pipe cleaner into the straw.
4. Repeat Step 3 with your left eye closed.

Inferring How does closing one eye affect your ability to judge distances?

FIGURE 13
How You See

Light coming from an object enters your eye and is focused by the cornea and lens. An upside-down image forms on your retina. Receptors in your retina then send impulses to your cerebrum, which turns the image right-side up.

Comparing and Contrasting *Which receptors work best in dim light?*

Rods and Cones
Receptors in the retina include rods (shown in green) and cones (shown in blue).

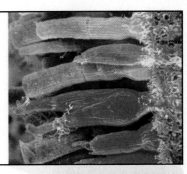

Object

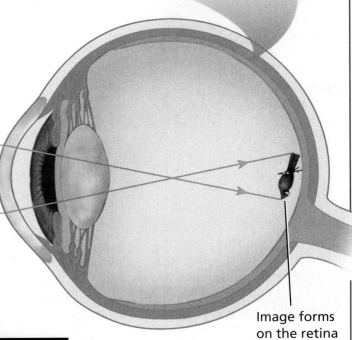

Image forms on the retina

◄ An image is focused on the retina. Notice that the image is upside down.

Hearing and Balance

Have you ever watched a dog listen for its owner's voice? Dogs and other mammals have muscles that enable their external ears to move. This movement helps the animals detect faint sounds and identify where the sounds come from. Though your ears don't move like those of a dog, they do detect sound. 🔑 **Your ears are the sense organs that respond to the stimulus of sound. The ears convert sound to nerve impulses that your brain interprets.** So when you hear an alarm clock, your brain tells you that it's time to wake up.

How Sound Is Produced Sound is produced by vibrations that travel as waves. The material that is vibrating, or moving rapidly back and forth, may be almost anything—a guitar string, an insect's wings, or a stereo speaker.

The vibrations, or sound waves, move outward from the source of the sound, something like ripples moving out from a stone dropped in water. The sound waves cause particles, such as the gas molecules that make up air, to vibrate. In this way, sound is carried. When you hear a friend's voice, for example, sound waves have traveled from your friend's larynx to your ears. Sound waves can also travel through liquids, such as water, and solids, such as wood.

FIGURE 14
Sensing Sound
A dog can cock its external ear when listening to sounds.

Math ► **Analyzing Data**

Math: Number Sense 7.1.1

Sound Intensity

Sound intensity, or loudness, is measured in units called decibels. The threshold of hearing for the human ear is 0 decibels. For every 10-decibel increase, the sound intensity increases ten times. Thus, a 20-decibel sound is ten times more intense than a 10-decibel sound, not twice as intense. A 30-decibel sound is 100 times more intense than a 10-decibel sound. Sound levels for several sound sources are shown in the bar graph.

1. **Interpreting Data** What is the sound intensity in decibels of a whisper? Normal talking? A rock concert?

2. **Calculating** How much more intense is normal talking than a whisper? Explain.

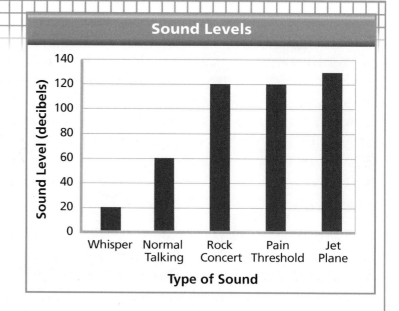

Sound Levels

3. **Predicting** Based on the graph, what sounds could be painful if you were exposed to them?

FIGURE 15
The Ear

Sound waves enter the outer ear and make structures in the middle ear vibrate. When the vibrations reach the inner ear, nerve impulses travel to the cerebrum through the auditory nerve. **Predicting** *What would happen if the bones of the middle ear could not move?*

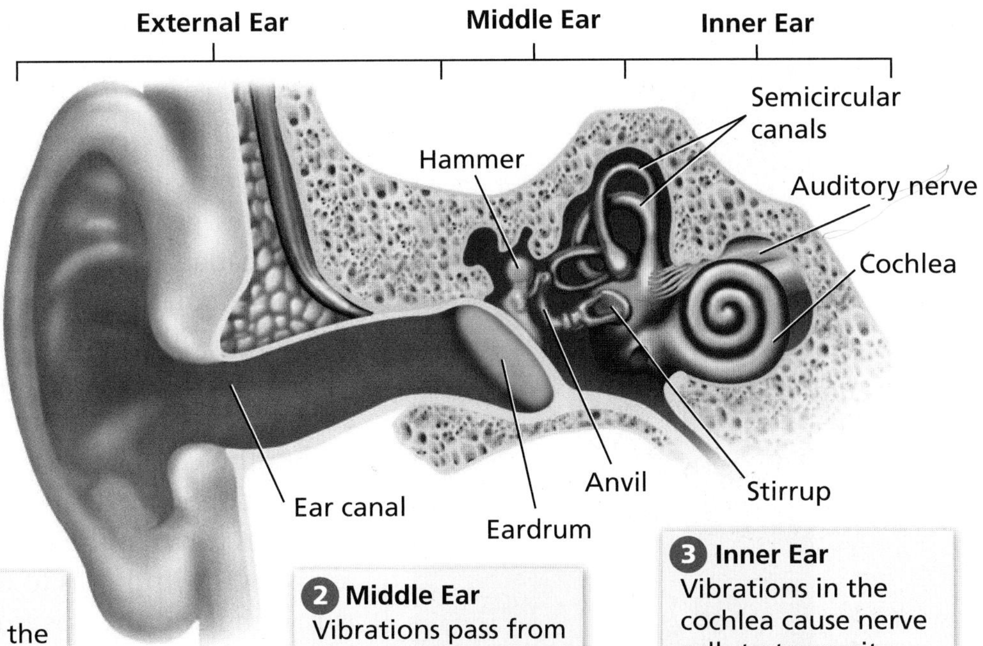

Hammer

Semicircular canals

Auditory nerve

Cochlea

Ear canal

Anvil

Eardrum

Stirrup

1 External Ear
Sound waves enter the external ear and reach the eardrum.

2 Middle Ear
Vibrations pass from the hammer to the anvil and stirrup.

3 Inner Ear
Vibrations in the cochlea cause nerve cells to transmit signals to the brain.

The External Ear The three regions of the ear—the external ear, middle ear, and inner ear—are shown in Figure 15. Notice that the visible part of the external ear is shaped like a funnel. This funnel-like shape enables the external ear to collect sound waves, which then travel down the ear canal.

The Middle Ear The ear canal directs sound waves to the middle ear, where they strike the eardrum. The **eardrum,** or tympanic membrane, vibrates when struck by sound waves. Your eardrum vibrates much as a drum does when it is struck. Within the middle ear are three small bones called the **hammer** (or malleus), **anvil** (or incus), and **stirrup** (or stapes). These tiny bones act as a series of levers that transfer vibrations from one place to another. Vibrations pass first from the eardrum to the hammer. Then they pass to the anvil, and next to the stirrup. Muscles adjust the tension on the eardrum and the three bones in response to the loudness of the sound.

The Inner Ear The stirrup vibrates against a thin membrane that covers the opening of the inner ear, also called the labyrinth. This membrane channels the vibrations into fluid in the cochlea. The **cochlea** (KAHK le uh) is a snail-shaped tube that is lined with receptor cells that respond to sound. When the fluid in the cochlea vibrates, it stimulates these receptors. Sensory neurons then send nerve impulses to the cerebrum through the auditory nerve. These impulses are interpreted as sounds that you hear.

Lab zone Skills Activity

Making Models
Use simple materials to build a model of the ear. Items such as a funnel, clay, pipe cleaners, and a piece of balloon may be used to model different parts of the ear. Make a sketch of your model and label each structure. Then write a brief paragraph that explains how the parts of the ear work together to transmit sound to the brain.

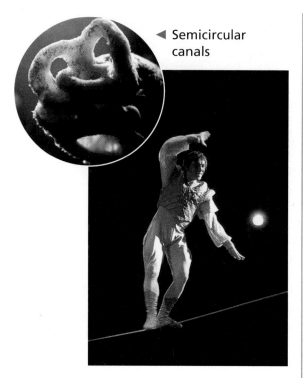

◄ Semicircular canals

FIGURE 16
Balancing Act
This tightrope walker is able to keep his balance due to the functioning of his semicircular canals.
Relating Cause and Effect *How do the semicircular canals help you to maintain balance?*

The Inner Ear and Balance  **Structures in your inner ear control your sense of balance.** Above the cochlea in your inner ear are the **semicircular canals,** which are the structures in the ear that are responsible for your sense of balance. You can see how these structures got their name if you look at Figure 16. These canals, as well as the two tiny sacs located behind them, are full of fluid. The canals and sacs are also lined with tiny cells that have hairlike extensions.

When your head moves, the fluid in the semicircular canals is set in motion. The moving fluid makes the cells' hairlike extensions bend. This bending produces nerve impulses in sensory neurons. The impulses travel to the cerebellum. The cerebellum then analyzes the impulses to determine the way your head is moving and the position of your body. If the cerebellum senses that you are losing your balance, it sends impulses to muscles that help you restore your balance.

Have you ever spun around and then stopped suddenly? You probably felt dizzy afterward. Dizziness happens because the fluid in the semicircular canals keeps moving for a while after your body stops moving.

✓ Reading Checkpoint Where in the ear are the semicircular canals located?

Section 3 Assessment

S 7.5.g, 7.6.b, E-LA: Reading: 7.1.2, Writing 7.2.5

Vocabulary Skill Suffixes Use the meaning of the suffix *-ness* to explain the meaning of *dizziness.*

Reviewing Key Concepts

1. a. **Listing** What are the parts of the eye?
   b. **Sequencing** Describe the process by which the eye produces an image. Begin at the point at which light is focused by the lens.
   c. **Predicting** If you closed one eye, could you thread a needle easily? Explain your answer.
2. a. **Identifying** What are the three regions of the ear?
   b. **Describing** Describe how sound is transmitted from the eardrum to the cochlea.
   c. **Relating Cause and Effect** Why may an infection of the inner ear cause you to lose your balance?

Writing in Science

Summary Paragraph Write a summary paragraph that describes what happens to your eyes when you walk from a dark movie theater into bright sunshine. Include the main ideas and important details about the structures in the eye and how they change.

Smell, Taste, and Touch

CALIFORNIA
Standards Focus

S 7.5.b Students know organ systems function because of the contributions of individual organs, tissues, and cells. The failure of any part can affect the entire system.

 How do your senses of smell and taste work together?

 How is your skin related to your sense of touch?

Key Terms

• taste bud

Lab zone Standards **Warm-Up**

What's in the Bag?

1. Your teacher will give you a paper bag that contains several objects. Your challenge is to use only your sense of touch to identify each object. You will not look inside the bag.

2. Put your hand in the bag and carefully touch each object. Observe the shape of each object. Note whether its surface is rough or smooth. Also note other characteristics, such as its size, what it seems to be made of, and whether it can be bent.

3. After you have finished touching each object, write your observations on a sheet of paper. Then, write your inference about what each object is.

Think It Over
Interpreting Data What did your sense of touch help you learn? What could you not determine?

You grip the steering wheel as the bumper car jerks into motion. The wheel's surface feels smooth. Next, you are zipping around and bumping into other cars. You feel air rush past your face and the jolt of another car hitting yours. As you zoom to a far corner of the floor, you smell the aromas of the snack bar.

Like your other senses, your senses of smell, taste, and touch get information from your environment. This information travels by nerve impulses to your brain. Then you can decide how to act on the information. For example, you can choose which way to move the bumper car or when to eat.

Enjoy the ride, and ▶
thank your senses!

Lab zone Skills **Activity**

Designing Experiments

Can people tell one food from another if they can taste the foods but not smell them? Design an experiment to find out. Use these foods: a peeled pear, a peeled apple, and a peeled raw potato. Be sure to control all variables except the one you are testing. Write your hypothesis and a description of your procedure. Obtain your teacher's approval before carrying out your experiment.

Smell and Taste

You walk into the house and smell the aroma of freshly baked cookies. You bite into one and taste its rich chocolate flavor. When you smelled the cookies, receptors in your nose reacted to chemicals carried by the air from the cookies to your nose. When you took a bite of a cookie, your taste buds were stimulated. **Taste buds** are organs on your tongue that respond to chemicals in food. These chemicals were dissolved in saliva, which came in contact with your taste buds.

The senses of smell and taste work closely together. Both depend on chemicals in food or in the air. The chemicals trigger responses in receptors in the nose and mouth. Nerve impulses then travel to the brain, where they are interpreted as smells or tastes.

The nose can distinguish at least 50 basic odors. In contrast, there are only five main taste sensations—sweet, sour, salty, bitter, and a meatlike taste called *umami*. When you eat, however, you experience a much wider variety of tastes. The flavor of food is influenced by both smell and taste. When you have a cold, foods may not seem very flavorful. That is because a stuffy nose decreases your ability to smell food.

Reading Checkpoint What basic tastes can the tongue detect?

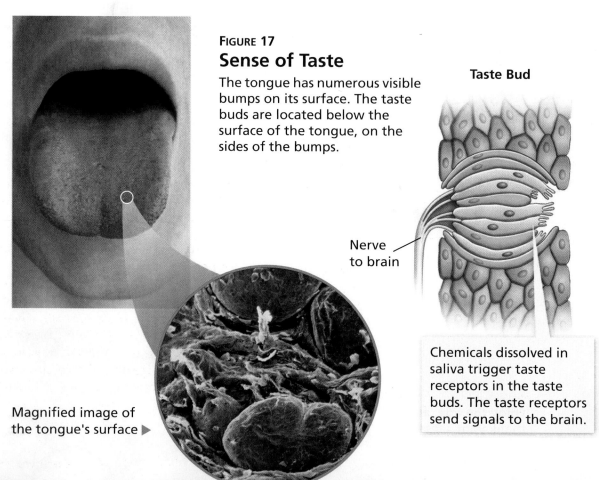

FIGURE 17
Sense of Taste

The tongue has numerous visible bumps on its surface. The taste buds are located below the surface of the tongue, on the sides of the bumps.

Taste Bud

Nerve to brain

Chemicals dissolved in saliva trigger taste receptors in the taste buds. The taste receptors send signals to the brain.

Magnified image of the tongue's surface ▶

Touch

Unlike vision, hearing, balance, smell, and taste, the sense of touch is not found in one specific place. Instead, the sense of touch is found in all areas of your skin. Your skin is your largest sense organ! ◑ **Your skin contains different kinds of touch receptors that respond to a number of stimuli.** Some of these receptors respond to light touch and others to heavy pressure. Still other receptors pick up sensations of pain and temperature change.

The receptors that respond to a light touch are close to the surface of your skin. They tell you when something brushes against your skin. These receptors also let you feel the textures of objects, such as smooth glass and rough sandpaper. Receptors deeper in the skin pick up the feeling of pressure. Press down hard on the top of your desk, for example, and you will feel pressure in your fingertips.

The skin also contains receptors that respond to temperature and pain. Pain is unpleasant, but it can be one of the body's most important feelings because it alerts the body to possible danger. Have you ever stepped into a bathtub of very hot water and then immediately pulled your foot out? If so, you can appreciate how pain can trigger an important response in your body.

FIGURE 18
Reading by Touch
People who are blind use their sense of touch to read. To do this, they run their fingers over words written in Braille. Braille uses raised dots to represent letters and numbers. Here, a teacher shows a blind child how to read Braille.

Section 4 Assessment

S 7.5.b, E-LA: Reading: 7.2.0

◑ **Target Reading Skill** **Identify Main Ideas**
Reread the text following the heading Touch. Which sentence states the main idea?

◑ **Reviewing Key Concepts**

1. a. **Reviewing** What two senses work together to influence the flavor of food?
   b. **Comparing and Contrasting** How are the senses of taste and smell similar? How are they different?
   c. **Sequencing** Describe the process by which you are able to taste food. Begin at the point when you put a piece of food into your mouth. Identify each of the key structures involved.
2. a. **Identifying** What kinds of touch receptors are found in the skin?
   b. **Relating Cause and Effect** What happens in the skin when you accidentally touch a hot stove?

c. **Drawing Conclusions** The brain itself has no pain receptors. What can you conclude about the brain from this information?

Lab zone **At-Home Activity**

Light Touch Ask family members to keep their eyes closed while you help them touch simple objects from around your home. Choose different items, such as a metal spoon, fuzzy fabric, a nailbrush, a warm mug, and a chilled apple. Explain to your family that they can feel the differences in texture and temperature of the objects because of the different receptors present in skin.

Alcohol and Other Drugs

CALIFORNIA
Standards Focus

S 7.5.b Students know organ systems function because of the contributions of individual organs, tissues, and cells. The failure of any part can affect the entire system.

- Which body system is immediately endangered by drug abuse?

- What are some commonly abused drugs and how does each affect the body?

- How does alcohol abuse harm the body?

Key Terms
- drug
- drug abuse
- tolerance
- addiction
- withdrawal
- depressant
- stimulant
- alcoholism

Lab zone Standards **Warm-Up**

What Is Alcohol's Effect?

1. Look at the graph to the right. It relates the percent of alcohol in the blood to changes in reaction time. Reaction time is the time it takes someone to respond to a stimulus.

2. How does the percent of alcohol in the blood change from left to right in the graph?

3. Describe how reaction time changes as the alcohol level in the blood changes. What is the difference between the least and greatest change in reaction time?

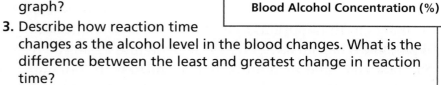

Think It Over

Inferring How might alcohol affect a person's ability to drive safely? Explain your answer.

Drugs! You probably hear and see that word in a lot of places. Drugstores sell drugs to relieve headaches, soothe upset stomachs, and stop coughs. Radio and television programs and magazine articles explore drug-related problems. Your school probably has a program to educate students about drugs. When people talk about drugs, what do they mean? To a scientist, a **drug** is any chemical taken into the body that causes changes in a person's body or behavior. Many drugs affect the functioning of the central nervous system.

Drug Abuse

The deliberate misuse of drugs for purposes other than medical ones is called **drug abuse.** Even medicines can be abused drugs if they are used in a way for which they were not intended. Many abused drugs, however, such as cocaine and heroin, are illegal under any circumstances. The use of these drugs is against the law because their effects on the body are almost always dangerous.

Effects of Abused Drugs Most abused drugs, such as marijuana, alcohol, and cocaine, are especially dangerous because of their immediate effects on the brain and other parts of the nervous system. In addition, long-term drug abuse can lead to addiction and other health and social problems.

Different drugs have different effects. Some drugs cause nausea and a fast, irregular heartbeat. Others can cause sleepiness. Drug abusers may also experience headaches, dizziness, and trembling. Alcohol can cause confusion, poor muscle coordination, and blurred vision. These effects are especially dangerous in situations in which an alert mind is essential, such as driving a car.

Most abused drugs can alter, or change, a person's mood and feelings. For example, alcohol can sometimes make a person angry and even violent. Mood-altering drugs also affect of thinking and interpretation information from the senses.

Tolerance and Addiction If a person takes a drug regularly, the body may develop a tolerance to the drug. **Tolerance** is a state in which a drug user needs larger and larger amounts of the drug to produce the same effect on the body. Tolerance can cause people to take too much, or an overdose, of a drug. People who take an overdose may become unconscious or even die.

Repeated use of some abused drugs can lead to **addiction,** a condition in which the body becomes physically dependent on a drug. If a person stops using a drug suddenly, headaches, dizziness, fever, vomiting, and muscle cramps may result. These symptoms are signs of **withdrawal,** a period of adjustment that occurs when a person stops taking a drug on which the body is dependent. Some drugs may also cause a person to become emotionally dependent on them.

 **Reading Checkpoint** What is addiction?

FIGURE 19
Drug Abuse
Drug abuse can have serious consequences. However, if someone is abusing drugs, there are ways to help that person.
Interpreting Diagrams *What are two ways you can help if someone you know is abusing drugs?*

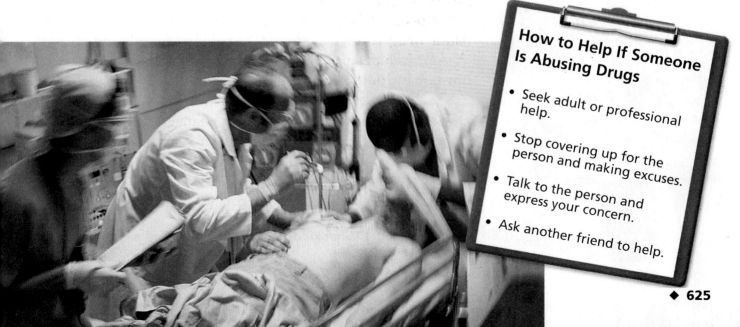

How to Help If Someone Is Abusing Drugs
- Seek adult or professional help.
- Stop covering up for the person and making excuses.
- Talk to the person and express your concern.
- Ask another friend to help.

Go Online
SciLINKS NSTA

For: Links on drug addiction
Visit: www.SciLinks.org
Web Code: scn-0464

FIGURE 20
Making a Statement About Drug Abuse
Many teens are becoming active in antidrug campaigns.

Kinds of Abused Drugs

There are many kinds of drugs, with a wide range of effects on the body. Some are legitimate medicines that a doctor prescribes to help the body fight disease and injury. However, many kinds of drugs are frequently abused. **Commonly abused drugs include depressants, stimulants, inhalants, hallucinogens, anabolic steroids, and alcohol. Many drugs affect the central nervous system, while others affect the overall chemical balance in the body.** Figure 21 lists and describes characteristics of some commonly abused drugs.

Depressants Notice in Figure 21 that some drugs are classified as depressants. **Depressants** are drugs that slow down the activity of the central nervous system. When people take depressants, their muscles relax and they may become sleepy. They may fail to respond to stimuli in a normal amount of time. For example, depressants may prevent people from reacting quickly to the danger of a car rushing toward them. Alcohol and narcotics, such as heroin, are depressants.

Stimulants In contrast to depressants, **stimulants** speed up body processes. They make the heart beat faster and make the breathing rate increase. Cocaine and nicotine are stimulants, as are amphetamines (am FET uh meenz). Amphetamines are prescription drugs that are sometimes sold illegally.

Inhalants and Hallucinogens Some substances, called inhalants, produce mood-altering effects when they are inhaled, or breathed in. Inhalants include paint thinner, nail polish remover, and some kinds of cleaning fluids. Hallucinogens, such as LSD and mescaline, can make people see or hear things that do not really exist.

Steroids Some athletes try to improve their performance by taking drugs known as steroids. Anabolic steroids (an uh BAH lik STEER oydz) are synthetic chemicals that are similar to hormones produced in the body.

Anabolic steroids may increase muscle size and strength. However, steroids can cause mood changes that lead to violence. In addition, steroid abuse can cause serious health problems, such as heart damage, liver damage, and increased blood pressure. Steroid use is especially dangerous for teenagers, whose growing bodies can be permanently damaged.

 **Reading Checkpoint** What kinds of drugs are classified as stimulants?

FIGURE 21
Abused drugs can have many serious effects on the body. Most of the drugs listed below cause addiction and emotional dependence. **Interpreting Tables** *What are the long-term effects of using methamphetamines?*

Some Effects of Commonly Abused Drugs		
Drug Type	**Short-Term Effects**	**Long-Term Effects**
Marijuana (including hashish)	Unclear thinking, loss of coordination, increased heart rate	Difficulty with concentration and memory; respiratory disease and lung cancer
Nicotine (in cigarettes, cigars, chewing tobacco)	Stimulant; nausea, loss of appetite, headache	From tobacco smoke: heart and lung disease, difficulty breathing, heavy coughing
Alcohol	Depressant; decreased alertness, poor reflexes, nausea, emotional depression	Liver and brain damage, heart disease, digestive problems, inadequate nutrition
Inhalants (glue, household cleaners)	Sleepiness, nausea, headaches, loss of consciousness, death	Damage to liver, kidneys, and brain; loss of bladder control
Cocaine (including crack)	Stimulant; nervousness, disturbed sleep, loss of appetite	Mental illness, damage to lining of nose, irregular heartbeat, heart or breathing failure, liver damage
Amphetamines	Stimulant; restlessness, rapid speech, dizziness	Restlessness, irritability, irregular heartbeat, liver damage
Methamphetamine (crystal meth)	Increased respiration, elevated body temperature, stroke	Psychotic behavior, memory loss, aggression, damage to brain and heart, severe tooth and gum disease, stroke
Hallucinogens (LSD, mescaline, PCP)	Hallucinations, anxiety, panic; thoughts and actions not connected to reality	Mental illness; fearfulness; behavioral changes, including violence
Barbiturates (Phenobarbital, Nembutal, Seconal)	Depressant; decreased alertness, slowed thought processes, poor muscle coordination	Sleepiness, irritability, confusion
Tranquilizers (Valium, Xanax)	Depressant; blurred vision, sleepiness, unclear speech, headache, skin rash	Blood and liver disease
Opiates (opium, codeine, morphine, heroin)	Depressant; sleepiness, nausea, reduced respiration	Constipation, convulsion, coma, death
Anabolic steroids	Mood swings	Heart, liver, and kidney damage; hypertension; overgrowth of skull and facial bones; aggression

Alcohol

Alcohol is a drug found in many beverages, including beer, wine, cocktails, and hard liquor. Alcohol is a powerful depressant. In all states, it is illegal for people under the age of 21 to buy or possess alcohol. In spite of this fact, alcohol is the most commonly abused legal drug in people aged 12 to 17.

How Alcohol Affects the Body Alcohol is absorbed by the digestive system quickly. If a person drinks alcohol on an empty stomach, the alcohol enters the blood and gets to the brain and other organs almost immediately. If alcohol is drunk with a meal, it takes longer to get into the blood.

The chart in Figure 22 describes what alcohol does to the body. The more alcohol in the blood, the more serious the effects. The amount of alcohol in the blood is usually expressed as blood alcohol concentration, or BAC. A BAC value of 0.1 percent means that one tenth of one percent of the fluid in the blood is alcohol. In some states, if car drivers have a BAC of 0.08 percent or more, they are legally drunk. In other states, drivers with a BAC of 0.1 are considered legally drunk.

Alcohol produces serious negative effects, including loss of normal judgment, at a BAC of less than 0.08 percent. This loss of judgment can have serious consequences. People who have been drinking may not realize that they cannot drive a car safely. About every two minutes, a person in the United States is injured in a car crash related to alcohol.

FIGURE 22
Alcohol's Effects
Alcohol affects every system of the body. It also impacts a person's thought processes, judgment, and reaction time. In the bottom photo, a police officer tests the blood alcohol concentration of a driver suspected of drinking.

Short-Term Effects of Alcohol	
Body System	**Effect**
Cardiovascular system	First, heartbeat rate and blood pressure increase. Later, they may decrease.
Digestive system	Alcohol is absorbed directly from the stomach and small intestine, which allows it to enter the bloodstream quickly.
Excretory system	The kidneys produce more urine, causing the drinker to excrete more water than usual.
Nervous system	Vision blurs. Speech becomes unclear. Control of behavior is reduced. Judgment becomes poor.
Skin	Blood flow to the skin increases, causing rapid loss of body heat.

Long-Term Alcohol Abuse Many adults drink occasionally and in moderation, without serious safety or health problems. However, heavy drinking, especially over a long period, can result in significant health problems. 🔑 **Alcohol abuse can cause the destruction of cells in the brain and liver, and can lead to addiction and emotional dependence.** Damage to the brain can cause mental disturbances, such as hallucinations and loss of consciousness. The liver, which breaks down alcohol for elimination from the body, can become so scarred that it fails to function properly. Liver failure affects body systems and processes. For example, without certain chemicals produced by the liver, blood may not clot properly. In addition to liver and brain damage, long-term alcohol abuse can increase the risk of getting certain kinds of cancer.

Abuse of alcohol can result in **alcoholism,** a disease in which a person is both physically addicted to and emotionally dependent on alcohol. To give up alcohol, as with any addictive drug, alcoholics must go through withdrawal. To give up drinking, alcoholics need both medical and emotional help. Medical professionals, psychologists, and organizations such as Alcoholics Anonymous can help a person stop drinking.

 **Reading Checkpoint** **What organs are affected by alcohol abuse?**

Healthy Liver

Alcohol-damaged Liver

FIGURE 23
Alcohol's Effect on the Liver
Long-term alcohol abuse can cause serious damage to the liver.
Relating Cause and Effect *What other effects can alcohol abuse have on the body?*

Section **5** **Assessment**

S 7.5.b, E-LA: Reading: 7.1.2

Vocabulary Skill **Suffixes** One meaning of the verb *depress* is "to decrease the force or activity of." If you add the suffix *-ant* to the verb *depress,* what Key Term do you get? What is the meaning of this Key Term?

🔑 **Reviewing Key Concepts**

1. a. Identifying Which major organ of the body is quickly affected by commonly abused drugs?
   b. Applying Concepts What reasons would you give to discourage someone from abusing drugs?
2. a. Listing Name two commonly abused depressants and two commonly abused stimulants.
   b. Comparing and Contrasting Contrast the effects that depressants and stimulants have on the body.

   c. Inferring Why might a person's risk of a heart attack increase with the use of stimulants?
3. a. Reviewing What type of drug is alcohol?
   b. Explaining What immediate effects does alcohol have on the body?
   c. Relating Cause and Effect Based on alcohol's effect on the nervous system, explain why drinking and driving is extremely dangerous.

Lab zone **At-Home Activity**

Medicine Labels With a family member, collect several medicine bottles found in your home. Read the warning labels and then discuss them with your family. Identify which body systems could be placed at risk by use of these medicines. Why do you think medicines provide warnings?

The BIG Idea Structures that enable the nervous system to function include the brain, spinal cord, neurons, and sense organs, such as the eye and ear.

1 How the Nervous System Works

Key Concepts   S 7.5.b

- The nervous system directs how your body responds to information about what is happening inside and outside your body. Your nervous system also helps maintain homeostasis.

- The three kinds of neurons found in the body are sensory neurons, interneurons, and motor neurons.

- For a nerve impulse to be carried along at a synapse, it must cross the gap between an axon and the next structure.

Key Terms

- stimulus • response • neuron
- nerve impulse • dendrite • axon • nerve
- sensory neuron • interneuron
- motor neuron • synapse

2 Divisions of the Nervous System

Key Concepts   S 7.5.b

- The central nervous system is the control center of the body. It includes the brain and spinal cord.

- The three main regions of the brain are the cerebrum, cerebellum, and brain stem.

- The peripheral nervous system consists of a network of nerves that branch out from the central nervous system and connect it to the rest of the body.

- A reflex is an automatic response that occurs very rapidly and without conscious control.

- Concussions and spinal cord injuries are two ways the central nervous system can be damaged.

Key Terms

- central nervous system
- peripheral nervous system • brain
- spinal cord • cerebrum • cerebellum
- brain stem • somatic nervous system
- autonomic nervous system • reflex
- concussion

3 Sight and Hearing

Key Concepts   S 7.5.g, 7.6.b

- The eyes convert light into nerve impulses that your brain interprets, enabling you to see.

- The ears convert sound into nerve impulses that your brain interprets, enabling you to hear.

- Structures in your inner ear control your sense of balance.

Key Terms

- cornea • pupil • iris • lens • retina • rods
- cones • optic nerve • eardrum • hammer
- anvil • stirrup • cochlea • semicircular canal

4 Smell, Taste, and Touch

Key Concepts   S 7.5.b

- The senses of smell and taste work together when chemicals in food or in the air trigger receptors in the nose and mouth.

- The skin contains touch receptors that respond to a number of stimuli.

Key Terms

- taste bud

5 Alcohol and Other Drugs

Key Concepts   S 7.5.b

- Most abused drugs are dangerous because of their immediate effects on the nervous system.

- Commonly abused drugs include depressants, stimulants, inhalants, steroids, and alcohol.

- Alcohol use can destroy cells in the brain and liver, and lead to addiction.

Key Terms

- drug • drug abuse • tolerance • addiction
- withdrawal • depressant • stimulant
- alcoholism

Review and Assessment

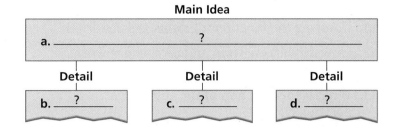
Target Reading Skill

Identifying Main Ideas Review the two paragraphs following the heading Concussions on page 613. Use a graphic organizer like the one to the right to identify the main idea and three details.

Main Idea

a. _____ ? _____

| Detail | Detail | Detail |

b. ___ ?   c. ___ ?   d. ___ ?

Reviewing Key Terms

Choose the letter of the best answer.

1. The structures that carry messages toward a neuron's cell body are
   a. axons.
   b. dendrites.
   c. nerves.
   d. nerve impulses.

2. Which structure links the brain to most of the nerves of the peripheral nervous system?
   a. the cerebrum
   b. the cerebellum
   c. the cochlea
   d. the spinal cord

3. Which structure focuses light as it passes through the eye?
   a. the pupil
   b. the retina
   c. the lens
   d. the iris

4. Taste buds contain sensory receptors that detect
   a. odors.
   b. flavors.
   c. textures.
   d. heat.

5. Physical dependence on a drug is called
   a. withdrawal.
   b. response.
   c. addiction.
   d. tolerance.

Complete the following sentences so that your answers clearly explain the key term.

6. Answering the door when the bell rings is an example of a **response,** which is _____ .

7. Your understanding of the words on this page occurs in your **cerebrum,** which is _____ .

8. The **cornea** in your eye plays an important role in seeing because it _____ .

9. Sound waves strike the **eardrum,** which then _____ .

10. Alcohol is classified as a **depressant** because _____ .

Writing in Science

Descriptive Paragraph Draw a diagram of the human eye, and label the key parts. Then, write a paragraph that describes how each part helps a person "see" an image.

Video Assessment
Discovery Channel School
The Nervous System

Review and Assessment

Checking Concepts

11. Compare the functions of axons and dendrites.

12. How do the cerebrum and cerebellum work together when you ride a bicycle?

13. What is the function of the autonomic nervous system?

14. What is the result if the spinal cord is cut?

15. What enables a person to see depth?

16. What type of stimuli trigger receptors that enable you to taste food?

17. How do anabolic steroids affect the body?

Thinking Critically

18. **Interpreting Diagrams** The diagram below shows a synapse. Explain how a nerve impulse crosses the gap.

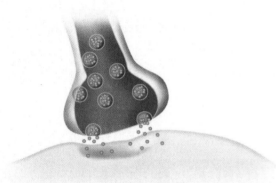

19. **Relating Cause and Effect** When a person has a stroke, blood flow to part of the brain is reduced, and some brain cells die. Suppose that after a stroke, a woman is unable to move her right arm and right leg. In which side of her brain did the stroke occur? Explain.

20. **Applying Concepts** As a man walks barefoot along a beach, he steps on a sharp shell. His foot automatically jerks upward, even before he feels pain. What process is this an example of? How does it help protect the man?

21. **Inferring** Suppose a person has an injury that results in a torn eardrum. Explain how you think the person's hearing would be affected.

Applying Skills

Use the graph to answer Questions 22–25.

A person with normal vision stood at different distances from an eye chart and tried to identify the letters on the chart. The line graph gives the results.

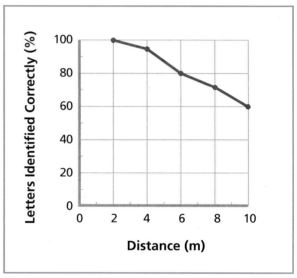

Eye Chart Results

22. **Reading Graphs** What variable is plotted on the x-axis? On the y-axis?

23. **Interpreting Data** As the distance from the eye chart increases, what happens to the percentage of letters identified correctly?

24. **Controlling Variables** What was the manipulated variable in this experiment? What was the responding variable?

25. **Predicting** Based on the graph, what would you expect the percent of correctly identified letters to be when the distance is 12 meters?

Lab zone Standards Investigation

Performance Assessment Explain to your classmates how you set up your experiment, which illusions you used, which senses were involved in the illusions, and why the illusions worked. Include information on how the nervous system was involved in your illusions.

Choose the letter of the best answer.

1. A scientist studying the brain is studying part of the
   A peripheral nervous system.
   B somatic nervous system.
   C autonomic nervous system.
   D central nervous system.   **S 7.5.b**

2. Suppose you step on a tack. Which of the following choices represents the order of response of your nervous system?
   A Sensory neuron stimulated; impulse to spinal cord; impulse to brain; impulse to motor neuron; foot moves
   B Sensory neuron stimulated; impulse to spinal cord; impulse to motor neuron; foot moves; message to brain
   C Impulse to motor neuron; foot moves; impulse to sensory neuron; impulse to spinal cord; impulse to brain
   D Foot moves; sensory neuron stimulated; impulse to brain; impulse to motor neuron   **S 7.5.b**

3. What is the function of the part labeled *A* on the neuron shown below?

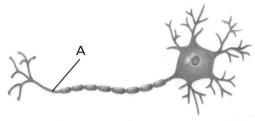

   A It carries the nerve impulse toward the cell body.
   B It protects the neuron from damage.
   C It carries the nerve impulse away from the cell body.
   D It picks up stimuli from the environment.
                                      S 7.5.b

Use the diagram below and your knowledge of science to answer Question 4.

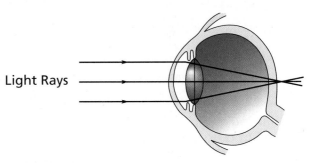

Light Rays

4. The person with this eye probably has trouble seeing because the light rays focus
   A behind the retina.   B on the eye's lens.
   C on the cornea.   D on the iris.
                                      S 7.5.g

5. A disease damages a person's semicircular canals. That person will most likely have difficulty
   A seeing.
   B hearing.
   C maintaining balance.
   D tasting food.   **S 7.5.g**

6. Which of the following structures in the ear changes sound waves into nerve impulses that go to the brain?
   A hammer
   B cochlea
   C eardrum
   D anvil   **S 7.5.g**

7. You can infer that a person who has lost his or her sense of smell is also likely to have a poor
   A sense of balance.
   B sense of touch.
   C sense of taste.
   D sense of hearing.
                                      S 7.5.b

Apply the
BIG Idea

8. Identify the structures of the eye and other parts of the nervous system that allow you to read and understand this sentence. Explain the order in which the structures are involved and how each one functions.   **S 7.5.g**

Chapter 16

The Endocrine System and Reproduction

CALIFORNIA Standards Preview

S 7.1 All living organisms are composed of cells, from just one to many trillions, whose details usually are visible only through a microscope. As a basis for understanding this concept:

f. Students know that as multicellular organisms develop, their cells differentiate.

S 7.5 The anatomy and physiology of plants and animals illustrate the complementary nature of structure and function. As a basis for understanding this concept:

b. Students know organ systems function because of the contributions of individual organs, tissues, and cells. The failure of any part can affect the entire system.

d. Students know how the reproductive organs of the human female and male generate eggs and sperm and how sexual activity may lead to fertilization and pregnancy.

e. Students know the function of the umbilicus and placenta during pregnancy.

S 7.7 Scientific progress is made by asking meaningful questions and conducting careful investigations. As a basis for understanding this concept and addressing the content in the other three strands, students should develop their own questions and perform investigations.

Identical twins form when a fertilized egg splits in two.

634 ◆

S 7.5.d

Focus on the
BIG Idea

How do the endocrine and reproductive systems work together to contribute to reproduction?

Check What You Know

Suppose you hear someone say, "She has her father's eyes," or "The twins look just like their grandmother." How do traits pass from one generation to the next? Explain how sexual reproduction results in children that resemble their parents or grandparents. Which body cells play key roles in this process?

Build Science Vocabulary

The images shown here represent some of the Key Terms in this chapter. You can use this vocabulary skill to help you understand the meaning of some key terms in this chapter.

Vocabulary Skill

Identify Related Word Forms

You can increase your vocabulary by learning related forms of a word. For example, if you know the verb *produce* means "to make," you can figure out the meaning of the noun *product*—"something that is made." You can also figure out the meaning of the noun *production*—"the process of making." The table below shows some key terms in this chapter and their related word forms.

Verb	Noun	Adjective
differentiate To change and become specialized in the process of embryo development	**differentiation** The process in which cells change and become specialized during the development of an embryo	**differentiating** Undergoing change and specialization
menstruate To lose blood and tissue in a monthly cycle	**menstruation** The process in which blood and tissue pass from the female body	**menstrual** Relating to the process in which blood and tissue pass from the body
ovulate To release an egg from an ovary	**ovulation** The process in which an egg is released from an ovary	**ovulating** Releasing an egg from an ovary

Apply It!

Review the words related to *ovulation*. Complete the following sentences with the correct form of the word.

1. After _____ occurs, the egg may be fertilized.
2. Women usually _____ about halfway through the menstrual cycle.

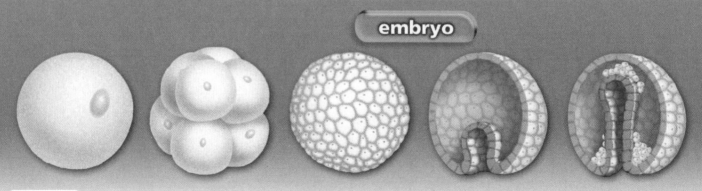

embryo

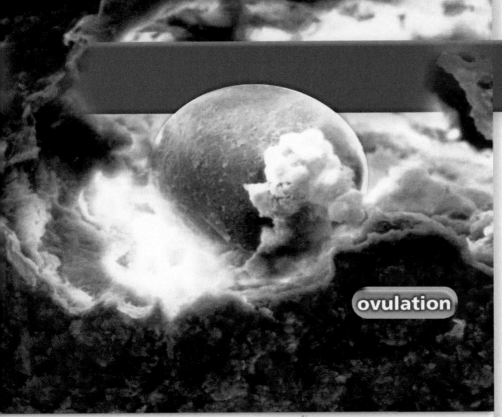
ovulation

negative feedback

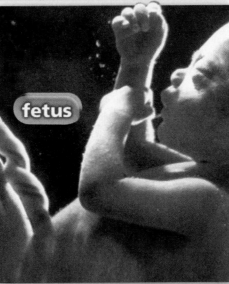
fetus

egg and sperm

Chapter 16 Vocabulary

interactive Textbook

Build Science Vocabulary
Online
Visit: PHSchool.com
Web Code: cvj-4160

Chapter 16 ◆ **637**

How to Read Science

Analyze Cause and Effect

Science involves many cause-and-effect relationships. A cause makes something happen. An effect is what happens. When you recognize that one event causes another, you are relating cause and effect. Words such as *cause, because, effect, affect,* and *result* often signal a cause-and-effect relationship. Other words such as *so, since,* and *therefore* may also signal cause-and-effect relationships.

Read the following paragraph, which is about some of the effects of hormones. Then copy the graphic organizer below. Complete it to show some of the effects of hormones.

Chemicals called hormones <u>affect</u> many processes in the body. One hormone, for example, helps <u>cause</u> the immune system to develop. A second hormone regulates growth. In addition, as a <u>result</u> of the combined action of two hormones, the level of glucose in the blood stays fairly constant.

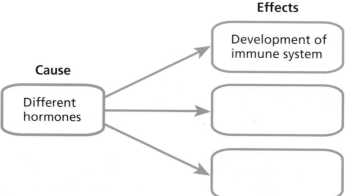

Apply It!

1. Review the completed graphic organizer. Then answer the following question: What are three effects of hormones?
2. After you read Section 1, make a cause-and-effect graphic organizer similar to the one above to show the effects of hormones produced by the adrenal glands.

Standards Investigation

S 7.1.f

Taking Shape

As a human embryo develops, differentiation gives rise to many different kinds of cells. This process occurs in all multicellular organisms. In fact, in its early stages, a human embryo develops much like embryos of other vertebrates. Cells divide and differentiate into ever more specialized tissues, organs, and other structures. In this investigation, you'll model the important tissues of an embryo and find out where the different body systems develop.

Your Goal

To design and construct a display showing the tissues of an early embryo and the structures that develop when cells in those tissues undergo differentiation

Your display must

- illustrate the structure of an embryo
- include tissues outside the embryo that help protect and nourish the embryo
- identify the organs, systems, and other body structures that develop from each layer of the embryos
- be made following the safety guidelines in Appendix A

Plan It!

Preview the diagram in the chapter that shows the development of an early embryo and the body systems that arise from each of its tissue layers. Use print and electronic resources to learn the scientific names of the three layers and more details about the body structures that develop from each. Also, identify the roles of four tissues called the amnion, chorion, allantois, and yolk sac.

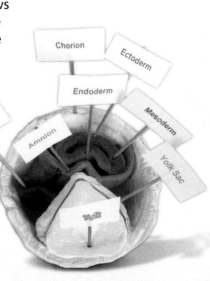

The Endocrine System

CALIFORNIA
Standards Focus

S 7.5.b Students know organ systems function because of the contributions of individual organs, tissues, and cells. The failure of any part can affect the entire system.

- How does the endocrine system control body processes?
- What are the endocrine glands?
- How does negative feedback control hormone levels?

Key Terms

- endocrine gland
- hormone
- target cell
- hypothalamus
- pituitary gland
- negative feedback

Lab zone Standards **Warm-Up**

What's the Signal?

1. Stand up and move around the room until your teacher says "Freeze!" Then, stop moving immediately. Stay perfectly still until your teacher says "Start!" Then, begin moving again.
2. Anyone who moves between the "Freeze!" command and the "Start!" command has to leave the game.
3. When only one person is left, that person wins.

Think it Over

Inferring Why is it important for players in this game to respond to signals? What types of signals function in the human body?

Imagine that you are trapped in a damp, dark dungeon. Somewhere near you is a deep pit with water at the bottom. Overhead swings a pendulum with a razor-sharp edge. With each swing, the pendulum lowers closer and closer to your body.

The main character in Edgar Allan Poe's story "The Pit and the Pendulum" finds himself in that very situation. Here is his reaction: "A fearful idea now suddenly drove the blood in torrents upon my heart. . . . I at once started to my feet, trembling convulsively in every fibre. . . . Perspiration burst from every pore, and stood in cold, big beads upon my forehead."

Poe's character is terrified. When people are badly frightened, their bodies react in the ways that the character describes. These physical reactions, such as sweating and rapid heartbeat, are caused mainly by the body's endocrine system.

Hormones and the Endocrine System

The human body has two systems that regulate its activities, the nervous system and the endocrine system. The nervous system regulates most activities by sending nerve impulses throughout the body. ⊙ **The endocrine system produces chemicals that control many of the body's daily activities. The endocrine system also regulates long-term changes such as growth and development.**

The endocrine system is made up of glands. A gland is an organ that produces or releases a chemical. Some glands, such as those that produce saliva and sweat, release their chemicals into tiny tubes. The tubes deliver the chemicals to a specific location within the body or to the skin's surface.

Unlike sweat glands, the glands of the endocrine system do not have delivery tubes. **Endocrine glands** (EN duh krin) produce and release their chemical products directly into the bloodstream. The blood then carries those chemicals throughout the body.

Hormones The chemical product of an endocrine gland is called a **hormone.** Hormones turn on, turn off, speed up, or slow down the activities of different organs and tissues. You can think of a hormone as a chemical messenger. Hormones are carried throughout the body by the blood. Therefore, hormones can regulate activities in tissues and organs that are not close to the glands that produce them.

FIGURE 1
Endocrine Control
The endocrine system controls the body's response to an exciting situation such as a roller-coaster ride. Endocrine glands also regulate the changes that occur as a baby grows.
Applying Concepts *What are the substances produced by endocrine glands called?*

Hormone Production What causes the release of hormones? Often, nerve impulses from the brain make that happen. Suppose, for example, a person sees a deadly, knife-edged pendulum. Nerve impulses travel from the person's eyes to the brain. The brain interprets the information and then sends an impulse to the adrenal glands. These glands, in turn, release the hormone adrenaline into the bloodstream. Adrenaline makes the heart rate and breathing rate increase.

Hormone Action In contrast to the body's response to a nerve impulse, hormones usually cause a longer-lasting response. For example, the brain sends a quick, short signal to the adrenal glands, which then release adrenaline. When the adrenaline reaches the heart, it makes the heart beat more rapidly. The heart continues to race until the amount of adrenaline in the blood drops to a normal level.

Target Cells When a hormone enters the bloodstream, it affects some organs but not others. Why? The answer lies in the hormone's chemical structure. A hormone interacts only with specific target cells. **Target cells** are specialized cells that recognize the hormone's chemical structure. A hormone and its target cell fit together the way a key fits into a lock. Hormones will travel through the bloodstream until they find the "lock"—or particular cell type—that they fit.

 **Reading Checkpoint** What is a target cell?

Functions of Endocrine Glands

Each endocrine gland releases different hormones and thus controls different processes. 🔑 **The endocrine glands include the hypothalamus, pituitary, thyroid, parathyroid, adrenal, thymus, and pancreas. They also include the ovaries in females and testes in males.** Figure 2 shows the locations of the endocrine glands and describes some activities they control.

The Hypothalamus The nervous system and the endocrine system work together. The **hypothalamus** (hy poh THAL uh mus), a tiny part of the brain near the middle of your head, is the link between the two systems. Nerve messages controlling sleep, hunger, and other basic body processes come from the hypothalamus. The hypothalamus also produces hormones that control other endocrine glands and organs. The hypothalamus plays a major role in maintaining homeostasis because of the nerve impulses and hormones it produces.

FIGURE 2
Glands of the Endocrine System

Each of the endocrine glands has an important regulatory role in the body. **Interpreting Diagrams** *What are two systems that are regulated by endocrine glands?*

Hypothalamus
The hypothalamus links the nervous and endocrine systems and controls the pituitary gland.

Pituitary Gland
The pituitary gland controls other endocrine glands and regulates growth, blood pressure, and water balance.

Thyroid Gland
This gland controls the release of energy from food molecules inside cells.

Thymus Gland
Hormones from this gland help the immune system develop during childhood.

Parathyroid Glands
These tiny glands regulate the amount of calcium in the blood.

Adrenal Glands
These glands release several hormones. Adrenaline triggers the body's response to emergency situations. Other hormones affect salt and water balance in the kidneys and sugar in the blood.

Pancreas
The pancreas produces the hormones insulin and glucagon, which control the level of glucose in the blood. (The pancreas also produces enzymes used in digestion.)

Testes
The testes release the sex hormone testosterone, which controls changes in a male's body and regulates sperm production.

Ovaries
The ovaries release female sex hormones. Estrogen controls changes in a female's body. Estrogen and progesterone trigger egg development.

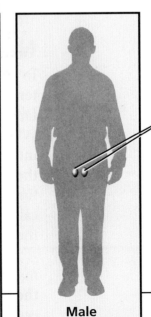

Female

Male

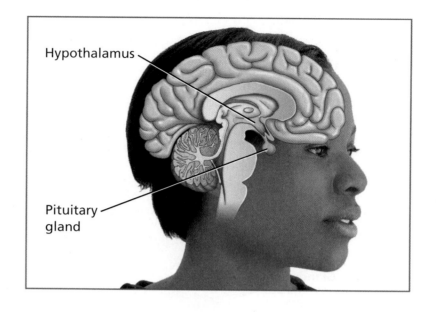

FIGURE 3
The Pituitary Gland
The pituitary gland is located below the hypothalamus. The pituitary controls several important body functions either directly or indirectly by signaling other endocrine glands.

Hypothalamus

Pituitary gland

The Pituitary Gland Just below the hypothalamus is an endocrine gland about the size of a pea. The **pituitary gland** (pih TOO ih tehr ee) communicates with the hypothalamus to control many body activities. In response to nerve impulses or hormone signals from the hypothalamus, the pituitary gland releases its hormones. Some of those hormones act as an "on" switch for other endocrine glands. For example, one pituitary hormone signals the thyroid gland to produce hormones. Other pituitary hormones control body activities directly. Growth hormone regulates growth from infancy to adulthood. Another pituitary hormone directs the kidneys to regulate the amount of water in the blood.

Reading Checkpoint What causes the pituitary gland to release hormones?

Negative Feedback

In some ways, the endocrine system works like a heating system. Suppose you set a thermostat at 20°C. If the temperature falls below 20°C, the thermostat signals the heater to turn on. When the heater warms the area to the proper temperature, information about the warm conditions "feeds back" to the thermostat. The thermostat then gives the heater a signal that turns the heat off. The type of signal used in a heating system is called **negative feedback** because the system is turned off by the condition it produces.

The endocrine system often uses negative feedback to maintain homeostasis.  **Through negative feedback, when the amount of a particular hormone in the blood reaches a certain level, the endocrine system sends signals that stop the release of that hormone.**

644 ◆

You can see an example of negative feedback in Figure 4. Like a thermostat in a cool room, the endocrine system senses when there's not enough thyroxine in the blood. Thyroxine is a thyroid hormone that controls how much energy is available to cells. When there's not enough energy available, the hypothalamus signals the pituitary gland to release thyroid-stimulating hormone (TSH). That hormone signals the thyroid gland to release thyroxine. When the amount of thyroxine reaches the right level, the endocrine system signals the thyroid gland to stop releasing thyroxine.

 **Reading Checkpoint** **How is thyroxine involved in negative feedback?**

Go Online
active art

For: Negative Feedback activity
Visit: PHSchool.com
Web Code: cep-4071

Hypothalamus senses cells need more energy.

Thyroid stops producing thyroxine.

Pituitary releases TSH.

Pituitary stops producing TSH.

Thyroid produces thyroxine.

Hypothalamus senses cells have enough energy.

FIGURE 4
Negative Feedback
The release of the hormone thyroxine is controlled through negative feedback. When enough thyroxine is present, the system signals the thyroid gland to stop releasing the hormone.
Predicting *What happens when the amount of thyroxine becomes too low?*

Section 1 Assessment

S 7.5.b, E-LA: Reading 7.2.3, Writing 7.2.5

Target Reading Skill **Analyze Cause and Effect** Look at your graphic organizer about the effects of hormones produced by the adrenal glands. Identify three effects of those hormones.

Reviewing Key Concepts

1. a. **Identifying** What is the role of the endocrine system?
   b. **Explaining** How does adrenaline affect the heart?
   c. **Predicting** What could happen if your body continued to release adrenaline into your bloodstream, and the amount of adrenaline did not return to normal?

2. a. **Listing** List the endocrine glands.
   b. **Summarizing** How do the hypothalamus and the pituitary gland interact?

3. a. **Defining** Define negative feedback.
   b. **Applying Concepts** How does negative feedback help to maintain homeostasis?

Writing in Science

Summary In your own words, summarize how the nervous system and endocrine system work together when adrenaline is released. Include main ideas and significant details.

Modeling Negative Feedback

S 7.5.b, 7.7

Problem

How can you model negative feedback?

Skills Focus

observing, making models, evaluating the design

Materials

- duct tape
- round balloon
- scissors
- rubber stopper
- string, 40 cm
- large plastic soda bottle (2-L) with bottom removed
- small plastic soda bottle (1-L)
- plastic tray
- water

Procedure

PART 1 Research and Investigate

1. Figure 1 shows how a flush toilet uses negative feedback to regulate the water level. In your notebook, describe which part of the process involves negative feedback.

FIGURE 1

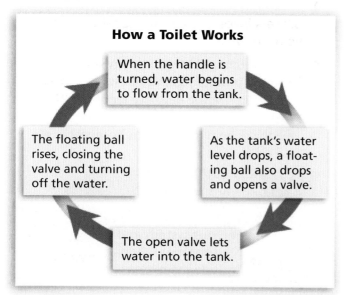

How a Toilet Works

When the handle is turned, water begins to flow from the tank.

As the tank's water level drops, a floating ball also drops and opens a valve.

The open valve lets water into the tank.

The floating ball rises, closing the valve and turning off the water.

FIGURE 2

PART 2 Design and Build

2. As you hold the open end of a balloon, push its closed end through the mouth of a small plastic bottle. Do not push the open end of the balloon into the bottle. Then, slide a straw partway into the bottle so that the air inside the bottle can escape as you blow up the balloon.

3. Partially blow up the balloon inside the bottle as shown in Figure 2. The partially inflated balloon should be about the size of a tennis ball. Remove the straw. Tie the balloon tightly, then push it into the bottle.

4. Place the large plastic bottle mouth to mouth with the small bottle. Tape the two bottles together. Make sure that the seal is waterproof.

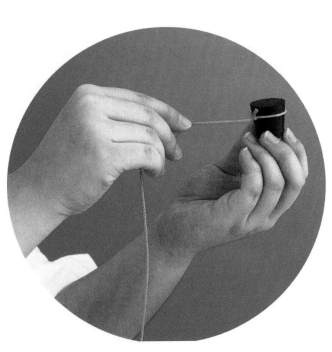

FIGURE 3

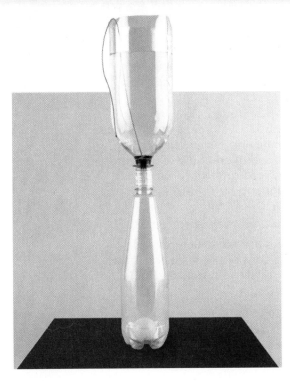

FIGURE 4

5. Tie one end of a piece of string around the top of a rubber stopper as shown in Figure 3.

6. Place the attached bottles on the tray with the smaller bottle on the bottom. Place the stopper loosely into the mouth of the larger bottle as shown in Figure 4.

7. While one partner holds the bottles upright, add water to the large bottle until it is about three fourths full. Then gently pull the string to remove the stopper. Watch what happens. Pay close attention to the following: What does the balloon do as water rises in the small bottle? Does the small bottle completely fill with water? Record your observations.

8. In your notebook, record which part of your device models negative feedback.

PART 3 Evaluate and Redesign

9. In the human endocrine system, negative feedback occurs as part of a cycle. With your partner, think of one or more ways that you could modify the model from Part 2 to show a cycle.

Analyze and Conclude

1. **Inferring** Summarize what you learned from Part 1 by describing an example of negative feedback.

2. **Observing** Describe the events you observed in Step 7.

3. **Making Models** In Step 7, which part of the process involves negative feedback? Explain your answer.

4. **Evaluating the Design** Suggest one way that you could change the model to show that negative feedback can be part of a cycle.

Communicating

Suppose you are a TV health reporter preparing a program on human hormones. You need to do a 30-second segment on hormones and negative feedback. Write a script for your presentation. Include references to a model to help viewers understand how negative feedback works in the endocrine system.

The Male and Female Reproductive Systems

CALIFORNIA
Standards Focus

S 7.5.d Students know how the reproductive organs of the human female and male generate eggs and sperm and how sexual activity may lead to fertilization and pregnancy.

- What is sexual reproduction?
- What are the structures and functions of the male and female reproductive systems?
- What events occur during the menstrual cycle?

Key Terms

- egg • sperm • testis
- testosterone • scrotum
- semen • penis • urethra
- ovary • estrogen
- fallopian tube • uterus
- vagina • menstrual cycle
- follicle • ovulation
- menstruation

Lab zone Standards **Warm-Up**

What's the Big Difference?

1. Your teacher will provide prepared slides of eggs and sperm.
2. Examine each slide under the microscope, first under low power, then under high power. Be sure you view more than one example of each kind of cell.
3. Sketch and label each sample.

Think It Over

Observing What differences did you observe between sperm cells and egg cells? How are these differences examples of the complementary nature of structure and function?

Many differences between an adult animal and its young are controlled by the endocrine system. In humans, two endocrine glands—the ovaries and the testes—control many of the changes that occur as a child matures. These glands release hormones that cause the body to develop as a person grows older. They also produce mature sex cells that are part of sexual reproduction.

Hormones control growth and development.

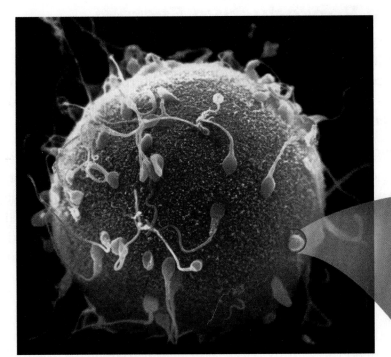

FIGURE 5
Egg and Sperm
An egg is one of the largest cells in the body. A sperm, which is much smaller than an egg, has a head (rounded end) and a tail that allows it to move. In the photograph on the left, sperm are swarming around the large egg. On the right, a sperm, which has been colored blue, has penetrated the egg. **Applying Concepts** *What structure results when the sperm fertilizes the egg?*

Sexual Reproduction

You began life as a single cell. That single cell was produced by the joining of two other cells, an egg and a sperm. An **egg** is the female sex cell. A **sperm** is the male sex cell. It has a tail, or flagellum, that enables it to move.

The joining of a sperm and an egg is called fertilization. Fertilization is an important part of sexual reproduction, the process by which male and female living things produce new individuals. ⬭ **Sexual reproduction involves the production of eggs by the female and sperm by the male. The egg and sperm join together during fertilization.** When fertilization occurs, a fertilized egg, or zygote, is produced. Every one of the trillions of cells in your body is descended from the single cell that formed during fertilization.

Like other cells in the body, sex cells contain rod-shaped structures called chromosomes. Chromosomes carry the information that controls inherited characteristics, such as eye color and blood type. Every cell in the human body that has a nucleus, except the sex cells, contains 46 chromosomes. Each sex cell contains half that number, or 23 chromosomes. During fertilization, the 23 chromosomes in a sperm join the 23 chromosomes in an egg. The result is a zygote with 46 chromosomes. The zygote contains all of the information needed to produce a new human being.

Reading Checkpoint What happens to the number of chromosomes when a male sex cell and a female sex cell join?

Male Reproductive System

The organs of the male reproductive system are shown in Figure 6. 🔑 **The male reproductive system is specialized to produce sperm and the hormone testosterone. The structures of the male reproductive system include the testes, scrotum, and penis.**

The Testes The oval-shaped **testes** (TES teez) (singular *testis*) are the organs of the male reproductive system in which sperm are produced. The testes contain clusters of tiny coiled tubes, called seminiferous tubules. Immature sperm form in the walls of these tubes. As each sperm cell matures, it gains a flagellum. Sperm are then carried to the epididymis. Within this structure, the sperm continue to mature and are stored.

Notice in Figure 6 that the testes are located in an external pouch of skin called the **scrotum** (SKROH tum). This location keeps the testes about 2°C to 3°C below body temperature. Sperm need the slightly cooler conditions to develop normally.

The testes also produce testosterone. **Testosterone** (tes TAHS tuh rohn) is a hormone that controls the development of physical characteristics in mature men. Some of those characteristics include facial hair, deepening of the voice, broadening of the shoulders, and the ability to produce sperm.

FIGURE 6
The Male Reproductive System
In the male reproductive system, the testes produce sperm and the hormone testosterone.
Interpreting Diagrams *Trace the pathway of sperm in the male reproductive system. What structures does a sperm cell pass through before exiting the body?*

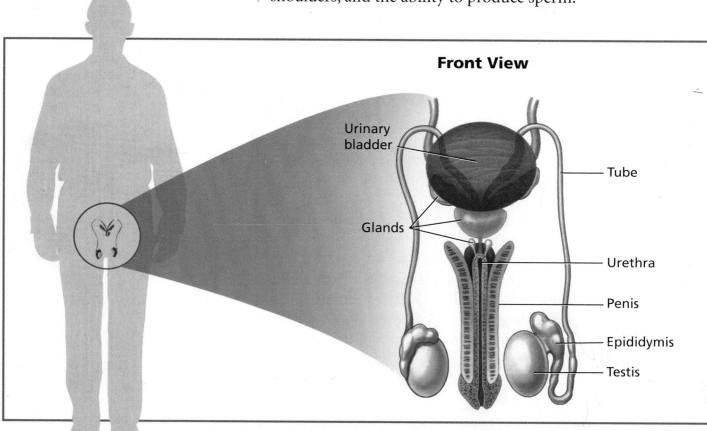

Front View

Urinary bladder

Tube

Glands

Urethra

Penis

Epididymis

Testis

The Path of Sperm Cells The production of sperm cells begins in the testes at some point during the teenage years. Each sperm cell has a head, which contains chromosomes, and a long, whiplike flagellum. Once sperm cells form, they move to the epididymis. From there, sperm travel through other structures in the male reproductive system. As the sperm move, they mix with fluids produced by nearby glands. This mixture of sperm cells and fluids is called **semen** (SEE mun). The fluids in semen provide an environment in which sperm are able to swim. Semen also contains nutrients that the moving sperm use as a source of energy.

Semen leaves the body through an organ called the **penis.** The tube in the penis through which the semen travels is the **urethra** (yoo REE thruh). Urine also leaves the body through the urethra. However, when semen passes through the urethra, muscles near the bladder contract. Those muscles prevent urine and semen from mixing.

Semen contains a huge number of sperm cells—about 5 to 10 million per drop! Sperm leave the penis in a process called ejaculation, which can release 2 to 3 milliliters of semen. The release of sperm during sexual activity may lead to the fertilization of an egg and pregnancy.

 **Reading Checkpoint** What is the pouch of skin in which the testes are located?

Go Online
SCiLINKS™ NSTA

For: Links on the reproductive system
Visit: www.SciLinks.org
Web Code: scn-0472

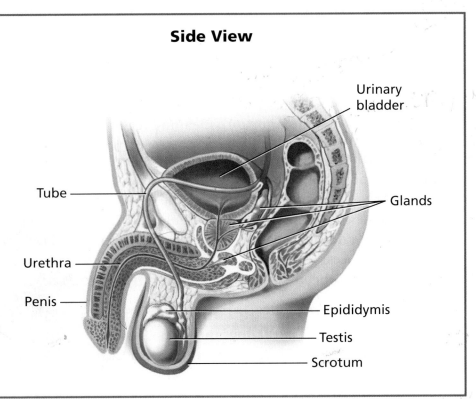

Side View

Urinary bladder

Tube

Glands

Urethra

Penis

Epididymis

Testis

Scrotum

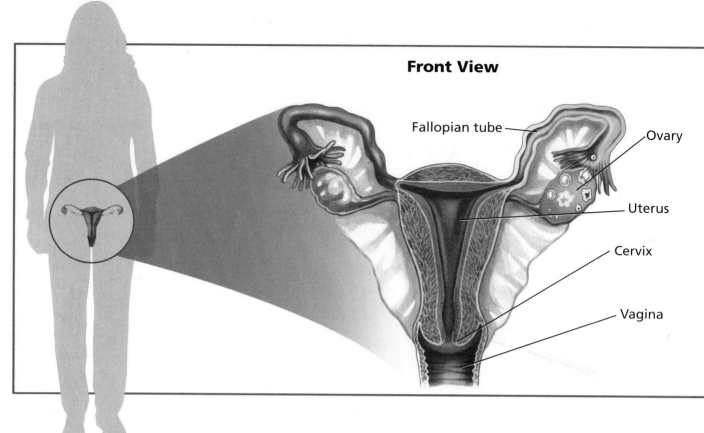

Front View

Fallopian tube

Ovary

Uterus

Cervix

Vagina

FIGURE 7

The Female Reproductive System

In the female reproductive system, the two ovaries produce eggs and hormones, such as estrogen and progesterone.
Relating Cause and Effect What changes does estrogen produce in a female's body?

Female Reproductive System

🔑 **The role of the female reproductive system is to produce eggs and, if an egg is fertilized, to nourish a developing baby until birth. The organs of the female reproductive system include the ovaries, fallopian tubes, uterus, and vagina.**

The Ovaries The **ovaries** (OH vuh reez) are the female reproductive structures that produce and store eggs. The ovaries are located slightly below the waist, one ovary on each side of the body. The name for these organs comes from the Latin word *ova* (singular *ovum*), meaning "eggs."

Female Hormones Like the testes in males, the ovaries also are endocrine glands that produce hormones. One hormone, **estrogen** (ES truh jun), triggers the development of some adult female characteristics. For example, estrogen causes the hips to widen and the breasts to develop. Estrogen also plays a role in the process by which egg cells mature. Another hormone, progesterone, maintains the uterus during pregnancy.

The Path of the Egg Cell Each ovary is located near a fallopian tube. The **fallopian tubes,** also called oviducts, are passageways for eggs as they travel from the ovary to the uterus. Each month, one of the ovaries releases a mature egg, known as an oocyte (OH oh sight). The egg enters the nearest fallopian tube. Fertilization usually occurs within a fallopian tube.

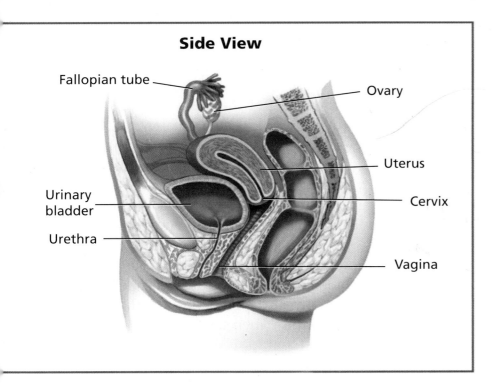

Side View

Fallopian tube

Ovary

Uterus

Cervix

Urinary bladder

Urethra

Vagina

The egg moves through the fallopian tube, which leads to the uterus. The **uterus** (YOO tur us) is a hollow muscular organ about the size of a pear. If an egg has been fertilized, it becomes attached to the wall of the uterus and pregnancy begins.

An egg that has not been fertilized starts to break down in the uterus. It leaves the uterus through an opening at the base of the uterus, called the cervix. The egg then enters the vagina. The **vagina** (vuh JY nuh) is a muscular passageway leading to the outside of the body. The vagina, or birth canal, is the passageway through which a baby leaves the mother's body.

 **Reading Checkpoint**   **What is the role of the fallopian tube?**

The Menstrual Cycle

When the female reproductive system becomes mature, usually during the teenage years, there are about 400,000 undeveloped eggs in the ovaries. However, only about 500 of those eggs will actually leave the ovaries and reach the uterus. An egg is released about once a month in a mature woman's body. The monthly cycle of changes that occur in the female reproductive system is called the **menstrual cycle** (MEN stroo ul).

➤ **During the menstrual cycle, an egg matures in an ovary. At the same time, the lining of the uterus becomes thicker.** In this way, the menstrual cycle prepares the woman's body for pregnancy, which begins after fertilization.

Lab zone Skills **Activity**

Calculating
An egg is about 0.1 mm in diameter. In contrast, the head of a sperm is about 0.005 mm. Calculate how much bigger an egg is than a sperm.

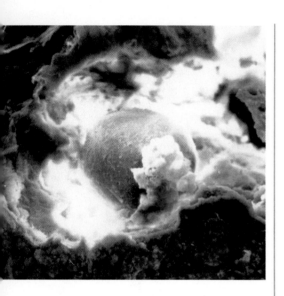

FIGURE 8
Release of an Egg
The ovary releases an egg, shown here in pink. The egg will then travel down the fallopian tube to the uterus. **Applying Concepts** *Through what structure does an unfertilized egg pass after leaving the uterus?*

Stages of the Menstrual Cycle Follow the stages of the menstrual cycle in Figure 9. Early in the menstrual cycle, an egg starts to mature in one of the ovaries. Each egg matures within its own grouping of cells, called a **follicle** (FAHL ih kuhl). At the same time, the lining of the uterus begins to thicken. About halfway through a typical menstrual cycle, the follicle ruptures and the mature egg is released from the ovary into a fallopian tube. The process in which an egg is released is called **ovulation** (ahv yuh LAY shun).

Once the egg is released, it can be fertilized for the next few days if sperm are in or near the vagina and travel into the fallopian tube. If the egg is not fertilized, or if it fails to implant, it begins to break down. The lining of the uterus also breaks down. The extra blood and tissue of the thickened lining are sloughed off and pass out of the body through the vagina in a process called **menstruation** (men stroo AY shun). On average, menstruation lasts about four to six days. At the same time that menstruation takes place, a new egg begins to mature in the ovary, and the cycle continues.

Endocrine Control The menstrual cycle is controlled by hormones of the endocrine system. Hormones also trigger a girl's first menstruation. Many girls begin menstruation between the ages of 10 and 14 years. Some girls start earlier, while others start later. Women continue to menstruate until about age 50. Then, the production of sex hormones drops. As a result, the ovaries stop releasing mature egg cells.

Math: Algebra and Functions 7.1.5

Math Analyzing Data

Changing Hormone Levels

A woman's hormone levels change throughout the menstrual cycle. The graph shows the levels of one female hormone, known as LH, which causes the egg to mature.

1. **Reading Graphs** What does the *y*-axis show?

2. **Interpreting Data** What is the level of LH on day 1? On day 17? On day 21?

3. **Calculating** What is the difference between LH levels on days 9 and 13?

4. **Drawing Conclusions** On what day does LH reach its highest level? What event do you think takes place at about the same time?

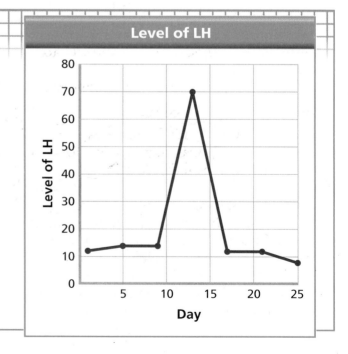

Level of LH

FIGURE 9
The Menstrual Cycle

During the menstrual cycle, the lining of the uterus builds up with extra blood and tissue. About halfway through a typical cycle, ovulation takes place. **Predicting** *What happens if the egg is not fertilized?*

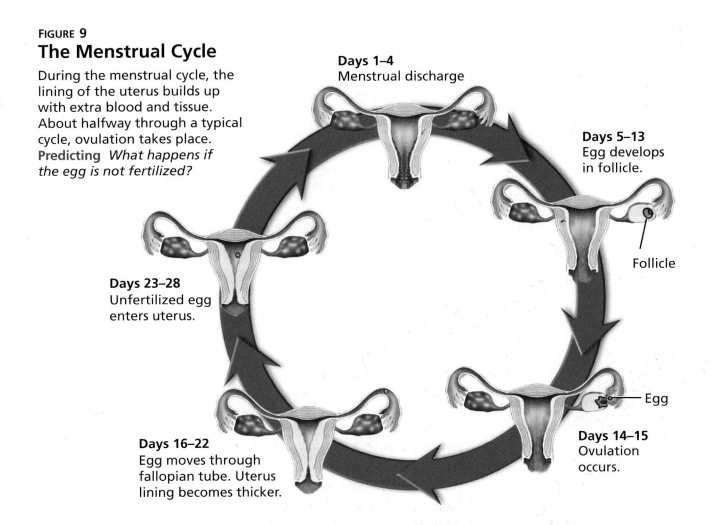

Days 1–4
Menstrual discharge

Days 5–13
Egg develops in follicle.

Follicle

Egg

Days 14–15
Ovulation occurs.

Days 16–22
Egg moves through fallopian tube. Uterus lining becomes thicker.

Days 23–28
Unfertilized egg enters uterus.

Section 2 Assessment

S 7.5.d, E-LA: Reading 7.1.0, Writing 7.2.0

Vocabulary Skill **Identify Related Word Forms** Choose one of the following words—*menstruate, menstruation,* or *menstrual*—to complete the following sentence:
The _____ cycle is controlled by hormones.

Reviewing Key Concepts

1. a. **Reviewing** What is fertilization?
   b. **Explaining** Explain how fertilization produces a new individual.
   c. **Comparing and Contrasting** Contrast the number of chromosomes in sex cells and in a zygote. Explain why the zygote has the number of chromosomes that it does.
2. a. **Listing** List the structures of the male and female reproductive systems.
   b. **Describing** Describe the functions of the structures you named in Question 2a.
   c. **Comparing and Contrasting** In what ways are the functions of the ovaries and the testes similar? How do their functions differ?
3. a. **Defining** What is the menstrual cycle?
   b. **Sequencing** At what point in the menstrual cycle does ovulation occur?
   c. **Relating Cause and Effect** How is ovulation related to fertilization?

Writing in Science

Explanatory Paragraph Write a paragraph explaining why the ovaries and testes are part of both the endocrine system and the reproductive system.

Pregnancy, Development, and Birth

S 7.1.f Students know that as multicellular organisms develop, their cells differentiate.

S 7.5.e Students know the function of the umbilicus and placenta during pregnancy.

- What are the changes that occur to the zygote, embryo, and fetus during development?
- How is the developing embryo protected and nourished?
- What happens during childbirth?
- What changes occur as a person develops from infancy to adulthood?

Key Terms

- embryo
- differentiation
- fetus
- amniotic sac
- placenta
- umbilical cord
- adolescence
- puberty

Lab zone Standards **Warm-Up**

Is It Safe From Harm?

1. Place a foam packing peanut in a uninflated balloon. Blow up the balloon and tie it closed.
2. Try to crush or break the peanut without breaking the balloon. You can shake or drop the balloon, or try other approaches that are approved by your teacher.

Think It Over

Drawing Conclusions How easy or difficult was it to crush or break the peanut? How did the presence of the air in the bag contribute to your results?

An egg can be fertilized during the first few days after ovulation. When sexual activity occurs, sperm may be deposited in or near the vagina. Sperm move through the vagina, into and through the uterus, and then into the fallopian tubes. If a sperm fertilizes an egg, pregnancy can occur. One of the earliest signs of pregnancy is that a woman's menstrual cycle stops. About nine months after fertilization, a baby is born.

Development Before Birth

A fertilized egg, or zygote, is no larger than the period at the end of this sentence. Yet after fertilization, the zygote undergoes changes that result in the formation of a new human. **The zygote develops into an embryo and then into a fetus. Differentiation leads to specialized cells, tissues, and organs.**

Zygote

Eight-Cell Stage

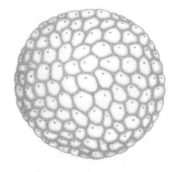

Hollow Ball

From Zygote to Embryo After an egg and sperm join, the zygote moves down the fallopian tube toward the uterus. During this trip, which takes about four days, the zygote begins to divide. The original cell divides to make two cells. These two cells divide to make four, and so on. Eventually, the mass of hundreds of cells forms a hollow ball not very different in size from the zygote. The ball attaches to the lining of the uterus. From the two-cell stage through the eighth week of development, the developing human is called an **embryo** (EM bree oh).

Differentiation of the Embryo Figure 10 shows the early stages that occur when a zygote divides and an embryo develops. Within the first day or two, cell divisions in the 4-cell stage produce 8 cells, 16 cells, and so on. At this point, all the cells still look alike. During the first week after fertilization, these cells rearrange into a hollow ball. Just a few days later, this ball of cells attaches to the wall of the uterus.

At about three weeks, some cells of the embryo begin to fold into the center of the ball. Then other cells fill in spaces between the folds. These changes lead to three layers of cells.

The layer in which a cell is located determines, or fixes, how it will differentiate. **Differentiation** is the process by which cells change and become specialized. For example, cells that will eventually give rise to the stomach and intestines are located in a different layer from cells that will give rise to the central nervous system and eyes. These two types of cells become distinguished from one another at a very early stage. As development continues, some cells become more finely differentiated. For example, certain cells of the retina in the eye become rod cells, and others become cone cells.

 **Reading Checkpoint** How many layers of cells in the embryo give rise to differentiated cells?

FIGURE 10
Early Changes in an Embryo
Cell division occurs rapidly in an embryo. Location helps control how the cells will differentiate. Some of the structures that form from the layers of the embryo are listed below. *Interpreting Diagrams Which layer gives rise to the skeletal system?*

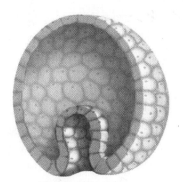

Stage When Folding Begins

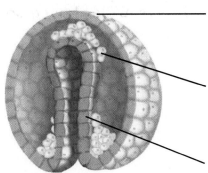

Embryo With Three Layers

Outer Layer
Skin, nervous system, pituitary gland, salivary glands

Middle Layer
Heart, bones, muscles, kidneys, lymphatic system testes, ovaries

Inner Layer
Pancreas, thyroid gland, liver, parts of the digestive system

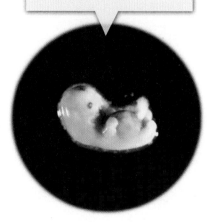

Four-week embryo Heart beats in a regular rhythm. Eyes and ears begin to form.

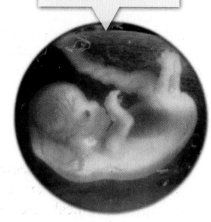

Eight-week embryo Heart has left and right chambers.

24-week fetus All parts of the eye are present. Fingerprints are forming.

FIGURE 11
Development of the Fetus
As a fetus grows and develops, it gains mass and increases in length. Its body systems also develop.
Applying Concepts *What process leads to the development of the different body systems?*

Development of the Fetus From about the ninth week of pregnancy until birth, the developing human is called a **fetus** (FEE tus). At first the fetus is only the size of a walnut shell, but it now looks more like a human. Many internal organs have formed. The head is about half the body's total size and the brain is developing rapidly. The fetus also has dark eye patches, fingers, and toes. At three months, the fetus is about 9 centimeters long and has a mass of about 26 grams.

Between the fourth and sixth months, bones become distinct. A heartbeat can be heard with a stethoscope. A layer of soft hair grows over the skin. The arms and legs develop more completely. The fetus begins to move and kick, a sign that its muscles are growing. At the end of the sixth month, the mass of the fetus is approaching 700 grams. Its body is about 30 centimeters long.

The final three months prepare the fetus to survive outside the mother's body. The brain surface develops grooves and ridges. The lungs become ready to carry out the exchange of oxygen and carbon dioxide. The eyelids can open. The fetus doubles in length. Its mass may reach 3 kilograms or more.

 **Reading Checkpoint** At what point during development can a heartbeat be detected in a fetus?

Protection and Nourishment

Just like you, the embryo and fetus need nourishment and protection to develop properly. Soon after the embryo attaches to the uterus, changes take place. In addition to the three layers of the embryo, new membranes form. ◯ **The membranes and other structures that form during development protect and nourish the developing embryo, and later the fetus.**

Go Online
SciLINKS NSTA

For: Links on before birth
Visit: www.SciLinks.org
Web Code: scn-0473

Amniotic Sac One membrane surrounds the embryo and develops into a fluid-filled sac called the **amniotic sac** (am NEE aht ik). Locate the amniotic sac in Figure 12. The fluid in the amniotic sac cushions and protects the developing baby.

Placenta and Umbilical Cord Another membrane helps to form the placenta. The **placenta** (pluh SEN tuh) is an organ that develops from fetal tissue during pregnancy. In the placenta, the embryo's blood vessels are located next to the mother's blood vessels. A ropelike structure called the **umbilical cord** forms between the embryo and the placenta. It contains veins and arteries that link the fetus to the mother.

Although the blood systems do not mix, many substances pass between the mother and fetus through the placenta. As blood travels back and forth through the umbilical cord, the fetus receives nutrients, oxygen, and other substances from the mother. Carbon dioxide and other wastes move from the fetus to the mother. The mother's body then releases the wastes through her excretory and respiratory systems.

Keeping the Fetus Healthy The barrier that separates the two blood supplies stops some diseases from spreading from the mother to the fetus. But some infectious viruses can pass through easily. One example is HIV, the virus that causes AIDS. Substances such as alcohol, chemicals in tobacco, and other drugs also can pass through the barrier. For this reason, pregnant women should not smoke, drink alcohol, or take any drug without a doctor's approval.

FIGURE 12
A Vital Link
The placenta provides a link between the mother and fetus. Blood vessels in the umbilical cord carry materials to and from the fetus. The point where the cord enters the fetus's body is the umbilicus. It remains as the navel after the baby is born.

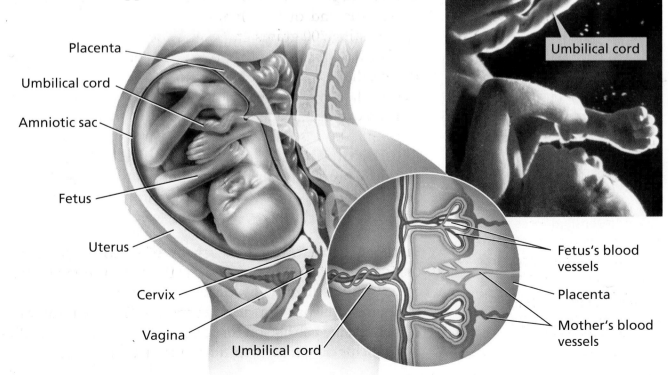

Placenta
Umbilical cord
Amniotic sac
Fetus
Uterus
Cervix
Vagina
Umbilical cord

Umbilical cord
Fetus's blood vessels
Placenta
Mother's blood vessels

FIGURE 13
Birth
After about nine months of
growth and development inside
the uterus, a baby is born. You can
see where the umbilical cord of
this newborn was tied and cut.

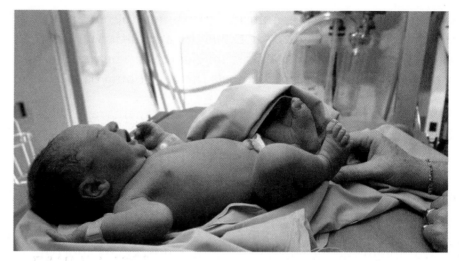

Way to Grow!
The table lists the average
mass of a developing baby at
each month of pregnancy.

Month of Pregnancy	Mass (grams)
1	0.02
2	2.0
3	26
4	150
5	460
6	640
7	1,500
8	2,300
9	3,200

1. Use a balance to identify
an everyday object with a
mass approximately equal
to each mass listed in the
table. You may need to use
different balances to cover
the range of masses listed.
2. Arrange the objects in
order by month.

Making Models What did you
learn by gathering these
physical models?

Birth

After about 40 weeks of development inside the uterus, the baby is ready to be born. 🔑 **The birth of a baby takes place in three stages—labor, delivery, and afterbirth.**

Labor During the first stage of birth, strong muscular contractions of the uterus begin. These contractions are called labor. The contractions cause the cervix to open, eventually allowing the baby to fit through the opening. Labor may last from about 2 hours to more than 20 hours.

Delivery The second stage of birth is called delivery. During normal delivery, the baby is pushed completely out of the uterus, through the vagina, and out of the mother's body. At this time, the baby is still connected to the placenta by the umbilical cord. Delivery of the baby usually takes less time than labor does—from several minutes to an hour or so.

Shortly after delivery, the umbilical cord is clamped, then cut about 5 centimeters from the baby's abdomen. Within seven to ten days, the remainder of the umbilical cord dries up and falls off, leaving a scar called the navel, or belly button.

Afterbirth About 15 minutes after delivery, the third stage of the birth process begins. Contractions push the placenta and other membranes out of the uterus through the vagina. This stage, called afterbirth, is usually completed in less than an hour.

Birth and the Baby As the baby is pushed and squeezed, muscle contractions put pressure on the placenta and umbilical cord. This pressure briefly decreases the baby's supply of oxygen. In response, the baby's heart rate increases. Within a few seconds of delivery, the baby begins breathing with a cry or a cough. This action helps rid the lungs of fluid and fills them with air.

Multiple Births The delivery of more than one baby from a single pregnancy is called a multiple birth. In the United States, about 1 out of every 30 babies born each year is a twin. Multiple births of more than two babies, such as triplets and quadruplets, occur less frequently than do twin births.

There are two types of twins: identical twins and fraternal twins. Identical twins develop from a single fertilized egg, or zygote. Early in development, the embryo splits into two identical embryos. The two embryos have identical inherited traits and are the same sex. Fraternal twins develop when two eggs are released from the ovary and are fertilized by two different sperm. Fraternal twins are no more alike than any other brothers or sisters. Fraternal twins may or may not be the same sex.

 **Reading Checkpoint** What are the two types of twins?

FIGURE 14

Twins

Identical twins (left) develop from the same fertilized egg. They share identical characteristics. Fraternal twins (right) develop from two different fertilized eggs. **Applying Concepts** *Why can fraternal twins be different sexes while identical twins cannot?*

Identical Twins

A sperm fertilizes a single egg.

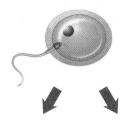

The single egg splits and forms two identical embryos.

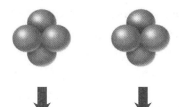

Identical twins result.

Fraternal Twins

Two different sperm fertilize two eggs.

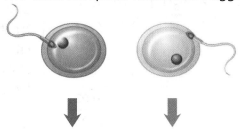

Each of the eggs develops into an embryo.

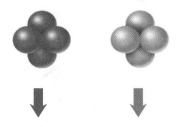

Fraternal twins result.

FIGURE 15
Development
You can see the changes in development from infancy through adolescence.
Applying Concepts *What mental development takes place during childhood?*

▲ **Adolescence**

▲ **Childhood**

▲ **Infancy**

Video Field Trip
Discovery Channel School
The Endocrine System and Reproduction

Growth and Development

You've changed a lot since you were a baby. And more changes are yet to come. ⬤ **The changes that take place between infancy and adulthood include physical changes, such as an increase in size and coordination, and mental changes, such as the ability to communicate and solve complex problems.**

Infancy During infancy—the first two years of life—a baby grows quickly. Its weight may double within just the first year! The baby's nervous and muscular systems become better coordinated. After about 3 months, a baby can hold its head up and reach for objects. Within the next 4 to 14 months, most infants begin to crawl, and then walk, by themselves. They also learn to speak. By two years old, children can do many things for themselves, such as understand simple directions, feed themselves, and play with toys.

Childhood Infancy ends and childhood begins at about two years of age. Children grow taller and heavier as their bones and muscles increase in size. They become more coordinated as they practice such skills as walking, using a pencil, and playing games. Children show a growing curiosity and increased mental abilities. Skills improve rapidly, as children learn to read, carry on conversations, and solve problems.

Adolescence The stage of development during which children mature into adults physically and mentally is called **adolescence** (ad ul ES uns). Adolescents gradually become able to think like adults and take on adult responsibilities. The bodies of adolescents also undergo specific physical changes.

Between the ages of 9 and 15 years, girls and boys enter puberty. **Puberty** (PYOO bur tee) is the period of development in which the body becomes able to reproduce. Girls begin to menstruate, and boys produce sperm. Other physical changes in girls include enlargement of the breasts and widening of the hips. In boys, facial and chest hair appears, and the voice deepens.

Adulthood Mental and emotional growth continue after adolescence. It is difficult to say when adolescence ends and adulthood begins. As adults, people continue to learn new things. After about age 30, a process known as aging begins. As people age, the skin becomes wrinkled and muscle strength decreases. The eyes may lose their ability to focus on close objects, and hair may lose its coloring. Aging becomes more noticeable between the ages of 40 and 65. However, the effects of aging can be slowed if people follow sensible diets and good exercise plans. Many adults can remain active throughout their lives. Older people have learned a lot from their experiences. Because of this learning, many older people have a great deal of wisdom they can share with younger people.

FIGURE 16
Adulthood
Young adults often enjoy helping older adults.

 Reading Checkpoint   **What are the physical effects of aging?**

Section **3** **Assessment**

S 7.1.f, 7.5.e,
E-LA: Reading 7.1.0

Vocabulary Skill Identify Related Word Forms
Which word—*differentiate* or *differentiation*—correctly completes the following sentence?
During _____, cells in an embryo change and become specialized.

Reviewing Key Concepts

1. a. Identifying What three stages of development does a fertilized egg go through before birth?
   b. Describing How does differentiation change an embryo as it develops?
   c. Interpreting Diagrams Using Figure 10, predict which cell layer of the embryo will likely differentiate into brain cells.
2. a. Reviewing What is the general function of the membranes that surround a fetus?
   b. Explaining What are the specific functions of the placenta and the umbilical cord?
   c. Relating Cause and Effect Why is it dangerous for a pregnant woman to drink alcohol or to smoke cigarettes?

3. a. Listing What are the three stages of birth?
   b. Summarizing What happens during labor?
4. a. Identifying Identify two general kinds of change that occur between infancy and adulthood. Give an example of each.
   b. Describing Describe physical changes that happen in males and females during puberty.

Lab zone At-Home **Activity**

Understanding Risk Check the labels on nonprescription drugs that may be in your home to see if they carry warnings about use during pregnancy. Show the warnings to a family member, and explain why these labels are important.

The BIG Idea

Hormones regulate the functions of the female and male reproductive systems. The reproductive organs produce sex cells and enable fertilization and pregnancy to occur.

① The Endocrine System

Key Concepts S 7.5.b

- The endocrine system produces chemicals that control many of the body's daily activities as well as growth and development.

- The endocrine glands include the pituitary, hypothalamus, thyroid, parathyroid, adrenal, thymus, and pancreas. They also include ovaries in females and testes in males.

- Through negative feedback, when the amount of a particular hormone in the blood reaches a certain level, the endocrine system sends signals that stop the release of that hormone.

Key Terms
- endocrine gland • hormone • target cell
- hypothalamus • pituitary gland
- negative feedback

② The Male and Female Reproductive Systems

Key Concepts S 7.5.d

- Sexual reproduction involves the production of eggs by the female and sperm by the male. The egg and sperm join during fertilization.

- The male reproductive system produces sperm and the hormone testosterone. The structures include the testes, epididymis, scrotum, and penis.

- The female reproductive system produces eggs and nourishes a developing baby until birth. The structures include the ovaries, fallopian tubes, uterus, and vagina.

- During the menstrual cycle, an egg develops in an ovary. At the same time, the uterus prepares for the arrival of an embryo.

Key Terms
- egg • sperm • testis • testosterone
- scrotum • semen • penis • urethra
- ovary • estrogen • fallopian tube • uterus
- vagina • menstrual cycle • follicle
- ovulation • menstruation

③ Pregnancy, Development, and Birth

Key Concepts S 7.1.f, 7.5.e

- The zygote develops into an embryo and then into a fetus. Differentiaton leads to specialized cells, tissues, and organs.

- The membranes and other structures that form during development protect and nourish the developing embryo, and later the fetus.

- The birth of a baby takes place in three stages— labor, delivery, and afterbirth.

- The changes that take place between infancy and adulthood include physical changes, such as an increase in size and coordination, and mental changes, such as the ability to communicate and solve complex problems.

Key Terms
embryo
differentiation
fetus
amniotic sac
placenta
umbilical cord
adolescence
puberty

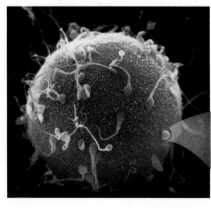

Review and Assessment

Target Reading Skill

Analyze Cause and Effect To review part of Section 3, copy and complete the graphic organizer to the right, which describes some effects of aging.

Cause

Aging

Effect

Muscle strength decreases.

a. _____

b. _____

c. _____

Reviewing Key Terms

Choose the letter of the best answer.

1. The structure that links the nervous system and the endocrine system is the
   a. thyroid gland.
   b. target cell.
   c. umbilical cord.
   d. hypothalamus.

2. The male sex cell is called the
   a. testis.
   b. sperm.
   c. egg.
   d. ovary.

3. The release of an egg from an ovary is known as
   a. ovulation.
   b. fertilization.
   c. menstruation.
   d. negative feedback.

4. In which stage of development does differentiation lead to specialized cells?
   a. unfertilized egg
   b. fertilized egg
   c. zygote
   d. embryo

5. The structure that transports materials between the fetus and the placenta is called the
   a. umbilical cord.
   b. scrotum.
   c. amniotic sac.
   d. ovary.

Complete the following sentences so that your answers clearly explain the key term.

6. The decrease in release of the hormone thyoxine occurs as a result of **negative feedback,** which is _____.

7. Sexual reproduction depends on **fertilization,** which is _____.

8. After an egg is fertilized and begins to develop, it becomes attached to the inner wall of the **uterus** which is _____.

9. **Differentiation** leads to the development of organ systems because _____.

10. The mother's body can provide nourishment to the fetus through the **placenta** which is _____.

Writing in Science

Creative Writing Imagine you just found out that you have an identical twin who was raised in another country. Write a description of what you think your twin would be like. Be sure to include information about what your twin looks like, his or her interests, and unique characteristics of your twin.

Video Assessment

Discovery Channel School
The Endocrine System and Reproduction

Review and Assessment

Checking Concepts

11. What is the function of the pituitary gland?

12. When enough thyroxine has been released into the blood, what signal is sent to the thyroid gland? How is that signal sent?

13. Identify two functions of the testes.

14. Describe the path of an unfertilized egg, beginning with its release and ending when it leaves the body.

15. What changes occur in the uterus during the menstrual cycle?

16. How does a zygote form? What happens to the zygote during the first four days after it forms?

17. How are the cell layers of an embryo related to the way the cells differentiate? Give an example.

18. Describe how a fetus receives food and oxygen and gets rid of wastes.

Thinking Critically

19. Inferring Study the diagram below. Then, suggest how the two hormones, glucagon and insulin, might work together to maintain homeostasis in the body.

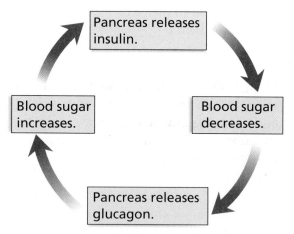

Pancreas releases insulin.

Blood sugar decreases.

Pancreas releases glucagon.

Blood sugar increases.

20. Calculating The average menstrual cycle is 28 days in length but can vary from 24 to 32 days. Ovulation usually occurs 14 days before the end of the cycle. How long after the start of a 24-day cycle will ovulation occur? A 32-day cycle?

21. Comparing and Contrasting Contrast the ways in which identical twins and fraternal twins form.

22. Applying Concepts Why is the umbilical cord not necessary after a baby is born?

Applying Skills

Use the table to answer Questions 23–25.

The data table below shows how the length of a developing baby changes during pregnancy.

Length of Fetus

Week of Pregnancy	Average Length (mm)	Week of Pregnancy	Average Length (mm)
4	4	24	300
8	30	28	350
12	75	32	410
16	180	36	450
20	250	38	500

23. Measuring Use a metric ruler to mark each length on a piece of paper. During which four-week period did the greatest increase in length occur?

24. Graphing Graph the data by plotting time on the *x*-axis and length on the *y*-axis.

25. Interpreting Data At the twelfth week, a developing baby measures about 75 mm. By which week has the fetus grown to four times that length? Six times that length?

Lab zone Standards Investigation

Performance Assessment You should now be ready to present your display. Be prepared to summarize what you learned from your research and to discuss the different parts of your model and their functions.

Choose the letter of the best answer.

1. You are riding your bike when a small child suddenly darts out in front of you. Which of your endocrine glands is most likely to release a hormone in response to this situation?

   A pituitary gland
   B adrenal glands
   C thyroid gland
   D parathyroid gland   **S 7.5.b**

2. In what part of the male reproductive system are sperm cells produced?

   A epididymis   B testes
   C penis   D urethra   **S 7.5.d**

3. On day 10 of a woman's menstrual cycle, the egg is most likely

   A moving through the fallopian tube.
   B in the uterus.
   C in the ovary.
   D leaving the body   **S 7.5.d**

Use the figure below to answer Question 4.

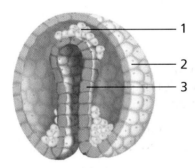

4. In the figure above, what process will begin to occur in areas 1, 2, and 3?

   A fertilization
   B ovulation
   C menstruation
   D differentiation   **S 7.1.f**

5. Which of the following is the correct sequence in the development of a fetus?

   A fertilization, zygote, embryo, differentiation
   B zygote, embryo, fertilization, differentiation
   C differentiation, fertilization, embryo, zygote
   D fertilization, embryo, zygote, differentiation
                                  S 7.1.f

Use the figure below to answer Question 6.

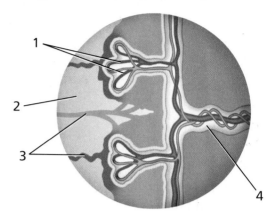

6. Which structure in the figure above connects the fetus to the placenta?

   A Structure 1
   B Structure 2
   C Structure 3
   D Structure 4   **S 7.5.e**

7. Which statement is true about the placenta?

   A The blood supplies must mix.
   B Carbon dioxide passes from the mother to the fetus.
   C Oxygen passes from the fetus to the mother.
   D Viruses can pass from the mother to the fetus.   **S 7.5.e**

Apply the BIG Idea

8. Identify the structures in the female and male reproductive systems that are also part of the endocrine system. Tell how the endocrine function and the reproductive function of each structure are related.   **S 7.5.d**

Chapter 13
Bones and Muscles

The BIG Idea

When muscles contract, they exert a force that pulls on a bone and makes it move. Many bones act as levers by rotating around a joint that acts as a fulcrum.

- What systems are in the human body, and what are their functions?
- What are the functions of the skeleton?
- What joints are examples of fulcrums for levers in the body?

Chapter 14
Circulation and Respiration

The BIG Idea

The circulatory and respiratory systems move blood through the body and enable the exchange of gases.

- What are the functions of the cardiovascular system?
- What are the components of the blood?
- What are the functions of the respiratory system?
- What are some diseases of the cardiovascular system?

Chapter 15
The Nervous System

The BIG Idea

Structures that enable the nervous system to function include the brain, spinal cord, neurons, and sense organs, such as the eye and ear.

- What are the functions of the nervous system?
- What are the structures and functions of the central nervous system?
- How do your eyes enable you to see?
- How do your senses of smell and taste work together?

Chapter 16
The Endocrine System and Reproduction

The BIG Idea

Hormones regulate the functions of the female and male reproductive systems. The reproductive organs produce sex cells and enable fertilization and pregnancy to occur.

- What are the structures and functions of the male and female reproductive systems?
- What are the changes that occur to the zygote, embryo, and fetus during development?

Unit 4 Assessment

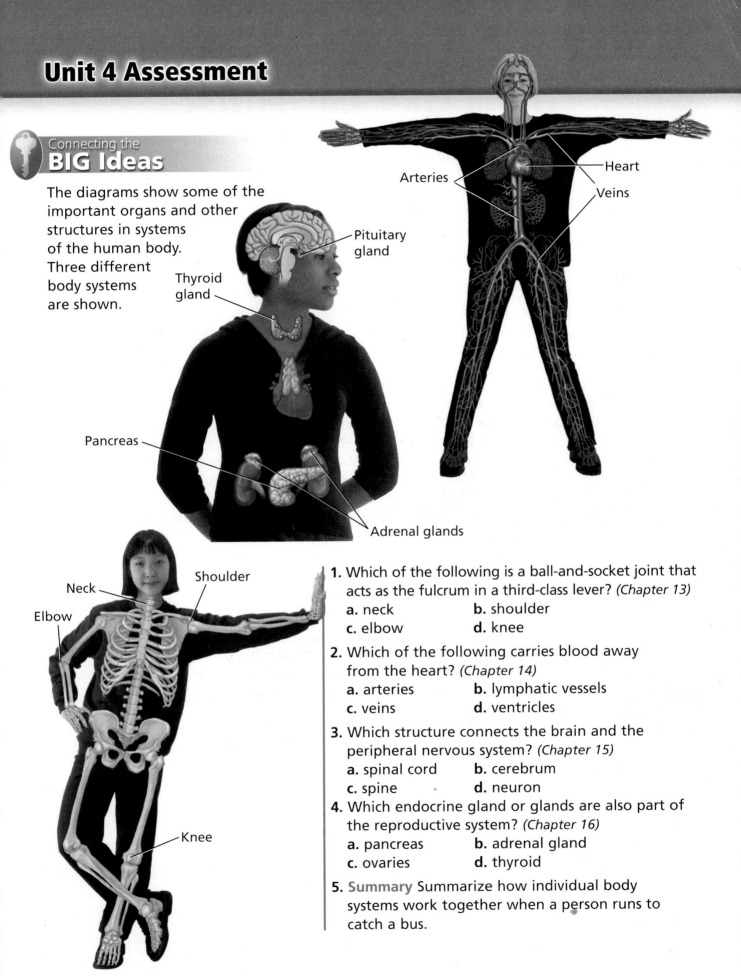

The diagrams show some of the important organs and other structures in systems of the human body. Three different body systems are shown.

Pituitary gland

Thyroid gland

Pancreas

Adrenal glands

Heart

Arteries

Veins

Neck

Shoulder

Elbow

Knee

1. Which of the following is a ball-and-socket joint that acts as the fulcrum in a third-class lever? *(Chapter 13)*
   a. neck   **b.** shoulder
   c. elbow   **d.** knee

2. Which of the following carries blood away from the heart? *(Chapter 14)*
   a. arteries   **b.** lymphatic vessels
   c. veins   **d.** ventricles

3. Which structure connects the brain and the peripheral nervous system? *(Chapter 15)*
   a. spinal cord   **b.** cerebrum
   c. spine   **d.** neuron

4. Which endocrine gland or glands are also part of the reproductive system? *(Chapter 16)*
   a. pancreas   **b.** adrenal gland
   c. ovaries   **d.** thyroid

5. **Summary** Summarize how individual body systems work together when a person runs to catch a bus.

Think Like a Scientist

Scientists have a particular way of looking at the world, or scientific habits of mind. Whenever you ask a question and explore possible answers, you use many of the same skills that scientists do. Some of these skills are described on this page.

Observing

When you use one or more of your five senses to gather information about the world, you are **observing.** Hearing a dog bark, counting twelve green seeds, and smelling smoke are all observations. To increase the power of their senses, scientists sometimes use microscopes, telescopes, or other instruments that help them make more detailed observations.

An observation must be an accurate report of what your senses detect. It is important to keep careful records of your observations in science class by writing or drawing in a notebook. The information collected through observations is called evidence, or data.

Inferring

When you interpret an observation, you are **inferring,** or making an inference. For example, if you hear your dog barking, you may infer that someone is at your front door. To make this inference, you combine the evidence— the barking dog—and your experience or knowledge—you know that your dog barks when strangers approach—to reach a logical conclusion.

Notice that an inference is not a fact; it is only one of many possible interpretations for an observation. For example, your dog may be barking because it wants to go for a walk. An inference may turn out to be incorrect even if it is based on accurate observations and logical reasoning. The only way to find out if an inference is correct is to investigate further.

Predicting

When you listen to the weather forecast, you hear many predictions about the next day's weather—what the temperature will be, whether it will rain, and how windy it will be. Weather forecasters use observations and knowledge of weather patterns to predict the weather. The skill of **predicting** involves making an inference about a future event based on current evidence or past experience.

Because a prediction is an inference, it may prove to be false. In science class, you can test some of your predictions by doing experiments. For example, suppose you predict that larger paper airplanes can fly farther than smaller airplanes. How could you test your prediction?

Activity

Use the photograph to answer the questions below.

Observing Look closely at the photograph. List at least three observations.

Inferring Use your observations to make an inference about what has happened. What experience or knowledge did you use to make the inference?

Predicting Predict what will happen next. On what evidence or experience do you base your prediction?

Classifying

Could you imagine searching for a book in the library if the books were shelved in no particular order? Your trip to the library would be an all-day event! Luckily, librarians group together books on similar topics or by the same author. Grouping together items that are alike in some way is called **classifying.** You can classify items in many ways: by size, by shape, by use, and by other important characteristics.

Like librarians, scientists use the skill of classifying to organize information and objects. When things are sorted into groups, the relationships among them become easier to understand.

> **Activity**
>
> Classify the objects in the photograph into two groups based on any characteristic you choose. Then use another characteristic to classify the objects into three groups.

> **Activity**
>
> This student is using a model to demonstrate what causes day and night on Earth. What do the flashlight and the tennis ball in the model represent?

Making Models

Have you ever drawn a picture to help someone understand what you were saying? Such a drawing is one type of model. A model is a picture, diagram, computer image, or other representation of a complex object or process. **Making models** helps people understand things that they cannot observe directly.

Scientists often use models to represent things that are either very large or very small, such as the planets in the solar system, or the parts of a cell. Such models are physical models—drawings or three-dimensional structures that look like the real thing. Other models are mental models—mathematical equations or words that describe how something works.

Communicating

Whenever you talk on the phone, write a report, or listen to your teacher at school, you are communicating. **Communicating** is the process of sharing ideas and information with other people. Communicating effectively requires many skills, including writing, reading, speaking, listening, and making models.

Scientists communicate to share results, information, and opinions. Scientists often communicate about their work in journals, over the telephone, in letters, and on the Internet.

They also attend scientific meetings where they share their ideas with one another in person.

> **Activity**
>
> On a sheet of paper, write out clear, detailed directions for tying your shoe. Then exchange directions with a partner. Follow your partner's directions exactly. How successful were you at tying your shoe? How could your partner have communicated more clearly?

Making Measurements

By measuring, scientists can express their observations more precisely and communicate more information about what they observe.

Measuring in SI

The standard system of measurement used by scientists around the world is known as the International System of Units, which is abbreviated as SI (**Système International d'Unités,** in French). SI units are easy to use because they are based on multiples of 10. Each unit is ten times larger than the next smallest unit and one tenth the size of the next largest unit. The table lists the prefixes used to name the most common SI units.

Common SI Prefixes		
Prefix	**Symbol**	**Meaning**
kilo-	k	1,000
hecto-	h	100
deka-	da	10
deci-	d	0.1 (one tenth)
centi-	c	0.01 (one hundredth)
milli-	m	0.001 (one thousandth)

Length To measure length, or the distance between two points, the unit of measure is the **meter (m).** The distance from the floor to a doorknob is approximately one meter. Long distances, such as the distance between two cities, are measured in kilometers (km). Small lengths are measured in centimeters (cm) or millimeters (mm). Scientists use metric rulers and meter sticks to measure length.

Common Conversions	
1 km	= 1,000 m
1 m	= 100 cm
1 m	= 1,000 mm
1 cm	= 10 mm

Activity

The larger lines on the metric ruler in the picture show centimeter divisions, while the smaller, unnumbered lines show millimeter divisions. How many centimeters long is the shell? How many millimeters long is it?

Liquid Volume To measure the volume of a liquid, or the amount of space it takes up, you will use a unit of measure known as the **liter (L).** One liter is the approximate volume of a medium-size carton of milk. Smaller volumes are measured in milliliters (mL). Scientists use graduated cylinders to measure liquid volume.

Activity

The graduated cylinder in the picture is marked in milliliter divisions. Notice that the water in the cylinder has a curved surface. This curved surface is called the *meniscus.* To measure the volume, you must read the level at the lowest point of the meniscus. What is the volume of water in this graduated cylinder?

Common Conversion
1 L = 1,000 mL

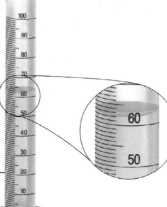

Mass To measure mass, or the amount of matter in an object, you will use a unit of measure known as the **gram (g).** One gram is approximately the mass of a paper clip. Larger masses are measured in kilograms (kg). Scientists use a balance to find the mass of an object.

Common Conversion

1 kg = 1,000 g

Activity

The mass of the potato in the picture is measured in kilograms. What is the mass of the potato? Suppose a recipe for potato salad called for one kilogram of potatoes. About how many potatoes would you need?

Temperature To measure the temperature of a substance, you will use the **Celsius scale.** Temperature is measured in degrees Celsius (°C) using a Celsius thermometer. Water freezes at 0°C and boils at 100°C.

Time The unit scientists use to measure time is the **second (s).**

Activity

What is the temperature of the liquid in degrees Celsius?

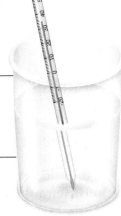

Converting SI Units

To use the SI system, you must know how to convert between units. Converting from one unit to another involves the skill of **calculating,** or using mathematical operations. Converting between SI units is similar to converting between dollars and dimes because both systems are based on multiples of ten.

Suppose you want to convert a length of 80 centimeters to meters. Follow these steps to convert between units.

1. Begin by writing down the measurement you want to convert—in this example, 80 centimeters.

2. Write a conversion factor that represents the relationship between the two units you are converting. In this example, the relationship is 1 meter = 100 centimeters. Write this conversion factor as a fraction, making sure to place the units you are converting from (centimeters, in this example) in the denominator.

3. Multiply the measurement you want to convert by the fraction. When you do this, the units in the first measurement will cancel out with the units in the denominator. Your answer will be in the units you are converting to (meters, in this example).

Example

80 centimeters = ■ meters

$$80 \text{ centimeters} \times \frac{1 \text{ meter}}{100 \text{ centimeters}} = \frac{80 \text{ meters}}{100}$$

$$= 0.8 \text{ meters}$$

Activity

Convert between the following units.
1. 600 millimeters = ■ meters
2. 0.35 liters = ■ milliliters
3. 1,050 grams = ■ kilograms

Conducting a Scientific Investigation

In some ways, scientists are like detectives, piecing together clues to learn about a process or event. One way that scientists gather clues is by carrying out experiments. An experiment tests an idea in a careful, orderly manner. Although experiments do not all follow the same steps in the same order, many follow a pattern similar to the one described here.

Posing Questions

Experiments begin by asking a scientific question. A scientific question is one that can be answered by gathering evidence. For example, the question "Which freezes faster—fresh water or salt water?" is a scientific question because you can carry out an investigation and gather information to answer the question.

Developing a Hypothesis

The next step is to form a hypothesis. A **hypothesis** is a possible explanation for a set of observations or answer to a scientific question. A hypothesis may incorporate observations, concepts, principles, and theories about the natural world. Hypotheses lead to predictions that can be tested. A prediction can be worded as an *If . . . then . . .* statement. For example, a prediction might be *"If I add salt to fresh water, then the water will take longer to freeze."* A prediction worded this way serves as a rough outline of the experiment you should perform.

Designing an Experiment

Next you need to plan a way to test your hypothesis. Your plan should be written out as a step-by-step procedure and should describe the observations or measurements you will make.

Two important steps involved in designing an experiment are controlling variables and forming operational definitions.

Controlling Variables In a well-designed experiment, you need to keep all variables the same except for one. A **variable** is any factor that can change in an experiment. The factor that you change is called the **manipulated variable**. In this experiment, the manipulated variable is the amount of salt added to the water. Other factors, such as the amount of water or the starting temperature, are kept constant.

The factor that changes as a result of the manipulated variable is called the **responding variable.** The responding variable is what you measure or observe to obtain your results. In this experiment, the responding variable is how long the water takes to freeze.

An experiment in which all factors except one are kept constant is called a **controlled experiment.** Most controlled experiments include a test called the control. In this experiment, Container 3 is the control. Because no salt is added to Container 3, you can compare the results from the other containers to it. Any difference in results must be due to the addition of salt alone.

Forming Operational Definitions Another important aspect of a well-designed experiment is having clear operational definitions. An **operational definition** is a statement that describes how a particular variable is to be measured or how a term is to be defined. For example, in this experiment, how will you determine if the water has frozen? You might decide to insert a stick in each container at the start of the experiment. Your operational definition of "frozen" would be the time at which the stick can no longer move.

Experimental Procedure
1. Fill 3 containers with 300 milliliters of cold tap water.
2. Add 10 grams of salt to Container 1; stir. Add 20 grams of salt to Container 2; stir. Add no salt to Container 3.
3. Place the 3 containers in a freezer.
4. Check the containers every 15 minutes. Record your observations.

Interpreting Data

The observations and measurements you make in an experiment are called **data.** At the end of an experiment, you need to analyze the data to look for any patterns or trends. Patterns often become clear if you organize your data in a data table or graph. Then think through what the data reveal. Do they support your hypothesis? Do they point out a flaw in your experiment? Do you need to collect more data?

Drawing Conclusions

A **conclusion** is a statement that sums up what you have learned from an experiment. When you draw a conclusion, you need to decide whether the data you collected support your hypothesis or not. You may need to repeat an experiment several times before you can draw any conclusions from it. Conclusions often lead you to pose new questions and plan new experiments to answer them.

Activity

Is a ball's bounce affected by the height from which it is dropped? Using the steps just described, plan a controlled experiment to investigate this problem.

Technology Design Skills

Engineers are people who use scientific and technological knowledge to solve practical problems. To design new products, engineers usually follow the process described here, even though they may not follow these steps in the exact order. As you read the steps, think about how you might apply them in technology labs.

Identify a Need

Before engineers begin designing a new product, they must first identify the need they are trying to meet. For example, suppose you are a member of a design team in a company that makes toys. Your team has identified a need: a toy boat that is inexpensive and easy to assemble.

Research the Problem

Engineers often begin by gathering information that will help them with their new design. This research may include finding articles in books, magazines, or on the Internet. It may also include talking to other engineers who have solved similar problems. Engineers often perform experiments related to the product they want to design.

For your toy boat, you could look at toys that are similar to the one you want to design. You might do research on the Internet. You could also test some materials to see whether they will work well in a toy boat.

Drawing for a boat design ▼

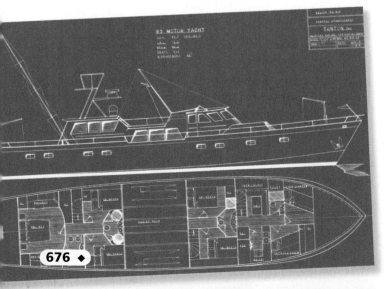

Design a Solution

Research gives engineers information that helps them design a product. When engineers design new products, they usually work in teams.

Generating Ideas Often design teams hold brainstorming meetings in which any team member can contribute ideas. **Brainstorming** is a creative process in which one team member's suggestions often spark ideas in other group members. Brainstorming can lead to new approaches to solving a design problem.

Evaluating Constraints During brainstorming, a design team will often come up with several possible designs. The team must then evaluate each one.

As part of their evaluation, engineers consider constraints. **Constraints** are factors that limit or restrict a product design. Physical characteristics, such as the properties of materials used to make your toy boat, are constraints. Money and time are also constraints. If the materials in a product cost a lot, or if the product takes a long time to make, the design may be impractical.

Making Trade-offs Design teams usually need to make trade-offs. In a **trade-off,** engineers give up one benefit of a proposed design in order to obtain another. In designing your toy boat, you will have to make trade-offs. For example, suppose one material is sturdy but not fully waterproof. Another material is more waterproof, but breakable. You may decide to give up the benefit of sturdiness in order to obtain the benefit of waterproofing.

Build and Evaluate a Prototype

Once the team has chosen a design plan, the engineers build a prototype of the product. A **prototype** is a working model used to test a design. Engineers evaluate the prototype to see whether it works well, is easy to operate, is safe to use, and holds up to repeated use.

Think of your toy boat. What would the prototype be like? Of what materials would it be made? How would you test it?

Troubleshoot and Redesign

Few prototypes work perfectly, which is why they need to be tested. Once a design team has tested a prototype, the members analyze the results and identify any problems. The team then tries to **troubleshoot,** or fix the design problems. For example, if your toy boat leaks or wobbles, the boat should be redesigned to eliminate those problems.

Communicate the Solution

A team needs to communicate the final design to the people who will manufacture and use the product. To do this, teams may use sketches, detailed drawings, computer simulations, and word descriptions.

Activity

You can use the technology design process to design and build a toy boat.

Research and Investigate

1. Visit the library or go online to research toy boats.

2. Investigate how a toy boat can be powered, including wind, rubber bands, or baking soda and vinegar.

3. Brainstorm materials, shapes, and steering for your boat.

Design and Build

4. Based on your research, design a toy boat that
   - is made of readily available materials
   - is no larger than 15 cm long and 10 cm wide
   - includes a power system, a rudder, and an area for cargo
   - travels 2 meters in a straight line carrying a load of 20 pennies

5. Sketch your design and write a step-by-step plan for building your boat. After your teacher approves your plan, build your boat.

Evaluate and Redesign

6. Test your boat, evaluate the results, and troubleshoot any problems.

7. Based on your evaluation, redesign your toy boat so it performs better.

Creating Data Tables and Graphs

How can you make sense of the data in a science experiment? The first step is to organize the data to help you understand them. Data tables and graphs are helpful tools for organizing data.

Data Tables

You have gathered your materials and set up your experiment. But before you start, you need to plan a way to record what happens during the experiment. By creating a data table, you can record your observations and measurements in an orderly way.

Suppose, for example, that a scientist conducted an experiment to find out how many Calories people of different body masses burn while doing various activities. The data table shows the results.

Notice in this data table that the manipulated variable (body mass) is the heading of one column. The responding variable (for

Calories Burned in 30 Minutes			
Body Mass	Experiment 1: Bicycling	Experiment 2: Playing Basketball	Experiment 3: Watching Television
30 kg	60 Calories	120 Calories	21 Calories
40 kg	77 Calories	164 Calories	27 Calories
50 kg	95 Calories	206 Calories	33 Calories
60 kg	114 Calories	248 Calories	38 Calories

Experiment 1, the number of Calories burned while bicycling) is the heading of the next column. Additional columns were added for related experiments.

Bar Graphs

To compare how many Calories a person burns doing various activities, you could create a bar graph. A bar graph is used to display data in a number of separate, or distinct, categories. In this example, bicycling, playing basketball, and watching television are the three categories.

To create a bar graph, follow these steps.

1. On graph paper, draw a horizontal, or *x*-, axis and a vertical, or *y*-, axis.

2. Write the names of the categories to be graphed along the horizontal axis. Include an overall label for the axis as well.

3. Label the vertical axis with the name of the responding variable. Include units of measurement. Then create a scale along the axis by marking off equally spaced numbers that cover the range of the data collected.

4. For each category, draw a solid bar using the scale on the vertical axis to determine the height. Make all the bars the same width.

5. Add a title that describes the graph.

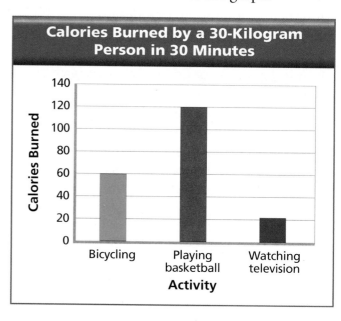

Line Graphs

To see whether a relationship exists between body mass and the number of Calories burned while bicycling, you could create a line graph. A line graph is used to display data that show how one variable (the responding variable) changes in response to another variable (the manipulated variable). You can use a line graph when your manipulated variable is **continuous,** that is, when there are other points between the ones that you tested. In this example, body mass is a continuous variable because there are other body masses between 30 and 40 kilograms (for example, 31 kilograms). Time is another example of a continuous variable.

Line graphs are powerful tools because they allow you to estimate values for conditions that you did not test in the experiment. For example, you can use the line graph to estimate that a 35-kilogram person would burn 68 Calories while bicycling.

To create a line graph, follow these steps.

1. On graph paper, draw a horizontal, or *x*-, axis and a vertical, or *y*-, axis.

2. Label the horizontal axis with the name of the manipulated variable. Label the vertical axis with the name of the responding variable. Include units of measurement.

3. Create a scale on each axis by marking off equally spaced numbers that cover the range of the data collected.

4. Plot a point on the graph for each piece of data. In the line graph above, the dotted lines show how to plot the first data point (30 kilograms and 60 Calories). Follow an imaginary vertical line extending up from the horizontal axis at the 30-kilogram mark. Then follow an imaginary horizontal line extending across from the vertical axis at the 60-Calorie mark. Plot the point where the two lines intersect.

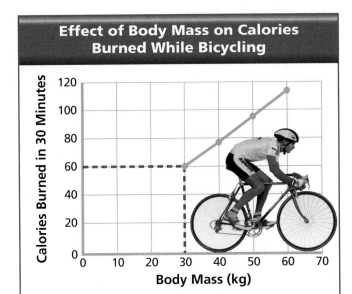

Effect of Body Mass on Calories Burned While Bicycling

5. Connect the plotted points with a solid line. (In some cases, it may be more appropriate to draw a line that shows the general trend of the plotted points. In those cases, some of the points may fall above or below the line. Also, not all graphs are linear. It may be more appropriate to draw a curve to connect the points.)

6. Add a title that identifies the variables or relationship in the graph.

Activity

Create line graphs to display the data from Experiment 2 and Experiment 3 in the data table.

Activity

You read in the newspaper that a total of 4 centimeters of rain fell in your area in June, 2.5 centimeters fell in July, and 1.5 centimeters fell in August. What type of graph would you use to display these data? Use graph paper to create the graph.

Circle Graphs

Like bar graphs, circle graphs can be used to display data in a number of separate categories. Unlike bar graphs, however, circle graphs can only be used when you have data for *all* the categories that make up a given topic. A circle graph is sometimes called a pie chart. The pie represents the entire topic, while the slices represent the individual categories. The size of a slice indicates what percentage of the whole a particular category makes up.

The data table below shows the results of a survey in which 24 teenagers were asked to identify their favorite sport. The data were then used to create the circle graph at the right.

Favorite Sports	
Sport	Students
Soccer	8
Basketball	6
Bicycling	6
Swimming	4

To create a circle graph, follow these steps.

1. Use a compass to draw a circle. Mark the center with a point. Then draw a line from the center point to the top of the circle.

2. Determine the size of each "slice" by setting up a proportion where x equals the number of degrees in a slice. (*Note:* A circle contains 360 degrees.) For example, to find the number of degrees in the "soccer" slice, set up the following proportion:

$$\frac{\text{Students who prefer soccer}}{\text{Total number of students}} = \frac{x}{\text{Total number of degrees in a circle}}$$

$$\frac{8}{24} = \frac{x}{360}$$

Cross-multiply and solve for x.

$$24x = 8 \times 360$$
$$x = 120$$

The "soccer" slice should contain 120 degrees.

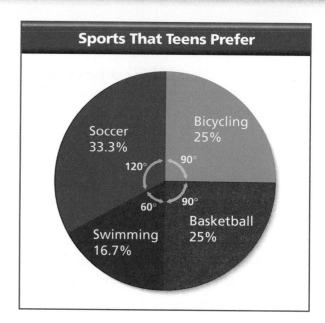

Sports That Teens Prefer

Soccer 33.3%
Bicycling 25%
120°
90°
60°
90°
Swimming 16.7%
Basketball 25%

3. Use a protractor to measure the angle of the first slice, using the line you drew to the top of the circle as the 0° line. Draw a line from the center of the circle to the edge for the angle you measured.

4. Continue around the circle by measuring the size of each slice with the protractor. Start measuring from the edge of the previous slice so the wedges do not overlap. When you are done, the entire circle should be filled in.

5. Determine the percentage of the whole circle that each slice represents. To do this, divide the number of degrees in a slice by the total number of degrees in a circle (360), and multiply by 100%. For the "soccer" slice, you can find the percentage as follows:

$$\frac{120}{360} \times 100\% = 33.3\%$$

6. Use a different color for each slice. Label each slice with the category and with the percentage of the whole it represents.

7. Add a title to the circle graph.

Activity

In a class of 28 students, 12 students take the bus to school, 10 students walk, and 6 students ride their bicycles. Create a circle graph to display these data.

Math Review

Scientists use math to organize, analyze, and present data.
This appendix will help you review some basic math skills.

Mean, Median, and Mode

The **mean** is the average, or the sum of the data divided by the number of data items. The middle number in a set of ordered data is called the **median**. The **mode** is the number that appears most often in a set of data.

Example

A scientist counted the number of distinct songs sung by seven different male birds and collected the data shown below.

Male Bird Songs							
Bird	A	B	C	D	E	F	G
Number of Songs	36	29	40	35	28	36	27

To determine the mean number of songs, add the total number of songs and divide by the number of data items—in this case, the number of male birds.

$$\text{Mean} = \frac{231}{7} = 33 \text{ songs}$$

To find the median number of songs, arrange the data in numerical order and find the number in the middle of the series.

27 28 29 35 36 36 40

The number in the middle is 35, so the median number of songs is 35.

The mode is the value that appears most frequently. In the data, 36 appears twice, while each other item appears only once. Therefore, 36 songs is the mode.

Practice

Find out how many minutes it takes each student in your class to get to school. Then find the mean, median, and mode for the data.

Probability

Probability is the chance that an event will occur. Probability can be expressed as a ratio, a fraction, or a percentage. For example, when you flip a coin, the probability that the coin will land heads up is 1 in 2, or $\frac{1}{2}$, or 50 percent.

The probability that an event will happen can be expressed in the following formula.

$$P(\text{event}) = \frac{\text{Number of times the event can occur}}{\text{Total number of possible events}}$$

Example

A paper bag contains 25 blue marbles, 5 green marbles, 5 orange marbles, and 15 yellow marbles. If you close your eyes and pick a marble from the bag, what is the probability that it will be yellow?

$$P(\text{yellow marbles}) = \frac{15 \text{ yellow marbles}}{50 \text{ marbles total}}$$

$$P = \frac{15}{50}, \text{ or } \frac{3}{10}, \text{ or } 30\%$$

Practice

Each side of a cube has a letter on it. Two sides have *A*, three sides have *B*, and one side has *C*. If you roll the cube, what is the probability that *A* will land on top?

Area

The **area** of a surface is the number of square units that cover it. The front cover of your textbook has an area of about 600 cm².

Area of a Rectangle and a Square To find the area of a rectangle, multiply its length times its width. The formula for the area of a rectangle is

$$A = \ell \times w, \text{ or } A = \ell w$$

Since all four sides of a square have the same length, the area of a square is the length of one side multiplied by itself, or squared.

$$A = s \times s, \text{ or } A = s^2$$

Example

A scientist is studying the plants in a field that measures 75 m × 45 m. What is the area of the field?

$$A = \ell \times w$$
$$A = 75 \text{ m} \times 45 \text{ m}$$
$$A = 3,375 \text{ m}^2$$

Area of a Circle The formula for the area of a circle is

$$A = \pi \times r \times r, \text{ or } A = \pi r^2$$

The length of the radius is represented by r, and the value of π is approximately $\frac{22}{7}$.

Example

Find the area of a circle with a radius of 14 cm.

$$A = \pi r^2$$
$$A = 14 \times 14 \times \frac{22}{7}$$
$$A = 616 \text{ cm}^2$$

Practice

Find the area of a circle that has a radius of 21 m.

Circumference

The distance around a circle is called the **circumference**. The formula for finding the circumference of a circle is

$$C = 2 \times \pi \times r, \text{ or } C = 2\pi r$$

Example

The radius of a circle is 35 cm. What is its circumference?

$$C = 2\pi r$$
$$C = 2 \times 35 \times \frac{22}{7}$$
$$C = 220 \text{ cm}$$

Practice

What is the circumference of a circle with a radius of 28 m?

Volume

The volume of an object is the number of cubic units it contains. The volume of a wastebasket, for example, might be about 26,000 cm³.

Volume of a Rectangular Object To find the volume of a rectangular object, multiply the object's length times its width times its height.

$$V = \ell \times w \times h, \text{ or } V = \ell w h$$

Example

Find the volume of a box with length 24 cm, width 12 cm, and height 9 cm.

$$V = \ell w h$$
$$V = 24 \text{ cm} \times 12 \text{ cm} \times 9 \text{ cm}$$
$$V = 2,592 \text{ cm}^3$$

Practice

What is the volume of a rectangular object with length 17 cm, width 11 cm, and height 6 cm?

Fractions

A **fraction** is a way to express a part of a whole. In the fraction $\frac{4}{7}$, 4 is the numerator and 7 is the denominator.

Adding and Subtracting Fractions To add or subtract two or more fractions that have a common denominator, first add or subtract the numerators. Then write the sum or difference over the common denominator.

To find the sum or difference of fractions with different denominators, first find the least common multiple of the denominators. This is known as the least common denominator. Then convert each fraction to equivalent fractions with the least common denominator. Add or subtract the numerators. Then write the sum or difference over the common denominator.

> **Example**
>
> $$\frac{5}{6} - \frac{3}{4} = \frac{10}{12} - \frac{9}{12} = \frac{10 - 9}{12} = \frac{1}{12}$$

Multiplying Fractions To multiply two fractions, first multiply the two numerators, then multiply the two denominators.

> **Example**
>
> $$\frac{5}{6} \times \frac{2}{3} = \frac{5 \times 2}{6 \times 3} = \frac{10}{18} = \frac{5}{9}$$

Dividing Fractions Dividing by a fraction is the same as multiplying by its reciprocal. Reciprocals are numbers whose numerators and denominators have been switched. To divide one fraction by another, first invert the fraction you are dividing by—in other words, turn it upside down. Then multiply the two fractions.

> **Example**
>
> $$\frac{2}{5} \div \frac{7}{8} = \frac{2}{5} \times \frac{8}{7} = \frac{2 \times 8}{5 \times 7} = \frac{16}{35}$$

> **Practice**
>
> Solve the following: $\frac{3}{7} \div \frac{4}{5}$.

Decimals

Fractions whose denominators are 10, 100, or some other power of 10 are often expressed as decimals. For example, the fraction $\frac{9}{10}$ can be expressed as the decimal 0.9, and the fraction $\frac{7}{100}$ can be written as 0.07.

Adding and Subtracting With Decimals To add or subtract decimals, line up the decimal points before you carry out the operation.

> **Example**
>
> $$\begin{array}{r} 27.4 \\ + 6.19 \\ \hline 33.59 \end{array} \qquad \begin{array}{r} 278.635 \\ - 191.4 \\ \hline 87.235 \end{array}$$

Multiplying With Decimals When you multiply two numbers with decimals, the number of decimal places in the product is equal to the total number of decimal places in each number being multiplied.

> **Example**
>
> $$\begin{array}{r} 46.2 \text{ (one decimal place)} \\ \times\ 2.37 \text{ (two decimal places)} \\ \hline 109.494 \text{ (three decimal places)} \end{array}$$

Dividing With Decimals To divide a decimal by a whole number, put the decimal point in the quotient above the decimal point in the dividend.

> **Example**
>
> $$15.5 \div 5$$
> $$\begin{array}{r} 3.1 \\ 5{\overline{)15.5}} \end{array}$$

To divide a decimal by a decimal, you need to rewrite the divisor as a whole number. Do this by multiplying both the divisor and dividend by the same multiple of 10.

> **Example**
>
> $$1.68 \div 4.2 = 1.68 \div 4.2$$
> $$\begin{array}{r} 0.4 \\ 42{\overline{)16.8}} \end{array}$$

> **Practice**
>
> Multiply 6.21 by 8.5.

Ratio and Proportion

A **ratio** compares two numbers by division. For example, suppose a scientist counts 800 wolves and 1,200 moose on an island. The ratio of wolves to moose can be written as a fraction, $\frac{800}{1,200}$, which can be reduced to $\frac{2}{3}$. The same ratio can also be expressed as 2 to 3 or 2 : 3.

A **proportion** is a mathematical sentence saying that two ratios are equivalent. For example, a proportion could state that $\frac{800 \text{ wolves}}{1,200 \text{ moose}} = \frac{2 \text{ wolves}}{3 \text{ moose}}$. You can sometimes set up a proportion to determine or estimate an unknown quantity. For example, suppose a scientist counts 25 beetles in an area of 10 square meters. The scientist wants to estimate the number of beetles in 100 square meters.

Example

1. Express the relationship between beetles and area as a ratio: $\frac{25}{10}$, simplified to $\frac{5}{2}$.

2. Set up a proportion, with x representing the number of beetles. The proportion can be stated as $\frac{5}{2} = \frac{x}{100}$.

3. Begin by cross-multiplying. In other words, multiply each fraction's numerator by the other fraction's denominator.

   5 × 100 = 2 × *x*, or 500 = 2*x*

4. To find the value of x, divide both sides by 2. The result is 250, or 250 beetles in 100 square meters.

Practice

Find the value of x in the following proportion: $\frac{6}{7} = \frac{x}{49}$.

Percentage

A **percentage** is a ratio that compares a number to 100. For example, there are 37 granite rocks in a collection that consists of 100 rocks. The ratio $\frac{37}{100}$ can be written as 37%. Granite rocks make up 37% of the rock collection.

You can calculate percentages of numbers other than 100 by setting up a proportion.

Example

Rain falls on 9 days out of 30 in June. What percentage of the days in June were rainy?

$$\frac{9 \text{ days}}{30 \text{ days}} = \frac{d\%}{100\%}$$

To find the value of d, begin by cross-multiplying, as for any proportion:

9 × 100 = 30 × *d* $d = \frac{900}{30}$ *d* = 30

Practice

There are 300 marbles in a jar, and 42 of those marbles are blue. What percentage of the marbles are blue?

Significant Figures

The **precision** of a measurement depends on the instrument you use to take the measurement. For example, if the smallest unit on the ruler is millimeters, then the most precise measurement you can make will be in millimeters.

The sum or difference of measurements can only be as precise as the least precise measurement being added or subtracted. Round your answer so that it has the same number of digits after the decimal as the least precise measurement. Round up if the last digit is 5 or more, and round down if the last digit is 4 or less.

Example

Subtract a temperature of 5.2°C from the temperature 75.46°C.

75.46 − 5.2 = 70.26

5.2 has the fewest digits after the decimal, so it is the least precise measurement. Since the last digit of the answer is 6, round up to 3. The most precise difference between the measurements is 70.3°C.

Practice

Add 26.4 m to 8.37 m. Round your answer according to the precision of the measurements.

Significant figures are the number of nonzero digits in a measurement. Zeroes between nonzero digits are also significant. For example, the measurements 12,500 L, 0.125 cm, and 2.05 kg all have three significant figures. When you multiply and divide measurements, the one with the fewest significant figures determines the number of significant figures in your answer.

Example

Multiply 110 g by 5.75 g.

110 × 5.75 = 632.5

Because 110 has only two significant figures, round the answer to 630 g.

Scientific Notation

A **factor** is a number that divides into another number with no remainder. In the example, the number 3 is used as a factor four times.

An **exponent** tells how many times a number is used as a factor. For example, $3 \times 3 \times 3 \times 3$ can be written as 3^4. The exponent 4 indicates that the number 3 is used as a factor four times. Another way of expressing this is to say that 81 is equal to 3 to the fourth power.

Example

$$3^4 = 3 \times 3 \times 3 \times 3 = 81$$

Scientific notation uses exponents and powers of ten to write very large or very small numbers in shorter form. When you write a number in scientific notation, you write the number as two factors. The first factor is any number between 1 and 10. The second factor is a power of 10, such as 10^3 or 10^6.

Example

The average distance between the planet Mercury and the sun is 58,000,000 km. To write the first factor in scientific notation, insert a decimal point in the original number so that you have a number between 1 and 10. In the case of 58,000,000, the number is 5.8.

To determine the power of 10, count the number of places that the decimal point moved. In this case, it moved 7 places.

$58{,}000{,}000 \text{ km} = 5.8 \times 10^7 \text{ km}$

Practice

Express 6,590,000 in scientific notation.

Safety Symbols

These symbols warn of possible dangers in the laboratory and remind you to work carefully.

 Safety Goggles Wear safety goggles to protect your eyes in any activity involving chemicals, flames or heating, or glassware.

 Lab Apron Wear a laboratory apron to protect your skin and clothing from damage.

 Breakage Handle breakable materials, such as glassware, with care. Do not touch broken glassware.

 Heat-Resistant Gloves Use an oven mitt or other hand protection when handling hot materials such as hot plates or hot glassware.

 Plastic Gloves Wear disposable plastic gloves when working with organisms and harmful chemicals. Keep your hands away from your face, and dispose of the gloves according to your teacher's instructions.

 Heating Use a clamp or tongs to pick up hot glassware. Do not touch hot objects with your bare hands.

 Flames Before you work with flames, tie back loose hair and clothing. Follow instructions from your teacher about lighting and extinguishing flames.

 No Flames When using flammable materials, make sure there are no flames, sparks, or other exposed heat sources present.

 Corrosive Chemical Avoid getting acid or other corrosive chemicals on your skin or clothing or in your eyes. Do not inhale the vapors. Wash your hands after the activity.

 Poison Do not let any poisonous chemical come into contact with your skin, and do not inhale its vapors. Wash your hands when you are finished with the activity.

 Fumes Work in a ventilated area when harmful vapors may be involved. Avoid inhaling vapors directly. Only test an odor when directed to do so by your teacher, and use a wafting motion to direct the vapor toward your nose.

 Sharp Object Scissors, scalpels, knives, needles, pins, and tacks can cut your skin. Always direct a sharp edge or point away from yourself and others.

 Animal Safety Treat live or preserved animals or animal parts with care to avoid harming the animals or yourself. Wash your hands when you are finished with the activity.

 Plant Safety Handle plants only as directed by your teacher. If you are allergic to certain plants, tell your teacher; do not do an activity involving those plants. Avoid touching harmful plants such as poison ivy. Wash your hands when you are finished with the activity.

 Electric Shock To avoid electric shock, never use electrical equipment around water, or when the equipment is wet or your hands are wet. Be sure cords are untangled and cannot trip anyone. Unplug equipment not in use.

 Physical Safety When an experiment involves physical activity, avoid injuring yourself or others. Alert your teacher if there is any reason you should not participate.

 Disposal Dispose of chemicals and other laboratory materials safely. Follow the instructions from your teacher.

 Hand Washing Wash your hands thoroughly when finished with the activity. Use soap and warm water. Rinse well.

 General Safety Awareness When this symbol appears, follow the instructions provided. When you are asked to develop your own procedure in a lab, have your teacher approve your plan before you go further.

Science Safety Rules

General Precautions

Follow all instructions. Never perform activities without the approval and supervision of your teacher. Do not engage in horseplay. Never eat or drink in the laboratory. Keep work areas clean and uncluttered.

Dress Code

Wear safety goggles whenever you work with chemicals, glassware, heat sources such as burners, or any substance that might get into your eyes. If you wear contact lenses, notify your teacher.

Wear a lab apron or coat whenever you work with corrosive chemicals or substances that can stain. Tie back long hair. Remove or tie back any article of clothing or jewelry that can hang down and touch chemicals, flames, or equipment. Roll up long sleeves. Never wear open shoes or sandals.

First Aid

Report all accidents, injuries, or fires to your teacher, no matter how minor. Be aware of the location of the first-aid kit, emergency equipment such as the fire extinguisher and fire blanket, and the nearest telephone. Know whom to contact in an emergency.

Heating and Fire Safety

Keep all combustible materials away from flames. When heating a substance in a test tube, make sure that the mouth of the tube is not pointed at you or anyone else. Never heat a liquid in a closed container. Use an oven mitt to pick up a container that has been heated.

Using Chemicals Safely

Never put your face near the mouth of a container that holds chemicals. Never touch, taste, or smell a chemical unless your teacher tells you to.

Use only those chemicals needed in the activity. Keep all containers closed when chemicals are not being used. Pour all chemicals over the sink or a container, not over your work surface. Dispose of excess chemicals as instructed by your teacher.

Be extra careful when working with acids or bases. When mixing an acid and water, always pour the water into the container first and then add the acid to the water. Never pour water into an acid. Wash chemical spills and splashes immediately with plenty of water.

Using Glassware Safely

If glassware is broken or chipped, notify your teacher immediately. Never handle broken or chipped glass with your bare hands.

Never force glass tubing or thermometers into a rubber stopper or rubber tubing. Have your teacher insert the glass tubing or thermometer if required for an activity.

Using Sharp Instruments

Handle sharp instruments with extreme care. Never cut material toward you; cut away from you.

Animal and Plant Safety

Never perform experiments that cause pain, discomfort, or harm to animals. Only handle animals if absolutely necessary. If you know that you are allergic to certain plants, molds, or animals, tell your teacher before doing an activity in which these are used. Wash your hands thoroughly after any activity involving animals, animal parts, plants, plant parts, or soil.

During field work, wear long pants, long sleeves, socks, and closed shoes. Avoid poisonous plants and fungi as well as plants with thorns.

End-of-Experiment Rules

Unplug all electrical equipment. Clean up your work area. Dispose of waste materials as instructed by your teacher. Wash your hands after every experiment.

The microscope is an essential tool in the study of life science. It allows you to see things that are too small to be seen with the unaided eye.

You will probably use a compound microscope like the one you see here. The compound microscope has more than one lens that magnifies the object you view.

Typically, a compound microscope has one lens in the eyepiece, the part you look through. The eyepiece lens usually magnifies 10 ×. Any object you view through this lens would appear 10 times larger than it is.

The compound microscope may contain one or two other lenses called objective lenses. If there are two objective lenses, they are called the low-power and high-power objective lenses. The low-power objective lens usually magnifies 10 ×. The high-power objective lens usually magnifies 40 ×.

To calculate the total magnification with which you are viewing an object, multiply the magnification of the eyepiece lens by the magnification of the objective lens you are using. For example, the eyepiece's magnification of 10 × multiplied by the low-power objective's magnification of 10 × equals a total magnification of 100 ×.

Use the photo of the compound microscope to become familiar with the parts of the microscope and their functions.

The Parts of a Compound Microscope

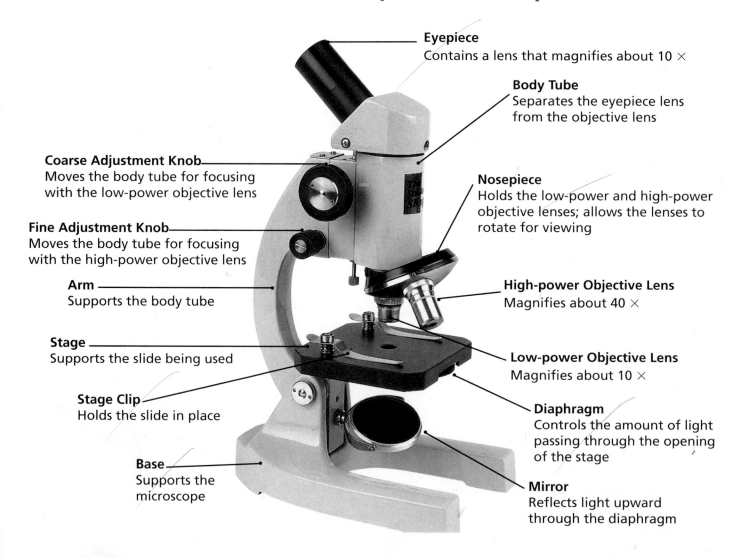

Eyepiece
Contains a lens that magnifies about 10 ×

Body Tube
Separates the eyepiece lens from the objective lens

Coarse Adjustment Knob
Moves the body tube for focusing with the low-power objective lens

Fine Adjustment Knob
Moves the body tube for focusing with the high-power objective lens

Arm
Supports the body tube

Stage
Supports the slide being used

Stage Clip
Holds the slide in place

Base
Supports the microscope

Nosepiece
Holds the low-power and high-power objective lenses; allows the lenses to rotate for viewing

High-power Objective Lens
Magnifies about 40 ×

Low-power Objective Lens
Magnifies about 10 ×

Diaphragm
Controls the amount of light passing through the opening of the stage

Mirror
Reflects light upward through the diaphragm

Using the Microscope

Use the following procedures when you are working with a microscope.

1. To carry the microscope, grasp the microscope's arm with one hand. Place your other hand under the base.
2. Place the microscope on a table with the arm toward you.
3. Turn the coarse adjustment knob to raise the body tube.
4. Revolve the nosepiece until the low-power objective lens clicks into place.
5. Adjust the diaphragm. While looking through the eyepiece, also adjust the mirror until you see a bright white circle of light. **CAUTION:** *Never use direct sunlight as a light source.*
6. Place a slide on the stage. Center the specimen over the opening on the stage. Use the stage clips to hold the slide in place. **CAUTION:** *Glass slides are fragile.*
7. Look at the stage from the side. Carefully turn the coarse adjustment knob to lower the body tube until the low-power objective almost touches the slide.
8. Looking through the eyepiece, very slowly turn the coarse adjustment knob until the specimen comes into focus.
9. To switch to the high-power objective lens, look at the microscope from the side. Carefully revolve the nosepiece until the high-power objective lens clicks into place. Make sure the lens does not hit the slide.
10. Looking through the eyepiece, turn the fine adjustment knob until the specimen comes into focus.

Making a Wet-Mount Slide

Use the following procedures to make a wet-mount slide of a specimen.

1. Obtain a clean microscope slide and a coverslip. **CAUTION:** *Glass slides and coverslips are fragile.*
2. Place the specimen on the slide. The specimen must be thin enough for light to pass through it.
3. Using a plastic dropper, place a drop of water on the specimen.
4. Gently place one edge of the coverslip against the slide so that it touches the edge of the water drop at a 45° angle. Slowly lower the coverslip over the specimen. If air bubbles are trapped beneath the coverslip, tap the coverslip gently with the eraser end of a pencil.
5. Remove any excess water at the edge of the coverslip with a paper towel.

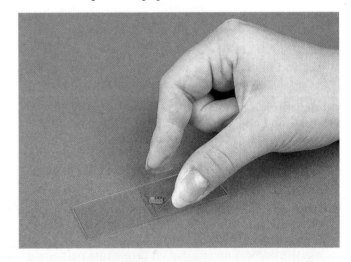

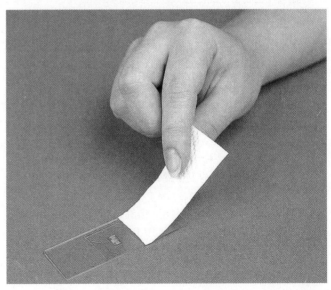

English and Spanish Glossary

A

abdomen The hind section of an arthropod's body that contains its reproductive organs and part of its digestive tract. (p. 438)
abdomen Sección posterior del cuerpo de un artrópodo que contiene sus órganos reproductores y parte de su aparato digestivo.

absolute age The age of a rock given as the number of years since the rock formed. (p. 272)
edad absoluta Edad de una roca basada en el número de años desde que se formó la roca.

active transport The movement of materials through a cell membrane using energy. (p. 106)
transporte activo Movimiento de materiales a través de la membrana celular que usa energía.

adaptation A behavior or physical characteristic that allows an organism to survive or reproduce in its environment. (p. 227)
adaptación Comportamiento o característica física que ayuda a un organismo a sobrevivir o a reproducirse en su medio ambiente.

addiction Physical dependence on a substance. (p. 625)
adicción Dependencia física de una sustancia.

adolescence The stage of development between childhood and adulthood when children become adults physically and mentally. (p. 662)
adolescencia Etapa del desarrollo entre la niñez y la adultez cuando los niños empiezan a ser adultos física y mentalmente.

alcoholism A disease in which a person is both physically addicted to and emotionally dependent on alcohol. (p. 629)
alcoholismo Enfermedad en la que una persona es adicta físicamente y dependiente emocionalmente del alcohol.

algae Plantlike protists. (p. 339)
algas Protistas con características vegetales.

alleles The different forms of a gene. (p. 157)
alelos Diferentes formas de un gen.

alveoli Tiny sacs of lung tissue specialized for the movement of gases between air and blood. (p. 574)
alveolos Sacos diminutos de tejido pulmonar especializados en el intercambio de gases entre el aire y la sangre.

amino acid A small molecule that is linked chemically to other amino acids to form proteins.
amino ácido Pequeña molécula que se une químicamente a otros aminoácidos para formar proteínas. (p. 100)

amniotic egg An egg with a shell and internal membranes that keep the embryo moist (p. 474)
huevo amniótico Huevo con cáscara y membranas internas que mantiene al embrión húmedo.

amniotic sac A fluid-filled sac that cushions and protects the embryo and fetus in the uterus. (p. 659)
saco amniótico Saco lleno de líquido que amortigua y protege al embrión y al feto en desarrollo en el útero.

amphibian An animal that spends its early life in water and its adult life on land. (pp. 290, 468)
anfibio Vertebrado ectotérmico que pasa la primera etapa de su vida en el agua y la madurez en la tierra.

amplitude The maximum distance the particles of a medium move away from their rest positions as a wave passes through the medium. (p. 40)
amplitud Distancia máxima a la que se separan las partículas de un medio de sus posiciones de reposo, cuando una onda atraviesa el medio.

anabolic steroids Synthetic chemicals that are similar to hormones produced in the body. (p. 626)
esteroides anabólicos Sustancias químicas sintéticas que son semejantes a las hormonas producidas por el cuerpo.

anatomy The study of the structure of organisms.
anatomía Estudio de la estructura de los organismos. (p. 411)

angiosperm A flowering plant that produces seeds enclosed in a protective structure. (p. 392)
angiosperma Planta con flores que produce semillas encerradas en una estructura protectora.

antenna An appendage on the head of an arthropod that contains sense organs. (p. 436)
antena Apéndice en la cabeza de un animal que contiene órganos sensoriales.

antibody A protein produced by a B cell of the immune system that destroys pathogens. (p. 514)
anticuerpo Proteína producida por una célula B del sistema inmunológico que destruye un tipo específico de patógeno.

anus A muscular opening at the end of the rectum through which waste material is eliminated. (p. 428)
ano Abertura muscular al final del recto a través de la cual se elimina el material de desecho digestivo del cuerpo.

anvil A small bone in the middle ear that transmits vibrations from the hammer to the stirrup; also called the "incus." (p. 619)
yunque Pequeño hueso en el medio del oído, que transmite vibraciones desde el martillo al estribo, también llamado incus.

aorta The largest artery in the body. (p. 557)
aorta La arteria más grande del cuerpo.

arachnid An arthropod with two body sections, four pairs of legs, and no antennae. (p. 438)
arácnido Artrópodo con dos secciones corporales, cuatro pares de patas y sin antenas.

artery A blood vessel that carries blood away from the heart. (p. 556)
arteria Vaso sanguíneo que transporta la sangre que sale del corazón.

arthropod An invertebrate that has an external skeleton, a segmented body, and jointed appendages. (p. 434)
artrópodo Invertebrado que tiene esqueleto externo, cuerpo segmentado y apéndices anexos.

asexual reproduction A reproductive process that involves only one parent and produces offspring that are identical to the parent. (p. 328)
reproducción asexual Proceso de reproducción que implica a sólo un progenitor y produce descendencia que es idéntica al progenitor.

asthma A respiratory disorder in which the airways in the lungs narrow significantly. (p. 586)
asma Trastorno fisiológico por el cual las vías respiratorias se estrechan considerablemente.

atherosclerosis A condition in which an artery wall thickens from a buildup of fatty materials. (p. 581)
arteriosclerosis Condición en la que la pared de una arteria se hace más gruesa debido a la acumulación de materiales grasos.

atom The smallest particle of an element. (p. 280)
átomo Partícula más pequeña de un elemento.

atrium Each of the two upper chambers of the heart that receives blood that comes into the heart.
aurícula Cada una de las dos cámaras superiores del corazón que reciben la sangre que entra en el corazón. (pp. 470, 555)

autonomic nervous system The group of nerves in the peripheral nervous system that controls involuntary actions. (p. 611)
sistema nervioso autónomo Grupo de nervios en el sistema nervioso periférico que controla las acciones involuntarias.

autotroph An organism that makes its own food.
autótrofo Organismo que produce su propio alimento. (p. 119)

axon A threadlike extension of a neuron that carries nerve impulses away from the cell body. (p. 602)
axón Extensión con forma de hilo de una neurona que lleva los impulsos nerviosos del cuerpo de la célula.

 B

bacteria Single-celled organisms that lack a nucleus; prokaryotes. (p. 326)
bacteria Organismo unicelular que no tiene núcleo.

bacteriophage A virus that infects bacteria. (p. 319)
bacteriófago Virus que infecta bacterias.

bilateral symmetry Body plan with two halves that are mirror images. (p. 414)
simetría bilateral La cualidad de ser divisible en mitades que son imágenes reflejas.

binary fission A form of asexual reproduction in which one cell divides to form two identical cells.
fisión binaria Forma de reproducción asexual en la que una célula se divide para formar dos células idénticas. (p. 328)

binomial nomenclature The system for naming organisms in which each organism is given a unique, two-part scientific name. (p. 250)
nomenclatura binaria Sistema para nombrar organismos, en el cual a cada organismo se le da un nombre científico único de dos partes.

biology The study of life. (p. 13)
biología El estudio de la vida.

bird An endothermic vertebrate that has feathers and a four-chambered heart, and lays eggs. (p. 481)
ave Vertebrado endotérmico que tiene plumas, un corazón de 4 cámaras y pone huevos.

bivalve A mollusk that has two shells held together by hinges and strong muscles. (p. 431)
bivalvo Molusco que tiene dos conchas unidas por charnelas y fuertes músculos.

blood pressure The pressure that is exerted by the blood against the walls of blood vessels. (p. 560)
presión arterial Presión que ejerce la sangre contra las paredes de los vasos sanguíneos.

brain The part of the nervous system that controls most functions in the body. (pp. 425, 607)
encéfalo Parte del sistema nervioso que controla la mayoría de las funciones del cuerpo.

brain stem The part of the brain that lies between the cerebellum and spinal cord, and controls the body's involuntary actions. (p. 608)
tronco encefálico Parte del encéfalo que se encuentra entre el cerebelo y la médula espinal, y controla las acciones involuntarias del cuerpo.

English and Spanish Glossary

branching tree diagram A diagram that shows how scientists think different groups of organisms are related. (p. 255)
diagrama ramificado de árbol Diagrama ramificado que muestra las probables relaciones evolutivas entre los organismos.

bronchi The passages that direct air into the lungs.
bronquios Conductos que dirigen el aire hacia los pulmones. (p. 574)

bronchitis An irritation of the breathing passages in which the small passages become narrower than normal and may be clogged with mucus. (p. 585)
bronquitis Irritación de los conductos respiratorios en la que los conductos pequeños se hacen más estrechos de lo normal y se pueden obstruir con mucosidad.

budding A form of asexual reproduction of yeast in which a new cell grows out of the body of a parent.
gemación Forma de reproducción asexual de las levaduras, en la que una nueva célula crece del cuerpo de su progenitor. (p. 346)

cambium A layer of cells in a plant that produces new phloem and xylem cells. (p. 383)
cámbium Una capa de células de una planta que produce nuevas células de floema y xilema.

camera An optical instrument that uses lenses to focus light, and film to record an image of an object.
cámara Instrumento óptico que usa lentes para enfocar la luz, y película para grabar la imagen de un objeto. (p. 66)

capillary A tiny blood vessel where substances are exchanged between the blood and the body cells.
capilar Vaso sanguíneo minúsculo donde se intercambian las sustancias de la sangre y las células del cuerpo. (p. 556)

carbohydrate An energy-rich organic compound made of the elements carbon, hydrogen, and oxygen. (p. 99)
carbohidrato Compuesto orgánico altamente energético hecho de elementos de carbono, hidrógeno y oxígeno.

cardiac muscle Muscle tissue found only in the heart.
músculo cardiaco Tejido muscular que sólo se encuentra en el corazón. (p. 528)

cardiovascular system The body system that consists of the heart, blood vessels, and blood; circulatory system. (p. 552)
sistema cardiovascular Sistema corporal que está formado por el corazón, los vasos sanguíneos y la sangre; tambien llamado sistema circulatoria.

carrier A person who has one recessive allele for a trait, but does not have the trait. (p. 197)
portador Persona que tiene un alelo recesivo para un determinado rasgo, pero que no tiene el rasgo.

cartilage A connective tissue that is more flexible than bone and that protects the ends of bones and keeps them from rubbing together. (pp. 465, 521)
cartílago Tejido conectivo que es más flexible que el hueso y que protege los extremos de los huesos y evita que se rocen.

cast A type of fossil that forms when a mold becomes filled in with minerals that then harden. (p. 236)
vaciado Tipo de fósil que se forma cuando un molde se llena con minerales que luego se endurecen.

cell The basic unit of structure and function in living things. (p. 81)
célula Unidad básica de estructura y función de los seres vivos.

cell cycle The regular sequence of growth and division that cells undergo. (p. 130)
ciclo celular Secuencia regular de crecimiento y división de las células.

cell membrane The outside cell boundary that controls which substances can enter or leave the cell.
membrana celular Estructura celular que controla qué sustancias pueden entrar y salir de la célula. (p. 89)

cell theory A widely accepted explanation of the relationship between cells and living things. (p. 84)
teoría celular Explicación ampliamente aceptada sobre la relación entre las células y los seres vivos.

cell wall A rigid layer of nonliving material that surrounds the cells of plants and some other organisms. (p. 89)
pared celular Capa rígida de material no vivo que rodea las células vegetales y de algunos organismos.

central nervous system The division of the nervous system consisting of the brain and spinal cord.
sistema nervioso central División del sistema nervioso formado por el encéfalo y la médula espinal. (p. 606)

cephalopod An ocean-dwelling mollusk whose foot is adapted as tentacles that surround its mouth.
cefalópodo Molusco que vive en el océano, cuyas extremidades se adaptaron a la forma de tentáculos alrededor de su boca. (p. 432)

cerebellum The part of the brain that coordinates muscle action and helps maintain balance. (p. 608)
cerebelo Parte del encéfalo que coordina las acciones de los músculos y ayuda a mantener el equilibrio.

cerebrum The part of the brain that interprets input from the senses, controls movement, and carries out complex mental processes. (p. 608)
cerebro Parte del encéfalo que interpreta los estímulos de los sentidos, controla el movimiento y realiza procesos mentales complejos.

chlorophyll The main photosynthetic pigment found in the chloroplasts of plants, algae, and some bacteria. (p. 120)
clorofila Pigmento verde que se encuentra en los cloroplastos de las plantas, algas y algunas bacterias.

chloroplast A structure in the cells of plants and some other organisms that captures energy from sunlight and uses it to produce food. (p. 94)
cloroplasto Estructura en las células vegetales y algunos otros organismos que captan la energía de la luz solar y la usan para producir alimento.

chordate The phylum whose members have a notochord, a nerve cord, and slits in their throat area at some point in their lives. (p. 456)
cordado Fílum cuyos micmbros poseen un notocordio, un cordón nervioso y aberturas en el área de la garganta en alguna etapa de su vida.

chromosome A doubled rod of condensed chromatin.
cromosoma Doble bastón de cromatina condensada; contiene ADN que transporta información genética. (p. 131)

cilia The hairlike projections on the outside of cells that move in a wavelike manner. (pp. 337, 573)
cilios Finas proyecciones en el exterior de las células, que se mueven de manera ondulante.

classification The process of grouping things based on their similarities. (pp. 10, 249)
clasificación Proceso de agrupar cosas según sus semejanzas.

clone An organism that is genetically identical to the organism from which it was produced. (p. 207)
clon Organismo que es genéticamente idéntico al organismo del que proviene.

closed circulatory system A circulatory system in which blood moves only within a connected network of tubes called blood vessels. (p. 429)
sistema circulatorio cerrado Sistema circulatorio en el cual la sangre se mueve sólo dentro de una red conectada de conductos llamados vasos sanguíneos.

cnidarian An invertebrate animal that uses stinging cells to capture food and defend itself. (p. 419)
cnidario Animal invertebrado que usa células punzantes para capturar alimento y defenderse.

cochlea A snail-shaped tube in the inner ear that is lined with receptor cells that respond to sound.
cóclea Tubo en forma de caracol en el oído interno que está recubierto de células receptoras que responden al sonido. (p. 619)

codominance A condition in which neither of two alleles of a gene is dominant or recessive. (p. 167)
codominancia Condición en la que ninguno de los dos alelos de un gen es dominante ni recesivo.

communicating The process of sharing ideas with others through writing and speaking. (p. 21)
comunicar Proceso de compartir ideas con otras personas a través de la escritura o el lenguage hablado.

compact bone Hard, dense bone tissue that is beneath the outer membrane of a bone. (p. 522)
hueso compacto Tejido de hueso denso y duro que se encuentra debajo de la membrana externa de un hueso.

comparative anatomy The comparison of the structures of different organisms. (p. 235)
anatomía comparativa Comparación de las estructuras de diferentes organismos.

complementary Working together to meet the needs of an organism, as structure and function do. (p. 16)
complementario Que trabaja en conjunto para satisfacer las necesidades de un organismo, como lo hacen la estructura y la función.

complementary colors Any two colors that combine to form white light or black pigment. (p. 49)
colores complementarios Dos colores cualesquiera que se combinan para crear luz blanca o pigmento negro.

complete metamorphosis A type of metamorphosis characterized by four dramatically different stages. (p. 440)
metamorfosis completa Tipo de metamorfosis caracterizado por cuatro etapas muy diferentes.

compound Two or more elements that are chemically combined. (p. 98)
compuesto Dos o más elementos que se combinan químicamente.

concave lens A lens that is thinner in the center than at the edges. (p. 60)
lente cóncava Lente que es más fina en el centro que en los extremos.

concave mirror A mirror with a surface that curves inward. (p. 55)
espejo cóncavo Espejo cuya superficie se curva hacia dentro.

concussion A bruiselike injury of the brain that occurs when the soft tissue of the brain collides against the skull. (p. 613)
contusión Magulladura en el encéfalo que ocurre cuando el tejido suave del encéfalo choca contra el cráneo.

cone The reproductive structure of a gymnosperm.
cono Estructura reproductora de una gimnosperma. (p. 390)

cone cells Receptor cells in the eye that work best in bright light and enable you to see color. (pp. 63, 616)
células cono Receptores en la retina del ojo que funcionan mejor cuando hay luz brillante y te permiten ver los colores.

conjugation The process in which a unicellular organism transfers some of its genetic material to another unicellular organism. (p. 328)
conjugación Proceso por el cual un organismo unicelular transfiere parte de su material genético a otro organismo unicelular.

connective tissue A body tissue that provides support for the body and connects all of its parts.
tejido conectivo Tejido que da soporte al cuerpo y conecta todas sus partes. (p. 510)

continental drift The very slow motion of the continents. (p. 284)
deriva continental Movimiento muy lento de los continentes.

contour feather A large feather that helps give shape to a bird's body. (p. 481)
pluma remera Pluma grande que ayuda a dar forma al cuerpo del ave.

contractile vacuole The cell structure that collects extra water from the cytoplasm and then expels it from the cell. (p. 336)
vacuola contráctil Estructura celular que recoge el agua sobrante del citoplasma y luego la expulsa de la célula.

control The part of an experiment to which you can compare the results of the other tests. (p. 20)
control Parte de un experimento con la cual se pueden comparar los resultados de otras pruebas.

controlled experiment An experiment in which only one variable is manipulated at a time. (p. 20)
experimento controlado Experimento en el cual sólo una variable es manipulada a la vez.

convex lens A lens that is thicker in the center than at the edges. (p. 59)
lente convexa Lente que es más gruesa en el centro que en los extremos.

convex mirror A mirror with a surface that curves outward. (p. 56)
espejo convexo Espejo cuya superficie se curva hacia fuera.

cornea The clear tissue that covers the front of the eye.
córnea Tejido transparente que cubre el frente del ojo. (pp. 63, 615)

coronary artery An artery that supplies blood to the heart itself. (p. 558)
arteria coronaria Arteria que lleva sangre al corazón en sí.

cotyledon A seed leaf. (p. 377)
cotiledón Hoja de una semilla.

crest The highest part of a wave. (p. 40)
cresta Parte más alta de una onda.

crop A bird's internal storage pouch that allows it to store food inside its body after swallowing it.
buche Depósito de almacenamiento interno del ave que permite guardar el alimento dentro del ave después de tragarlo. (p. 483)

crustacean An arthropod that has two or three body sections, five or more pairs of legs, and two pairs of antennae. (p. 437)
crustáceo Artrópodo que tiene dos o tres secciones corporales, cinco o más pares de patas y dos pares de antenas.

cuticle The waxy, waterproof layer that covers the leaves and stems of most plants. (p. 364)
cutícula Capa cerosa e impermeable que cubre las hojas y los tallos de la mayoría de las plantas.

cytokinesis The final stage of the cell cycle, in which the cell's cytoplasm divides, distributing the organelles into each of the two new cells. (p. 134)
citocinesis Fase final del ciclo celular en la cual se divide el citoplasma de la célula y se distribuyen los organelos en cada una de las dos nuevas células.

cytoplasm The material within a cell apart from the nucleus. (p. 93)
citoplasma Material que hay en una célula, pero fuera del núcleo.

cytoskeleton A protein "framework" inside a cell that gives the cell a shape. (p. 89)
citoesqueleto "Estructura" proteica dentro de una célula que da su forma a la célula.

data Facts, figures, and other evidence gathered through observations. (p. 21)
dato Hecho, cifra u otra evidencia reunida por medio de las observaciones.

decomposer An organism that breaks down chemicals from wastes and dead organisms, and returns important materials to the soil and water. (p. 332)
descomponedor Organismo que separa sustancias químicas de los organismos muertos y devuelve materiales importantes al suelo y al agua.

dendrite A threadlike extension of a neuron that carries nerve impulses toward the cell body.
dendrita Extensión en forma de hilo de una neurona que lleva los impulsos nerviosos hacia el cuerpo de las células. (p. 602)

depressant A drug that slows down the activity of the central nervous system. (p. 626)
sustancia depresora Droga que disminuye la velocidad de la actividad del sistema nervioso central.

development The process of change that occurs during an organism's life to produce a more complex organism. (p. 15)
desarrollo Proceso de cambio que ocurre durante la vida de un organismo, mediante el cual se desarrolla un organismo más complejo.

diaphragm A large muscle located at the bottom of a mammal's rib cage that functions in breathing.
diafragma Músculo grande ubicado en la parte inferior de la caja torácica de un mamífero, que participa en la respiración. (pp. 488, 576)

dicot An angiosperm that has two seed leaves.
dicotiledónea Angiosperma cuyas semillas tienen dos cotiledones. (p. 396)

differentiation The process by which cells change in structure and become capable of carrying out specialized functions. (pp. 138, 657)
diferenciación Proceso por el cual las células cambian en estructura y son capaces de realizar funciones especializadas.

diffusion The process by which molecules move from an area of higher concentration to an area of lower concentration. (pp. 103, 559)
difusión Proceso por el cual las moléculas se mueven de un área de mayor concentración a otra de menor concentración.

digestion The process by which the body breaks down food into small nutrient molecules. (p. 512)
digestión Proceso por el cual el cuerpo descompone la comida en pequeñas moléculas de nutrientes.

diploid Describes a cell that has two sets of chromosomes, one from each parent. (p. 171)
diploide Describe a una célula que tiene dos juegos de cromosomas, un juego de cada progenitor.

DNA Deoxyribonucleic acid; the genetic materal that carries information about an organism and is passed from parent to offspring. (p. 101)
ADN Ácido desoxirribonucleico; material genético que lleva información sobre un organismo y que se pasa de padres a hijos.

dominant allele An allele whose trait always shows up in the organism when the allele is present.
alelo dominante Alelo cuyo rasgo siempre se manifiesta en el organismo, cuando el alelo está presente. (p. 157)

down feather A short, fluffy feather that traps heat and keeps a bird warm. (p. 481)
plumones Plumas cortas y mullidas que atrapan el calor y mantienen al ave abrigada.

drug Any chemical taken into the body that causes changes in a person's body or behavior. (p. 624)
droga Cualquier sustancia química que se incorpora al cuerpo, que causa cambios en el cuerpo o comportamiento de una persona.

drug abuse The deliberate misuse of drugs for purposes other than medical. (p. 624)
abuso de drogas Uso indebido deliberado de drogas para fines no médicos.

eardrum The membrane that separates the outer ear from the middle ear, and that vibrates when sound waves strike it. (p. 619)
tímpano Membrana que separa el oído externo del oído medio, y que vibra cuando le llegan ondas sonoras.

echinoderm A radially symmetrical invertebrate with an internal skeleton and a water vascular system.
equinodermo Invertebrado con simetría radial que vive en el suelo oceánico y tienen un esqueleto interno. (p. 443)

ectotherm An animal whose body does not produce much internal heat. (p. 459)
ectotermo Animal cuyo cuerpo no produce mucho calor interno.

effort arm For a lever, the distance from the fulcrum to the effort force. (p. 536)
brazo de potencia Para una palanca, la distancia desde el fulcro a la fuerza aplicada.

English and Spanish Glossary

effort distance The distance you push down on a lever. (p. 534)
distancia de potencia La distancia que empujas hacia abajo una palanca.

effort force The force you exert on a lever. (p. 534)
fuerza de potencia La fuerza que ejerces sobre una palanca.

egg A female sex cell. (p. 649)
óvulo Célula sexual femenina.

electromagnetic radiation The energy transferred through space by electromagnetic waves. (p. 42)
radiación electromagnética Energía transferida por ondas electromagnéticas a través del espacio.

electromagnetic spectrum The complete range of electromagnetic waves placed in order of increasing frequency. (p. 43)
espectro electromagnético Gama completa de ondas electromagnéticas colocadas en orden de menor a mayor frecuencia.

electromagnetic waves Waves that transfer electrical and magnetic energy. (p. 42)
ondas electromagnéticas Ondas que transfieren energía eléctrica y magnética.

electron microscope A microscope that uses a beam of electrons to produce a magnified image. (p. 69)
microscopio electrónico microscopio que forma una imagen al centrar un haz de electrones en un espécimen.

element Any substance that cannot be broken down into simpler substances. (pp. 97, 280)
elemento Cualquier sustancia que no puede descomponerse en sustancias más pequeñas.

embryo A young organism that develops from a zygote (p. 377); a developing human during the first eight weeks after fertilization. (p. 657)
embrión Organismo joven que se desarrolla a partir de un cigoto; humano en desarrollo durante las primeras ocho semanas después de ocurrir la fecundación.

emphysema A serious disease that destroys lung tissue and causes breathing difficulties. (p. 585)
enfisema Enfermedad grave que destruye el tejido pulmonar y causa dificultades respiratorias.

endocrine gland A structure of the endocrine system that produces and releases its chemical products directly into the bloodstream. (p. 641)
glándula endocrina Estructura del sistema endocrino que produce y libera sus productos químicos directamente a la corriente sanguínea.

endoplasmic reticulum A cell structure that forms passageways in which proteins and other materials are carried through the cell. (p. 93)
retículo endoplasmático Estructura celular que forma un laberinto de pasajes por los que se transportan las proteínas y otros materiales de una parte de la célula a otra.

endoskeleton An internal skeleton. (p. 443)
endoesqueleto Esqueleto interno.

endospore A small, rounded, thick-walled, resting cell that forms inside a bacterial cell. (p. 329)
endospora Célula pequeña y redonda de paredes gruesas que se encuentra en reposo, que se forma dentro de una célula bacteriana.

endotherm An animal whose body controls and regulates its temperature by controlling the internal heat it produces. (p. 460)
endotermo Animal cuyo cuerpo controla y regula su temperatura controlando el calor interno que produce.

energy The ability to do work or cause change (p. 39)
energía Capacidad para realizar trabajo o causar un cambio.

enzyme A protein that speeds up chemical reactions in a living thing. (p. 100)
enzima Proteína que acelera las reacciones químicas en un ser vivo.

epithelial tissue A body tissue that covers the surfaces of the body, inside and out. (p. 510)
tejido epitelial Tejido corporal que cubre la superficie del cuerpo, por dentro y por fuera.

era One of the three long units of geologic time between the Precambrian and the present. (p. 286)
era Cada una de las tres unidades largas del tiempo geológico entre el Precámbrico y el presente.

erosion The process by which water, ice, or wind breaks down rocks. (p. 268)
erosión Proceso por el cual el agua, el hielo, el viento, o la gravedad des plazan rocas degastadas y suelo.

estimate An approximation of a number, based on reasonable assumptions. (p. 712)
estimación Cálculo aproximado de un número, basándose en supuestos razonables.

estrogen A hormone produced by the ovaries that controls the development of eggs and adult female characteristics. (p. 652)
estrógeno Hormona producida por los ovarios que controla el desarrollo de los óvulos y de las características femeninas adultas.

eukaryote An organism whose cells contain nuclei.
eucariota Organismo cuyas células contienen núcleo. (p. 254)

evolution The gradual change in a species over time.
evolución Cambio gradual de una especie a través del tiempo. (p. 228)

excretion The process by which wastes are removed from the body. (p. 579)
excreción Proceso por el cual se eliminan los desechos del cuerpo.

exoskeleton A waxy, waterproof outer shell or outer skeleton that protects the animal and helps prevent evaporation of water. (p. 435)
exoesqueleto Concha externa cerosa e impermeable o esqueleto externo que protege al animal y ayuda a evitar la evaporación del agua.

extinction The disappearance of all members of a species from Earth. (p. 245)
extinción Desaparición de la Tierra de todos los miembros de una especie.

extrusion An igneous rock layer formed when lava flows onto Earth's surface and hardens. (p. 274)
extrusión Capa de roca ígnea formada cuando la lava fluye hacia la superficie de la Tierra y se endurece.

eyepiece A lens that magnifies the image formed by the objective. (p. 67)
ocular Lente que aumenta la imagen formada por el objetivo.

fallopian tube A passageway for eggs from an ovary to the uterus. (p. 652)
trompa de falopio Pasaje por el que pasan los óvulos desde un ovario al útero.

farsighted Able to see distant objects clearly. (p. 64)
hipermetropía Condición en la que una persona puede ver claramente los objetos distantes.

fault A break or crack in Earth's crust along which the rocks move. (p. 274)
falla Fisura o grieta en la corteza de la Tierra a lo largo de la cual se mueven las rocas.

fermentation The process by which cells break down molecules to release energy without using oxygen.
fermentación Proceso por el cual las células descomponen las moléculas para liberar energía sin usar oxígeno. (p. 126)

fertilization The joining of a sperm and an egg.
fecundación Unión de un espermatozoide y un óvulo. (p. 155)

fetus A developing human from the ninth week of development until birth. (p. 658)
feto Humano en desarrollo desde la novena semana de desarrollo hasta el nacimiento.

fish An ectothermic vertebrate that lives in the water and has fins. (p. 463)
pez Vertebrado ectotérmico que vive en el agua y tiene branquias.

flagellum A long, whiplike structure that helps a cell to move. (p. 326)
flagelo Estructura larga con forma de látigo que ayuda a la célula para moverse.

flower The reproductive structure of an angiosperm. (p. 392)
flor Estructura reproductora de una angiosperma.

focal point The point at which light rays parallel to the optical axis meet, or appear to meet, after being reflected (or refracted) by a mirror (or a lens).
punto de enfoque Punto en el que se encuentran, o parecen encontrarse, los rayos de luz paralelos al eje óptico después de reflejarse (o refractarse) en un espejo (o lente). (p. 55)

follicle Structure in the dermis of the skin from which a strand of hair grows; a grouping of cells in which an egg matures in an ovary. (p. 654)
folículo Estructura en la dermis de la piel de donde crece un pelo; agrupación de células en las cuales un óvulo madura en un ovario.

force A push or pull exerted on an object. (p. 533)
fuerza Empuje o atracción que se ejerce sobre un objeto.

fossil The preserved remains or traces of an organism that lived in the past. (p. 225)
fósil Restos o huellas preservados de un organismo que vivió en el pasado.

frequency The number of complete waves that pass a given point in a certain amount of time. (p. 41)
frecuencia Número de ondas completas que pasan por un punto dado en cierto tiempo.

frond The leaf of a fern plant. (p. 373)
fronda Hoja de un helecho.

fruit The ripened ovary and other structures of an angiosperm that enclose one or more seeds. (p. 394)
fruto Ovario maduro y otras estructuras que encierran una o más semillas de una angiosperma.

English and Spanish Glossary

fruiting body Reproductive structure of a fungus that contains many hyphae and produces spores. (p. 346)
órgano fructífero Estructura reproductora de un hongo que contiene muchas hifas y produce esporas.

fulcrum A fixed point on which a lever pivots. (p. 534)
fulcro Punto fijo en torno al cual gira una palanca.

function A process that enables an organism to survive.
función Proceso que permite a un organismo sobrevivir. (p. 16)

fungus A eukaryotic organism that has cell walls, uses spores to reproduce, and is a heterotroph that feeds by absorbing its food. (p. 344)
hongo Organismo eucariótico que posee paredes celulares, usa esporas para reproducirse y es un heterótrofo que se alimenta absorbiendo su comida.

gametophyte The stage in the life cycle of a plant in which the plant produces gametes, or sex cells.
gametofito Etapa en el ciclo de vida de una planta en la cual la planta produce gametos, es decir, células sexuales. (p. 368)

gastropod A mollusk with a single shell or no shell.
gasterópodo Molusco con una única concha o sin concha. (p. 431)

gene The set of information that controls a trait; a segment of DNA on a chromosome that codes for a specific trait. (p. 157)
gen Conjunto de información que controla un rasgo; un segmento de ADN en un cromosoma el cual codifica un rasgo determinado.

gene therapy The insertion of working copies of a gene into the cells of a person with a genetic disorder in an attempt to correct the disorder. (p. 209)
terapia génica Inserción de copias activas de un gen en las células de una persona con un trastorno genético para intentar corregir dicho trastornó.

genetic disorder An abnormal condition that a person inherits through genes or chromosomes.
trastorno genético Condición anormal que hereda una persona a través de genes o cromosomas. (p. 199)

genetic engineering The transfer of a gene from the DNA of one organism into another organism, in order to produce an organism with desired traits.
ingeniería genética Transferencia de un gen desde el ADN de un organismo a otro, para producir un organismo con los rasgos deseados. (p. 208)

genetics The scientific study of heredity. (p. 154)
genética Ciencia que estudia la herencia.

genetic variation Any difference between individuals of the same species. (p. 229)
variación genética Cualquier diferencia entre individuos de la misma especie.

genome All of the DNA in one cell of an organism.
genoma Todo el ADN de una célula de un organismo. (p. 210)

genotype An organism's genetic makeup, or allele combinations. (p. 166)
genotipo Composición genética de un organismo, es decir, las combinaciones de los alelos.

genus A classification grouping that consists of a number of similar, closely related species. (p. 250)
género Clasificación por grupo formada por un número de especies similares y muy relacionadas.

geologic time scale A record of the geologic events and life forms in Earth's history. (p. 286)
escala geocronológica Registro de los sucesos geológicos y de las formas de vida en la historia de la Tierra.

geology The study of the structures of planet Earth and the forces that make and shape Earth. (p. 268)
geología ciencia que estudia la Tierra, su forma, su composición y los cambios que ha tenido y que continúa teniendo.

germination The sprouting of the embryo from a seed that occurs where the embryo resumes growth. (p. 379)
germinación La brotadura del embrión de una semilla; se occura cuando el embrión resuma su crecimiento.

gestation period The length of time between fertilization and birth of a mammal. (p. 490)
período de gestación Tiempo entre la fecundación y el nacimiento del mamífero.

gill An organ that removes oxygen from water. (p. 430)
branquia Órgano que extrae el oxígeno del agua.

gizzard A muscular, thick-walled part of a bird's stomach that squeezes and grinds partially digested food. (p. 483)
molleja Parte muscular, de paredes gruesas del estómago del ave que exprime y muele parcialmente el alimento digerido.

Golgi body A structure in a cell that receives proteins and other newly formed materials from the endoplasmic reticulum, packages them, and distributes them to other parts of the cell. (p. 94)

aparato de Golgi Estructura en la célula que recibe del retículo endoplasmático las proteínas y otros materiales recientemente formados, los empaqueta y los distribuye a otras partes de la célula.

gradual metamorphosis A type of metamorphosis in which an egg hatches into a nymph that resembles an adult, and which has no distinctly different larval stage. (p. 440)
metamorfosis gradual Tipo de metamorfosis en la que un huevo incubado pasa a la etapa de ninfa con aspecto de adulto, y no tiene una etapa de larva diferenciada.

gradualism The theory that evolution occurs slowly but steadily. (p. 240)
gradualismo Teoría que enuncia que la evolución ocurre lenta pero continuamente.

gymnosperm A plant that produces seeds that are not enclosed by a protective fruit. (p. 388)
gimnosperma Planta cuyas semillas no están encerradas en una fruta protectora.

H

habitat The specific environment that provides the things an organism needs to live, grow, and reproduce. (pp. 242, 471)
hábitat Medio ambiente específico que proporciona las cosas que un organismo necesita para vivir, crecer y reproducirse.

half-life The time it takes for half of the atoms in a radioactive element to decay. (p. 280)
vida media Tiempo que demoran en desintegrarse la mitad de los átomos de un elemento radiactivo.

hammer A small bone in the middle ear that transmits vibrations from the eardrum to the anvil; also called the "malleus." (p. 619)
martillo Pequeño hueso en el oído medio, que transmite vibraciones desde el tímpano hasta el yunque.

heart A hollow, muscular organ that pumps blood throughout the body. (p. 554)
corazón Órgano muscular hueco que bombea sangre a todo el cuerpo.

heart attack A condition in which blood flow to part of the heart muscle is blocked, causing heart cells to die. (p. 581)
infarto cardiaco Condición en la que se obstruye el flujo de sangre a una parte del músculo cardiaco, lo que causa la muerte de las células cardiacas.

hemoglobin An iron-containing protein that binds chemically to oxygen molecules. (p. 564)
hemoglobina Proteína que contiene hierro, y que se enlaza químicamente a las moléculas de oxígeno.

heredity The passing of traits from parents to offspring. (p. 154)
herencia Transmisión de rasgos de padres a hijos.

hertz (Hz) Unit of measurement for frequency. (p. 41)
hercio (Hz) Unidad de media de frecuencia.

heterotroph An organism that cannot make its own food. (p. 119)
heterótrofo Organismo que no puede producir su propio alimento.

heterozygous Having two different alleles for a trait.
heterocigoto Tener dos alelos diferentes para el mismo rasgo. (p. 166)

homeostasis The maintenance of stable internal conditions in an organism. (p. 516)
homeostasis Mantenimiento de condiciones internas estables.

homologous structures Body parts that are structurally similar in related species. (p. 235)
estructuras homólogas Partes del cuerpo que son estructuralmente similares entre las especies relacionadas.

homozygous Having two identical alleles for a trait.
homocigoto Tener dos alelos idénticos para el mismo rasgo. (p. 166)

hormone A chemical product of an endocrine gland that produces a specific effect such as growth or development. (p. 641)
hormona Sustancia química que afecta el crecimiento y desarrollo.

host The organism that a parasite or virus lives in or on.
huésped Organismo dentro o fuera del cual vive un parásito. (pp. 318, 426)

hybrid An organism that has two different alleles for a trait; an organism that is heterozygous for a particular trait. (p. 158)
híbrido Organismo que tiene dos alelos diferentes para un rasgo; un organismo que es heterocigoto para un rasgo en particular.

hybridization A selective breeding method in which two genetically different individuals are crossed. (p. 206)
hibridación Método de cruce selectivo en el cual se cruzan dos individuos genéticamente diferentes.

English and Spanish Glossary

hypertension A disorder in which a person's blood pressure is consistently higher than normal; also called high blood pressure. (p. 582)
hipertensión Trastorno en el que la presión arterial de una persona es constantemente más alta de lo normal; tambien se llama presión alta.

hyphae The branching, threadlike tubes that make up the bodies of multicellular fungi. (p. 345)
hifas Delgados tubos ramificados que constituyen el cuerpo de los hongos multicelulares.

hypothalamus A part of the brain that links the nervous system and the endocrine system. (p. 642)
hipotálamo Parte del encéfalo que une el sistema nervioso con el sistema endocrino.

hypothesis A possible explanation for a set of observations or answer to a scientific question; must be testable. (p. 19)
hipótesis Explicación posible a un conjunto de observaciones o respuesta a una pregunta científica; debe ser verificable.

igneous rock A type of rock that forms from the cooling of molten rock at or below the surface.
roca ígnea Tipo de roca que se forma cuando se enfrían las rocas fundidas en la superficie o debajo de la superficie. (p. 269)

image A copy of an object formed by reflected or refracted rays of light. (p. 54)
imagen Copia de un objeto formado por rayos de luz que se reflejan y se refractan.

immune response Part of the body's defense against pathogens, in which cells of the immune system react to each kind of pathogen with a defense targeted specifically at that pathogen. (p. 600)
reacción inmunológica Parte de la defensa del cuerpo contra los patógenos en la que las células del sistema inmunológico reaccionan a cada tipo de patógeno con una defensa específica.

immunity The body's ability to destroy pathogens before they can cause disease. (p. 514)
inmunidad Capacidad del cuerpo para destruir los patógenos antes de que causen enfermedades.

inbreeding A selective breeding method in which two individuals with identical or similar sets of alleles are crossed. (p. 206)
endogamia Método de cruce selectivo en el que se cruzan dos individuos con pares de alelos idénticos o semejantes.

inclusion A piece of rock that is contained in another rock; an inclusion is younger than the rock containing it. (p. 275)
intrusión Roca que está contenida en otra roca.; una intrusión tiene menos edad que la roca que la contiene.

index fossil Fossils of widely distributed organisms that lived during only one short period. (p. 276)
fósil indicador Fósiles de organismos ampliamente dispersos que vivieron durante un período corto.

inferring The process of making an inference, an interpretation based on observations and prior knowledge. (p. 8)
inferir Proceso de realizar una inferencia; una interpretación basada en observaciones y conocimiento previo.

insect An arthropod with three body sections, six legs, one pair of antennae, and usually one or two pairs of wings. (p. 439)
insecto Artrópodo con tres secciones corporales, seis patas, un par de antenas y normalmente uno o dos pares de alas.

interneuron A neuron that carries nerve impulses from one neuron to another. (p. 602)
interneurona Neurona que lleva los impulsos nerviosos de una neurona a otra.

interphase The stage of the cell cycle that takes place before cell division occurs. (p. 130)
interfase Fase del ciclo celular que ocurre antes de la división.

intrusion An igneous rock layer formed when magma hardens beneath Earth's surface. (p. 274)
intrusión Capa de roca ígnea formada cuando el magma se endurece bajo la superficie de la Tierra.

invertebrate An animal that does not have a backbone.
invertebrado Animal que no posee columna vertebral. (pp. 289, 416)

involuntary muscle A muscle that is not under conscious control. (p. 526)
músculos involuntarios Músculo que no se puede controlar conscientemente.

iris The circular structure that surrounds the pupil and regulates the amount of light entering the eye.
iris Estructura circular que rodea la pupila y regula la cantidad de luz que entra en el ojo. (pp. 63, 615)

J

joint A place in the body where two bones come together. (p. 520)
articulación Lugar en el cuerpo en donde se unen dos huesos.

K

karyotype A picture of all the chromosomes in a cell arranged in pairs. (p. 202)
cariotipo Imagen de todos los cromosomas de una célula, organizados en parejas.

kidney A major organ of the excretory system that removes urea and other wastes from the blood.
riñón Órgano principal del sistema excretor que elimina la urea y otros materiales de desecho de la sangre. (pp. 473, 513)

L

larva The immature form of an animal that looks very different from the adult. (p. 418)
larva Forma inmadura de un animal que se ve muy diferente al adulto.

larynx The voice box (p. 578)
laringe Dos pliegues de tejido que forman la caja sonora humana.

lava Liquid magma that reaches the surface. (p. 270)
lava Magma líquida que sale a la superficie.

law of reflection The rule that the angle of reflection equals the angle of incidence. (p. 53)
ley de reflexión Regla que enuncia que el ángulo de reflexión es igual al ángulo de incidencia.

law of superposition The geologic principle that states that in horizontal layers of sedimentary rock, each layer is older than the layer above it and younger than the layer below it. (p. 273)
ley de la superposición Principio geológico que enuncia que en las capas horizontales de la roca sedimentaria, cada capa es más vieja que la capa superior y más joven que la capa inferior.

lens A curved piece of glass or other transparent material that is used to refract light; the flexible structure that focuses light that has entered the eye. (pp. 58, 616)
cristalino Trozo de cristal u otro material transparente curvado que se usa para refractar la luz; estructura flexible que enfoca la luz que entra en el ojo.

lever A simple machine that consists of a rigid bar that pivots about a fixed point. (p. 534)
palanca Máquina simple que consiste en una barra rígida que gira en torno a un punto fijo.

lichen The combination of a fungus and either an alga or an autotrophic bacterium that live together in a mutualistic relationship. (p. 349)
liquen Combinación de un hongo y una alga o bien una bacteria autótrofa, que viven juntos en una relación de mutualismo.

life science The study of living things. (p. 13)
ciencias de la vida Estudio de los seres vivos.

ligament Strong connective tissue that holds bones together in movable joints. (p. 521)
ligamentos Tejido conectivo resistente que une los huesos en las articulaciones móviles.

lipid Energy-rich organic compound, such as a fat, oil, or wax, that is made of carbon, hydrogen, and oxygen.
lípido Compuesto orgánico rico en energía, como grasa, aceite y cera, formado por carbono, hidrógeno y oxígeno. (p. 99)

lung An organ found in air-breathing vertebrates that exchanges oxygen and carbon dioxide with the blood. (pp. 470, 574)
pulmón Órgano que se encuentra en los vertebrados que respiran aire, con el que intercambian oxígeno y dióxido de carbono con la sangre.

lymph The fluid that the lymphatic system collects and returns to the bloodstream. (p. 568)
linfa Fluido que el sistema linfático recoge y devuelve al torrente sanguíneo.

lymphatic system A network of veinlike vessels that returns the fluid that leaks out of blood vessels to the bloodstream. (p. 568)
sistema linfático Red de vasos semejantes a venas que devuelve al torrente sanguíneo el fluido que sale de los vasos sanguíneos.

lymph node A small knob of tissue in the lymphatic system that filters lymph, trapping bacteria and other microorganisms that cause disease. (p. 569)
ganglio linfático Pequeña prominencia de tejido en el sistema linfático que filtra la linfa, atrapando las bacterias y otros microorganismos que causan enfermedades.

lysosome A small, round cell structure containing chemicals that break down large food particles into smaller ones. (p. 94)
lisosoma Pequeña estructura celular redonda que contiene sustancias químicas que descomponen las partículas de alimento grandes en otras más simples.

machine A device that changes the amount of force exerted, the distance over which a force is exerted, or the direction in which force is exerted. (p. 533)
máquina Dispositivo que altera la cantidad de fuerza ejercida, la distancia sobre la que se ejerce la fuerza o la dirección en la que se ejerce la fuerza.

magma Molten material beneath Earth's surface.
magma Mezcla fundida de las sustancias que forman las rocas, gases y agua, proveniente del manto. (p. 270)

making models The process of creating representations of complex objects or processes.
hacer modelos Proceso de crear representaciones de objetos o procesos complejos. (p. 11)

mammal An endothermic vertebrate with a four-chambered heart, skin covered with fur or hair, and young fed with milk from the mother's body. (pp. 294, 486)
mamífero Vertebrado endotérmico con un corazón de cuatro cámaras y piel cubierta de pelaje o pelo, que alimenta a sus crías con leche materna.

mammary gland An organ in female mammals that produces milk for the mammal's young. (p. 487)
glándula mamaria Órgano en los mamíferos hembra que produce leche para alimentar a las crías.

manipulated variable The one factor that a scientist changes during an experiment; also called independent variable. (p. 20)
variable manipulada Único factor que un científico cambia durante un experimento; también llamada variable independiente.

marrow The soft connective tissue that fills the internal spaces in bone. (p. 522)
médula ósea Tejido conectivo suave que rellena los espacios internos de un hueso.

marsupial A mammal whose young are born alive at an early stage of development, and which usually continue to develop in a pouch on their mother's body. (p. 490)
marsupial Mamífero cuyas crías nacen vivas en una etapa muy temprana del desarrollo, y que normalmente sigue su desarrollo en una bolsa en el cuerpo de la madre.

mass extinction When many types of living things become extinct at the same time. (p. 291)
extinción en masa Cuando muchos tipos de seres vivos se extinguen al mismo tiempo.

mechanical advantage For a lever, the ratio of the resistance force to the effort force. (p. 536)
ventaja mecánica Para una palanca, la razón de la fuerza de resistencia a la fuerza de potencia.

medium The material through which a wave travels. (p. 39)
medio Material a través del cual viaja una onda.

medusa The cnidarian body plan having a bowl shape and adapted for a free-swimming life.
medusa Cnidario cuyo cuerpo se caracteriza por tener forma de cuenco, y que está adaptado para nadar libremente en el agua. (p. 419)

meiosis The process that occurs in the formation of sex cells (sperm and egg) by which the number of chromosomes is reduced by half. (p. 172)
meiosis Proceso que ocurre en la formación de las células sexuales (espermatozoide y óvulo) por el cual el número de cromosomas se reduce a la mitad.

menstrual cycle The cycle of changes that occurs in the female reproductive system, during which an egg develops and the uterus prepares for the arrival of a fertilized egg. (p. 653)
ciclo menstrual Ciclo de cambios que ocurre en el sistema reproductor femenino, durante el cual se desarrolla un óvulo, y el útero se prepara para la llegada del óvulo fecundado.

menstruation The process in which the thickened lining of the uterus breaks down, and blood and tissue then pass out of the female body. (p. 654)
menstruación Proceso en el cual el grueso recubrimiento del útero se descompone la sangre y el tejido salen del cuerpo femenino.

messenger RNA RNA that copies the coded message from DNA in the nucleus and carries the message into the cytoplasm. (p. 177)
ARN mensajero ARN que copia el mensaje codificado del ADN en el núcleo y lo lleva al citoplasma.

metamorphic rock A type of rock that forms from an existing rock that is changed by heat, pressure, or chemical reactions. (p. 269)
roca metamórfica Tipo de roca que se forma cuando una roca es transformada por el calor, presión o reacciones químicas.

metamorphosis A process in which an animal's body undergoes dramatic changes in form during its life cycle. (p. 437)
metamorfosis Proceso por el cual el cuerpo de un animal cambia de manera drástica durante su ciclo de vida.

microscope An instrument that makes small objects look larger. (p. 68)
microscopio Instrumento que hace que los objetos pequeños se vean más grandes.

mitochondria Rod-shaped cell structures that convert energy in food molecules to energy the cell can use to carry out its functions. (p. 93)
mitocondria Estructura celular con forma de bastón que transforma la energía de las moléculas de alimentos en energía que la célula puede usar para llevar a cabo sus funciones.

mitosis The stage of the cell cycle during which the cell's nucleus divides into two new nuclei and one copy of the DNA is distributed into each daughter cell. (p. 131)
mitosis Fase del ciclo celular durante la cual el núcleo de la célula se divide en dos nuevos nucleolos y se distribuye una copia del ADN a cada célula hija.

mold A type of fossil formed when a shell or other hard part of an organism dissolves, leaving an empty space in the shape of the part. (p. 236)
molde Tipo de fósil que se forma cuando el caparazón, concha u otra parte dura de un organismo enterrado se disuelve y deja un área hueca con la forma de esa parte.

mollusk An invertebrate with a soft, unsegmented body; most are protected by a hard outer shell.
molusco Invertebrado con cuerpo blando y sin segmentos; la mayoría están protegidos por una concha exterior dura. (p. 430)

molting The process of shedding an outgrown exoskeleton. (p. 435)
muda Proceso de cambio de un exoesqueleto a otro.

monocot An angiosperm with one seed leaf. (p. 396)
monocotiledónea Angiosperma cuyas semillas tienen un solo cotiledón.

monotreme A mammal that lays eggs. (p. 490)
monotrema Mamífero que pone huevos.

motor neuron A neuron that sends an impulse to a muscle or gland, causing the muscle or gland to react.
neurona motora Neurona que envía un impulso a un músculo o glándula, haciendo que el músculo o la glándula reaccione. (p. 602)

mucus A thick, sticky liquid produced by the body.
moco Líquido espeso y pegajoso producido por el cuerpo. (p. 573)

multicellular Consisting of many cells. (p. 85)
multicelular Que se compone de muchas células.

multiple alleles Three or more forms of a gene that code for a single trait. (p. 194)
alelo múltiple Tres o más formas de un gen que codifican un solo rasgo.

muscle tissue A body tissue that contracts or shortens, making body parts move. (p. 510)
tejido muscular Tejido corporal que se contrae o acorta, permitiendo así que se muevan las partes del cuerpo.

mutation A change in a gene or chromosome. (p. 180)
mutación Cambio en un gen o cromosoma.

mutualism A close relationship between organisms of two species in which both organisms benefit.
mutualismo Relación entre dos especies de la cual ambas se benefician. (p. 338)

natural selection A process by which individuals that are better adapted to their environment are more likely to survive and reproduce than others of the same species. (p. 229)
selección natural Proceso por el cual los individuos que se adaptan mejor a sus ambientes tienen más posibilidades de sobrevivir y reproducirse que otros miembros de la misma especie.

nearsighted Able to see nearby objects clearly. (p. 64)
miopía Condición en la que una persona puede ver claramente los objetos cercanos.

negative feedback A process in which a system is turned off by the condition it produces. (p. 644)
reacción negativa Proceso en el cual un sistema se apaga por la condición que produce.

nephron Small filtering structure found in the kidneys that removes wastes from blood and produces urine.
nefrón Estructura diminuta de filtración que hay en los riñones, que elimina los desechos de la sangre y que produce la orina. (p. 513)

nerve A bundle of nerve fibers. (p. 602)
nervio Conjunto de fibras nerviosas.

nerve impulse A message carried by a neuron. (p. 602)
impulso nervioso Mensaje que lleva una neurona.

nervous tissue A body tissue that carries electrical messages back and forth between the brain and every other part of the body. (p. 510)
tejido nervioso Tejido corporal que lleva mensajes eléctricos entre el encéfalo y todas las demás partes del cuerpo y viceversa.

neuron A cell that carries information through the nervous system. (p. 602)
neurona Célula que lleva información a través del sistema nervioso.

nonvascular plant A low-growing plant that lacks true vascular tissue. (p. 366)
planta no vascular Planta de crecimiento lento que carece de tejido vascular verdadero.

notochord A flexible rod that supports a chordate's back. (p. 456)
notocordio Bastoncillo flexible que sostiene el lomo de los cordados.

nucleic acid Very large organic molecule made of carbon, oxygen, hydrogen, nitrogen, and phosphorus, that contains the instructions cells need to carry out all the functions of life. (p. 101)
ácido nucléico Molécula orgánica muy grande compuesta de carbono, oxígeno, hidrógeno, nitrógeno y fósforo, que contiene las instrucciones que las células necesitan para realizar todas las funciones vitales.

nucleus The control center of a eukaryotic cell that directs the cell's activities and contains the information that determines the cell's form and function.
núcleo Centro de control de la célula eucariota que dirige las actividades de la célula y que contiene información que determina la forma y función de la célula. (p. 92)

nymph A stage of gradual metamorphosis that usually resembles the adult insect. (p. 440)
ninfa Etapa de la metamorfosis gradual en la que normalmente el insecto se parece a un insecto adulto.

objective A lens that gathers light from an object and forms a real image. (p. 67)
objetivo Lente que reúne la luz de un objeto y forma una imagen real.

observing The process of using one or more of your senses to gather information. (p. 7)
observar Proceso de usar uno o más de los cinco sentidos para reunir información.

opaque Reflecting or absorbing all of the light that strikes it. (p. 47)
opaco Lo que refleja o absorbe toda la luz que llega a él.

open circulatory system A circulatory system in which the heart pumps blood into a short vessel that opens into spaces in the body, and in which blood is not confined to blood vessels. (p. 430)
sistema circulatorio abierto Sistema circulatorio en el que el corazón bombea la sangre en espacios abiertos del cuerpo y la sangre no se mantiene en vasos sanguíneos.

operational definition A statement that describes how to measure a particular variable or how to define a particular term. (p. 20)
definición operativa Enunciado que describe cómo medir una variable determinada o cómo definir un término determinado.

optic nerve The short, thick nerve in the eye through which rods and cones send electrical impulses to the brain. (p. 616)
nervio óptico Nervio corto y grueso en el ojo, a través del cual los bastones y los conos envían impulsos eléctricos al cerebro.

optical axis An imaginary line that divides a mirror in half. (p. 55)
eje óptico Recta imaginaria que divide un espejo por la mitad.

organ A structure in the body that is composed of different kinds of tissue. (p. 85)
órgano Estructura del cuerpo compuesta de diferentes tipos de tejidos.

organ system A group of organs that work together to perform a major function in the body.
sistema de órganos Grupo de órganos que trabajan juntos para realizar una función importante del cuerpo. (pp. 85, 510)

organelle A tiny cell structure that carries out a specific function within the cell. (p. 88)
organelo Diminuta estructura celular que realiza una función específica dentro de la célula.

organism A living thing. (p. 13)
organismo Ser vivo.

osmosis The diffusion of water molecules through a selectively permeable membrane. (p. 104)
ósmosis Difusión de las moléculas de agua a través de una membrana con permeabilidad selectiva.

osteoporosis A condition in which the body's bones become weak and break easily. (p. 525)
osteoporosis Condición en la cual los huesos del cuerpo se debilitan y se rompen fácilmente.

ovary A flower structure that encloses and protects ovules and seeds as they develop; organ of the female reproductive system in which eggs and estrogen are produced. (pp. 393, 652)
ovario Estructura de la flor que encierra y protege a los óvulos y a las semillas durante su desarrollo; órgano del sistema reproductor femenino en el cual se producen los óvulos y el estrógeno.

ovulation The process in which a mature egg is released from the ovary into a fallopian tube.
ovulación Proceso en el cual el óvulo maduro sale del ovario y va a la trompa de falopio. (p. 654)

ovule A structure that contains an egg cell. (p. 390)
óvulo Estructura que contiene una célula reproductora femenina.

pacemaker A group of cells located in the right atrium that sends out signals that make the heart muscle contract and that regulates heartbeat rate.
marcapasos Grupo de células ubicado en la aurícula derecha que envía señales para que el músculo cardiaco se contraiga, y que regula el ritmo cardiaco. (p. 555)

paleontologist A scientist who studies fossils. (p. 238)
paleontólogo Científico que estudia los fósiles.

parasite The organism that benefits by living on or in a host in a parasitism interaction. (pp. 318, 426)
parásito Organismo que se beneficia de vivir en la superficie o en el interior de un huésped en una interacción de parasitismo.

passive transport The movement of materials through a cell membrane without using the cell's energy. (p. 106)
transporte pasivo Movimiento de materiales a través de la membrana celular sin el uso de energía.

pasteurization A process of heating food to a temperature that is high enough to kill most harmful bacteria without changing the taste of the food.
pasteurización Proceso de calentamiento del alimento a una temperatura suficientemente alta como para matar la mayoría de las bacterias dañinas sin cambiar el sabor de la comida. (p. 331)

pathogen An organism that causes disease. (p. 514)
patógeno Organismo que causa enfermedades.

pedigree A chart or "family tree" that tracks which members of a family have a particular trait.
genealogía Tabla o "árbol genealógico" que muestra qué miembros de una familia tienen un rasgo en particular. (p. 201)

penis The organ through which both semen and urine leave the male body. (p. 651)
pene Órgano a través del cual salen del cuerpo masculino tanto el semen como la orina.

period One of the units of geologic time into which geologists divide eras. (p. 286)
período Una de las unidades del tiempo geológico dentro de las cuales los geólogos dividen las eras.

peripheral nervous system The division of the nervous system consisting of all of the nerves located outside the central nervous system. (p. 606)
sistema nervioso periférico Parte del sistema nervioso formada por todos los nervios ubicados fuera del sistema central nervioso.

petal A colorful, leaflike structure of some flowers.
pétalo Estructura de color brillante, en forma de hoja que tienen algunas flores. (p. 392)

petrified fossil A fossil formed when minerals replace all or part of an organism. (p. 236)
fósil petrificado Fósil que se forma cuando los minerales reemplazan todo el organismo o parte de él.

pharynx The throat. (p. 573)
faringe Garganta.

phenotype An organism's physical appearance, or visible traits. (p. 166)
fenotipo Apariencia física de un organismo, es decir, los rasgos visibles.

phloem The vascular tissue through which food moves in some plants. (p. 376)
floema Tejido vascular por el que circula el alimento en algunas plantas.

photosynthesis The process by which a cell captures energy in sunlight and uses it to make food. (p. 119)
fotosíntesis Proceso por el cual los organismos usan el agua junto con la luz solar y el dióxido de carbono para producir su alimento.

phylum One of the major groups into which biologists classify members of a kingdom. (p. 416)
fílum Uno de alrededor de 35 grupos principales en los que los biólogos clasifican los miembros del reino animal.

physiology The study of the functions in organisms.
fisiología Estudio de las funciones en los organismos. (p. 411)

pigment A colored chemical compound that absorbs light and can be used to color other materials.
pigmento Compuesto químico de color que absorbe luz. (pp. 49, 120)

English and Spanish Glossary

pistil The female reproductive part of a flower. (p. 393)
pistilo Parte reproductora femenina de una flor.

pituitary gland An endocrine gland that controls many body activities. (p. 644)
glándula pituitaria Glándula endocrina que controla muchas actividades corporales.

placenta A membrane that becomes the link between the developing embryo or fetus and the mother. (pp. 491, 659)
placenta Membrana que se convierte en la unión entre el embrión o feto en desarrollo y la madre.

placental mammal A mammal that develops inside its mother's body until its body systems can function independently. (p. 491)
mamífero placentario Mamífero que se desarrolla dentro del cuerpo de la madre hasta que sus sistemas corporales pueden funcionar por sí solos.

plane mirror A flat mirror that produces an upright, virtual image the same size as an object. (p. 54)
espejo plano Espejo liso que produce una imagen virtual vertical del mismo tamaño que el objeto.

plasma The liquid part of blood. (p. 563)
plasma Parte líquida de la sangre.

plate One of the major pieces of Earth's rocky outer layer on which continents and oceans move. (p. 284)
placa Sección de la litosfera que se desplaza lentamente sobre la stenosfera, llevando consigo trozos de la corteza continental y de la oceánia.

platelet A cell fragment that plays an important part in forming blood clots. (p. 566)
plaqueta Fragmento de célula que juega un papel muy importante en la formación de coágulos sanguíneos.

pneumonia An infection that causes fluid to accumulate in the alveoli, decreasing the lungs' ability to take in oxygen and remove carbon dioxide. (p. 587)
neumonía Infección que causa la acumulación de fluido en los alveolos, lo que disminuye la capacidad de los pulmones para absorber oxígeno y eliminar dióxido de carbono.

pollen Tiny particles (male gametophytes) produced by seed plants that contain the cells that later become sperm cells. (p. 376)
polen Partículas diminutas (gametofitos masculinos) producidas por las plantas de semillas que contienen las células que posteriormente se convierten en células reproductoras masculinas.

pollination The transfer of pollen from male reproductive structures to female reproductive structures in plants. (p. 390)
polinización Transferencia de polen de las estructuras reproductoras masculinas a las estructuras reproductoras femeninas de las plantas.

polyp The cnidarian body plan characterized by a vaselike shape and usually adapted for a life attached to an underwater surface. (p. 419)
pólipo Cnidario cuyo cuerpo se caracteriza por tener forma cilíndrica, y que generalmente está adaptado para vivir adherido a una superficie submarina.

predicting The process of forecasting what will happen based on past experience or evidence. (p. 9)
predecir Proceso de pronosticar lo que va a suceder en el futuro, basado en la experiencia pasada o en evidencia.

pressure The force exerted on a surface divided by the total area over which the force is exerted. (p. 560)
presión La fuerza ejercida sobre una superficie, dividida por el área total sobre la cual se ejerce la fuerza; fuerza por unidad de área.

primary colors Three colors that can be used to make any other color. (p. 49)
colores primarios Tres colores que se pueden usar para hacer cualquier color.

probability A number that describes how likely it is that an event will occur. (p. 162)
probabilidad Número que describe la posibilidad de que ocurra un suceso.

prokaryote An organism whose cells lack a nucleus and some other cell structures. (p. 253)
procariota Organismo cuyas células carecen de núcleo y otras estructuras celulares.

protein Large organic molecule made of carbon, hydrogen, oxygen, nitrogen, and sometimes sulfur.
proteína Molécula orgánica grande compuesta de carbono, hidrógeno, oxígeno, nitrógeno y, a veces, azufre. (p. 100)

protist A eukaryotic organism that cannot be classified as an animal, plant, or fungus. (p. 335)
protista Organismo eucariótico que no se puede clasificar como animal, planta ni hongo.

protozoan An animal-like protist. (p. 335)
protozoario Protista con características animales.

pseudopod A "false foot" or temporary bulge of cytoplasm used for feeding and movement in some protozoans. (p. 336)
seudópodo "Falso pie" o abultamiento temporal del citoplasma, que algunos protozoarios usan para alimentarse o desplazarse.

puberty The period of sexual development in which the body becomes able to reproduce. (p. 663)
pubertad Período de desarrollo sexual durante la adolescencia en el que el cuerpo se vuelve capaz de reproducir.

pulse The alternating expansion and relaxation of an artery wall as blood travels through an artery. (p. 558)
pulso Expansión y relajación alternada de una pared arterial a medida que la sangre viaja por la arteria.

punctuated equilibria The theory that species evolve during short periods of rapid change.
equilibrio puntuado Teoría que enuncia que las especies evolucionan durante períodos breves de cambios rápidos. (p. 240)

Punnett square A chart that shows all the possible combinations of alleles that can result from a genetic cross. (p. 164)
cuadrado de Punnett Tabla que muestra todas las combinaciones posibles de los alelos que pueden resultar de una cruza genética.

pupa The third stage of complete metamorphosis, in which an insect changes from a larva to an adult.
pupa Tercera etapa de la metamorfosis completa, en la cual un insecto cambia de larva a adulto. (p. 440)

pupil The opening through which light enters the eye. (pp. 63, 615)
pupila Abertura por la que entra la luz al ojo.

purebred The offspring of many generations that have the same traits. (p. 155)
raza pura Descendiente de muchas generaciones que tienen los mismos rasgos.

Q

qualitative observation An observation that deals with characteristics that cannot be expressed in numbers. (p. 7)
observación cualitativa Observación que se centra en las características que no se pueden expresar con números.

quantitative observation An observation that deals with a number or amount. (p. 7)
observación cuantitativa Observación que se centra en un número o cantidad.

R

radial symmetry The quality of having many lines of symmetry that all pass through a central point.
simetría radial Cualidad de tener muchos ejes de simetría que pasan por un punto central. (p. 414)

radioactive decay The breakdown of a radioactive element, releasing particles and energy. (p. 280)
desintegración radiactiva Descomposición de un elemento radiactivo que libera partículas y energía.

radula A flexible ribbon of tiny teeth in mollusks.
rádula Hilera flexible de minúsculos dientes en los moluscos. (p. 431)

real image An upside-down image formed where rays of light meet. (p. 55)
imagen real Imagen invertida formada donde se encuentran los rayos de luz.

recessive allele An allele that is masked when a dominant allele is present. (p. 157)
alelo recesivo Alelo que queda oculto cuando está presente un alelo dominante.

red blood cell A cell in the blood that takes up oxygen in the lungs and delivers it to cells elsewhere in the body. (p. 564)
glóbulo rojo Célula de la sangre que capta el oxígeno en los pulmones y lo lleva a las células de todo el cuerpo.

reflecting telescope A telescope that uses a concave mirror to gather light from distant objects. (p. 67)
telescopio reflector Telescopio que usa un espejo cóncavo para reunir luz de los objetos distantes.

reflection The bouncing back of an object or wave when it hits a surface through which it cannot pass. (p. 53)
reflexión Rebote de un objeto o una onda cuando golpea una superficie por la cual no puede pasar.

reflex An automatic response that occurs rapidly and without conscious control. (p. 611)
reflejo Respuesta automática que ocurre muy rápidamente y sin control consciente.

refracting telescope A telescope that uses two convex lenses to form images. (p. 67)
telescopio refractor Telescopio que usa dos lentes convexas para formar imágenes.

refraction The bending of waves as they enter a new medium at an angle. (p. 57)
refracción Cambio de dirección de las ondas cuando entran en un nuevo medio en un determinado ángulo.

English and Spanish Glossary

relative age The age of a rock compared to the ages of rock layers. (p. 272)
edad relativa Edad de una roca comparada con la edad de las capas de roca.

replication The process by which a cell makes a copy of the DNA in its nucleus. (p. 130)
replicación Proceso por el cual una célula copia el ADN de su núcleo.

reptile An animal that lays eggs and has lungs and scaly skin. (pp. 290, 473)
reptil Vertebrado ectotermico que pono huevos, y que tiene pulmones y piel con excamas.

resistance arm For a lever, the distance from the fulcrum to the resistance force. (p. 536)
brazo de resistencia Para una palanca, la distancia desde el fulcro a la fuerza de resistencia.

resistance distance The distance a lever pushes up on an object. (p. 534)
distancia de resistencia Distancia que una palanca empuja un objeto hacia arriba.

resistance force The force a lever exerts on an object.
fuerza de resistencia Fuerza que una palanca ejerce sobre un objeto. (p. 534)

respiration The process by which cells break down simple food molecules such as glucose to release the energy they contain. (pp. 124, 571)
respiración Proceso por el cual las células descomponen moléculas simples de alimento para liberar la energía que contienen.

responding variable The factor that changes as a result of changes to the manipulated, or independent, variable in an experiment; also called dependent variable. (p. 20)
variable respuesta Factor que cambia como resultado del cambio de la variable manipulada, o independiente, en un experimento; también llamada variable dependiente.

response An action or change in behavior that occurs in reaction to a stimulus. (p. 601)
respuesta Acción o cambio en el comportamiento que ocurre como resultado de un estímulo.

retina A sheet of light-sensitive cells at the back of the eye on which an image is focused. (pp. 63, 616)
retina Capa de células receptoras en la parté posterior del ojo donde se enfoca una imagen.

rhizoid A thin, rootlike structure that anchors a moss and absorbs water and nutrients. (p. 371)
rizoide Estructura fina parecida a una raíz que sujeta un musgo al suelo, y que absorbe el agua y los nutrientes.

ribosome A small grain-like structure in the cytoplasm of a cell where proteins are made. (p. 93)
ribosoma Estructura pequeña parecida a un grano en el citoplasma de una célula donde se fabrican las proteínas.

RNA Ribonucleic acid; a nucleic acid that plays an important role in the production of proteins. (p. 101)
ARN Ácido ribonucleico; ácido nucleico que juega un papel importante en la producción de proteínas.

rock cycle A series of processes on the surface and inside Earth that slowly change rocks from one kind to another. (p. 270)
ciclo de las rocas Serie de processos en la superficie y dentro de la Tierra que lentamente transforman las rocas de un tipo de roca a otro.

rod cells Receptor cells in the eye that work best in dim light and enable you to see black, white, and gray.
células bastones Receptores en la retina del ojo, que funcionan mejor con poca luz y permiten ver negro, blanco y tonos de gris. (pp. 63, 616)

root cap A structure that covers the tip of a root, protecting the root from injury. (p. 381)
cofia Estructura que cubre la punta de una raíz y la protege contra daños.

S

scale model A model that accurately shows the proportions between its parts. (p. 12)
modelo a escala Modelo que muestra exactamente las proporciones entre sus partes.

science A way of learning about the natural world and the knowledge gained through the process.
ciencia Estudio del mundo natural a través de observaciones y del razonamiento lógico. (p. 6)

scientific inquiry The diverse ways in which scientists study the natural world and propose explanations based on evidence they gather. (p. 18)
investigación científica Diversidad de métodos con los que los científicos estudian el mundo natural y proponen explicaciones del mismo basadas en la evidencia que reúnen.

scientific theory A well-tested concept that explains a wide range of observations. (p. 228)
teoría científica Concepto comprobado que explica una amplia gama de observaciones.

scrotum An external pouch of skin in which the testes are located. (p. 650)
escroto Bolsa externa de piel en donde se ubican los testículos.

secondary color Any color produced by combining equal amounts of any two primary colors. (p. 49)
color secundario Color producido al combinar iguales cantidades de dos colores primarios cualquiera.

sedimentary rock Rock formed of hardened layers of sediments. (p. 269)
roca sedimentaria Roca formada por las capas endurecidas de sedimentos.

seed The plant structure that contains a young plant inside a protective covering. (p. 376)
semilla Estructura de una planta que contiene una plántula dentro de una cubierta protectora.

selective breeding The process of selecting a few organisms with desired traits to serve as parents of the next generation. (p. 206)
cruce selectivo Proceso de selección de algunos organismos con los rasgos deseados para que sirvan de como progenitores de la siguiente generación.

selectively permeable A property of cell membranes that allows some substances to pass through, while others cannot. (p. 102)
permeabilidad selectiva Propiedad de las membranas celulares que permite que algunas sustancias pasen y otras no.

semen A mixture of sperm and fluids. (p. 651)
semen Mezcla de células de espermatozoides y fluidos.

semicircular canals Structures in the inner ear that are responsible for the sense of balance. (p. 620)
canales semicirculares Estructuras en el oído interno responsables del sentido del equilibrio.

sensory neuron A neuron that picks up stimuli from the internal or external environment and converts each stimulus into a nerve impulse. (p. 602)
neurona sensorial Proceso de selección de algunos organismos con los rasgos deseados para servir como progenitores de la siguiente generación.

sepal A leaflike structure that encloses the bud of a flower. (p. 392)
sépalo Estructura, parecida a una hoja, que encierra el botón de una flor.

sex chromosomes A pair of chromosomes carrying genes that determine whether a person is male or female. (p. 195)
cromosomas sexuales Par de cromosomas portadores de genes que determinan si una persona es macho o hembra.

sex-linked gene A gene that is carried on the X or Y chromosome. (p. 196)
gen ligado al sexo Gen portador del cromosoma X o Y.

sexual reproduction A reproductive process that involves two parents that combine their genetic material to produce a new organism, which differs from both parents. (pp. 170, 328)
reproducción sexual Proceso de reproducción que implica a dos progenitores que combinan su material genético para producir un nuevo organismo diferente a los dos progenitores.

shared derived characteristic A characteristic—usually a homologous structure—shared by all organisms in a group. (p. 256)
características derivadas compartidas Una característica, normalmente una estructura homóloga, compartida por todos los organismos de un grupo.

shock The failure of the circulatory system to provide adequate oxygen-rich blood to all parts of the body.
conmoción Incapacidad del sistema circulatorio de proporcionar suministro adecuado de sangre rica en oxígeno a todas las partes del cuerpo. (p. 566)

skeletal muscle A muscle that is attached to the bones of the skeleton and provides the force that moves the bones. (p. 528)
músculos esqueléticos Músculo que está unido a los huesos del esqueleto y que proporciona la fuerza para que los huesos se muevan.

skeleton The inner framework made of all the bones of the body. (p. 518)
esqueleto Estructura formada por todos los huesos del cuerpo.

smooth muscle Involuntary muscle found inside many internal organs of the body. (p. 528)
músculos lisos Músculo involuntario que se encuentra dentro de muchos órganos internos del cuerpo.

somatic nervous system The group of nerves in the peripheral nervous system that controls voluntary actions. (p. 611)
sistema nervioso somático Grupo de nervios en el sistema nervioso periférico que controla las acciones voluntarias.

species A group of organisms that are physically similar and can mate with each other and produce offspring that can also mate and reproduce. (p. 225)
especie Grupo de organismos que son físicamente semejantes, se pueden cruzar y producen crías que también se pueden cruzar y reproducir.

sperm A male sex cell. (p. 649)
espermatozoide Célula sexual masculina.

spinal cord The thick column of nerve tissue that links the brain to most of the nerves in the peripheral nervous system. (p. 607)
médula espinal Columna gruesa de tejido nervioso que une el encéfalo con la mayoría de los nervios en el sistema nervioso periférico.

spongy bone Layer of bone tissue having many small spaces and found just inside the layer of compact bone. (p. 522)
hueso esponjoso Capa de tejido de un hueso que tiene muchos espacios pequeños y se encuentra justo dentro de la capa del hueso compacto.

spore A tiny cell that is able to grow into a new organism. (p. 342)
espora Célula diminuta que, al crecer, puede convertirse en un nuevo organismo.

sporophyte The stage in the life cycle of a plant in which the plant produces spores. (p. 368)
esporofito Etapa en el ciclo de vida de una planta en la que la planta produce esporas.

stamen A male reproductive part of a flower. (p. 392)
estambre Parte reproductora masculina de una flor.

stem cell A cell that can differentiate throughout life.
célula troncal Célula del cuerpo que se puede diferenciar durante toda la vida. (p. 140)

stimulant A drug that speeds up body processes.
estimulante Droga que acelera los procesos del cuerpo. (p. 626)

stimulus A change or signal in an organism's surroundings that causes the organism to react.
estímulo Cambio en el entorno de un organismo que le hace reaccionar. (p. 601)

stirrup A small bone in the middle ear that transmits vibrations from the anvil to a membrane of the inner ear; also called the "stapes." (p. 619)
estribo Pequeño hueso en el oído medio, que transmite vibraciones desde el yunque a una membrana del oído interno.

stomata Small openings on a leaf through which oxygen and carbon dioxide can move. (p. 121)
estomas Pequeños orificios en la superficie inferior de la hoja a través de los cuales se intercambia oxígeno y dióxido de carbono.

stress The reaction of a person's body to potentially threatening, challenging, or disturbing events. (p. 517)
estrés Reacción del cuerpo de un individuo a amenazas, retos o sucesos molestos potenciales.

striated muscle A muscle that appears banded; also called skeletal muscle. (p. 528)
músculo estriado Músculo con forma de franjas; también se llama músculo esquelético.

stroke Death of brain tissue that can result when a blood vessel in the brain is either blocked by a clot or bursts. (p. 583)
apoplejía Interrupción repentina del flujo de sangre a una parte del cerebro.

structure The way an organism is put together as a whole. (p. 16)
estructura La manera en que un organismo está armado como conjunto.

suffocation Dangerous condition in which insufficient gas exchange in the lungs leads to a lack of oxygen in the vital organs. (p. 586)
sofocación Condiciones peligrosas en las que el intercambio insuficiente de gases en los pulmones lleva a la carencia de oxígeno en los órganos vitales.

swim bladder An internal, gas-filled organ that helps a bony fish stabilize its body at different water depths.
vejiga natatoria Órgano interno lleno de gas que ayuda a un pez con esqueleto a estabilizar su cuerpo a diferentes profundidades. (p. 466)

symbiosis A close relationship between two organisms of different species that benefits at least one of the organisms. (p. 338)
simbiosis Relación estrecha entre especies de la que se beneficia al menos una de ellas.

synapse The junction where one neuron can transfer an impulse to another structure. (p. 604)
sinapsis Unión donde una neurona puede transferir un impulso a la siguiente estructura.

T

tadpole The larval form of a frog or a toad. (p. 469)
renacuajo Estado de larva de una rana o un sapo.

tar A dark, sticky substance that forms when tobacco burns. (p. 584)
alquitrán Sustancia oscura y pegajosa producida cuando se quema tabaco.

target cell A cell in the body that recognizes a hormone's chemical structure. (p. 642)
célula destinataria Célula del cuerpo que reconoce la estructura química de una hormona.

taste bud An organ on the tongue that contains receptors that detect chemicals in food. (p. 622)
papila gustativa Órgano en la lengua que contiene receptores que detectan los químicos en los alimentos.

taxonomy The scientific study of how living things are classified. (p. 249)
taxonomía Estudio científico de cómo se clasifican los seres vivos.

telescope An optical instrument that forms enlarged images of distant objects. (p. 67)
telescopio Instrumento óptico que forma imágenes aumentadas de los objetos lejanos.

tendon Strong connective tissue that attaches muscle to bone. (p. 528)
tendón Tejido conectivo resistente que une un músculo a un hueso.

testis Organ of the male reproductive system in which sperm and testosterone are produced.
testículo Órgano del sistema reproductor masculino en el cual se producen los espermatozoides y la testosterona. (p. 650)

testosterone A hormone produced by the testes that controls the development of physical characteristics in mature men. (p. 650)
testosterona Hormona producida por los testículos que controla el desarrollo de las características físicas del hombre maduro.

theory of plate tectonics Theory that states that Earth's plates move slowly in different directions. (p. 284)
tectonica de placas Teoría según la cual las partes de la litosfera de la Tierra están en continuo movimiento, impulsadas por las corrientes de convección del manto.

thorax An arthropod's midsection, to which its wings and legs are attached. (p. 439)
tórax Sección media de un insecto, a la que están unidas las alas y las patas.

tissue A group of similar cells that perform the same function. (p. 85)
tejido Grupo de células semejantes que realizan la misma función.

tolerance A state in which a drug user needs larger amounts of the drug to produce the same effect on the body. (p. 625)
tolerancia Estado en el que un consumidor de drogas necesita mayores cantidades de la droga para que produzca el mismo efecto en el cuerpo.

trace fossil A type of fossil that provides evidence of the activities of ancient organisms. (p. 237)
vestigios fósiles Tipo de fósil que da evidencia de las actividades de los organismos antiguos.

trachea The windpipe; a passage through which air moves in the respiratory system. (p. 574)
tráquea Conducto a través del cual se mueve el aire en el sistema respiratorio.

trait A characteristic that an organism can pass on to its offspring through its genes. (p. 154)
rasgo Característica que un organismo puede transmitir a su descendencia a través de sus genes.

transfer RNA RNA in the cytoplasm that carries an amino acid to the ribosome and adds it to the growing protein chain. (p. 177)
ARN de transferencia ARN en el citoplasma que lleva un aminoácido al ribosoma y lo suma a la cadena proteínica que se está formando.

translucent That which scatters light as it passes through. (p. 47)
material traslúcido Lo que dispersa la luz cuando ésta lo atraviesa.

transparent That which transmits light without scattering it. (p. 47)
material transparente Lo que transmite luz sin dispersarla.

transpiration The process by which water is lost through a plant's leaves. (p. 385)
transpiración Proceso por el cual las hojas de una planta eliminan agua.

trough The lowest part of a wave. (p. 40)
valle Parte más baja de una onda.

tube feet Extensions of an echinoderm's water vascular system that stick out from the body and function in movement and obtaining food. (p. 444)
pies ambulacrales Extensiones del sistema vascular de agua de un equinodermo que sobresalen del cuerpo y sirven para la locomoción y la obtención de alimento.

English and Spanish Glossary

U

umbilical cord A ropelike structure that forms between the embryo or fetus and the placenta. (p. 659)
cordón umbilical Estructura con forma de cuerda que se forma entre el embrión o feto y la placenta.

unconformity A place where an old, eroded rock surface is in contact with a newer rock layer. (p. 275)
discordancia Lugar donde una superficie rocosa erosionada y vieja está en contacto con una capa de rocas más nueva.

unicellular Made of a single cell. (p. 85)
unicelular Compuesto por una sola célula.

uniformitarianism The geologic principle that the same geologic processes that operate today operated in the past to change Earth's surface. (p. 269)
uniformismo Principio geológico que enuncia que los mismos procesos geológicos que cambian la superficie de la Tierra en la actualidad, ocurrían en el pasado.

ureter A narrow tube that carries urine from one of the kidneys to the urinary bladder. (p. 513)
ureter Conducto estrecho que lleva la orina desde cada uno de los riñones a la vejiga urinaria.

urethra A small tube through which urine flows from the body. (p. 651)
uretra Pequeño conducto a través del cual fluye la orina desde el cuerpo.

urinary bladder A sacklike muscular organ that stores urine until it is eliminated from the body.
vejiga urinaria Órgano muscular con forma de saco que almacena la orina hasta que es eliminada del cuerpo. (p. 513)

urine A watery fluid produced by the kidneys that contains urea and other wastes. (p. 473)
orina Fluido acuoso producido por los riñones que contiene urea y otros materiales de desecho.

uterus The hollow muscular organ of the female reproductive system in which a fertilized egg develops. (p. 653)
útero Órgano muscular hueco del sistema reproductor femenino en el que se desarrolla el bebé.

V

vaccine A substance used in a vaccination that consists of weakened or killed pathogens that can trigger the immune system into action. (p. 323)
vacuna Sustancia usada en una vacunación que está formada por patógenos que han sido debilitados o muertos pero que todavía pueden activar el sistema inmunológico.

vacuole A sac inside a cell that acts as a storage area.
vacuola Saco dentro de la célula que actúa como área de almacenamiento. (p. 94)

vagina A muscular passageway leading to the outside of the body; also called the birth canal. (p. 653)
vagina Pasaje muscular que lleva hacia afuera del cuerpo; también llamado canal de nacimiento.

valve A flap of tissue in the heart or a vein that prevents blood from flowing backward. (p. 555)
válvula Tapa de tejido en el corazón o en una vena que impide que la sangre fluya hacia atrás.

variable A factor in an experiment that can change.
variable Factor que puede cambiar en un experimento. (p. 20)

vascular plant A plant that has true vascular tissue.
planta vascular Planta que tiene tejido vascular verdadero. (p. 366)

vascular tissue The internal transporting tissue in some plants that is made up of tubelike structures.
tejido vascular Tejido de transporte interno en algunas plantas que está formado por estructuras parecidas a tubos. (p. 365)

vegetative reproduction Reproduction in plants by asexual methods. (p. 365)
reproducción vegetativa Reproducción en las plantas a través de métodos asexuales.

vein A blood vessel that carries blood back to the heart.
vena Vaso sanguíneo que devuelve la sangre al corazón. (p. 556)

ventricle A lower chamber of the heart that pumps blood out to the lungs and body. (pp. 470, 555)
ventrículo Cámara inferior del corazón que bombea la sangre hacia los pulmones y el cuerpo.

vertebrae The small bones that make up the backbone. (pp. 457, 519)
vértebras Los huesecillos que forman la columna vertebral de un animal.

vertebrate An animal that has a backbone. (pp. 289, 416)
vertebrado Animal que posee columna vertebral.

vibration A repeated back-and-forth or up-and-down motion. (p. 39)
vibración Movimiento repetido hacia delante y hacia atrás o hacia arriba y hacia abajo.

virtual image An upright image formed where rays of light appear to meet or come from. (p. 54)
imagen virtual Imagen vertical que se forma desde donde parecen provenir los rayos de luz.

virus A tiny, nonliving particle that invades and then reproduces inside a living cell. (p. 318)
virus Partícula diminuta no viva que invade una célula viva y luego se reproduce dentro de ella.

visible light Electromagnetic waves that are visible to the human eye. (p. 43)
luz visible Ondas electromagnéticas visibles al ojo humano.

vocal cords Folds of connective tissue that stretch across the opening of the larynx and produce a person's voice. (p. 578)
cuerdas vocales Pliegues de tejido conectivo que se extienden a lo largo de la abertura de la laringe y producen la voz de la persona.

voluntary muscle A muscle that is under conscious control. (p. 527)
músculos voluntarios Músculo que se puede controlar conscientemente.

water vascular system A system of fluid-filled tubes in an echinoderm's body. (p. 444)
sistema vascular de agua Sistema de vasos llenos de líquidos en el cuerpo de un equinodermo.

wave A disturbance that transfers energy from place to place. (p. 39)
onda Perturbación que transfiere energía de un lugar a otro.

wavelength The distance between two corresponding parts of a wave. (p. 41)
longitud de onda Distancia entre dos partes correspondientes de una onda.

white blood cell A blood cell that fights disease.
glóbulo blanco Célula de la sangre que protege contra las enfermedades. (p. 565)

withdrawal A period of adjustment that occurs when a drug-dependent person stops taking the drug.
síndrome de abstinencia Período de ajuste que ocurre cuando una persona adicta a las drogas deja de consumirlas. (p. 625)

work Force exerted on an object that causes it to move.
trabajo Fuerza ejercida sobre un objeto para moverlo. (p. 533)

xylem The vascular tissue through which water and nutrients move in some plants. (p. 376)
xilema Tejido vascular por el que circulan agua y nutrientes en algunas plantas.

zygote A fertilized egg, produced by the joining of a sperm and an egg. (p. 365)
cigoto Óvulo fecundado, producido por la unión de un espermatozoide y un óvulo.

Index

Index

Page numbers for key terms are printed in **boldface** type.
Page numbers for illustrations, maps, and charts are printed in *italics*.

Index

DNA 15, 17, *101*, 112, 416, 509
  analyzing 213
  cell differentiation and 140
  evolution and 235
  genes and *176*
  mitochondrial 210
  replication **130**, *135–136*
  RNA compared to 177
  species relationships and *244*
  structure of *135–136*
DNA fingerprinting 210, 212–213
domains 251, *253–254*
dominant allele *157*, 158
down feathers **481**, *484*
Down syndrome 200, 203
downy mildews *343*
Drew, Charles *582*
drug abuse **624**–627
drugs 624
duck-billed platypus 490

E

ear 618, *619–620*. See also **hearing**
ear canal *619*
eardrum *619*
Earth
  age of 282
  early *288*
earthworm *424, 429*
Echinodermata 443
echinoderms *415*, **443**–445
ecologist *14*
ectotherms 459
effort arm *536*
effort distance **534**–535
effort force **534**–535, *537*
egg(s) *170*, 172, 413, **649**, 653–654
  amniotic **474**
  amphibians 469
  of birds 484–485
  insect *440, 441*
  of mammals 490–491
  reptile 473, *477*
  trout *464*
egg cells 368
  sponge 418
ejaculation 651
elbow joint 539
electric field *42*
electromagnetic radiation **42**
electromagnetic spectrum **43**–45
electromagnetic wave 39, **42**–45
electron microscopes 67, **69**, *83*

element(s) **97, 280**, 281
  daughter 281
  parent 281
embryo **377**, *395*, **657**, *658*
  differentiation of 657
  protection and nourishment
    658–659
emotional dependence 629
emperor penguins *460*
emphysema **585**
endangered species 242, 471
endocrine glands *641*
  functions of 642–644
endocrine system *515*, 640–647
  hormones and **641**–642, 652,
    654
  negative feedback in **644**–645
endoplasmic reticulum *90, 91*, **93**
endoskeleton **443**, 458
endospores *329*
endotherms **460**
energy 15, **39**, 118
  of electromagnetic waves *42*
  for photosynthesis 119
  respiration and *124*
  stored *122*
  from sun *119*, 120
  waves and 39
environment(s)
  bacterial cleanup of *332*
  extinction and 245
  heredity and *198*
  ice-age *296*
  natural selection and 230
  of the past *238–239*
  species variety and 242
enzymes **100**, 130, 513
epidermis *511*
epididymis *650, 651*
epiglottis *573*, 574
epithelial tissue *510*
equilibria, punctuated **240**
eras **286**
erosion **268**, 270, *271*
Escherichia coli 327
*Essay on the Principle of
  Population* (Malthus) 229
estrogen **652**
euglena *340*
Eukarya *253*
eukaryotes **254**
evidence in scientific theories 222

evolution 16, 218–261, **228**
  branching tree and 416
  classification and 248–257
  Darwin's theory of 224–231
  developmental similarities and
    235
  DNA and protein similarities
    235
  evidence of 234–240
  fossils 225, 236–240
  plate movement and 284, 285
  rate of 238, 240
  of species 241–246
  of vertebrates 458–*459*
excretory system 511, *513, 628*
exercise *580*
exhalation *577*
exoskeleton **435**
experiments
  controlled **20, 675**
external ear *619*
external fertilization 464
extinction **245**–246
  in Cretaceous Period 295
  of dinosaurs 295, 296
  mass **291**, 295
  in Permian Period 291
extrusion **274**, 275
eyepiece **67**, 68
eyes 48–49, *615*. See also **vision**
  compound 439
  simple 439
  structure and function of *16–17*
eyespot *340*, 427

F

fallopian tubes **652**, *653*
family 251
farsighted 64
fats 99, 510
faults *274*, 275
feathers 460
  contour *481*
  down **481**, *484*
feedback, negative **644**–645
female reproductive system
  652–655
femur (thighbone) *519, 522*
fermentation **126**–127
  alcoholic 127
  lactic acid *127*
ferns *373*

Index

Page numbers for key terms are printed in **boldface** type.
Page numbers for illustrations, maps, and charts are printed in *italics*.

Index

Index

Page numbers for key terms are printed in **boldface** type.
Page numbers for illustrations, maps, and charts are printed in *italics*.

Index

Page numbers for key terms are printed in **boldface** type.
Page numbers for illustrations, maps, and charts are printed in *italics*.

Index

Page numbers for key terms are printed in **boldface** type.
Page numbers for illustrations, maps, and charts are printed in *italics*.

Acknowledgments

Science Content Standards for California Public Schools reproduced by permission, California Department of Education, CDE Press, 1430 N Street, Suite 3207, Sacramento, CA 95814.

Acknowledgment for page 310: Excerpt from *James Herriot's Dog Stories*. Copyright ©1986 by James Herriot. Published by St. Martin's Press.

Staff Credits

Ernest Albanese, Scott Andrews, Carole Anson, Becky Barra, Peggy Bliss, Anne M. Bray, Katherine Bryant, Michael A. Burstein, Sarah Carroll, Sara Castrignano, Kenneth Chang, Jonathan Cheney, Bob Craton, Patricia M. Dambry, Glen Dixon, Jonathan Fisher, Kathryn Fobert, Robert M. Graham, Anne Jones, Kelly Kelliher, Toby Klang, Russ Lappa, Greg Lam, Dotti Marshall, Tim McDonald, Brent McKenzie, Ranida McKneally, Julia Osborne, Caroline Power, Gerry Schrenk, Siri Schwartzman, Malti Sharma, Laurel Smith, Emily Soltanoff, Paul Ramos, Linda Zust Reddy, Rashid Ross, Marcy Rose, Diane Walsh

Additional Credits

Michelle Chaison, Lisa Clark, Angela Clarke, Brad Conger, Roger Dowd, Paula Gogan-Porter, Tom Greene, Kama Holder, Rich McMahon, Robyn Salbo, Ted Smykal, Laura Smyth, Chris Willson, Heather Wright

Illustration

Articulate Graphics, Morgan Cain & Associates, David Corrente, Warren Cutler, Dorling Kindersley, John Edwards & Associates, Forge FX, Chris Forsey, Geosystems Global Corporation, Dale Gustafson, Robert Hynes, Kevin Jones Associates, Jared D. Lee, Martucci Design, Steve McEntee, Rich McMahon, Rich McMahon with J/B Woolsey Associates, Karen Minot, Paul Mirocha, Ortelius Design, Inc., Matthew Pippin, Brucie Rosch, Ted Smykal, Walter Stuart, J/B Woolsey Associates, XNR Productions, Rose Zgodzinski

Charts and Graphs

Ernest Albanese, Matt Mayerchak

Photography

Photo Research Kerri Hoar, John Judge, Sue McDermott, Paula Wehde
Cover Images: Kelp, Ralph A. Clevenger/Corbis; **Shark,** Amos Noucham

CHAPTER 1

Pages 0–1, Barrett and MacKay; **2l,** Richard Haynes; **3b,** AP/Wide World Photos; **3m,** Piotr Naskrecki /Minden Pictures; **5b,** Burke/Triolo Productions/Getty Images, Inc.; **7t,** Michael Nichols/National Geographic Society; **7b,** Manoh Shah/Getty Images, Inc.; **8l,** K. & K. Ammann/Bruce Coleman, Inc.; **9t,** Wild Chimpanzees.org; **10tr,** Wild Chimpanzees.org; **11r,** Adrian Warren/Lastrefuge.co.uk; **11l,** Irven De Vore/Anthrophoto file; **12,** Russ Lappa; **13l,** Davies & Starr/Getty Images, Inc.; **13mr,** David Wrobel/Visuals Unlimited; **13m,** Nancy Rotenberg/Animals Animals/Earth Scenes; **14mr,** Chris Stowers/Panos Pictures; **14bl,** Frans Lanting/Minden Pictures; **14tl,** AP/Wide World Photos; **16m,** Corbis **16l,** Joe McDonald/Animals Animals/Earth Scenes; **16r,** Rod Planck/Dembinsky Photo Associates; **17r,** James Robinson/ Animals Animals/Earth Scenes; **17l,** Robert Stahl/Getty Images, Inc.; **17m,** Hans Strand/Getty Images, Inc.; **18l,** M.T. Frazier/ Photo Researchers, Inc.; **18t,** Houghton Mifflin Company; **19r,** Richard Haynes; **20b,** Richard Haynes; **21t,** Richard Haynes; **23t,** Russ Lappa; **23b,** Russ Lappa; **24–25,** Richard Haynes; **28bl,** Renee Stockdale/Animals Animals.

CHAPTER 2

Pages 32–33, Hank Morgan/Photo Researchers, Inc.; **34bl,** Diane Hirsch/Fundamental Photographs; **34r,** Peter A. Simon/Corbis; **35t,** Reno Tucillo; **37** inset, Richard Haynes; **38b,** Image Bank/Getty Images, Inc.; **38t,** Richard Haynes; **43b,** Corbis; **46b,** E.R. Degginger/Color Pic; **46t,** Richard Haynes; **47r,** Richard Haynes; **48t,** PhotoDisc/Gettty Images, Inc.; **50t,** Russ Lappa; **51t,** Richard Haynes; **52t,** Richard Haynes; **52b,** Tony Freeman/PhotoEdit; **53b,** Reno Tucillo; **54r,** Sergio Piumatti; **55r,** David Young-Wolff/Photo Edit; **56r,** David Young-Wolff/Photo Edit; **58l,** Getty Images, Inc.; **59l,** Getty Images, Inc.; **59l,** Donald Specker/Animals Animals.; **61t,** Richard Haynes; **62t,** Richard Haynes; **65b,** Sinclair Stammers/SPL/Photo Researchers, Inc.; **65t,** Richard Haynes; **66l,** Joseph Van Os/Getty Images; **68tl,** Photo Researchers, Inc.; **68ml,** Dr. John D. Cunningham/Visuals Unlimited; **68bl,** Dr. John D. Cunningham/Visuals Unlimited; **69t,** CRNI/SPL/Photo Researchers, Inc.; **72t,** PhotoDisc/ Gettty Images, Inc.

CHAPTER 3

Pages 74–75, Dr. David E. Scott/Phototake; **75br,** Dorling Kindersley; **77t,** Digital Vision/Getty Images, Inc.; **79** inset, Richard Haynes; **80t,** Richard Haynes; **80b,** McDonald Wildlife Photo, Inc./DRK Photo; **81t,** SPL/Photo Researchers, Inc.; **81b,** Richard Haynes; **82m,** The Granger Collection; **82r,** Bettmann/Corbis; **82l,** FSU Research Foundation; **83l,** Bettmann/Corbis; **83r,** Lawrence Migdale/Stock Boston; **83m,** Pascal Goetgheluck/SPL/Photo Researchers; **84l,** John Locke/Dembinsky Photo Associates; **85tr,** Steve Shott/Dorling Kindersley Media Library; **86br,** Richard Haynes; **88t,** Runk/Schoenberger/Grant Heilman Photography, Inc.; **88b,** Corbis; **89r,** Mike Abbey/Visuals Unlimited; **89l,** Runk/Schoenberger/Grant Heilman Photography; **92t,** Alfred Paskieka/SPL/Photo Researchers, Inc.; **93t,** Bill Longcore/Photo Researchers, Inc.; **93l,** Photo Researcher, Inc.; **94t,** Photo Researchers, Inc.; **95t,** Dr. David Scott/CRNI/Phototake; **95b,** Motta & S. Correr/SPL/Photo Researchers, Inc.; **97t,** Russ Lappa; **98t,** Digital Vision/Getty Images, Inc.; **99bl,** Vittoriano Rastelli/Corbis; **99t,** Japack Company/Corbis; **99m,** Andrew Syred/Science Photo Library/Photo Researchers, Inc.; **99br,** Getty Images, Inc.; **101t,** CRNI/Science Photo Library; **102–103,** Damilo P. Donadomi/Bruce Coleman, Inc.; **107t,** M. Abbey/Visuals Unlimited; **110l,** Runk Schoenberger/Grant Heilman Photography.

CHAPTER 4

Pages 112–113, Michael J. Doolittle/The Image Works; **112,** Michael J. Doolittle/The Image Works; **113br,** Robert A. Tyrrell; **114l,** Ian O'Leary/Dorling Kindersley; **114r,** Ian O'Leary/Dorling Kindersley; **115b,** Dr. Dennis Kunkel/ Visuals Unlimited; **115mr,** Dr. Jeremy Burgess/Photo Researchers, Inc.; **115ml,** Dr. Jeremy Burgess/Photo Researchers, Inc.; **117b,** Russ Lappa; **118t,** Russ Lappa; **118–119,** Todd Gustafson/Panoramic Images; **119** inset, Stephen J. Krasemann/Photo Researchers, Inc.; **120l,** Biophoto Associates/Photo Researchers, Inc.; **121r,** Dr. Jeremy Burgess/SPL/Photo Researchers, Inc.; **122l,** Superstock; **123b,** Royalty-Free/Corbis; **124tr,** John Downer/NaturePL; **124tl,** Stephen Dalton/Photo Researchers, Inc.; **127t,** Richard Hutchins/PhotoEdit; **129tr,** David Scharf/Peter Arnold, Inc.; **129bl,** AP/Wide World Photos; **130–131,** Royalty Free/Corbis; **131b,** Biophoto Associates/Science Source/Photo Researchers,; Inc.; **132t,** M. Abbey/Photo Researchers, Inc.; **132b,** M. Abbey/Photo Researchers, Inc.; **132m,** M. Abbey/Photo Researchers, Inc.; **133t,** M. Abbey/Photo Researchers, Inc.; **133m,** M. Abbey/Photo Researchers, Inc.; **133b,** M. Abbey/Photo Researchers, Inc.; **134b,** Visuals Unlimited; **137t,** Runk/Schoenberger/Grant Heilman Photography; **138bl,** Steve Gschmeissner/Science Photo Library/Photo Researchers, Inc.; **138tr,** J. Brown/OSF/Animals Animals/Earth Scenes; **140tr,** Eye of Science/Photo Researchers, Inc; **140mr,** Eye of Science/ Photo Researchers, Inc; **140br,** Dr. Dennis Kunkel/Visuals Unlimited; **140l,** Dr. Dennis Kunkel/Visuals Unlimited; **141t,** Matthew Ward/Dorling Kindersley.

CHAPTER 5

Pages 148–149, Ron Kimball Studios; **153br,** Richard Haynes; **154tr,** Getty Images, Inc.; **154br,** Jerry Howard/ Positive Images; **154bl,** Hulton Archive/Getty Images, Inc.; **157mr,** Dorling Kindersley; **158br,** Meinrad Faltner/Corbis Stock Market; **158bl,** Meinrad Faltner/Corbis Stock Market;**159tr,** Villanova University; **160bl,** Mary Kate Denny/Photoedit; **160tl,** Michael Newman/PhotoEdit; **160tml,** David Young-Wolf/PhotoEdit; **160tmr,** David Young Wolf/ PhotoEdit; **160bmr,** David Young Wolf/PhotoEdit; **160tr,** David Young Wolf/PhotoEdit; **160br,** Corbis; **160bml,** Nicolas Russell/Getty Images, Inc.; **162r,** David Young-Wolff/Photo Edit; **162l,** U.S. Mint/Omni-Photo Communications, Inc.; **163b,** Jim Cummins/Getty Images, Inc.; **168t,** Dorling Kindersley; **169b,** Richard Haynes; **169t,** Dorling Kindersley; **170bl,** Dennis Kunkel/PhotoTake; **171r,** E.R. Degginger/Color-Pic, Inc.; **171l,** Michael Abbey/Photo Researchers, Inc.; **175b,** George Nikitin/AP/Wide World Photos; **181t,** Dorling Kindersley.

CHAPTER 6

Pages 186–187, Royalty-Free/Corbis; 188bl, Foodpix; 188bm, Photo Researchers, Inc.; 188br, Foodpix; 189t, The Image Works; 191r, Richard Haynes; 192t, Richard Haynes; 192b, Michael Newman/PhotoEdit; 193, David Young-Wolf/ PhotoEdit; 193, David Young-Wolf/PhotoEdit; 193, David Young-Wolf/ PhotoEdit; 193br, David Young-Wolf/PhotoEdit; 193tr, David Urbina/PhotoEdit; 193, Michael Newman/ PhotoEdit; 193bl, David Young-Wolff/PictureQuest; 194b, Camille Tokerud/Stone/Getty Images, Inc.; 196l, Corbis; 196r, Michael Douma, Institute for Dynamic Educational Advancement; 198t, Amy Etra/PhotoEdit; 199tr, CNRI/ Science Photo Library/Photo Researchers, Inc.; 199bl, Jonathan Nourok/ PhotoEdit; 200t, Stanley Flegler/Visuals Unlimited; 200b, Stanley Flegler/Visuals Unlimited; 201b, Craig Farraway; 203l, National Hemophilia Foundation; 203r, National Hemophilia Foundation; 205b, South West News Service; 206ml, Grant Heilman; 206bl, Foodpix; 206bm, Photo Researchers, Inc.; 206br, Foodpix; 206tl, Paul McCormick/Getty Images, Inc.; 207br, The Image Works; 209tr, 5-D and Segrest Farms/AP/Wide World Photos; 209tl, Animals Animals/Earth Scenes; 210l, Photo Researchers, Inc.; 211t, David Parker/Photo Researchers, Inc.; 212tr, Nathan Benn/Corbis; 212mr, Getty Images, Inc.; 213m, Loida J. Escote-Carlson; 213tr, Andrew Brooks/Corbis; 214r, Biophoto Associates/Photo Researchers, Inc.; 214l, Biophoto Associates/Photo Researchers, Inc.

CHAPTER 7

Pages 218–219, Tui De Roy/Minden Pictures; 219br, Ray Lacey / Science Photo Library/Photo Researchers; 220b, Daniel J. Krasemann/DRK Photo; 220l, Carolina Biological/Visuals Unlimited; 220m, W. Wayne Lockwood, M.D./Corbis; 220r, Photodisc/Getty Images, Inc.; 223br, Tom McHugh/ Photo Researchers, Inc.; 224t, Portrait by George Richmond/ Down House, Downe/Bridgeman Art Library; 224b, Christopher Ralling; 225b, Tui De Roy/Minden Pictures; 225t, Tui De Roy/Minden Pictures; 226b, Jeremy Woodhouse/Masterfile; 226t, Photo Researchers, Inc.; 228b, AP/Wide World Photos; 228t, Barbara D. Livingston; 228m, Barbara D. Livingston; 233r, Richard Haynes; 234b, Vincent P. Walter/PH College; 234t, James L. Amos/Photo Researchers, Inc.; 235m, Photo Researchers, Inc.; 235l, G. Alamany & E. Vicouns/Corbis; 235r, Robert Pearcy; 237tr, Peter Pavlovsky/Fossils.de; 238t, Peabody Museum of Natural History; 239t, T. Wiewandt/DRK Photo; 241tl, Klein/ Peter Arnold, Inc.; 241tm, Klein/Peter Arnold, Inc.; 241tr, Newman and Associates/Phototake NY; 241bl, Gerald & Buff Corsi/Visuals Unlimited; 242b, Frans Lanting/ Minden Pictures; 243l, Pat & Tom Leeson/Photo Researchers, Inc.; 243r, Pat & Tom Leeson Photo Researchers, Inc.; 244r, Gary Milburn/Tom Stack & Associates, Inc.; 244l, Frans Lanting/Minden Pictures; 248t, Russ Lappa; 248b, Inga Spence/The Picture Cube, Inc.; 249t, Biophoto Associates/Photo Researchers, Inc.; 250l, Gerard Lacz/Animals Animals; 250m, Ron Kimball Studios; 250r, Gavriel Jecan/Art Wolfe, Inc.; 251t, Lynn Stone/Animals Animals; 252b, Thomas Kitchin/Tom Stack & Associates, Inc.; 254tm, Dr. David Patterson/Photo Researchers, Inc.; 254tr, Jaime Plaza Van Roon/Auspace/Minden Pictures; 254l, Michael & Patricia Fogden/Minden Pictures; 254bl, Marian Bacon/Animals Animals/ Earth Scenes; 257t Colin Keates/Dorling Kindersley.

CHAPTER 8

Pages 262–263, Dave G. Houser/Corbis; 263br, B. Runks/S. Schoenberger/Grant Heilman Photography; 264b, Photo Researchers, Inc.; 264–265, Penny Tweedie/ TSI/Getty Images, Inc.; 265tl, Francois Gohier/Photo Researchers, Inc.; 265tr, Douglas Henderson; 265b, Penny Tweedie/TSI; 267 inset, Richard Haynes; 268l, Tom Lazar/Animals Animals/Earth Scenes; 269r, N J Clark/Robert Harding World Imagery/Getty Images, Inc.; 269l, Dr. Marli Miller/Visuals Unlimited; 272t, Richard Haynes; 272b, Zephyr Picture/Index Stock Imagery/PictureQuest; 273l, 274r, PH Photo; 274l, PH Photo; 276t, Maria Stenzel/National Geographic/Getty Images, Inc.; 277t, Photo Researchers, Inc.; 279t, Richard Haynes; 279b, Michael Fogden/ DRK Photo; 279 inset, Dr.Dennis Kunkel/Visuals Unlimited; 282t, NASA; 283b, NASA; 285t, Penny Tweedie/TSI; 290b, The Field Museum, Neg.#CSGEO 75400c.; 290t, Chip Clark/Smithsonian Institution; 294t, Dorling Kindersley; 295tr, David M. Dennis/Tom Stack & Associates, Inc.; 295b, D. Van Ravenswaay/Photo Researchers, Inc.; 297t, Photo Researchers, Inc.; 298tr, Richard Haynes.

CHAPTER 9

Pages 312–313, Dennis Kunkel/Phototake; 313br, Anne W. Rosenfeld/Animals Animals/Earth Scenes; 314b, Geoff Brightling/Dorling Kindersley; 315b, Jan Hinsch/Science Photo Library/Photo; Researchers, Inc.; 317 inset, Richard Haynes; 319t, Lee D. Simon/Science Source/Photo Researchers, Inc.; 320b, Peter Minister/ Dorling Kindersley; 322r, Institut Pasteur/CNRI/Phototake; 323t, Esbin-Anderson/ Omni-Photo; 324b, Dr. Linda Stannard, UCT/Science Photo Library/ Photo Researchers, Inc.; 325r, Richard Haynes; 326l, USDA/Visuals Unlimited; 327l, Dennis Kunkel/Phototake; 327m, Dennis Kunkel/Phototake; 327r, Photo courtesy of Agriculture and Agri-Food Canada; 328r, Dr. K.S. Kim/Peter Arnold, Inc.; 328l, Dr. Dennis Kunkel/Phototake; 329r, Alfred Pasieka/Peter Arnold, Inc.; 330l, Stock Food/Raben; 330r, Richard Haynes; 331m, J. C. Carton/Bruce Coleman; 331l, DK Images; 331r, Neil Marsh/DK Images; 332b, Ben Osborne; 332 inset, Michael Abbey/Photo Researchers, Inc.; 332t, John Riley/Getty Images; 333t, David Young-Wolff/PhotoEdit; 334t, Science VU/Visuals Unlimited; 334b, Jan Hinsch/Science Photo Library/Photo Researchers, Inc.; 335t, O.S.F./Animals Animals/Earth Scenes; 335m, A. Le Toquin/Photo Researchers, Inc.; 335b, Gregory G. Dimijian/Photo Researchers, Inc.; 336t, Astrid & Hanns-Frieder Michler/Photo Researchers, Inc.; 337t, Eric Grave/Photo Researchers, Inc.; 338 inset, Jerome Paulin/Visuals Unlimited; 338t, Layne Kennedy/Corbis; 338b, Oliver Meckes/Photo Researchers, Inc.; 339b, David M. Phillips/Visuals Unlimited; 340l, Sinclair Stammers Oxford Scientific Films/Animals Animals/Earth Scenes; 341t, Runk/Schoenberger/Grant Heilman Photography; 342l, David M. Dennis/Tom Stack & Associates, Inc.; 342r, David M. Dennis/Tom Stack & Associates, Inc.; 343b, G.R. Roberts/Omni-Photo; 344b, Michael Fogden/Animals Animals/Earth Scenes; 345b, Fred Unverhau/ Animals Animals/Earth Scenes; 346b, David Scharf/ Peter Arnold, Inc.; 347l inset, Scott Camazine I; 347l, Michael Fogden/Animals Animals/ Earth Scenes; 347r inset, E.R. Degginger/Photo Researchers, Inc.; 347tr, Carolina Biological/Visuals Unlimited; 347br, Runk/Schoenberger/Grant Heilman Photography, Inc.; 348b, Photo courtesy of David Read; 349t, Rod Planck/Tom Stack & Associates, Inc.; 349 inset, V. Ahmadjian/Visuals Unlimited; 350b, Richard Haynes; 351b, Richard Haynes; 352t, Geoff Brightling/Dorling Kindersley.

CHAPTER 10

Pages 356–357,Barrett and MacKay/DRK Photo; 357br, Barry Runk/Grant Heilman Photography, Inc.; 361br, Jon Chomitz; 362t, Richard Haynes; 364t, Kjell B. Sandved/Photo Researchers, Inc.; 365r, Ludovic Maisant/Corbis; 366l, Randy M. Ury/Corbis; 366r, John Shaw/Bruce Coleman; 367tl, R. Van Nostrand/Photo Researchers, Inc.; 367mr, Brenda Tharp/Photo Researchers, Inc.; 367ml, Runk/ Schoenberger/Grant Heilman Photography; 367br, Eastcott Momatiuk/Getty Images; 367bl, Ron Thomas/Getty Images; 368tl, Runk/Schoenberger/Grant Heilman Photography, Inc.; 368tr, Peter Chadwick/DK Images; 368bl, Frans Lanting/ Minden Pictures; 370–371, J. Lotter Gurling/Tom Stack & Associates, Inc.; 371l, Runk/Schoenberger/Grant Heilman Photography, Inc.; 374l, Gerald Moore; 374r, Runk/Schoenberger/Grant Heilman Photography, Inc.; 375bl, Michael Keller/Corbis; 378br, D. Cavagnaro/Visuals Unlimited; 378bl, Frans Lanting/ Minden Pictures; 378ml, Color-Pic/Animals Animals/Earth Scenes; 378mr, John Pontier/Animals Animals/Earth Scenes; 378mm, Heather Angel/Natural Visions; 380bl, Max Stuart/Alamy; 380br, Runk/Schoenberger/Grant Heilman Photography, Inc.; 380b, Color-Pic/Earth Scenes; 382br, David Sieren/Visuals Unlimited; 386r, Richard Haynes; 387b, Richard Haynes; 388t, Russ Lappa; 389r, Breck Kent/ Animals Animals/Earth Scenes; 389m, Ken Brate/ Photo Researchers, Inc.; 389tl, Michael Fogden/Animals Animals/Earth Scenes; 389tm, Jim Strawser/Grant Heilman Photography, Inc.; 391t, Grant Heilman/Grant Heilman Photography, Inc.; 391b inset, Breck P. Kent; 391t inset, Breck P. Kent/Animals Animals/Earth Scenes; 391b, Patti Murray/Animals Animals/Earth Scenes; 392l, Frans Lanting/Minden Pictures; 394br, Jules Selmes and Debi Treloar/Dorling Kindersley; 394 2nd from right-b, Philip Dowell/Dorling Kindersley; 394bl, Perennou et Nuridsany/Photo Researchers, Inc.; 394 2nd from left-b,Russ Lappa; 395l, Nancy Rotenberg/Animals Animals/Earth Scenes; 395br, Dwight Kuhn; 397t, Alan Pitcairn/Grant Heilman Photography, Inc.; 398t, Richard Haynes.

CHAPTER 11

Pages 404–405, Norm Thomas/Photo Researchers, Inc.; 405br, B. Runk/ S. Schoenberger/Grant Heilman Photography; 406m, Brandon D. Cole/Corbis; 406r, Ed Bravendam/Minden Pictures; 406l, Brian Parker/Tom Stack & Associates, Inc.; 407br, G. S. Grant/Photo Researchers, Inc.; 407bl, Dale Sanders/Masterfile; 407t, William Leonard/DRK Photo; 409 inset, Richard Haynes; 410t, Richard Haynes; 410br, Heather Angel/Natural Visions; 410bl, Heather Angel/Natural Visions; 411 2nd from right, Neil Flether/Oxford University Museum; 412b, Frank Oberle/Getty Images; 412t, Frank Greenaway /Dorling Kindersley Media Library; 413b, Michael Quinton/Minden Pictures; 414l, Tom and Pat Leeson; 414m, Andrew J. Martinez/Photo Researchers, Inc.; 414r, James Watt/Visuals Unlimited; 416r, Wolfgang Bayer/Bruce Coleman, Inc.; 417b, Michael DeFreitas/Bruce Coleman, Inc.; 419b, Dale Sanders/Masterfile; 419br, G. S. Grant/Photo Researchers, Inc.; 420t, Jeff Rotman/www.jeffrotman.com; 422–423, Jeff Hunter/Getty Images; 422t, Richard Cummins/Corbis; 424t, Richard Haynes; 424b, Dr. Alan L. Yen; 426t, Hans Strand/Getty Images; 426 inset, David M. Dennis/Tom Stack & Associates, Inc.; 428t, Sinclair Stammers/Photo Researchers, Inc.; 431b, Digital Vision/Getty Images; 432t, Ken Lucas/Visuals Unlimited; 434t, Richard Haynes; 434b, R.J.Erwin/Photo Researchers, Inc.; 435t, John Gerlach/Tom Stack &

...ociates, Inc.; **435b,** Frank Greenaway/Dorling Kindersley Media Library; **438b,** Marty Cordano/DRK Photo; **438t,** Geoff Dann/Dorling Kindersley; **442t,** Wilson Lourenço/Museum National d'Histoire Naturelle, Paris; **443t,** Richard Haynes; **445tr,** Brandon D. Cole/ Corbis; **445tm,** Brian Parker/Tom Stack & Associates, Inc.; **445br,** Ed Bravendam/Minden Pictures; **445t,** Kerrick James; **445tl,** Darrell Gulin/ Dembinsky Photo Associates.

CHAPTER 12

Pages 450–451, Norbert Wu/Minden Pictures; **452b,** Rod Planck/Science Photo Library/Photo Researchers, Inc.; **453tr,** Michael & Patricia Fogden/Corbis; **453mr,** Gary Meszaros/Photo Researchers, Inc.; **453b,** Dave King/Dorling Kindersley Media Library; **453tl,** Art Wolfe/Getty Images, Inc.; **453ml,** Ian & Karen Stewart/Bruce Coleman Inc.; **455br,** Richard Haynes; **456t,** Russ Lappa; **457b,** Tom Flach/Getty Images, Inc.; **458t,** Dave King/Dorling Kindersley Media Library; **460r,** Michael Fogden/DRK Photo; **460l,** Frans Lanting/ Minden Pictures; **462t,** Gerard Lacz/ Animals Animals; **462b,** Flip Nicklin/Minden Pictures; **463t,** NHPA/LUTRA; **464tl,** John D. Cunningham/Visuals Unlimited; **464tr,** Michael Patrick O'Neil/Photo Researchers, Inc.; **464bl,** Mark Stouffer Enterprises/Animals Animals/Earth Scenes; **465b,** Animals Animals/Earth Scenes; **465t,** Bruce Coleman, Inc.; **465** inset, Herve Berthoule Jacana/Photo Researchers, Inc.; **466l,** Mike Parry/Minden Pictures; **466t,** Frank Burek/Animals Animals; **468b,** Rod Planck/Science Photo Library/Photo Researchers, Inc.; **470b,** Gerry Ellis/Minden Pictures; **471t,** Michael Fogden/OSF/ Animals Animals; **472t,** Richard Haynes; **472b,** Joe McDonald/Tom Stack & Associates, Inc.; **473t,** Thomas Wiewandt/wildhorizons.com; **474b,** Jay Ireland & Georgienne Bradley/Bradleyireland.com; **475t,** Kim Taylor & Jane Burton/DK Images; **475b,** Art Wolfe/Getty Images; **476r,** Ernst Mayr Library of the Museum of Comparative Zoology, Harvard University. ©President and Fellows of Harvard; **476l,** Typ 605.77.700 F, Department of Printing and Graphic Arts, Houghton Library, Harvard College Library; **476m,** Natural History Museum, London; **477r,** Louis Psihoyos/Matrix; **477l,** Andy Crawford/DK Images; **478b,** T.A. Wiewandt/DRK Photo; **480t,** Richard Haynes; **480b,** John Downes/DK Images; **483b,** Geoff Higgins/PhotoLibrary.com; **484** inset, Jerome Wexler/ Photo Researchers, Inc.; **484t,** Stephen J. Krasemann/DRK Photo; **485l,** Kim Taylor/DK Images; **485r,** Richard Wagner; **486t,** Richard Haynes; **486b,** Eric Valli/Minden Pictures; **487tl,** Hilary Pooley/Animals Animals; **487tr,** Phillip Dowell/DK Images; **487mr,** Philip Dowell/ Dorling Kindersley; **487br,** Dave King/DK Images; **488l,** Daryl Balfour/Getty Images, Inc.; **488r,** Art Wolfe; **489t,** Frans Lanting/Minden Pictures; **489b,** Frans Lanting/ Minden Pictures; **490b,** Dave Watts/Tom Stack & Associates, Inc.; **490t,** Tom McHugh/Photo Researchers; **491t,** Joe McDonald/Visuals Unlimited; **492ml,** Chuck Davis/Getty Images, Inc.; **492br,** Stephen J. Krasemann/DRK Photo; **492br,** Johnny Johnson/DRK Photo; **492tr,** Roger Aitkenhead/Animals Animals; **492bl,** Dave Welling; **493tl,** Dwight Kuhn; **493tr,** Art Wolfe/Getty Images, Inc.; **493bl,** M.P. Kahl/DRK Photo; **493br,** Renee Lynn/Getty Images, Inc.; **493ml,** Charlie Heidecker/ Visuals Unlimited; **494t,** Johnny Johnson/DRK Photo.

CHAPTER 13

Pages 502–503, Matthew Stockman/Getty Images, Inc.; **503br,** Sean Kernan/ Getty Images, Inc.; **504l,** Astrid & Hans-Frieder/Photo Researchers, Inc.; **504m,** Eric Grave/Photo Researchers, Inc.; **504r,** Ed Reschke/Peter Arnold, Inc.; **505tl,** Richard Haynes; **505tr,** Rudi Von Briel/PhotoEdit; **507** inset, Richard Haynes; **508t,** Richard Haynes; **509l,** Richard Haynes; **509r,** K.G. Murti/Visuals Unlimited; **510bm,** James Hayden, RBP/Phototake; **510tm,** Fred Hossler/Visuals Unlimited; **510t,** John D. Cunningham/Visuals Unlimited; **510b,** Biophoto Associates/Science Source/Photo Researchers, Inc.; **511r,** Richard Haynes; **512b,** Michael S. Yamashita/ Corbis; **512t,** Richard Haynes; **513l,** Richard Haynes; **513r,** Richard Haynes; **514t,** Lennart Nilsson/Boehringer Ingelheim International GmbH; **515b,** Richard Haynes; **515l,** Park Street/PhotoEdit; **515** 2nd from left, Tom Grill/Getty Images, Inc.; **515** 2nd from right, Image Source/Getty Images, Inc.; **515r,** Trinette Reed/Getty Images, Inc.; **515m,** D Falconer/PhotoLink/Getty Images; **516l,** Jon Feingersh/Corbis; **517t,** Mike Powell/Getty Images, Inc.; **518r,** Russ Lappa; **519r,** Richard Haynes; **519l,** Dorling Kindersley; **520l,** David Young-Wolff/PhotoEdit; **520r,** Rudi Von Briel/ PhotoEdit; **521l,** Journal-Courier/Steve Warmowski/The Image Works; **521r,** Peter Hvizdak/The Image Works; **523r,** David Madison Sports Images, Inc 2003; **524l,** David Young-Wolff/PhotoEdit; **524r,** Marc Romanelli/Getty Images, Inc.; **525l,** Innerspace Imaging/Photo Researchers, Inc.; **525r,** Zephyr/Photo Researchers, Inc.; **526t,** Richard Haynes; **527m,** Dorling Kindersley; **527tl,** Astrid & Hans-Frieder/ Photo Researchers, Inc.; **527bl,** Eric Grave/Photo Researchers, Inc.; **527r,** Ed Reschke/Peter Arnold, Inc.; **528l,** Richard Haynes; **529t,** Dorling Kindersley; **530t,** David Madison Sports Images, Inc. 2003; **531t,** Richard Haynes; **532b,** Jim West/The Image Works; **533l,** Richard Haynes; **533r,** Richard Haynes; **537t,** Richard Haynes; **537m,** David Brownell; **537b,** Karl Weatherly/Corbis; **539l,** Richard Haynes; **539r,** Richard Haynes; **539m,** Richard Haynes; **542b,** David Young-Wolff/PhotoEdit.

CHAPTER 14

Pages 546–547, Dennis Kunkel/Phototake; **547br,** Dorling Kindersley; **549b,** Oliver Meckes/Photo Researchers, Inc.; **549t,** Richard Haynes; **549mr,** Du Cane Medical Imaging LTD/Science Photo Library/Photo Researchers, Inc.; **551** inset, Richard Haynes; **553b,** Richard Haynes; **555br,** SPL/Photo Researchers, Inc.; **556t,** Felix Stensson/Alamy; **557br,** Richard Haynes; **558b,** VVG/Science Photo Library/ Photo Researchers; **560t,** Cabisco/Visuals Unlimited; **561t,** Arthur Tilley/Getty Images, Inc.; **562t,** Richard Haynes; **563t,** Andrew Syred/SPL/Photo Researchers, Inc.; **565b,** National Cancer Institute/Science Photo Library/Photo Researchers, Inc.; **565t,** Bill Longcore/Science Source/Photo Researchers, Inc.; **565m,** Andrew Syred/Science Photo Library/Photo Researchers, Inc.; **566t,** Oliver Meckes/Photo Researchers, Inc.; **569t,** Richard Haynes; **570t,** Richard Haynes; **570b,** Dennie Cody/Getty Images; **572tl,** Richard Haynes; **572bl,** Richard Haynes; **572tm,** Richard Haynes; **572tr,** Richard Haynes; **573b,** Richard Haynes; **574b,** Richard Haynes; **576t,** Mark Gibson/Corbis; **577** both, Richard Haynes; **578t,** Dorling Kindersley; **579t,** Russ Lappa; **580t,** Bob Daemmrich/Stock Boston; **580b,** Thom Duncan/Adventure Photo/Image State; **581l,** Custom Medical Stock Photo; **581r,** Custom Medical Stock Photo; **582l,** The Granger Collection, NY; **582m,** Courtesy of the Baker Institute; **582r,** Layne Kennedy/Corbis; **583r,** Reuters NewMedia/ Corbis; **583l,** Liaison/Getty Images, Inc.; **583m,** Richard T. Nowitzky/Corbis; **584l,** Matt Meadows/Peter Arnold, Inc.; **584r,** Jonathan Nourok/PhotoEdit; **585tr,** SIV/Photo Researchers, Inc.; **585br,** Photo Researchers, Inc.; **585l,** Michael Heron/ Prentice Hall; **587b,** Du Cane Medical Imaging LTD/Science Photo Library/Photo Researchers, Inc.; **587t,** BSIP/Photo Researchers, Inc.; **588b,** Center for Biomedical Communications/Phototake; **590b,** Custom Medical Stock Photo.

CHAPTER 15

Pages 594–595, Michael Kevin Daly/CORBIS; **595b,** Russ Lappa/Prentice Hall; **597tl,** Richard Haynes; **597 Inset,** Prof. P. Motta / Photo Researchers, Inc.; **597tr,** Richard Haynes; **598–599,** Chabruken/Getty Images, Inc., **601b,** Mike Blake/Reuters New Media, Inc./Corbis; **603 all,** Rolf Brudere/Masterfile; **605,** Richard Haynes; **606t,** Richard Haynes; **606b,** Chet Gordon/The Image Works; **607,** Richard Haynes; **609,** Richard Haynes; **611t,** Tom Stewart/Corbis; **612b,** Richard Haynes; **612b,** Richard Haynes; **613t,** Barbara Stitzer/PhotoEdit; **614b,** David Young-Wolff/PhotoEdit; **615t,** Diane Schiumo/Fundamental Photographs; **615b,** Diane Hirsch/Fundamental Photographs; **617b,** Prof. P. Motta/Dept. of Anatomy/U. "La Sapienza," Rome/Science Photo Library/Photo Researchers; **618t,** GK Hart/Vikki Hart/Getty Images, Inc.; **620 inset,** Lee Snider/The Image Works; **620tl,** Lennart Nilsson; **621b,** Tony Freeman/PhotoEdit; **622tl,** Richard Haynes; **622 Inset,** Prof. P. Motta/Photo Researchers, Inc.; **623tr,** Mugshots/ Corbis; **625b,** Digital Vision/Getty Images, Inc.; **626bl,** David Young-Wolff/PhotoEdit; **628bl,** Stacy Pick/Stock Boston; **629tr,** CNRI/SPL/Photo Researchers, Inc.; **629br,** PhotoEdit.

CHAPTER 16

Pages 634–635, George Shelley/Corbis; **637b,** David M. Phillips/Photo Researchers, Inc.; **637** inset,David Phillips/SPL/Photo Researchers, Inc.; **637t,** Professors P. M. Motta & J. Van Blerkom/ SPL/Photo Researchers, Inc.; **637mr,** Petit Format/Photo Researchers, Inc.; **638–639,** Chabruken/Getty Images, Inc., **641tr,** PhotoEdit; **641tl,** Chad Slattery/Getty Images, Inc.; **643,** Richard Haynes; **644t,** Richard Haynes; **646t,** Richard Haynes; **647tr,** Richard Haynes; **647tl,** Richard Haynes; **648,** Michael Newman/PhotoEdit; **649l,** David Phillips/SPL/Photo Researchers, Inc.; **649tr,** David Phillips/SPL/Photo Researchers, Inc.; **654t,** Professors P. M. Motta & J. Van Blerkom/ SPL/Photo Researchers, Inc.; **658l,** CNRI/SPL/Photo Researchers, Inc.; **658m,** G. Moscoso/Photo Researchers, Inc.; **658r,** Neil Bromhall/SPL/Photo Researchers, Inc.; **659r,** Petit Format/Photo Researchers, Inc.; **660t,** Index Stock Imagery, Inc.; **661l,** Roy Morsch/Corbis; **661r,** Tony Freeman/PhotoEdit; **662tl,** Penny Gentieu; **662tm,** Spencer Grant/PhotoEdit; **662tr,** Tim Pannell/Corbis; **663,** Michael Newman/PhotoEdit; **664b,** David M. Phillips/Photo Researchers, Inc.; **664 inset,** David Phillips/SPL/Photo Researchers, Inc.; **668t,** Gerald D. Tang; **668bm,** Michael Kevin Daly/Corbis; **668tm,** Dennis Kunkel/Phototake; **668b,** George Shelley/Corbis; **669tr,** Richard Haynes; **669m,** Richard Haynes; **669b,** Richard Haynes.